Mechanisms of Molecular Migrations

VOLUME 2

Mechanisms of Molecular Migrations

VOLUME 2

EDITOR

B. S. THYAGARAJAN

UNIVERSITY OF MADRAS
MADRAS, INDIA

INTERSCIENCE PUBLISHERS

A DIVISION OF JOHN WILEY & SONS

NEW YORK · LONDON · SYDNEY · TORONTO

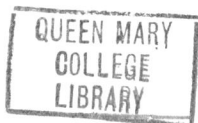

This volume and the others that follow in this series are dedicated to the many able investigators whose ceaseless efforts seek to secure the less obvious and more intricately woven pattern of order in the behavior of migrating molecular species in the domain of organic chemistry.

EDITOR

"The true worth of an experimenter consists in his pursuing not only what he seeks in his experiment, but also what he did not seek."

Claude Bernard

". . . It is truth very certain that, when it is not in our power to determine what is true, we ought to follow what is most probable."

Rene Descartes

"The first is that of gross over-simplification reflecting partly the need for practical working rules and even more a too enthusiastic aspiration after elegance of form. In the second stage the symmetry of the hypothetical systems is distorted and neatness marred as the recalcitrant facts increasingly rebel against uniformity. In the third stage, if and when this is attained, a new order emerges, more intricately contrived, less obvious, and with its parts more subtly interwoven, since it is of nature's and not of man's contriving."

Sir Cyril Hinshelwood

Preface

Volume 1 of this series presented six chapters dealing with the rearrangements of amidines, alpha halosulfones, azoxyarenes, cyclohexadienones, nitrones, and sulfoxides. Likewise the present volume carries chapters written by authors who have made highly significant research contributions to their chosen fields of study. These surveys deal with oxidative rearrangements of vinylic derivatives (Steltenkamp-Truce); rearrangements of O-acylated heterocyclic N-oxides (Traynelis); 1,3-alkyl migrations (Landis); base catalyzed rearrangements of acetylenic derivatives (Iwai); orbital symmetry and electrocyclic rearrangements (Fukui and Fujimoto); benzidine rearrangements (Shine); the Meisenheimer rearrangement of tertiary amine oxides (Johnstone); rearrangements involving nitrene intermediates (Boyer); and the uncatalyzed rearrangement of tervalent phosphorus esters (Mark). The cooperative and stimulating efforts of the contributing authors have made possible the early appearance of this second volume in quick succession to the first. The Editor wishes to thank them especially for the valuable time they have spared for these efforts.

The Editor hopes these surveys will stimulate continued growth of interests in these areas of research. The encouraging comments of many colleagues around the world have been of inestimable value in the organization of these volumes. While expressing his thankfulness for these comments, the Editor welcomes further suggestions and comments in the preparation of further volumes in this series.

B. S. THYAGARAJAN

Contents

Rearrangement of *O*-Acylated Heterocyclic *N*-Oxides

VINCENT J. TRAYNELIS

West Virginia University, Morgantown, West Virginia

I. INTRODUCTION

The extensive development of heterocyclic *N*-oxide chemistry in the past 15 to 20 years may be attributed to their unique reactions of synthetic and mechanistic interest. Although Meisenheimer (1) in 1926 reported a facile oxidative procedure for the preparation of pyridine *N*-oxide and related compounds, the chemistry of heterocyclic *N*-oxides lay dormant until 1940. At that time Linton (2) reported an unexpectedly low dipole moment for pyridine *N*-oxide ($\mu = 4.32$ D) and suggested structural representation of pyridine *N*-oxide as a resonance hybrid with contributing canonical structures that show electron release by the N—O oxygen

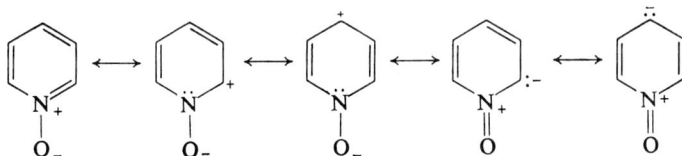

Figure 1

(Fig. 1). These considerations predicted that electrophilic substitution would be facilitated in the 4 or 2 position and led Ochiai in Japan and den Hertog in Holland to explore independently the nitration of heterocyclic

1

N-oxides. These two research groups confirmed the ease of nitration in pyridine which entered the 4 position, and proceeded to develop a considerable body of chemistry of heterocyclic *N*-oxides. In subsequent years many other workers entered the field and during the 1950's and 1960's brought this area to maturity. A number of reviews have appeared in the literature (3–7).

In considering the reactions of pyridine *N*-oxide, the oxygen atom assumes a key role both in its activation of the pyridine ring toward electrophilic and nucleophilic attack and in its reactions as a nucleophilic reagent. In the latter case the initial product of the reaction of pyridine *N*-oxide and electrophilic centers is an *O*-substituted oxypyridinium ion which may undergo subsequent reaction or be isolated as a salt. The reaction of heterocyclic *N*-oxides and acylating agents belongs in this category and forms the theme of this chapter.

A variety of products have resulted from the reaction of heterocyclic *N*-oxides with acid anhydrides, acid chlorides, and sulfonyl chlorides and seem dependent on the nature of the substituents on the heterocyclic *N*-oxide. Although the mechanisms for some of these reactions differ, a common unifying feature exists in the first step, the formation of an *N*-acyloxypyridinium (1) or *N*-sulfonyloxypyridinium (2) cation (Fig. 2).

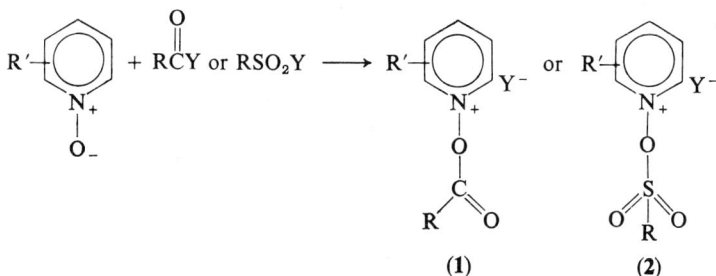

Figure 2

These cations, in general, are not isolable (however, see p. 26 for some stable cations) but readily undergo subsequent reactions which include molecular rearrangements, nucleophilic addition-elimination and other reactions. Since competition exists between rearrangement and non-rearrangement pathways, consideration is given in this chapter to all reactions proceeding via the oxypyridinium ions of types 1 and 2. These reactions may be cataloged into the following categories: (*1*) ring substitution, reaction at the heterocyclic ring which results in the substitution of a ring hydrogen and the loss of the *N*-oxygen function, or replacement of a ring nitro group by another substituent and retention of the *N*-oxide group; (2) deoxygenation, reaction at the N—O bond which results in deoxygenation of the heterocyclic N-oxide and an oxidative decarboxylation of the acyloxy group; and (3) side chain rearrangement, reaction at an alkyl side chain which entails rearrangement of the N-acyloxy substituent to the α-carbon on the side chain.

II. RING SUBSTITUTION

The first reaction of heterocyclic N-oxides with acylating agents was reported in 1947 by Katada (8), who isolated 2-pyridone (5, R = H) from the reaction of pyridine N-oxide with acetic or benzoic anhydride. However, the initial product of reaction was 2-acetoxypyridine (3, R = H) which was hydrolyzed on work-up to produce the 2-pyridone. Some years later Boekelheide (9), Cislak (10), and Bain and Saxton (11) extended this reaction to 3-methylpyridine N-oxide and 3,5-dimethylpyridine N-oxide

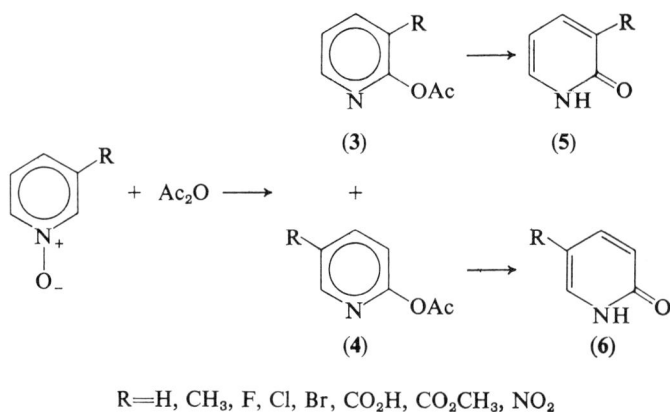

R=H, CH₃, F, Cl, Br, CO₂H, CO₂CH₃, NO₂

Figure 3

(Fig. 3). In the former case both 3-methyl-2-pyridone (5, R = CH₃) and 5-methyl-2-pyridone (6, R = CH₃) were found in comparable amounts. The conversion of 3-halopyridine N-oxides and 3-nitropyridine N-oxide via reaction with acetic anhydride to the corresponding 3-substituted 2-pyridones (5) was described by Cava (12) and Taylor (13), respectively; while Boekelheide (14) and Bain and Saxton (11) observed similar reactions with various pyridinecarboxylic acid N-oxides and their methyl esters.

Other heterocyclic *N*-oxide systems which react in a comparable manner with acetic anhydride include quinoline *N*-oxide (15,16), iso-quinoline *N*-oxide (17–19), benzimidazole *N*-oxide (16) and 8-hydroxy-purine 1-oxide (20a) (Fig. 4). In each of these cases the major product resulted from the introduction of an acetoxy group into a position adjacent

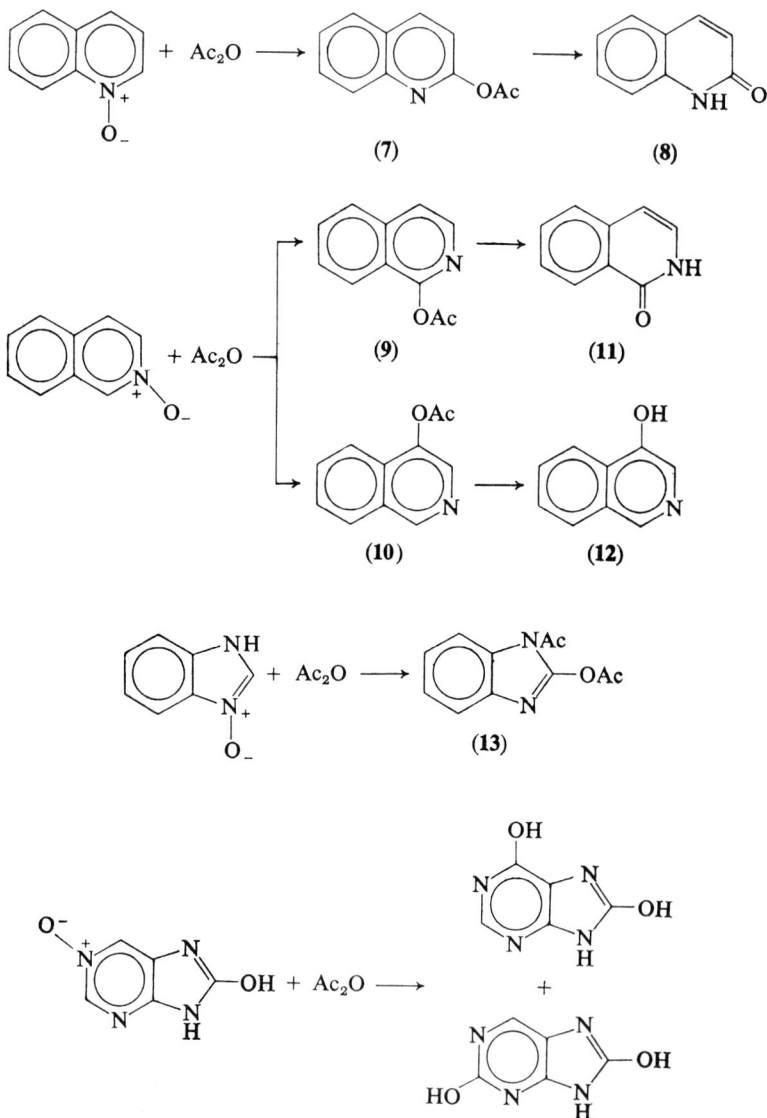

Figure 4

to the N-oxide function. In addition to compound **9** isoquinoline N-oxide and its 3-methyl derivative both gave a minor product **10** (converted to and isolated as **12**) which required introduction of an acetoxy function β to the N-oxide group. This position of attack became predominant with 3-chloroisoquinoline N-oxide (19).

An alternate reaction path was observed in the reaction of 6-amino-purine 1-oxide (**14**) and its 2-amino or 8-hydroxy derivatives with acetic anhydride (Fig. 5). The initial N-acetoxy acetate salt **15** undergoes cleavage

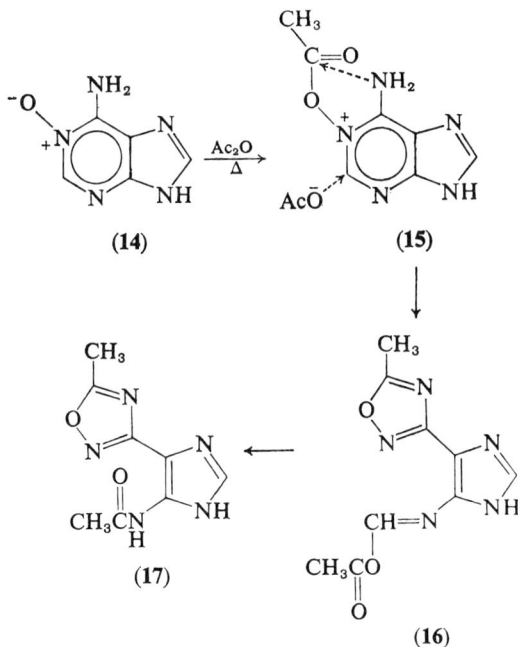

Figure 5

of the pyrimidine ring and reaction between the 6-amino and 1-acetoxy groups to produce a 1,2,4-oxadiazole ring (compound **16**). Subsequent reactions of **16** lead to the isolated product **17** (20b). Acridine N-oxide which has the α positions substituted with two fused benzene rings reacts with acetic anhydride to produce acridone and thus illustrates reaction of the position γ to the nitrogen (21).

Most of the mechanistic work on these reactions involved the pyridine N-oxide and acridine N-oxide systems and has been reported in the past several years. Although Ochiai and Okamoto (22) proposed the general mechanism for the reaction of pyridine *N*-oxide and acetic anhydride in 1948, the refinements of this mechanism along with supporting evidence were only recently provided by Markgraf (23) and Oae (24,25).

The mechanism which appears to emerge from these works may be described in the following manner (Fig. 6). Acetic anhydride undergoes

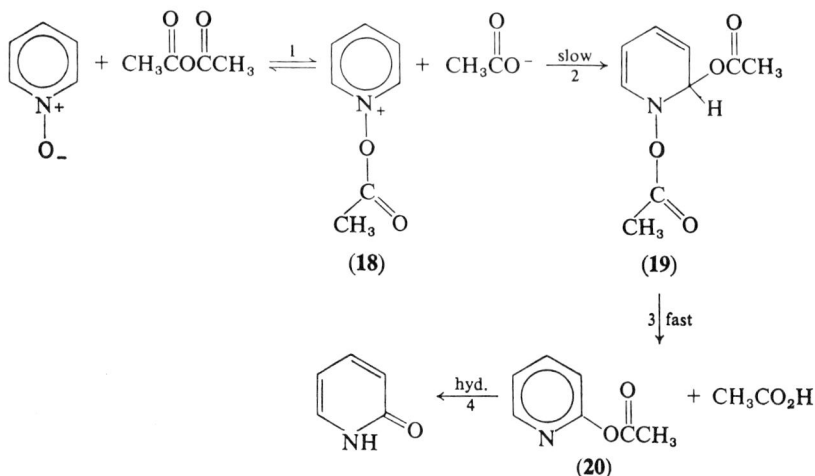

Figure 6

nucleophilic attack by pyridine *N*-oxide to produce the 1-acetoxypyridinium ion (18) and acetate ion in an equilibrium reaction. Although direct evidence for this equilibration or the formation of 18 is not available in this system, comparable reactions are well-established in the 2-alkyl-pyridine *N*-oxide series (26) and quinaldine *N*-oxide (27) and thus support by analogy the proposed equilibrium in step 1.

Markgraf (23) reported pseudo first-order kinetics for the reaction of pyridine *N*-oxide with excess acetic anhydride which were consistent with an intermolecular nucleophilic addition of acetate ion and agree with the formation of 1,2-diacetoxy-1,2-dihydropyridine (19). These data also permitted Markgraf to exclude the intramolecular pathway for the rearrangement of 19 to the product 20. The activation parameters were $\Delta H^{\ddagger}$ 29.2 kcal/mole and $\Delta S^{\ddagger}$ —5.5 eu. Further support for an inter-molecular reaction was advanced by Oae (24) via oxygen 18 labeling experiments. When 3-picoline *N*-oxide (^{18}O = 0.20 atom %) was treated with an equimolar amount of uniformly ^{18}O-labeled acetic anhydride (^{18}O = 0.89 atom %), the distilled mixture of 2-acetoxy-3-methylpyridine and 2-acetoxy-5-methylpyridine contained 0.73 atom % ^{18}O and the corresponding pyridone mixture contained 0.70 atom % ^{18}O. Control experiments excluded oxygen exchange of ester **20** with acetic anhydride or acetic acid and oxygen exchange during the hydrolysis of **20** to the pyridone. These results require an equilibration of all oxygen atoms, including the *N*-oxide oxygen, and are best accommodated by the inter-molecular addition in step 2 with subsequent loss of the *N*-acetoxy group. This latter group can then react with acetic anhydride leading to complete equilibration of all oxygens. Further confirmation of complete oxygen equilibration comes from experiments using an excess of ^{18}O-labeled acetic anhydride which produced esters and pyridones with the atom % ^{18}O content raised to the mean average concentration of all the oxygens in the reaction medium. Similar ^{18}O-labeling results were obtained using pyridine *N*-oxide in place of 3-methylpyridine *N*-oxide; however, in these experiments only 2-pyridone was isolated and analyzed (25).

In considering the rate controlling step the two alternatives, consistent with the kinetic and ^{18}O labeling data, are the nucleophilic addition of step 2 or the base-catalyzed elimination of step 3. Examination of the electronic effects exhibited by the C-3 substituents fail to distinguish between these two pathways. Although 3-methylpyridine *N*-oxide produced equal amounts of 3-methyl-2-pyridone and 5-methyl-2-pyridone (11), nicotinic acid *N*-oxide (11) and its methyl ester (14) gave 10–28% of the 3-sub-stituted-2-pyridone and 2–17% of the 5-substituted-2-pyridone, and the 3-halo- (12) and 3-nitropyridine *N*-oxides (13) gave only 3-substituted 2-pyridones; these findings can be rationalized by the inductive influence of the substituents on the C-2 position and satisfy either step 2 or step 3 as rate limiting. The strong electron-withdrawing groups favor nucleophilic attack at the C-2 position; however, the same inductive factors increase the acidity of the C-2 hydrogen over the C-6 hydrogen and facilitate the 1,2-elimination. Oae (25) resolved this question by determination of the hydrogen–deuterium kinetic isotope effect for pyridine *N*-oxide and 2,6-dideuteriopyridine *N*-oxide. Both compounds showed pseudo first-order behavior and exhibited the following kinetic isotope effect, $k_{\mathrm{H}}/k_{\mathrm{D}} = 0.92$. This small value and of the reverse order excludes cleavage of the C—H bond as the rate controlling process and leaves the nucleophilic addition of step 2 as rate determining. Thus the above evidence taken collectively supports the mechanistic pathway outlined in Figure 6.

The occurrence of step 4 is dependent on the ease of hydrolysis of **20** and simply reflects which product will be isolated.

The experimental approach in the mechanistic study of the reaction of acridine *N*-oxide with acetic anhydride parallels closely that for the pyridine *N*-oxide case. Markgraf and Ahn (28) observed pseudo-first-order kinetics for the reaction of acridine *N*-oxide in excess acetic anhydride and reported the following activation parameters $\Delta H^{\ddagger}$ 12.2 $\pm$ 0.1 kcal/mole, $\Delta S^{\ddagger}$ —32.2 $\pm$ 0.5 eu. In addition a small positive salt effect was found with the addition of sodium perchlorate and tetrabutylammonium acetate. A subsequent report by Markgraf and Carson (29) showed no kinetic isotope effect (k_H/k_D = 1) for this reaction. These data are rationalized by the mechanistic scheme outlined in Figure 7.

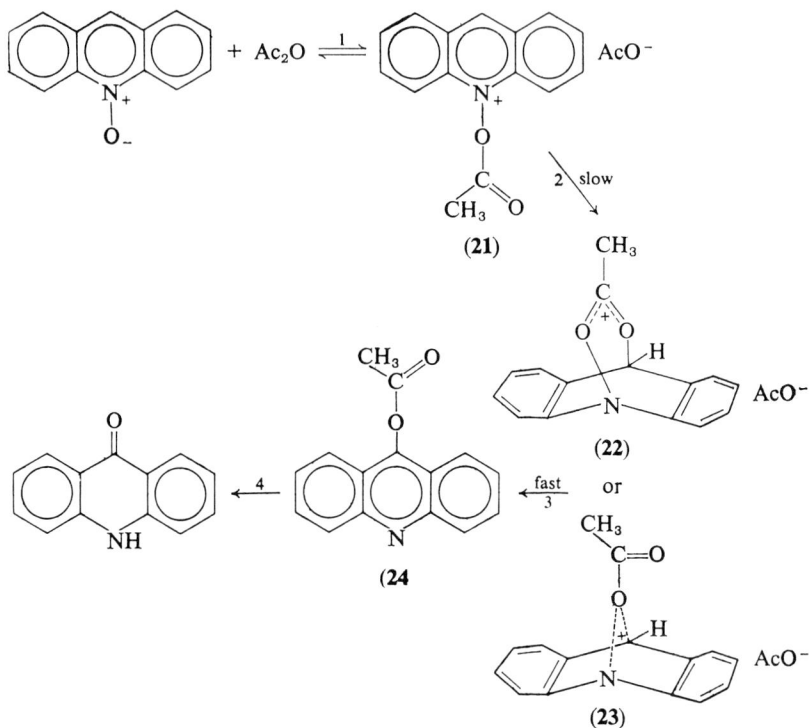

Figure 7

The equilibrium reaction in step 1 is generally accepted as described under the pyridine N-oxide discussion and initially produces a tight ion pair which equilibrates with a solvent separated ion pair (28). This proposal of ionic species appears consistent with the conductance measurements and the reported salt effects. Conversion of the solvent separated ion pair **21** to product **24** via a concerted intramolecular process (**22** or **23**) finds support in the activation parameters; and the absence of a kinetic isotope effect excludes the deprotonation of step 3 as rate controlling, thus favoring step 2 for the slow process.

The concerted intramolecular rearrangement can occur by attachment of the carbonyl oxygen (intermediate **22**) or the *N*-oxide oxygen (intermediate **23**) at the C-9 position of acridine. Oae and co-workers (30) employed ^{18}O-labeling experiments in an attempt to decide between these pathways; however, their results were inconclusive. The acridone isolated in each experiment was enriched with ^{18}O but there was never complete equilibration of all oxygens in the system. This result supports Markgraf's work in excluding an intermolecular reaction between **21** and acetate ion. If **22** were the intermediate, the use of ^{18}O-labeled acetic anhydride would introduce 100% labeling into the acridone; but with **23** as the intermediate, the resulting acridone would have 0% enrichment of ^{18}O. Oae's report shows 30–60% ^{18}O incorporation into acridone when acetic anhydride or sulfolane are used as solvents and 60–80% ^{18}O enrichment of acridone with chloroform as solvent. Oae's explanation invokes simultaneous formation of both **22** and **23** which proceed to product **24** and requires that intermediate **23** is favored when acetic anhydride or sulfolane are the solvents. This rationalization requires a unique solvent effect which must influence the two bond forming pathways of a single intramolecular process. The alternative possibility to explain the observed data which involves competing intermolecular and intramolecular processes does not appear consistent with the solvent effect observed. Therefore further experimentation and consideration must be given to this point.

A comparison of the reaction rates of acridine *N*-oxide and pyridine *N*-oxide with acetic anhydride both at 25° shows $k_{\text{acridine } N\text{-oxide}}/k_{\text{pyridine } N\text{-oxide}} = 4 \times 10^6$ (28). This striking difference in reaction rate along with a comparison of activation parameters for the two reactions is not surprising in view of the mechanistic differences for these reactions. However, the reaction of acridine *N* oxide with acetyl sulfide (Ac$_2$S) is currently under investigation by Markgraf (31) and appears to involve an intermolecular process. The product of this reaction is thioacridone which can be rationalized by an external nucleophilic attack of thioacetate ion on **21** with subsequent loss of acetic acid. Further details of this reaction must await the full experimental report.

In the reactions considered thus far an acetoxy group was introduced primarily into a position adjacent to the nitrogen atom of a variety of heterocyclic rings. These positions along with those comparable to the C-4 position in the pyridine ring appear to be sites of low electron density in the 1-oxypyridinium cations and thus are vulnerable to nucleophilic attack whether intra- or intermolecular. The C-3 position in pyridine *N*-oxide is not activated toward such a reaction and thus, with the exception of isoquinoline *N*-oxide, one fails to find β-acetoxy derivatives in these reactions. Therefore, the report by Murakami and Matsumura (32) that the reaction of pyridine *N*-oxide and tosyl chloride produced 3-tosyloxypyridine as the major product created considerable interest in the synthetic and theoretical aspects of this reaction. Subsequent work by den Hertog and collaborators (33,34) revealed a number of by-products as illustrated in Figure 8. This reaction has been extended by Matsumura to 3-picoline

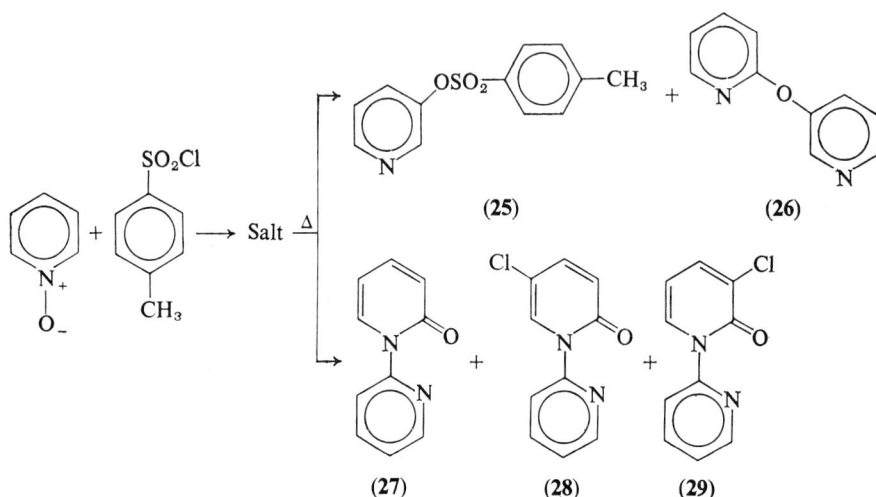

Figure 8

N-oxide (35) which produced 3-tosyloxy-5-methylpyridine and to picolinic acid *N*-oxide (36) which gave pyridine *N*-oxide, 2-pyridone, and 2,2′-dipyridyl ether. In the latter example one finds reaction affecting only the C-2 position.

The reaction of tosyl chloride with quinoline *N*-oxide (36,37) also produced a variety of products as illustrated in Figure 9. In other quinoline derivatives (38,39) reaction also proceeds primarily to the C-2 position unless blocked by the presence of a substituent, and no 3-substituted quinolines were reported in these cases. However, when the adduct of quinoline *N*-oxide and BF$_3$ was treated with tosyl chloride, both carbostyril (**8**) and 3-tosyloxy-quinoline (along with some 3-hydroxyquinoline) were found in low yield (40). The isoquinoline *N*-oxide series parallels pyridine *N*-oxide with the formation of 4-tosyloxyisoquinoline (*β*-substitution with respect to *N*) as the major product from the reaction of isoquinoline *N*-oxide and tosyl chloride (17). When the 4 position was blocked as in the case of 4-tosyloxyisoquinoline *N*-oxide, rearrangement proceeded

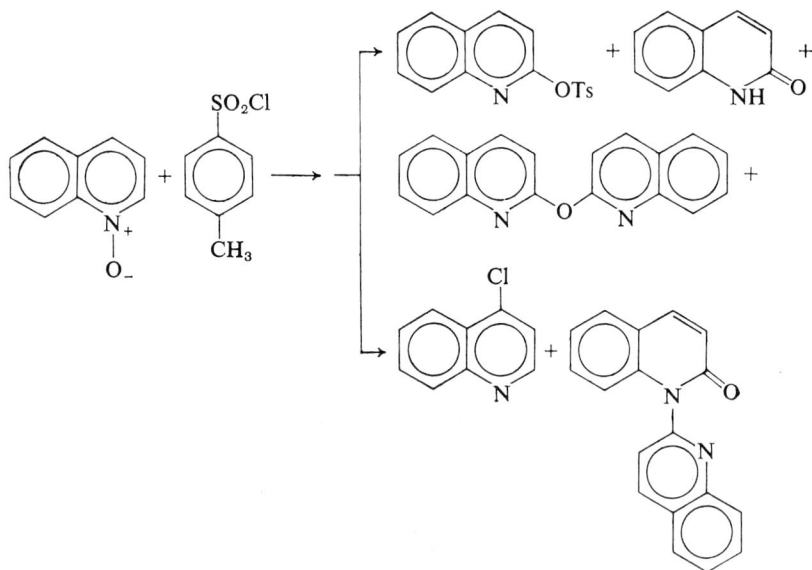

Figure 9

to the 1 position forming the isocarbostyril derivative (17). Phenazine N-oxides and tosyl chloride lead to substitution in the aromatic ring forming 1-tosyloxyphenazine (41).

In these reactions the first step is the formation of 1-tosyloxypyridinium chloride, represented as the resonance hybrid **30** (Fig. 10), or

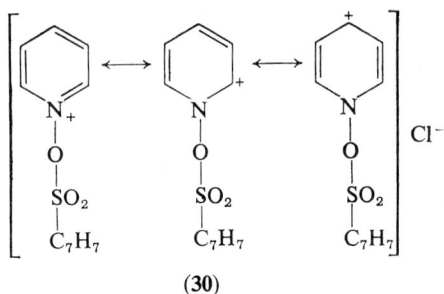

(**30**)

Figure 10

analogous salts for the other heterocyclic systems. These salts, although not characterized, have been the subject of numerous nucleophilic substitution studies (42–45). When **30** is heated, rearrangement appears to produce 3-tosyloxypyridine (**25**) and 2-tosyloxypyridine. The latter compound under experimental conditions reacts with unused pyridine N-oxide to produce 2,3'-dipyridyl ether (**26**), 1-(2'-pyridyl)-2-pyridone (**27**), 1-(2'-pyridyl)-5-chloro- (**28**), and -3-chloro-2-pyridone (**29**). Evidence to support this pathway was provided by den Hertog (46) who isolated compounds **26** and **27** from the reaction of pyridine N-oxide and 2-tosyloxypyridine and showed that chlorination of **27** gave the chloro derivatives **28** (major product) and **29**. The presence of chlorine in the initial reactions is attributed to the oxidation of chloride ion by pyridine N-oxide under reaction conditions. The formation of 1-(2'-pyridyl)-2-pyridone (**27**) may be rationalized by the mechanism (Fig. 11) analogous

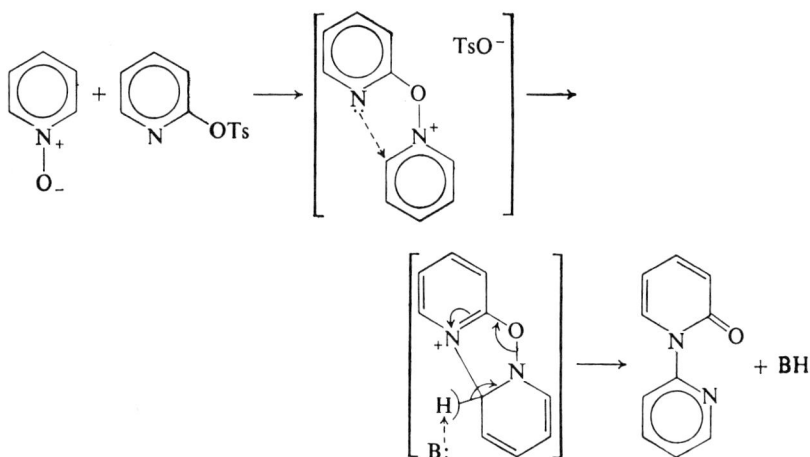

Figure 11

to the one offered by Ramirez and von Ostwalden (47) for the formation of **27** from 2-bromopyridine and pyridine N-oxide. However, the origin of 2,3'-dipyridyl ether remains obscure.

The above results imply the generation of 2-tosyloxypyridine as a reactive intermediate in the thermal decomposition of **30**; however, 2-tosyloxyquinoline has been isolated from the reaction of quinoline N-oxide and tosyl chloride. Furthermore quinoline N-oxide derivatives and tosyl chloride formed the corresponding 2-quinolones as the major products enhancing support for a 2-tosyloxy intermediate in these reactions. Thus far mechanistic studies have not been directed to account for the origin of the 2-tosyloxy compounds from the sulfonyloxypyridinium salts; however, it appears most likely that an intramolecular rearrangement is involved.

Introduction of the tosyloxy group β to the nitrogen cannot be accommodated by any of the mechanisms considered thus far. Ochiai and Ikehara (17) suggested a pathway to explain the formation of 4-tosyloxyisoquinoline from the reaction of isoquinoline *N*-oxide and tosyl chloride. In this scheme (Fig. 12) chloride ion adds to the C-1 position of the 2-tosyl-

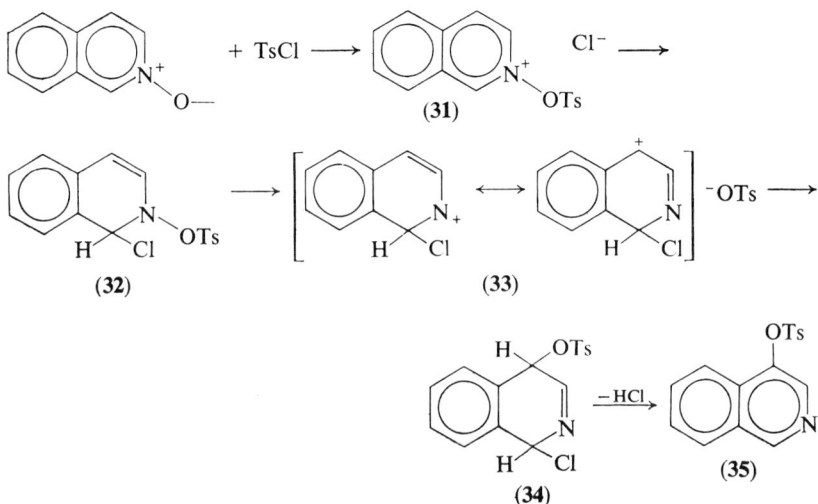

Figure 12

oxyisoquinolinium cation (31) to form adduct 32 which fragments heterolytically to form cation 33 and tosylate anion. Recombination of these ions to produce 1-chloro-4-tosyloxy-1,4-dihydroisoquinoline (34) followed by elimination of hydrogen chloride leads to 4-tosyloxyisoquinoline (35). Oae and co-workers (48) applied ^{18}O-labeling experiments to help elucidate this reaction mechanism and employed ^{18}O-enriched *p*-toluenesulfonyl chloride. The resulting 4-tosyloxyisoquinoline contained ^{18}O enrichment equivalent to the average from two ^{18}O-enriched oxygens and one natural oxygen, but upon saponification the 4-hydroxyisoquinoline contained primarily natural oxygen (about 14% enrichment with ^{18}O). These data permit the following conclusion regarding the ionization of 32 and the recombination of 33 to give 34: (1) the tosylate anion is not free of cation 33 to permit random substitution of all tosylate oxygens at C-4 and (2) the primary reaction involves attachment of the tosylate anion at C-4 through the *N*-oxide oxygen. Oae suggests structure 36, Figure 13, to represent the major pathway in this rearrangement. Since some ^{18}O enrichment occurred in the oxygen attached to C-4, this observation can be

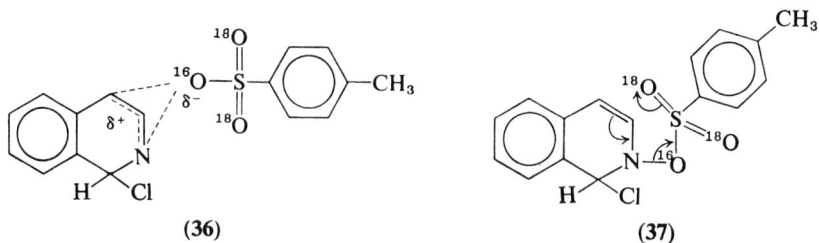

Figure 13

rationalized by a small contribution from another pathway, either a concerted cyclic process via **37** and/or solvent separated ion pairs permitting random attachment of all tosylate oxygens.

Oae and co-workers extended this mechanism to the pyridine N-oxide tosyl chloride reaction. In this case the ^{18}O-labeling experiments showed no ^{18}O enrichment in 3-pyridol and all the ^{18}O labeling was in the p-toluenesulfonate ion which resulted from hydrolysis of 4-tosyloxypyridine. These data again favor a tight ion pair arrangement via intermediate **38** (Fig. 14).

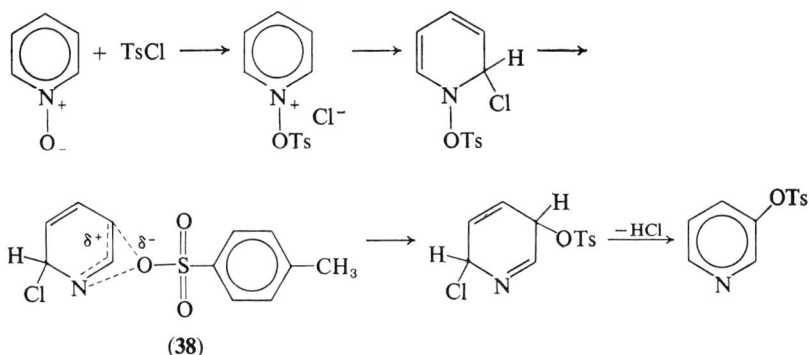

Figure 14

In all the previous examples an acetate or tosylate group was introduced into the pyridine ring replacing a hydrogen atom along with the loss of the N-oxide function. When 4-nitropyridine N-oxide (**39**, R = H) was treated with acetic anhydride, the reaction followed another course and gave as the major product 3-nitro-4-acetoxypyridine N-oxide (**40**, R = H) (28% yield) along with a small amount of 4-hydroxypyridine N-oxide (**41**, R = H) (Fig. 15) (49). If the same reaction were performed in the

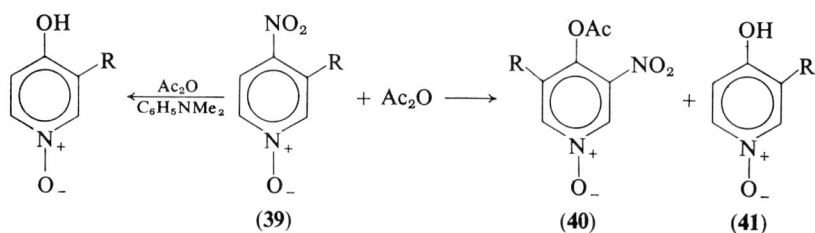

Figure 15

presence of *N,N*-dimethylaniline, only 4-hydroxypyridine *N*-oxide was isolated in 63% yield (49). Similar results were obtained with 4-nitro-3-picoline *N*-oxide (**39**, R = CH$_3$) (50), and the reaction was extended to the 4-nitroquinoline *N*-oxide series (51).

Although the mechanism of this reaction has not been elucidated, the scheme outlined in Figure 16 appears to offer one possible rationalization.

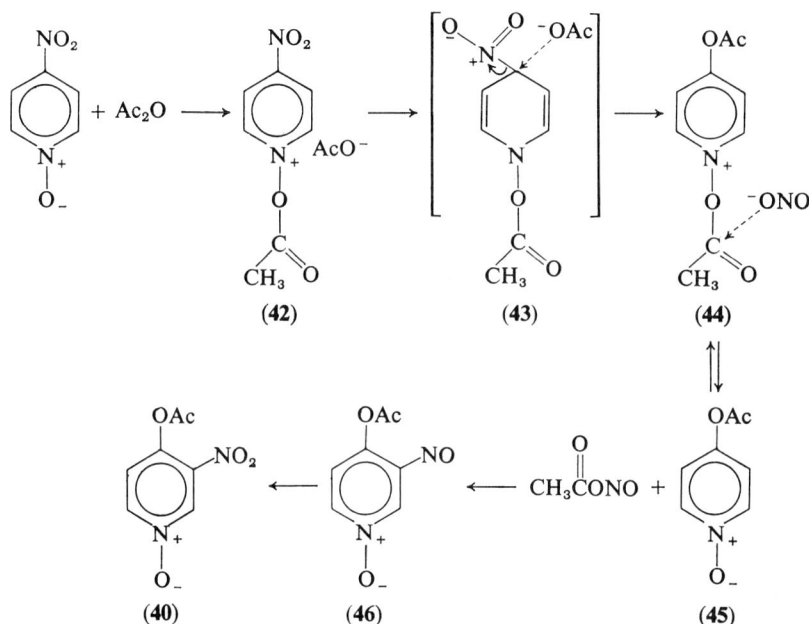

Figure 16

The conversion of 4-nitropyridine *N*-oxide to the salt 1-acetoxy-4-nitropyridinium acetate (**42**) enhances the activation of the pyridine ring toward nucleophilic attack. The reaction site at C-4 is further activated by the attachment of a nitro function and thus directs the nucleophilic attack of acetate to C-4 rather than C-2. The retention of the N-oxide function in the final product precludes an intramolecular migration of the 1-acetoxy group and thus leaves reaction of acetate anion at C-4. The displaced nitrite ion, via **43**, can react with the acyl carbon of **44** to produce 4-acetoxypyridine N-oxide (**45**) and acetyl nitrite. The latter substance nitrosates the activated N-oxide **45** and subsequent oxidation of compound **46** provides the nitro derivative **40**. When the reaction is performed in a current of air, the yield of **40** is increased from 28 to 38%; while the addition of N,N-dimethylaniline removes, by reaction, the nitrosating agent and thus permits the isolation of 4-hydroxypyridine N-oxide in good yield. Both of these observations are consistent with the mechanistic scheme just described.

A reaction parallel to the one above is the facile displacement of the nitro group by halide in the reaction of 2- or 4-nitropyridine N-oxides with acyl halides (50,52–54). In these cases the resulting 2- or 4-halopyridine N-oxides are not sufficiently activated to undergo subsequent nitrosation.

III. DEOXYGENATION

A second general class of reactions of pyridine N-oxide and acid anhydrides is the novel but complicated oxidative process recently discovered by Cohen (55), Rüchardt (56), and Koenig (57). In this reaction two equivalents of pyridine N-oxide are reduced to pyridine with concomitant oxidation of the acid anhydride to a carbonyl compound, carbon dioxide, and one equivalent of carboxylic acid as illustrated with phenylacetic anhydride in Figure 17. In addition the phenylacetic anhydride reaction gave diphenylmaleic anhydride and benzyl phenylacetate as by-products. Since acetic anhydride does not react readily with pyridine N-oxide below 100° or undergo this oxidative process, one can replace the acid anhydride with a mixture of the corresponding acid and acetic anhydride (55). Oxidative decarboxylation has also been observed in some cases using 4-picoline N-oxide.

This reaction has been successfully extended to diphenylacetic acid or anhydride and substituted phenylacetic anhydride (56); however, butyric and isobutyric anhydride were converted in low yield to propionaldehyde and acetone, respectively, while acetic anhydride, cyclohexanecarboxylic anhydride, cyclohexanedicarboxylic anhydride, glutaric anhydride, and pivalic anhydride failed to produce oxidative products and carbon dioxide (55). More recently, Rüchardt and Kratz (58) reported the conversion of a series of α,β- and β,γ-unsaturated aliphatic carboxylic acids with

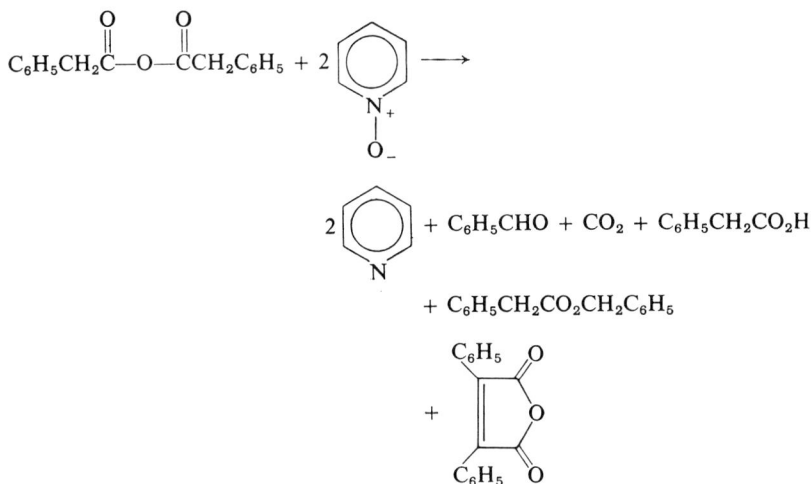

$$C_6H_5CH_2\overset{\overset{\displaystyle O}{\|}}{C}-O-\overset{\overset{\displaystyle O}{\|}}{C}CH_2C_6H_5 + 2 \; \underset{\underset{\displaystyle O_-}{\overset{\displaystyle |}{N_+}}}{\bigcirc} \longrightarrow$$

$$2 \; \underset{N}{\bigcirc} + C_6H_5CHO + CO_2 + C_6H_5CH_2CO_2H$$

$$+ \; C_6H_5CH_2CO_2CH_2C_6H_5$$

$$+ \quad \text{(maleic anhydride with } C_6H_5 \text{ substituents)}$$

Figure 17

pyridine *N*-oxide to α,β-unsaturated carbonyl compounds. In the same paper the reaction of phenoxyacetic and ethoxyacetic anhydrides with pyridine *N*-oxide resulted in carbon dioxide evolution and formation of the expected products.

The mechanism for this process has received considerable attention from the above three independent groups of workers and although a number of possible mechanisms have been excluded, no single mechanism can clearly accommodate all the current facts.

All workers agree that the most reasonable first step in these reactions is the formation of the 1-acyloxypyridinium salt. Subsequent conversion of this salt to products may involve radical or ionic species or may occur by some concerted fragmentation process. Free radical intermediates have been excluded as likely mechanistic prospects on the basis of the following observations (55,56): absence of products expected from free radical intermediates such as toluene, dibenzyl, etc. (although a small amount of 2- and 4-benzylpyridines were found, these may be accommodated by an alternative mechanism), lack of influence of oxygen on this process, no observed polymerization when the reaction was performed in the presence of styrene or acrylonitrile, and only 2% benzaldehyde production when *t*-butyl perphenylacetate was decomposed in pyridine *N*-oxide.

Numerous ionic species have been considered as possible intermediates in this reaction. The intermediacy of *N*-benzylpyridinium acetate has been excluded by Cohen (59) when he showed that *N*-benzylpyridinium acetate and pyridine *N*-oxide failed to give benzaldehyde and pyridine under the normal oxidative reaction conditions. A second ionic pathway involves generation of benzyl cations which can combine with pyridine *N*-oxide to form 1-benzyloxypyridine. The latter compound is known to undergo base-catalyzed fragmentation to produce benzaldehyde and pyridine (60). In general the failure of pivalic anhydride, which should provide *t*-butyl cations, to undergo reaction and the absence of carbonium ion rearrangements when the *n*-propyl cation or various allylic cations (58) would be the generated species, both support the rejection of the fragmentation of the intermediate salt to carbonium ions.

A carboxy inversion mechanism similar to that observed for diacyl-peroxide decompositions (61 and references cited therein) has been offered by Koenig (57) and Rüchardt (58) as a reasonable explanation for the origin of benzyl phenylacetate and comparable esters isolated in the oxidative decarboxylation reaction. This mechanism has been modified by Rüchardt (58) to rationalize, as well, the oxidative process leading to CO_2, pyridine and the carbonyl compounds (Fig. 18). However, Koenig

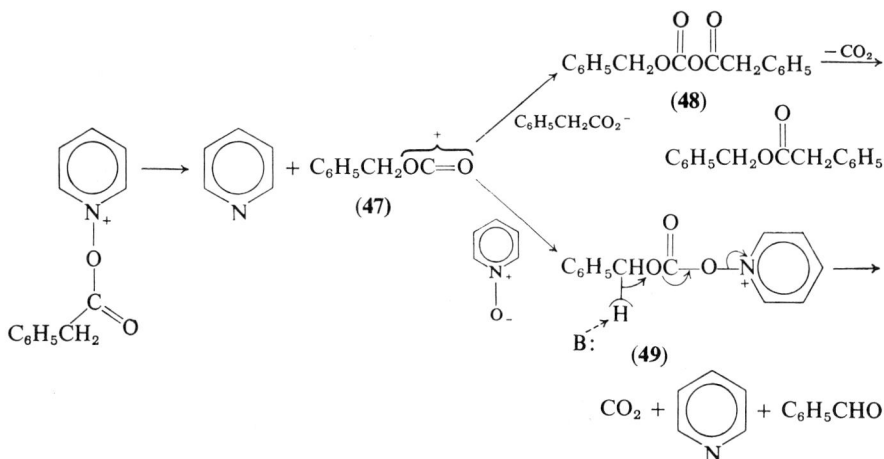

Figure 18

(62) has tested these proposed mechanistic possibilities and finds that the carboxy inversion mechanism may be applicable for the ester formation but must be discarded as a reasonable pathway for the oxidative process. Koenig generated a cation similar to **49** by reaction of benzyl chloro-formate with 4-picoline *N*-oxide and subsequent decomposition of **50** produced benzyl chloride (nearly quantitative), 4-picoline *N*-oxide (nearly

quantitative), and carbon dioxide (Fig. 19). Reaction of **50** with triethyl-amine, which should provide the most favorable conditions for oxidative decarboxylation, produced a rapid evolution of CO_2 with formation of benzyl chloride. These data rule out **49** and **50** as precursors to carbonyl

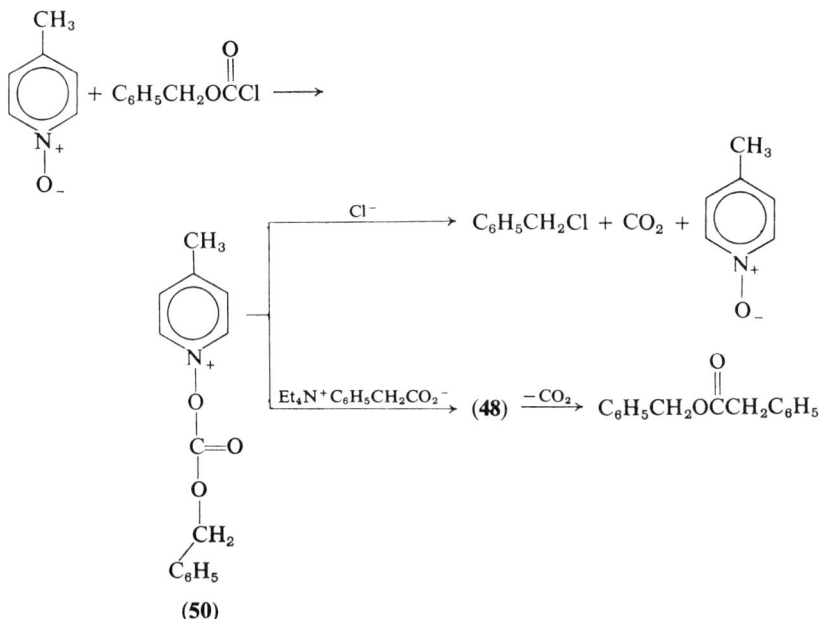

Figure 19

compounds. When **50** was mixed with tetraethylammonium phenylacetate, gas evolution was again rapid; however, the product was benzyl phenyl-acetate in high yield. The use of ^{18}O-enriched phenylacetate ions produced CO_2 containing 1.03 labeled oxygen atoms per molecule. These observa-tions may be rationalized by conversion of **50** to **48** followed by loss of CO_2 to produce benzyl phenylacetate and thus lend support to Koenig's (57) and Rüchardt's (58) proposals for ester formation by a carboxy inversion mechanism.

A mechanism for the oxidative decarboxylation reaction which seems to accommodate the majority of facts has been proposed by Cohen (59). The key intermediate (**55** for the phenylacetic anhydride reaction) involves the introduction of the pyridine *N*-oxide moiety into the α position of the carboxylic acid thus requiring the presence of at least one α-hydrogen in the anhydride or acid used in the reaction. This accounts for the failure of pivalic anhydride to effect the reduction of pyridine *N*-oxide.

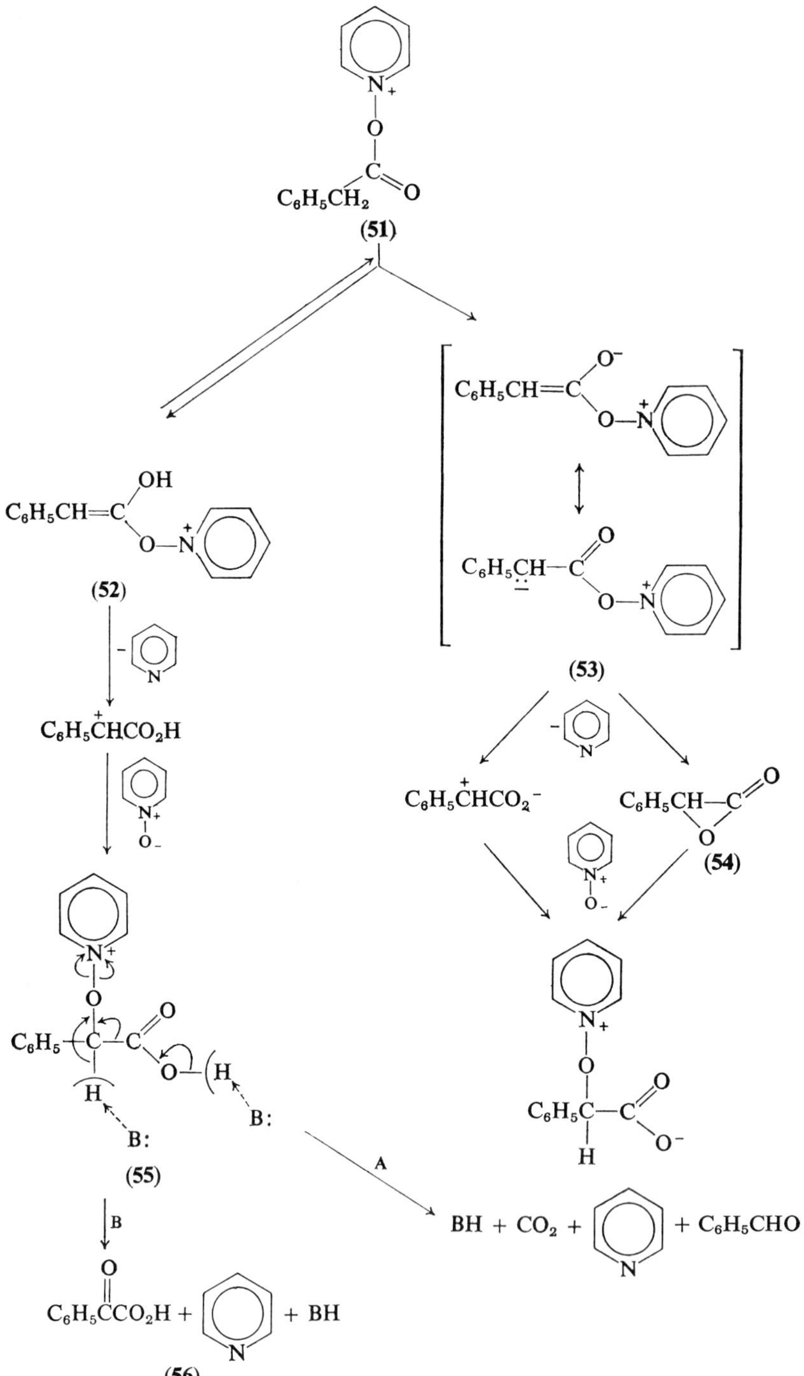

C₆H₅CH₂ — rendered as formulas:

$C_6H_5CH_2$

(51)

$C_6H_5CH=C$ OH / $O-N^+$ (pyridinium)

(52)

$C_6H_5CH=C$ O^- / $O-N^+$

$C_6H_5\underset{\cdot\cdot}{CH}-C$ $=O$ / $O-N^+$

(53)

$C_6H_5\overset{+}{C}HCO_2H$

$C_6H_5\overset{+}{C}HCO_2{}^-$

$C_6H_5CH-C=O$ / O

(54)

$C_6H_5-\overset{O}{\underset{\underset{\text{B:}}{H}}{C}}-C\overset{O}{\underset{O-(H}{}}$ B:

(55)

A

$BH + CO_2 + $ (pyridine) $+ C_6H_5CHO$

$C_6H_5-\overset{O}{C}-C\overset{O}{\underset{O^-}{}}$ / N^+—O / H

B

$C_6H_5\overset{O}{C}CO_2H +$ (pyridine) $+ BH$

(56)

Figure 20

Three alternatives have been proposed (59) to convert **51** to **55** (Fig. 20). A nucleophilic attack by pyridine *N*-oxide on the α-carbon of the enol (**52**) or enolate ion (**53**) can lead to **55** however the S_N1 type ionization of pyridine followed by addition of pyridine *N*-oxide would be more compatible with the effect of anhydride structure on this reaction. The third alternative is the intervention of an α-lactone (**54**) with subsequent ring opening by pyridine *N*-oxide. The feasibility of converting the enolate ion **53** to carbonyl compounds was elegantly demonstrated by Koenig (57) with the oxidation of diphenylketene by pyridine *N*-oxide which most

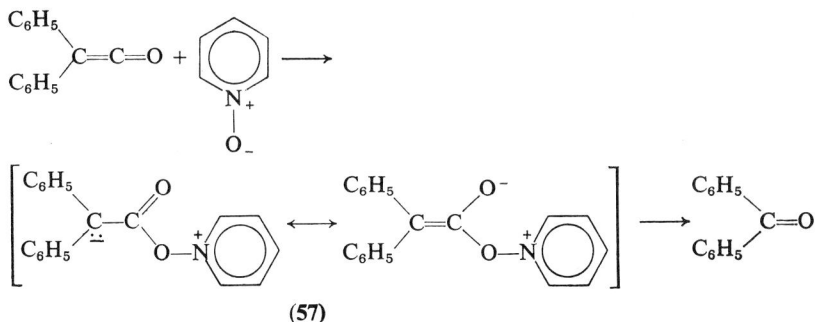

(57)

Figure 21

probably proceeds through enolate ion **57** (Fig. 21) to produce benzophenone. The isolation of phenylacetylmandelic acid and acetylmandelic acid, both as their methyl esters, demonstrates the capability of other nucleophiles interrupting the conversion of **51** to **55** and thus support the presence of an electrophilic intermediate.

Decomposition of **55** (Fig. 20) may occur by proton removal from the carboxyl function followed by a Grob type cleavage (63), path A, to yield carbon dioxide, benzaldehyde, and pyridine. An alternative reaction is shown in path B which is comparable to the base-catalyzed decomposition of benzyloxypyridinium ions (60) and leads to the production of phenylglyoxylic acid **56**. Cohen and Song (64) have confirmed these proposed pathways by isolating benzaldehyde (46%) and phenylglyoxylic acid (5%) from the reaction of pyridine *N*-oxide and α-bromophenylacetic acid which most likely proceeds via **55**. In addition **56** has been isolated in certain oxidative decarboxylation reactions and serves as a useful precursor to the formation of by-product diphenylmaleic anhydride. Cohen (59) has shown that phenylglyoxylic acid and phenylacetic anhydride undergo condensation promoted by pyridine to furnish diphenylmaleic anhydride.

The major difficulty with Cohen's mechanism is in rationalizing Rüchardt's (58) data with α,β-unsaturated anhydrides. In these reactions primarily a 1,4 enolization is required which forms a dienolate ion **58** (Fig. 22); however, one must propose exclusive reaction of the *N*-oxide at

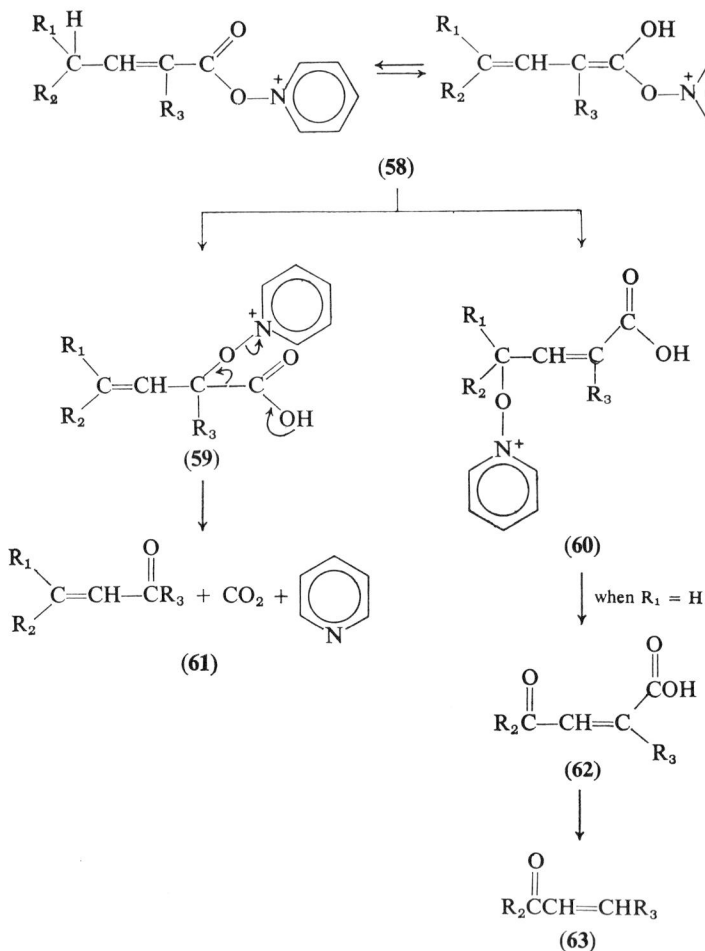

Figure 22

C-2 to produce intermediate **59** which proceeds to the product **61** isolated. Reaction at C-4 either fails to occur or takes place to a small extent producing intermediate **60**. Decarboxylation of **60** by path A (Fig. 20) cannot lead to **63**; however, the alternate path B (Fig. 20) forms **62** which should decarboxylate to **63**. The absence of products derived from **60** necessitating selective reaction at C-2 is difficult to justify. Thus the mechanism of the oxidative decarboxylation reaction is still under exploration and may require alternate proposals to satisfy the results for α,β-unsaturated anhydrides.

IV. SIDE CHAIN REARRANGEMENT

When 3-picoline *N*-oxide was treated with acetic anhydride, the acetoxy group was introduced into the α position of the pyridine ring; however, the reaction of 2- or 4-picoline *N*-oxide with acetic anhydride followed another course with the attachment of the acetoxy group primarily at the side chain. This rearrangement to the side chain has been extended to a large number of examples with varied alkyl substituents and using different acid anhydrides and acid chlorides. The mechanism for these rearrangements has received the greatest attention but a controversy still exists over certain aspects of the mechanism. Although there is close similarity in the rearrangement to the 2-alkyl and 4-alkyl groups, the discussion of these two systems will be treated separately and then unified in a comparative summary.

The initial observation that 2-alkylpyridine *N*-oxides react with acetic anhydride to form 2-α-acetoxyalkylpyridines was made independently by three groups of workers (9,65,66) with the most extensive report by Boekelheide and Linn (9). In all of the examples described only rearrangement to the side chain was reported, and the acetoxy group became attached to the α-alkylcarbon which contained no more than one other substituent. In 1954 Furukawa and co-workers (67) reported the isolation of 2,6-dimethyl-3-pyridol from the reaction of 2,6-lutidine *N*-oxide and acetic anhydride which represents the first example of β-ring attack in these reactions. Okuda (68) confirmed this competing β-substitution by isolation of 2-methyl-3-pyridol and 2-methyl-5-pyridol along with 2-pyridylmethanol upon saponification of the reaction mixture from 2-picoline *N*-oxide and acetic anhydride. These β-substituted by-products remained unexplored in the mechanistic studies that followed until Okuda's observations were unequivocally confirmed by Ford and Swan (69) and similar β-substituted picolines were used by Cohen (70) in his mechanistic interpretations. Rearrangements were also observed with 2-picoline *N*-oxide and acetyl chloride or benzoyl chloride to form the corresponding 2-pyridylmethyl esters (71).

Some synthetic applications of this rearrangement were reported by Cislak (72) in the preparation of pyridylalkandiols. Also the conversion of a 2-methyl group to an aldehyde function was described by Boekelheide and Linn (9) which entailed rearrangement of 2-picoline N-oxide and acetic anhydride to 2-pyridylmethyl acetate, oxidation to the N-oxide, a second reaction with acetic anhydride, and hydrolysis of the diacetate to produce 2-pyridinealdehyde. A similar sequence was employed by Elming (73) to prepare 3-hydroxy-2-pyridinealdehyde. Reactions with a variety of 4-substituted 2-picoline N-oxides and 2,6-lutidine N-oxides were described by Furukawa (74,75), who also noted the rearrangement of 2-styryl and 2(1-propenyl)pyridine N-oxides (64) by acetic anhydride to 65, 66, and 67 (Fig. 23).

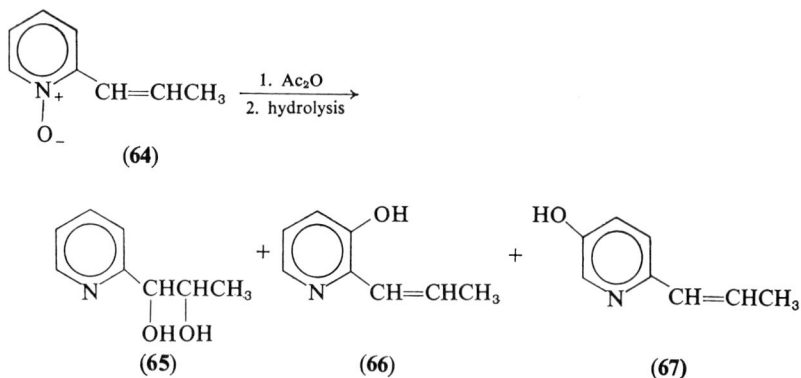

Figure 23

Similar rearrangements have been observed with quinaldine N-oxide and acetic anhydride (76) or benzoyl chloride and base (77) to yield the quinaldyl ester (69) (Fig. 24). In addition various methyldiazine N-oxides

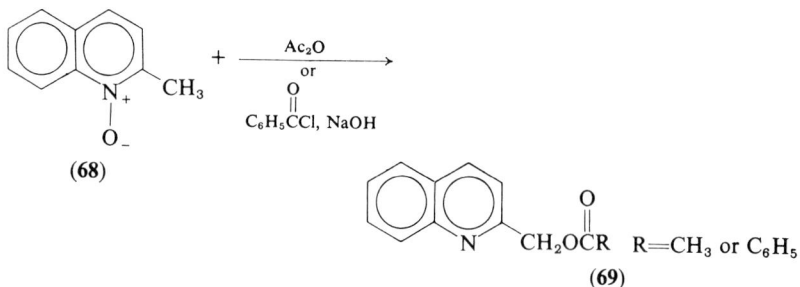

Figure 24

(pyrazines, pyrimidines, pyridazines) which have a methyl group on a carbon adjacent to the N-oxide function undergo reaction with acetic anhydride to produce acetoxy-methyldiazines (78–81) and 6-methylpurine 1-oxide undergoes rearrangement with acetic anhydride to form 6-acetoxymethylpurine (20a).

Since most of the mechanistic studies have involved the 2-picoline *N*-oxide and quinaldine *N*-oxide systems, data from these reactions will be offered interchangeably where appropriate. The reaction of 2-picoline *N*-oxide and acetic anhydride furnished a mixture of products as illustrated in Figure 25. Initial mechanistic suggestions (82) invoked a free

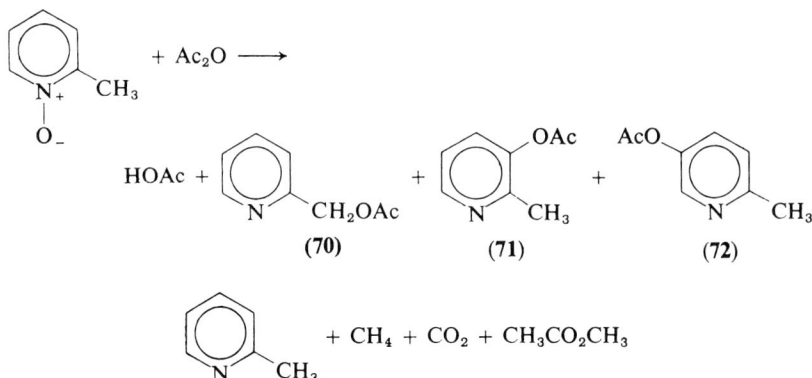

Figure 25

radical chain process to account for 2-pyridylmethyl acetate from 2-picoline *N*-oxide and acetic anhydride. A detailed product study (83) revealed the presence of free radicals in the reaction mixture; however, these intermediates were not involved in formation of 2-pyridylmethyl acetate. Evidence offered in support of these conclusions was derived from radical inhibitor studies which showed that such radical acceptors as quinone and *m*-dinitrobenzene, decrease the yield of radical generated products (polystyrene and methane, respectively), and have no influence on the generation of 2-pyridylmethyl acetate (83).

The generally accepted mechanism as outlined in Figure 26 requires a nucleophilic attack by the *N*-oxide oxygen on acetic anhydride forming 1-acetoxy-2-methylpyridinium (73) acetate in an equilibrium reaction. Abstraction of a proton from 73 by an acetate anion produces acetic acid and the anhydro base 74 which undergoes intramolecular rearrangement to 70, 71, and 72. Pachter (84) initially proposed a comparable mechanism for the reaction of quinaldine *N*-oxide with benzoyl chloride and sodium

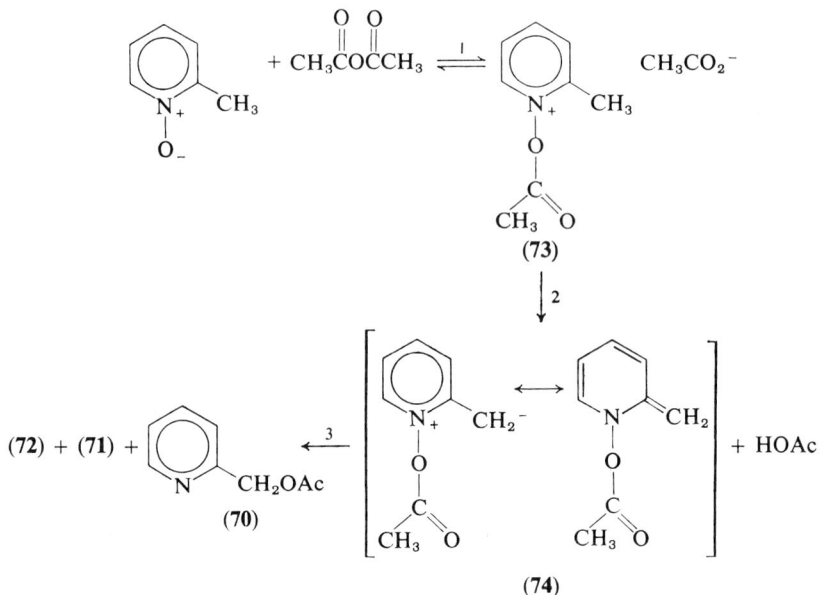

Figure 26

hydroxide. This mechanism was later applied to the 2-picoline N-oxide case (9,66,83) and subsequently modified to become the gross mechanistic interpretation of this reaction.

Studies in the 2-methylquinoline N-oxide system (85,27) provided spectral evidence that 2-methylquinoline N-oxide and acetic anhydride are converted completely to 1-acetoxy-2-methylquinolinium cation. The perchlorate salt (26,27) and picrate salt (86) of **73** have been isolated as well as 1-acetoxy-2-methylquinolinium perchlorate (27) and these salts upon treatment with a variety of bases, acetate ion, triethylamine, pyridine, or cyanide ion were converted to rearranged esters **70**. These results support the proposal that cation **73** can be an intermediate in this reaction. Evidence for the equilibrium nature of step 1 was reported by Muth (27), utilizing 1-acetoxy-2-methylquinolinium perchlorate tagged in the carbonyl position with ^{14}C. When this salt was treated with sodium acetate in acetic anhydride under conditions that would promote rearrangement to **69** and the reaction quenched with perchloric acid when partially complete, the recovered starting perchlorate retained only 10% of the original reactivity, while the rearranged product **69** contained about 25% of the radioactivity. A reversible reaction for step 1 conveniently accommodates the ^{14}C-labeling data.

The need for base in the conversion of **73** to **74** is supported by the reaction of **73** picrate or perchlorate with triethylamine and other bases to produce the rearranged product **70**. Attempts to demonstrate the presence of the anhydrobase via spectral measurements using the reaction of 1-acetoxy-2-benzyl- and 2-*p*-nitrobenzylpyridinium perchlorates and triethylamine (26) proved futile. However, the intermolecular process, nucleophilic attack of acetate ion or acetic acid on **74**, was excluded when experiments in the presence of foreign anions such as chloride (83), acid anions (83), and aryloxide anions (86) failed to produce products with these anions incorporated on the side chain methyl group. In particular, the reaction of 2,4,6-trichlorophenyl acetate and 2-picoline *N*-oxide leads to a salt with only 2,4,6-trichlorophenoxide anions and thus failure to incorporate these anions into the picolyl product strongly supports the intramolecular process. Oae's (87) experiments with ^{18}O-labeled acetic anhydride and 2-picoline *N*-oxide further strengthen the intramolecular pathway.

Although direct physical evidence for the presence of the anhydrobase **74** (or other anhydrobases) in the reaction medium is not available, the intermediacy of **74** still seems most probable. The alternative direct conversion of **73** to products requires a transition state in which proton abstraction from the α-side chain carbon must be accompanied by rupture of the nitrogen–oxygen bond with recombination of fragments producing the ester alkyl–oxygen bond. Such a mechanism requires extensive bond-breaking and bond-making acts and is not consistent with Oae's ^{18}O-labeling experiments to be discussed in the sequel. Thus the pathway from **73** to products may proceed by a reversible or irreversible formation of anhydrobase **74** followed by intramolecular rearrangement of **74** to products. The base-catalyzed conversion of salts such as **73** perchlorate to **70** was shown to proceed very rapidly in acetonitrile and seemed,

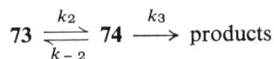

$$ 73 \underset{k_{-2}}{\overset{k_2}{\rightleftharpoons}} 74 \overset{k_3}{\longrightarrow} products $$

qualitatively, to be dependent on base strength (26). In addition the study of the reaction of 1-acetoxy-2(α,α-dideuteriobenzyl)pyridinium perchlorate with sodium acetate in acetic acid acetonitrile solvent carried to half completion showed no deuterium decrease in the starting material thus excluding the reversible formation of **74**. These results combined with the absence of spectral detection of **74** suggest that $k_3 \gg k_{-2}$ and that k_2 (step 2) appears to be the rate controlling step (26). Confirmatory evidence for this conclusion is found in the large kinetic isotope effect reported for 2-picoline *N*-oxide [$k_H/k_D = 3.1$ (50% D-content) at 30°] and 2-benzylpyridine *N*-oxide ($k_H/k_D = 7.6$ at 30°) (88); however, similar studies in the quinaldine N-oxide system revealed a lower kinetic isotope effect $k_H/k_D =$ 1.98 at 25°, 2.02 at 8° (89), and 1.5 at 30° (88). In his kinetic work Oae (88) employed the direct reaction of the N-oxide and acid anhydride in dioxane or acetonitrile as solvent and observed a small rate enhancement by electron withdrawing substituents in 2-p-substituted benzylpyridine N-oxides. The small influence of this substituent effect was attributed to the competing pre-equilibrium reaction (step 1, Fig. 26); however the direction of the effect is consistent with the proposed mechanistic scheme.

The remaining and most controversial point in the mechanism is the nature of the conversion of anhydrobase to products by an intramolecular process. Three alternatives are available: a concerted rearrangement via a quasi-six-membered ring, a homolytic rupture of the N—O bond generating radical pairs, or a heterolytic cleavage generating ion pairs, followed in each case by recombination. The concerted cyclic rearrangement is rejected on the basis of Oae's ^{18}O-labeling experiments in both the 2-picoline N-oxide series (87,90) and the quinaldine N-oxide system (91). The reaction of 2-picoline N-oxide and ^{18}O-labeled acetic anhydride (0.782 atom $\%$ ^{18}O) produced 2-pyridylmethyl acetate (0.498 atom $\%$ ^{18}O) with labeling equivalent to one natural oxygen and one labeled oxygen. When the ester was saponified, the resulting alcohol, 2-pyridylmethanol, contained 0.477 atom $\%$ ^{18}O. These results support an intramolecular rearrangement of anhydrobase and show equilibration of both N-acetoxy oxygens. Thus the N—O bond must rupture prior to formation of the alkyl oxygen bond in the ester. Similar results of ^{18}O scrambling of the N-benzoyloxy oxygens during rearrangement in the quinaldine N-oxide, benzoyl chloride and sodium hydroxide reaction again favor the N—O cleavage as the first step (91). In a more recent study of 2-picoline N-oxide, 2,6-lutidine N-oxide, and 2-quinaldine N-oxide with labeled acetic anhydride, Oae (92) separated the ester products in each reaction into individual components and analyzed each component for total ^{18}O content and determined the ^{18}O concentration in each ester oxygen. The results showed an unequal distribution of ^{18}O in the two oxygen positions which varied depending on the position taken by the acetoxy group (side chain or ring substitution) and the starting N-oxide. In the 2-picoline N-oxide case the resulting pyridylmethyl acetate contained greater enrichment of ^{18}O in the acyl oxygen position. Although a detailed analysis of these results must await the full experimental report, all of the above observations favor exclusions of a concerted rearrangement of the anhydro base to esters.

Cleavage of the N—O bond in **74** would form the resonance stabilized species **74a** [Fig. 27 (radical species via homolytic rupture and the charged species shown in brackets, by heterolytic fission)], and by recombination

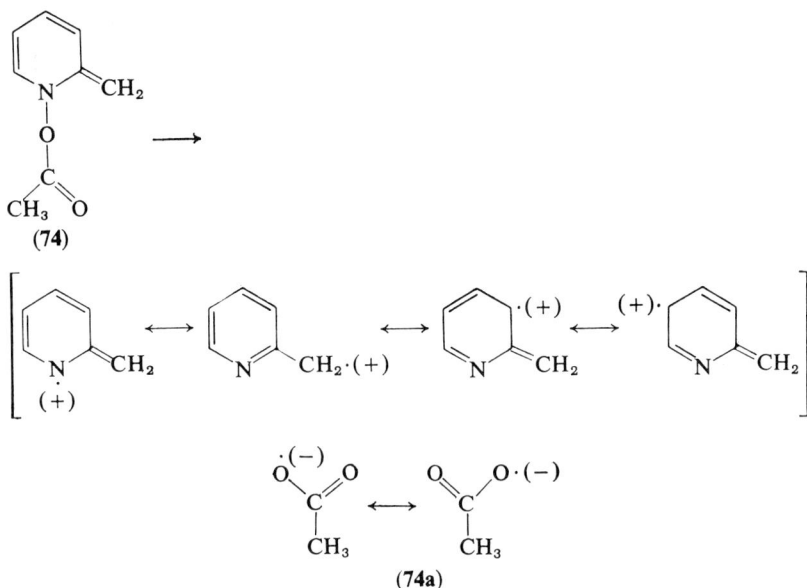

Figure 27

of **74a**, which can occur at the α-side chain or either β position on the ring, one can rationalize formation of all products. Recombination in the β position necessitates an allylic shift to regenerate the pyridine ring. Formation of either radical pairs or ions pairs requires a tight (solvent caged) association of these species, and recombination before separation of these pairs is necessary to accommodate an intramolecular process.

One advantage of the radical pair cleavage is that separation of the two radicals by diffusion produces a picolyl radical and an acetoxy radical, which can react further to form the by-products α-picoline, carbon dioxide, and methane. However, invoking radical pairs requires a rapid recombination [as suggested above $k_3 \gg k_{-2}$ (26)] or an efficient solvent cage to prevent the separation and further reaction of the radical pairs before recombination. In addition if the radical pairs are formed they do not appear to be affected even in nitrobenzene solvent or with the addition of m-dinitrobenzene or diphenylpicrylhydrazyl. Studies with phenylacetic anhydride and 2-picoline N-oxide showed formation of some 2-pyridyl-methyl phenylacetate and led Cohen (93) to favor ion pair intermediates. Koenig's (94) work with phenylacetic anhydride, trichloroacetic anhydride, and trifluoroacetic anhydride described good conversions to the corresponding 2-pyridylmethyl esters and essentially no CO_2 elimination with trichloroacetic anhydride. Acyloxy radicals resulting from these anhydrides are expected to be extremely short-lived and the absence of decomposition products from these radicals questions their presence. Most recently

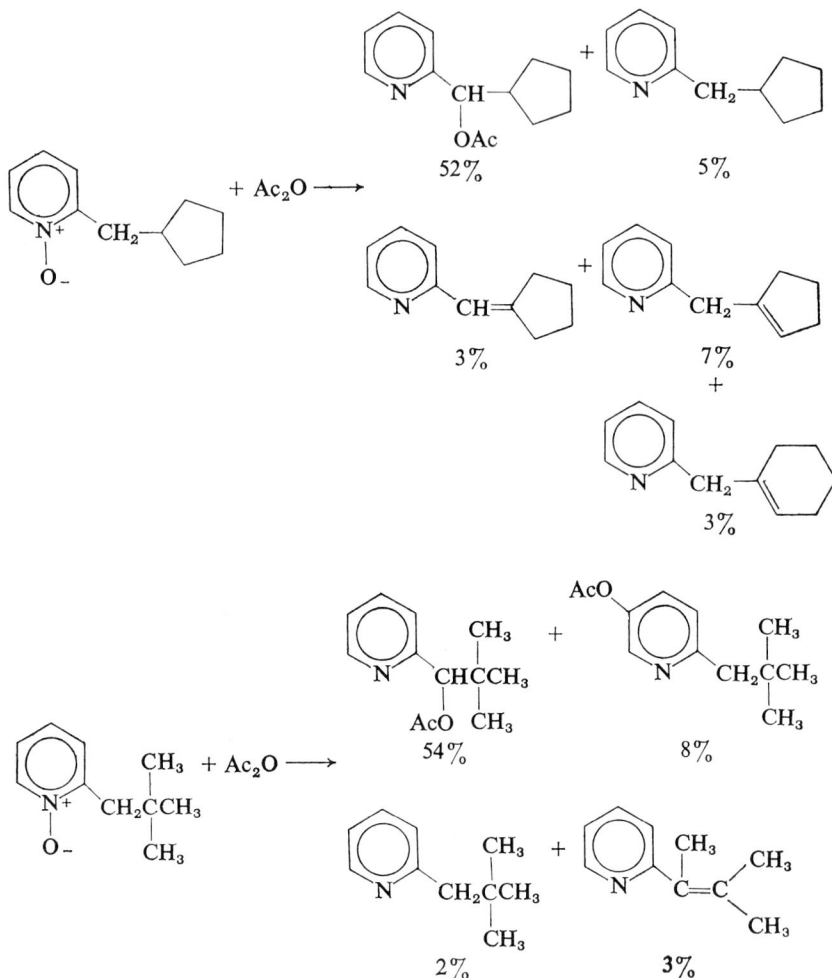

Figure 28

Katritzky (95) has reported very convincing evidence for the presence of ionic species in the reaction of 2-neopentyl- and 2-cyclopentylmethyl-pyridine N-oxide and acetic anhydride (Fig. 28). The presence of olefins with and without rearrangement of the side chain carbon skeleton strongly supports the appearance of picolyl cations (most likely from heterolytic

N—O bond fission in the corresponding anhydrobase). In addition the report cites the isolation of 15% of 2-(1-propenyl)pyridine from the reaction of 2-*n*-propylpyridine *N*-oxide and acetic anhydride.

In summary of the above studies minor products, best explained from free radical intermediates, are isolated from certain *N*-oxides and acid anhydrides; while other minor products, resulting from ionic species, are formed from different *N*-oxides and acid anhydrides. Evidence for the presence of both ionic and free radical species in the same reaction has not yet been reported. Thus if one proposes the anhydrobase as the potential source for both species, this leads one to consider a dual mechanism for the fragmentation of **74**, the competitive homolytic and heterolytic cleavage of the same N—O bond. Further experimentation appears necessary to resolve this last point.

The reaction of 4-alkylpyridine *N*-oxide and acid anhydrides parallels the reaction in the 2-picoline *N*-oxide system to form 4-(α-acyloxyalkyl)-pyridines (**75**) and 3-acyloxy-4-alkylpyridines (**76**) as the major products (9,66,72,96,97); however, this system is more prone to side reactions

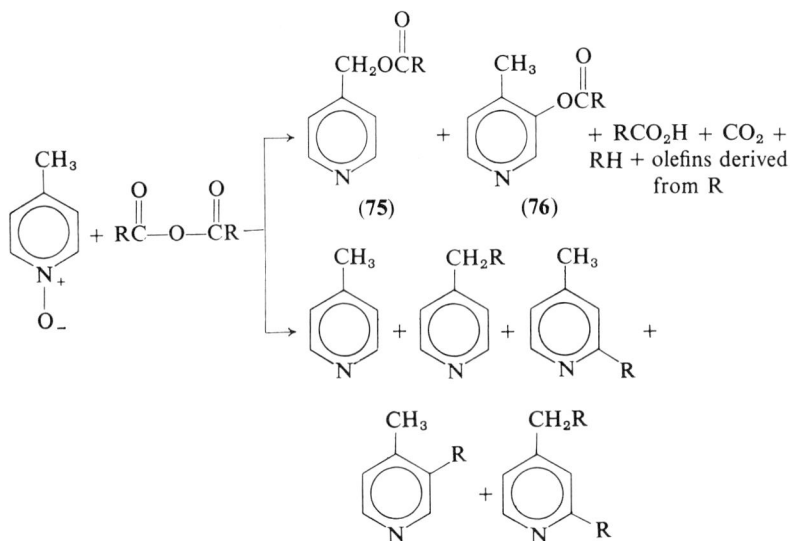

Figure 29

involving free radical intermediates (Fig. 29) and some contribution from the oxidative decarboxylation process discussed in Section II.

The general mechanistic scheme which accounts for the ester products in the 4-alkylpyridine *N*-oxide acid anhydride reaction is similar to the 2-alkylpyridine *N*-oxide case and is outlined in Figure 30. A free radical

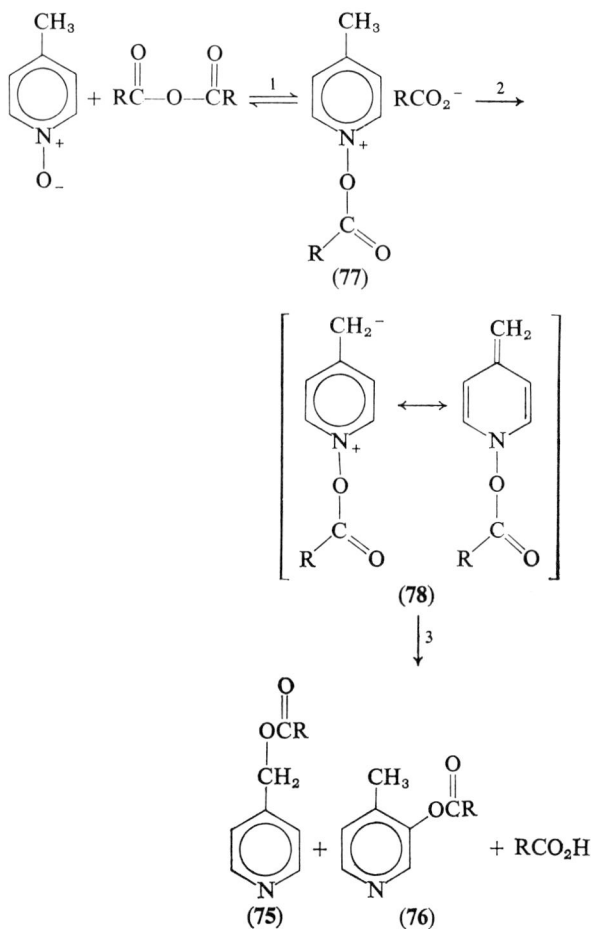

Figure 30

chain mechanism was excluded by radical inhibitor studies (98) similar to those in the 2-picoline *N*-oxide case. The reversible reaction in step 1 is offered by analogy with the 2-picoline *N*-oxide reaction; however, 1-acetoxy-4-methyl- (**77**), 4-benzyl-, and 4-*p*-nitrobenzyl-pyridinium perchlorates have been isolated and converted via base to the rearranged esters analogous to **75** and **76** (99). Also evidence for the anhydrobase was obtained by spectral studies (UV, visible) of the reaction of 1-acetoxy-4-benzylpyridinium perchlorate and triethylamine (99). Upon mixing these reactants a chromophore appeared immediately which resembled the anhydrobase derived from 1-methyl-4-benzylpyridinium iodide. This band decreased in time along with a corresponding change in carbonyl frequency denoting conversion of **78** to ester products **75** and **76**. Additional evidence in support of the anhydrobase is available in the lepidine *N*-oxide benzoyl chloride reaction (100). The reaction of lepidine *N*-oxide with benzoyl chloride produced 3-benzoyloxylepidine as the major product. When the same reaction was performed with 3-deuteriolepidine *N*-oxide (**79**), the resulting product was 3-benzoyloxylepidine (**83**) with one deuterium atom in the methyl group. These results are best rationalized by rearrangement of the anhydro base **81** to **82** followed by allylic rearrangement to **83** (Fig. 31).

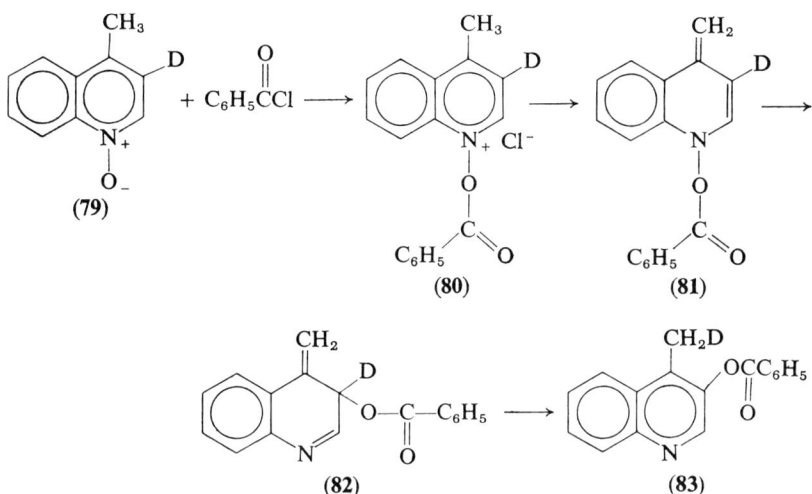

Figure 31

The study of the reaction of 1-acetoxy-4(α,α-dideuteriobenzyl)pyridine *N*-oxide with sodium acetate in acetic acid–acetonitrile carried to partial completion showed no deuterium loss in the starting material, which suggest the irreversible formation of the anhydrobase (99). Thus step 3 is much more rapid than the reverse of step 2 (see Fig. 30). These results along with an apparent dependence of anhydrobase formation on base strength (99) suggest that step 2 is rate controlling. Recent kinetic isotope studies by Oae (101) confirmed the proposed rate controlling step when he observed $k_H/k_D = 4.6$ at 30° for the 4-picoline *N*-oxide system and $k_H/k_D = 7.7$ at 30° for 4-methylquinoline *N*-oxide. These results clearly support the proton removal of **77** to produce the anhydrobase **78** as rate limiting.

The conversion of the anhydrobase **78** to ester products via step 3 (Fig. 30) requires that whether an inter- or intramolecular process is involved either must be more rapid than step 2. Evidence gathered thus far regarding the inter- or intramolecular nature of step 3 seems to suggest a process dependence on solvent and reaction conditions.

Reaction of 4-picoline *N*-oxide and acid anhydrides in the presence of foreign anions such as acid anions (98) or aryloxide anions (86) did not incorporate these anions into the ester products, thus favoring an intramolecular rearrangement of anhydrobase **78**. However, Oae (102) reported that the reaction of 4-picoline *N*-oxide and ^{18}O-labeled acetic anhydride produced esters in which the atom % of ^{18}O showed equilibration of all oxygens in the system. In addition complete scrambling of the two ester oxygens was observed. These results correspond to an intermolecular reaction by acid anion attack at the methylene position (path a) of **78** with loss of acid anion attached to nitrogen and production

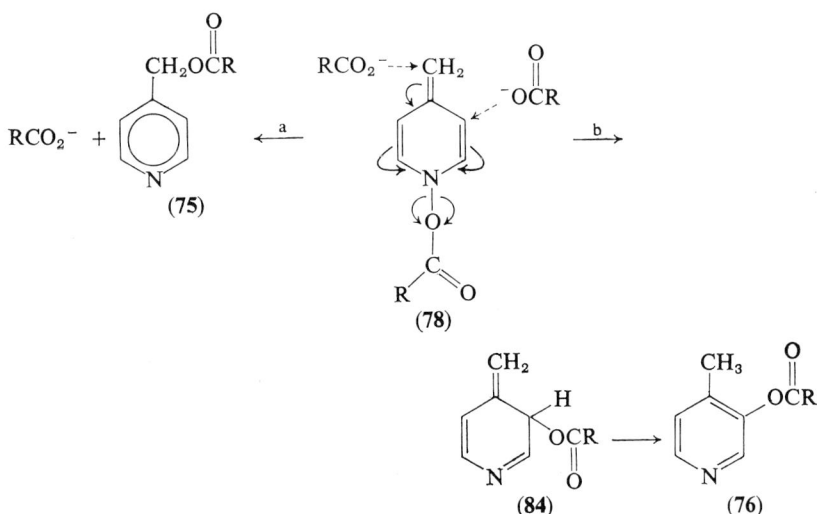

Figure 32

of **75**, or by acid anion attack at the C-3 position (path b) with the formation of intermediate **84** which undergoes an allylic rearrangement and forms **76** (Fig. 32). Support for the reaction pathway in the latter case is available from the lepidine *N*-oxide studies (100). Oae extended these labeling experiments to butyric anhydride (103) and observed a solvent effect which favored an intramolecular rearrangement as the primary path in xylene, while reaction in the presence of increasing amounts of butyric acid favored the intermolecular process. Similar observations of a solvent effect were made for 4-picoline *N*-oxide and acetic anhydride in xylene, chlorobenzene, and nitrobenzene, all of which promoted an intramolecular rearrangement as the major pathway (90). However, in all of these examples of solvent variation the intramolecular process seemed to contain contributions from an intermolecular pathway. In summary, evidence exists for an intramolecular rearrangement and an intermolecular reaction influenced by the nature of the solvent. For the present time one may consider both pathways participating in the reaction in varying degrees.

The reaction conditions which require an intermolecular interpretation provide a mechanism which is reasonably complete as described in Figure 32; however, the intramolecular rearrangement of **78** again raises the question of a concerted process, radical pair or ion pair cleavage of the N—O bond followed by recombination. ^{18}O-labeling experiments ruled out a concerted process (102,103). Cleavage of **78** to radical pairs is shown in Figure 33 and can readily explain the by-products in this reaction. Recombination of **78a** and **78b** as radicals or ion pairs gives the esters **75** and **76** but when **78a** and **78b** diffuse apart subsequent reactions of these free radicals such as fragmentation, radical abstraction, radical combination, and radical substitution can account for the alkylpyridines and the other products observed (104). As the R group in **78** is varied from methyl, *n*-propyl, *i*-propyl, to *t*-butyl, the amount of ester formation decreases with concurrent increase of radical products (104). Thus radical pair cleavage followed by diffusion is favored by bulky R groups which form more stable free radicals. Although the formation of carbon dioxide and alkylpyridines strongly supports the presence of radicals in the overall reaction, this still does not clearly establish that esters **75** and **76** result from radical recombination.

Cohen's studies (93) with phenylacetic anhydride and 4-picoline *N*-oxide again show a marked decrease in ester production; however this reaction is complicated by the competing oxidative decarboxylation process. The fact that any ester was isolated at all led Cohen to the conclusion that **78a** and **78b** recombine as ion pairs and cannot exist as radical pairs. Recently, Cohen (105) found evidence for the presence of ionic species in the reaction of 4-picoline *N*-oxide and acetic anhydride by trapping the picolyl cation in an electrophilic substitution of anisole. In addition when benzonitrile was used as solvent in a similar reaction no ring substitution was observed (as may be expected via picolyl free radical attack) but picolyl cation attack occurred at nitrogen and gave *N*-(4-picolyl)acetyl benzoyl imide. Additional evidence suggestive of ionic species in these reactions was found in the study of 4-isopropylpyridine *N*-oxide and 4-α-phenethylpyridine *N*-oxide with acetic anhydride (106). In both examples the major product was an olefin 2-(4-pyridyl)propene and

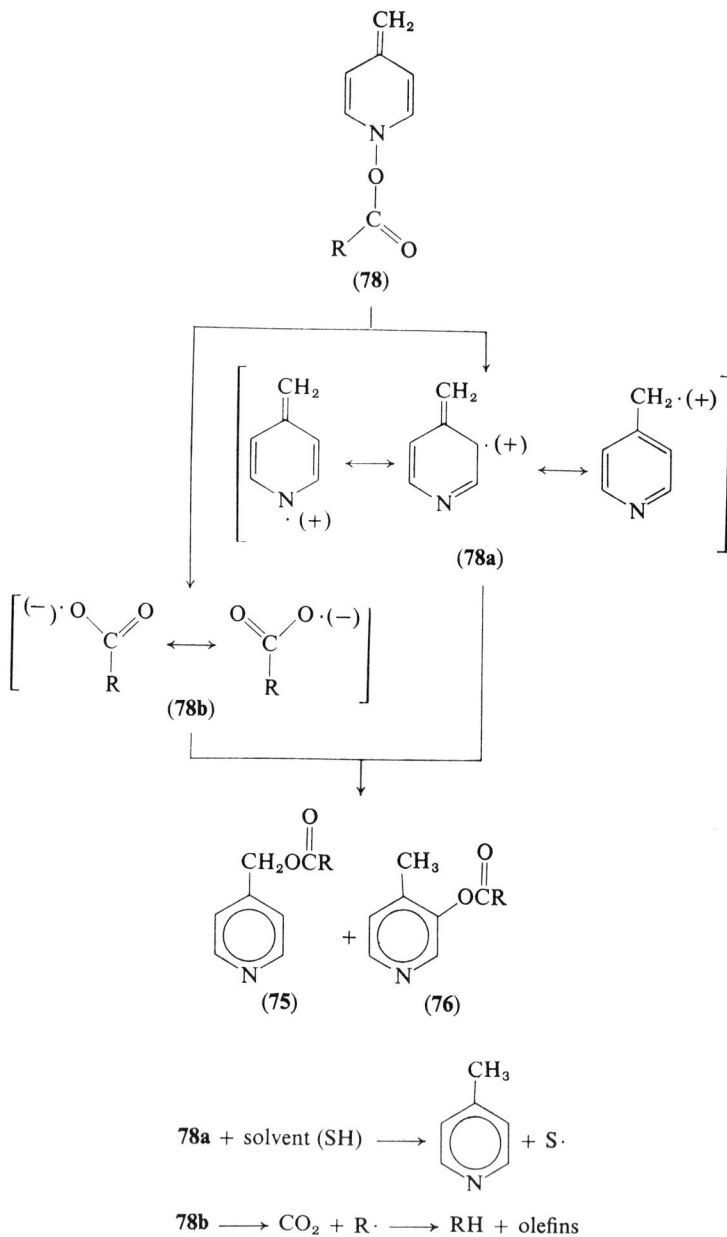

$$78a + \text{solvent (SH)} \longrightarrow \text{[4-methylpyridine]} + S\cdot$$

$$78b \longrightarrow CO_2 + R\cdot \longrightarrow RH + \text{olefins}$$

Figure 33

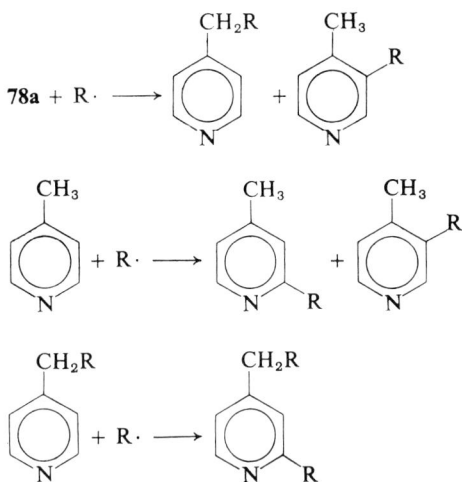

1-phenyl-1-(4-pyridyl)ethene, respectively. The expected ester products were also formed (in yields about half that of olefin) and were shown to be stable under reaction conditions. The origin of the olefins can be readily explained by proton loss from the tertiary picolyl cation arising from ion pair cleavage of the appropriate anhydro base. These results also provide the initial report of acid anhydride reactions with alkylpyridine *N*-oxides with 2-substituents on the α carbon of the side chain.

In summary of the above data some observations support the presence of ionic species while other results point to the presence of radical intermediates. In view of the intermediacy of the anhydrobase **78** a situation similar to the 2-alkylpyridine *N*-oxide case arises leading one to consider a dual mechanism in the cleavage of the N—O bond. This reaction appears to be further complicated by contributions from an intermolecular reaction of **78** with acid molecules or anions. These fine mechanistic points await additional study.

A comparison of the acetic anhydride *N*-oxide rearrangement to the 2-alkyl versus the 4-alkyl position in the pyridine or quinoline ring reveals a greater preference for the 2-alkyl group. This was demonstrated by Furukawa (107) in the reaction of 2,4-lutidine *N*-oxide and acetic anhydride, which gave after saponification 2-hydroxymethyl-4-methyl-pyridine (30%), 2-methyl-4-hydroxymethylpyridine (6%), and 2,4-dimethyl-3-hydroxypyridine (2%) and the 2,4-dimethylquinoline *N*-oxide acetic anhydride reaction which produced predominant rearrangement to the 2-methyl group, some reaction at the C-3 ring position, and no attack at the 4-methyl group. However, when the competition is between a 2-methyl group and a 4-benzyl substituent, rearrangement proceeds preferentially to the 4-benzyl group (97). These observations are consistent with the mechanistic studies described above where rearrangements to the 2-alkyl position occur more readily and with less complicating side reactions than to the 4-alkyl group. The proximity of the 2-alkyl group to the migrating acyloxy function appears to favor recombination of radicals or ions while migration of the acyloxy group to the more distant 4-alkyl position results in a greater production of free radicals. Comparing also the rearrangement to the side chain position versus reaction at the ring one finds that with nitro functions in the 4-position reaction first occurs predominately at the C-4 ring position followed by rearrangement to the 2-alkyl group (74). These conclusions are reviewed in Figure 34 where compound

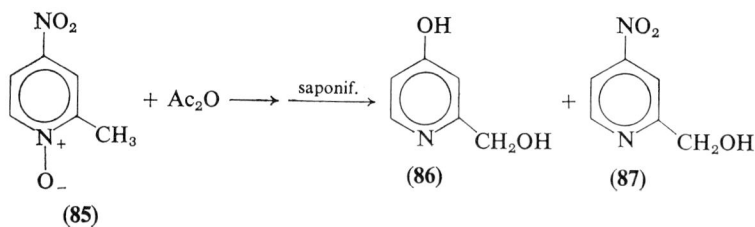

Figure 34

86, the major product, must result from displacement of the nitro first to form the 4-acetoxy-2-methylpyridine N-oxide followed by the normal rearrangement to the side chain. In addition the absence of reaction at the unsubstituted C-6 position of **85** relegates the acetate ion addition at the α position of pyridine as the least favored reaction in this group.

In the previous discussion in this section rearrangements of N-acyloxy-alkylpyridinium ions led to introduction of the acyloxy group into the side chain. A number of examples were reported in the quinoline system where reaction with benzoyl chloride also produced esters; however, when 2-picoline N-oxide is treated with benzoyl chloride or acetyl chloride, one finds some 2-picolyl chloride in addition to 2-pyridylmethyl esters (71). However, 2-picolyl chloride becomes the exclusive product when 2-picoline N-oxide is treated with p-toluenesulfonyl chloride (108) or benzenesulfonyl chloride (71). This reaction has been extended to substituted 2-picoline N-oxides (109,110), 2- and 4-methylquinoline N-oxides (111), and 2,4-dimethylthiazole N-oxide (110). Bauer and Gardella (112) reported an analogous side chain chlorination in the reaction of 4-picoline N-oxide and phosphorous oxychloride.

Although this reaction has received very little mechanistic study, in view of all previous discussions the formation of 1-tosyloxy-2-methyl-pyridinium chloride (**88**) seems to be the most reasonable first step (Fig. 35). Subsequent conversions to the anhydrobase **89** may occur which

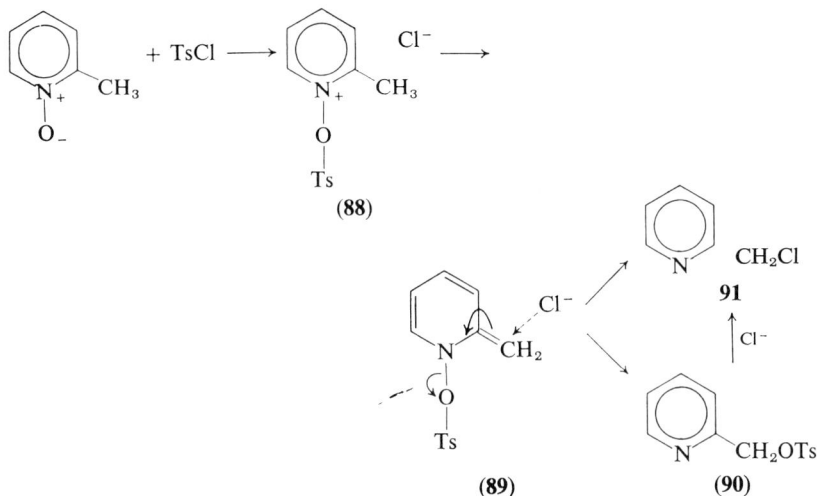

Figure 35

could undergo intermolecular reactions with chloride at the exo-methylene group to form the 2-chloromethylpyridine **91** directly or the anhydrobase may rearrange to produce 2-pyridylmethyl tosylate (**90**) which undergoes a nucleophilic displacement by chloride ion to give **91**. The mechanistic considerations remain to be tested and explored.

In conclusion a number of questions in this general area of aromatic *N*-oxides rearrangements remain to be answered. Many surprises have been discovered in past investigations and perhaps new unexpected observations are in store for the future workers in this interesting area of heterocyclic chemistry.

References

1. J. Meisenheimer, *Chem. Ber.*, **59**, 1848 (1926).
2. E. P. Linton, *J. Am. Chem. Soc.*, **62**, 1945 (1940).
3. E. Ochiai, *J. Org. Chem.*, **18**, 534 (1953).
4. H. J. den Hertog, *Chem. Weekblad.*, **52**, 387 (1956).
5. A. R. Katritzky, *Quart. Rev. (London)*, **10**, 395 (1956).
6. D. V. Ioffe and L. S. Efros, *Russ. Chem. Rev.*, **30**, 569 (1961).
7. E. Ochiai, *Aromatic Amine Oxides*, Elsevier, New York, 1967, Chapter 7.
8. M. Katada, *J. Pharm. Soc. Japan*, **67**, 51 (1947); *Chem. Abstr.*, **45**, 9536d (1951).

9. V. Boekelheide and W. J. Linn, *J. Am. Chem. Soc.*, **76**, 1286 (1954).

10. F. E. Cislak, U.S. Pat. 2,752,356, *Chem. Abstr.*, **51**, 4443e (1957).

11. B. M. Bain and J. E. Saxton, *Chem. Ind.* (*London*), 402 (1960).

12. M. P. Cava and B. Weinstein, *J. Org. Chem.*, **23**, 1616 (1958).

13. E. C. Taylor and J. S. Driscoll, *J. Org. Chem.*, **25**, 1716 (1960).

14. V. Boekelheide and W. L. Lehn, *J. Org. Chem.*, **26**, 428 (1961).

15. E. Ochiai and T. Okamoto, *J. Pharm. Soc. Japan*, **68**, 88 (1948); *Chem. Abstr.*, **47**, 8073e (1953).

16. F. Montanari and A. Risaliti, *Gazz. Chim. Ital.*, **83**, 278 (1953).

17. E. Ochiai and M. Ikehara, *Pharm. Bull.* (*Japan*), **3**, 454 (1955); *Chem. Abstr.*, **50**, 15560b (1956).

18. M. M. Robison and B. L. Robison, *J. Org. Chem.*, **21**, 1337 (1956).

19. M. M. Robison and B. L. Robison, *J. Am. Chem. Soc.*, **80**, 3443 (1958).

20. (a) M. A. Stevens, A. Giner-Sorolla, H. W. Smith, and G. B. Brown, *J. Org. Chem.*, **27**, 567 (1962); (b) M. A. Stevens, H. W. Smith, and G. B. Brown, *J. Am. Chem. Soc.*, **82**, 1148 (1960).

21. A. Kliegel and A. Fehrle, *Chem. Ber.*, **47**, 1629 (1914).

22. E. Ochiai and T. Okamoto, *J. Pharm. Soc.*, **68**, 88 (1948); *Chem. Abstr.*, **47**, 8073e (1953).

23. J. H. Markgraf, H. B. Brown, Jr., S. C. Mohr, and R. G. Peterson, *J. Am. Chem. Soc.*, **85**, 958 (1963).

24. S. Oae and S. Kozuka, *Tetrahedron*, **20**, 2691 (1964).

25. S. Oae and S. Kozuka, *Tetrahedron*, **21**, 1971 (1965).

26. V. J. Traynelis and P. L. Pacini, *J. Am. Chem. Soc.*, **86**, 4917 (1964).

27. C. W. Muth and R. S. Darlak, *J. Org. Chem.*, **30**, 1909 (1965).

28. J. H. Markgraf and M.-K. Ahn, *J. Am. Chem. Soc.*, **86**, 2699 (1964).

29. J. H. Markgraf and C. G. Carson, *J. Org. Chem.*, **29**, 2806 (1964).

30. S. Oae, S. Kozuka, Y. Sakaguchi, and K. Hiramatsu, *Tetrahedron*, **22**, 3143 (1966).

31. J. H. Markgraf, private communication, 1967.

32. M. Murakami and E. Matsumura, *J. Chem. Soc. Japan*, **70**, 393 (1949); *Chem. Abstr.*, **45**, 4698e (1951).

33. P. A. de Villiers and H. J. den Hertog, *Rec. Trav. Chim.*, **75**, 1303 (1956).

34. H. J. den Hertog, D. J. Buurman, and P. A. deVilliers, *Rec. Trav. Chim.*, **80**, 325 (1961).

35. E. Matsumura, *J. Chem. Soc., Japan*, **74**, 446 (1953); *Chem. Abstr.*, **48**, 6442e (1954).

36. M. Murakami and E. Matsumura, *J. Chem. Soc. Japan*, **72**, 509 (1951); *Chem. Abstr.*, **46**, 6648g (1952).

37. E. Ochiai, T. Watanabe, and S. Suzuki, *J. Pharm. Soc. Japan*, **76**, 1421 (1956); *Chem. Abstr.*, **51**, 6639h (1957).

38. H. Tanida, *Chem. Pharm. Bull.* (*Tokyo*), **7**, 887 (1959).

39. C. Kaneko, *Chem. Pharm. Bull.* (*Tokyo*), **7**, 273 (1959).

40. H. Tanida, *Yakugaku Zasshi*, **78**, 1083 (1958); *Chem. Abstr.*, **53**, 5266h (1959).

41. E. Matsumura and H. Takeda, *Nippon Kagaku Zasshi*, **81**, 515 (1960); *Chem. Abstr.*, **56**, 496h (1962).

42. M. Hamana and K. Funakoshi, *Yakugaku Zasshi*, **82**, 512, 518 (1962); *Chem. Abstr.*, **58**, 4512f, 4512h (1963).

43. H. Tanida, *Chem. Pharm. Bull.* (*Tokyo*), **7**, 887, 944 (1959).

44. (a) L. Bauer and T. E. Dickerhofe, *J. Org. Chem.*, **29**, 2183 (1964); (b) **31**, 939 (1966).

45. L. Bauer and A. L. Hirsch, *J. Org. Chem.*, **31**, 1210 (1966).
46. P. A. de Villiers and H. J. den Hertog, *Rec. Trav. Chim.*, **76**, 647 (1957).
47. F. Ramirez and P. W. von Ostwalden, *J. Am. Chem. Soc.*, **81**, 156 (1959).
48. S. Oae, T. Kitao, and Y. Kitaoka, *Tetrahedron*, **19**, 827 (1963).
49. E. Hayashi, *J. Pharm. Soc. Japan*, **70**, 145 (1950); *Chem. Abstr.*, **44**, 5881d (1950).
50. T. Itai and H. Ogura, *J. Pharm. Soc. Japan*, **75**, 292 (1955); *Chem. Abstr.*, **50** 1808g (1956).
51. E. Ochiai and C. Kaneko, *Pharm. Bull. (Tokyo)*, **5**, 56 (1957); *Chem. Abstr.*, **52** 1164 (1953).
52. T. Itai, *J. Pharm. Soc. Japan*, **65**, 70 (1945); *Chem. Abstr.*, **45**, 8528h (1951).
53. I. Suzuki, *J. Pharm. Soc. Japan*, **68**, 126 (1948); *Chem. Abstr.*, **47**, 8074b (1953).
54. E. V. Brown, *J. Am. Chem. Soc.*, **79**, 3565 (1957).
55. T. Cohen, I. Song, and J. Fager, *Tetrahedron Letters*, **1965**, No. 4, 237.
56. C. Rüchardt and O. Kratz, *Tetrahedron Letters*, **1965**, No. 4, 233.
57. T. Koenig, *Tetrahedron Letters*, **1965**, No. 35, 3127.
58. C. Rüchardt and O. Kratz, *Tetrahedron Letters*, **1966**, No. 47, 5915.
59. T. Cohen, I. Song, and J. Fager, *J. Am. Chem. Soc.*, **89**, 4968 (1967).
60. W. Feely, W. L. Lehn, and V. Boekelheide, *J. Org. Chem.*, **22**, 1135 (1957).
61. D. B. Denney and N. Sherman, *J. Org. Chem.*, **30**, 3760 (1965).
62. T. Koenig, *Tetrahedron Letters*, **1967**, No. 29, 2751.
63. C. A. Grob, *Angew. Chem. Intern. Ed. Eng.*, **6**, 1 (1967).
64. T. Cohen and I. H. Song, *J. Org. Chem.*, **31**, 3058 (1966).
65. Kobayashi and S. Furukawa, *Pharm. Bull. (Japan)*, **1**, 347 (1953); *Chem. Abstr.*, **49**, 10948e (1955).
66. O. H. Bullitt and J. T. Maynard, *J. Am. Chem. Soc.*, **76**, 1370 (1954).
67. G. Kobayashi, S. Furukawa, and Y. Kawada, *J. Pharm. Soc. Japan*, **74**, 790 (1954); *Chem. Abstr.*, **49**, 1164c (1955).
68. S. Okuda, *Pharm. Bull. (Japan)*, **3**, 316 (1955); *Chem. Abstr.*, **50**, 13056 (1956).
69. P. W. Ford and J. M. Swan, *Australian J. Chem.*, **18**, 867 (1965).
70. T. Cohen and J. H. Fager, *J. Am. Chem. Soc.*, **87**, 5701 (1965).
71. J. Vozza, *J. Org. Chem.*, **27**, 3856 (1962).
72. (a) F. E. Cislak, U. S. 2,743,277, *Chem. Abstr.*, **50**, 14001d (1956); (b) U.S. Pat. 2,748,141, *Chem. Abstr.*, **51**, 2878c (1957).
73. N. Elming, *Acta. Chem. Scand.*, **11**, 1496 (1957).
74. S. Furukawa, *J. Pharm. Soc. Japan*, **77**, 11 (1957); *Chem. Abstr.*, **51**, 8745g (1957).
75. S. Furukawa, *J. Pharm. Soc. Japan*, **79**, 487 (1959); *Chem. Abstr.*, **53**, 18028f (1959).
76. G. Kobayashi, S. Furukawa, Y. Akimoto, and T. Hoshi, *J. Pharm. Soc. Japan*, **74**, 791 (1954); *Chem. Abstr.*, **49**, 11659b (1955).
77. M. Henze, *Chem. Ber.*, **69B**, 534 (1936).
78. C. F. Koelsch and W. H. Gumprecht, *J. Org. Chem.*, **23**, 1603 (1958).
79. B. Klein, J. Berkowitz, and N. E. Hetman, *J. Org. Chem.*, **26**, 126 (1961).
80. R. R. Hunt, J. F. W. McOmie, and E. R. Sayer, *J. Chem. Soc.*, **1959**, 525.
81. M. Ogata and H. Kano, *Chem. Pharm. Bull. (Tokyo)*, **11**, 29 (1963); *Chem. Abstr.*, **59**, 2817b (1963).
82. V. Boekelheide and D. L. Harrington, *Chem. Ind. (London)*, **1955**, 1423.
83. V. J. Traynelis and R. F. Martello, *J. Am. Chem. Soc.*, **80**, 6590 (1958).
84. I. J. Pachter, *J. Am. Chem. Soc.*, **75**, 3026 (1953).

85. S. Furukawa, *J. Pharm. Soc. Japan*, **79**, 492 (1959); *Chem. Abstr.*, **53**, 18029b (1959).

86. V. J. Traynelis, A. I. Gallagher, and R. F. Martello, *J. Org. Chem.*, **26**, 4365 (1961).

87. S. Oae, T. Kitao, and Y. Kitaoka, *J. Am. Chem. Soc.*, **84**, 3359 (1962).

88. S. Oae, private communication, 1967; manuscript submitted for publication.

89. C. W. Muth, R. S. Darlak, M. L. DeMatte, and G. F. Chovanec, private communication, 1967; manuscript submitted for publication.

90. S. Oae, Y. Kitaoka, and T. Kitao, *Tetrahedron*, **20**, 2685 (1964).

91. S. Oae and S. Kozuka, *Tetrahedron*, **20**, 2671 (1964).

92. S. Oae, private communication, 1967; manuscript submitted for publication.

93. T. Cohen and J. H. Fager, *J. Am. Chem. Soc.*, **87**, 5701 (1965).

94. T. Koenig, *J. Am. Chem. Soc.*, **88**, 4045 (1966).

95. R. Bodalsk and A. R. Katritzky, *Tetrahedron Letters*, **1968**, No. 3, 257.

96. J. A. Berson and T. Cohen, *J. Am. Chem. Soc.*, **77**, 1281 (1955).

97. T. Kato, *J. Pharm. Soc. Japan*, **75**, 1233 (1955); *Chem. Abstr.*, **50**, 8664i (1956).

98. V. J. Traynelis and R. F. Martello, *J. Am. Chem. Soc.*, **82**, 2744 (1960).

99. V. J. Traynelis and A. I. Gallagher, unpublished results.

100. S. Oae, S. Tamagaki, and S. Kozuka, *Tetrahedron Letters*, **1966**, No. 14, 1513.

101. S. Oae, private communication, 1967; manuscript submitted for publication.

102. S. Oae, T. Kitao, and Y. Kitaoka, *J. Am. Chem. Soc.*, **84**, 3362 (1962).

103. S. Oae, Y. Kitaoka, and T. Kitao, *Tetrahedron*, **20**, 2677 (1964).

104. V. J. Traynelis and A. I. Gallagher, *J. Am. Chem. Soc.*, **87**, 5710 (1965).

105. T. Cohen and G. L. Deets, *J. Am. Chem. Soc.*, **89**, 3939 (1967).

106. V. J. Traynelis and K. Yamauchi, unpublished results.

107. S. Furukawa, *Pharm. Bull. (Japan)*, **3**, 413 (1955); *Chem. Abstr.*, **50**, 13926a (1956).

108. E. Matsumura, *J. Chem. Soc. Japan*, **74**, 363 (1953); *Chem. Abstr.*, **48**, 6442b (1954).

109. F. A. Daniher, B. E. Hackley, Jr., and A. B. Ash, *J. Org. Chem.*, **31**, 2709 (1966).

110. E. Matsumura, T. Kirooka, and K. Imagawa, *Nippon Kagaku Zasshi*, **82**, 616 (1961); *Chem. Abstr.*, **57**, 12466f (1962).

111. H. Tanida, *Yakaguka Zasshi*, **78**, 611 (1958); *Chem. Abstr.*, **50**, 18420e (1958).

112. L. Bauer and L. A. Gardella, *J. Org. Chem.*, **28**, 1323 (1963).

1,3-Alkyl Migrations

PHILLIP S. LANDIS

Mobil Oil Corporation, Central Research Division
Princeton, New Jersey

In contrast to the extensive literature on the Claisen rearrangement of allyl ethers (1), 1,3-rearrangements of alkyl groups from oxygen to carbon or from oxygen to nitrogen have received little attention. The diversity of these 1,3-rearrangements has compelled investigators to examine each system separately, and has thus far not permitted wide generalizations. The mechanistic paths of most 1,3-rearrangements are still merely conjecture.

I. 1,3-MIGRATIONS FROM OXYGEN TO CARBON

As early as 1896, Claisen (2a) observed the rearrangement of α-alkoxystyrenes (1) to the corresponding substituted acetophenone (2). The ease of rearrangement depended on the nature of the alkyl group where qualitatively *n*-propyl > ethyl > methyl (2b).

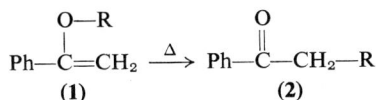

$$\underset{\textbf{(1)}}{\overset{\overset{\textstyle O-R}{|}}{Ph-C=CH_2}} \xrightarrow{\Delta} \underset{\textbf{(2)}}{\overset{\overset{\textstyle O}{\parallel}}{Ph-C-CH_2-R}}$$

Other early recorded examples of the rearrangement include the conversion of 2-ethoxy-4-methylcyclopent-2-eneone (3) to 3-ethyl-4-methyl-

43

1,2-cyclopentanedione (3) (4) and the rearrangement of methoxymethylene-phenyl acetic acid esters (5) to α-methyl-α-formylphenylacetic acid esters (4) (6).

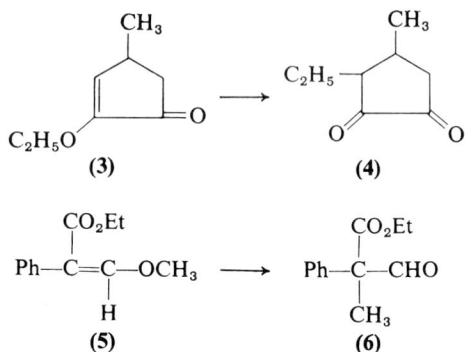

Subsequently, Lauer et al. examined the rearrangement of α-methoxy-styrene (7), noting by-product methane and 1,2-dibenzoylpropane (8), which arose from a secondary reaction that complicated kinetic studies (5). Analysis of gases evolved in the rearrangements of α-ethoxy- and α-n-

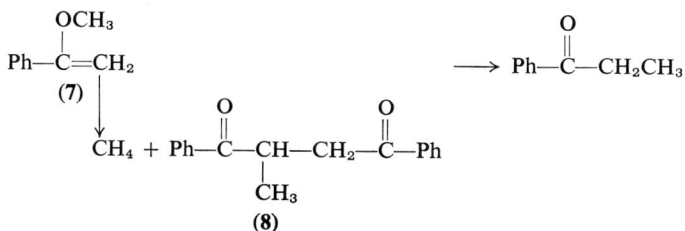

propoxystyrenes, which arose from this side condensation reaction, indicated that the side reaction was of minor importance unless the alkyl group in the styryl ether was large. Thus, gaseous product from rearranging α-ethoxystyrene consisted of 6% ethylene, and the gas from α-n-propoxystyrene rearrangement consisted of 16% propylene.

Wiberg and Rowland (6) reported the racemization of an optically active alkoxystyrene and the skeletal stability of the neopentyl group during rearrangement of α-neopentoxystyrene (9) to γ,γ-dimethylvalero-phenone (10).

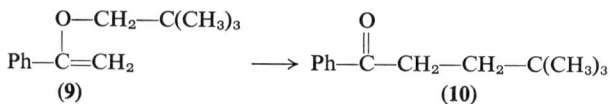

Arylmethyl vinyl ethers (11) undergo peroxide-initiated rearrangement to β-arylpropionaldehydes (7) (12), although yields are quite low.

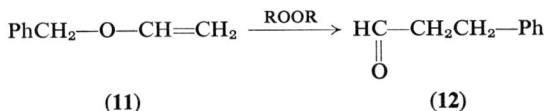

$$PhCH_2-O-CH=CH_2 \xrightarrow{\text{ROOR}} \underset{\underset{O}{\|}}{HC}-CH_2CH_2-Ph$$

$$\text{(11)} \qquad\qquad\qquad \text{(12)}$$

Simple alkyl vinyl ethers require temperatures of 400° to produce isomeric aldehydes and ketones (8). Thus, ethyl vinyl ether produces acetaldehyde and ethylene (9,10) at 400–600°, probably by a radical process. Two mechanisms have been proposed to account for the first-order kinetics of this decomposition; the first, A, based on activation energy considerations and the second, B, upon entropy considerations.

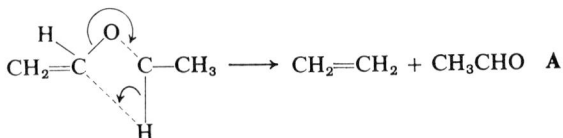

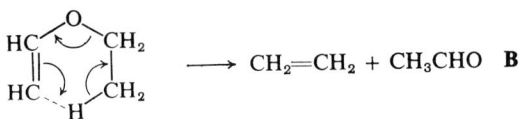

$$\longrightarrow CH_2=CH_2 + CH_3CHO \quad \textbf{A}$$

$$\longrightarrow CH_2=CH_2 + CH_3CHO \quad \textbf{B}$$

Pyrolysis of anisole (13) and phenetole (14) to 2-methylphenol (15) and 2-ethylphenol (16) in low yields may be analogous 1,3-rearrangements (11). The existence of free radical intermediates in such systems is

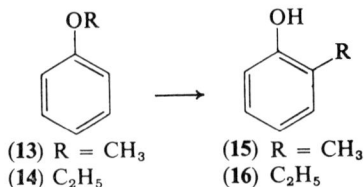

(13) R = CH_3   (15) R = CH_3
(14) C_2H_5   (16) C_2H_5

suggested by the observations of Hickenbottom (12), who heated benzyl-phenyl ether (17) to 250° in the presence of quinoline and obtained benzylquinoline (18) and hydroxyphenylquinoline (19).

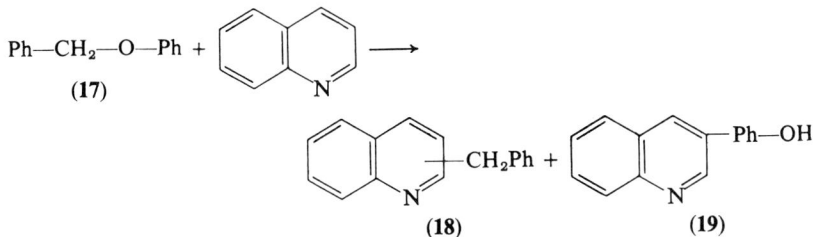

$$Ph-CH_2-O-Ph + \quad \longrightarrow$$

$$\text{(17)}$$

$$\text{(18)} \qquad\qquad \text{(19)}$$

It is possible that the rearrangements may not be general for alkyl vinyl ethers since β-methoxyphenylacrylonitrile (20) is reported not to rearrange at 190° (13), and Lauer and Spielman (5) found that 3-methoxyhexene-3 (21) and ethyl β-ethoxyacrylate (22) gave no rearrangement products on prolonged heating. However, the effects of high temperatures and radical initiators have not been studied with these compounds.

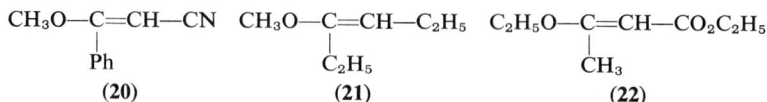

$$CH_3O—C=CH—CN \qquad CH_3O—C=CH—C_2H_5 \qquad C_2H_5O—C=CH—CO_2C_2H_5$$
$$\quad\quad\; | \qquad\qquad\qquad\qquad\quad\; | \qquad\qquad\qquad\qquad\qquad\; |$$
$$\quad\quad\; Ph \qquad\qquad\qquad\qquad\quad C_2H_5 \qquad\qquad\qquad\qquad\quad CH_3$$
$$\quad\quad\; (20) \qquad\qquad\qquad\qquad\quad (21) \qquad\qquad\qquad\qquad\quad (22)$$

A. Mechanisms for the Decomposition of Alkyl Vinyl Ethers

There is convincing evidence that the rearrangement of alkyl vinyl ethers proceeds by a free radical path.

1. The rearrangement is catalyzed by di-t-butylperoxide (6,7) and related initiators, including oxygen.

2. In the alkoxystyrene system, neopentyl (7), cyclohexyl, cyclopentyl, cycloheptyl, cyclopropylcarbinyl, norbornyl, and tetrahydrofurfuryl derivatives undergo rearrangement with no detectable skeletal isomerization of the migrating group. These observations would rule out heterolytic mechanisms that yield ionic intermediates.

3. Phenyl-α-naphthylamine inhibits the rearrangement although chloranil has no effect.

4. In the presence of easily abstractable hydrogen atoms, the leaving alkyl group forms an alkane (and minor amounts of olefin) and the newly generated, more stable, alkyl or preferably aralkyl radical is incorporated into the product. Free radical abstraction of hydrogen and halogen from alkanes and alkyl halides is well documented (14).

5. Optically active α-alkoxystyrenes undergo rearrangement with racemization of the optically active center.

These observations are consistent with the free radical pathway

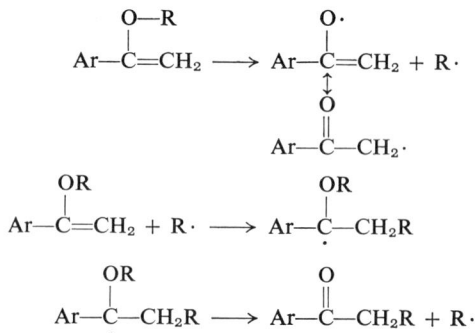

$$\begin{array}{c} O—R \\ | \\ Ar—C=CH_2 \end{array} \longrightarrow \begin{array}{c} O· \\ | \\ Ar—C=CH_2 + R· \\ \updownarrow \\ O \\ \| \\ Ar—C—CH_2· \end{array}$$

$$\begin{array}{c} OR \\ | \\ Ar—C=CH_2 + R· \end{array} \longrightarrow \begin{array}{c} OR \\ | \\ Ar—C—CH_2R \\ · \end{array}$$

$$\begin{array}{c} OR \\ | \\ Ar—C—CH_2R \\ · \end{array} \longrightarrow \begin{array}{c} O \\ \| \\ Ar—C—CH_2R + R· \end{array}$$

Possible termination reactions include

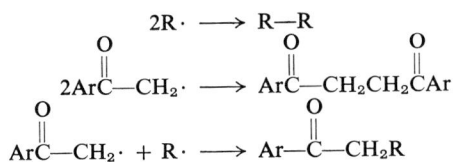

$$2R \cdot \longrightarrow R{-}R$$

$$2Ar\overset{\overset{\displaystyle O}{\|}}{C}{-}CH_2 \cdot \longrightarrow Ar\overset{\overset{\displaystyle O}{\|}}{C}{-}CH_2CH_2\overset{\overset{\displaystyle O}{\|}}{C}Ar$$

$$Ar\overset{\overset{\displaystyle O}{\|}}{C}{-}CH_2 \cdot + R \cdot \longrightarrow Ar{-}\overset{\overset{\displaystyle O}{\|}}{C}{-}CH_2R$$

Lack of inhibition of the reaction by several recognized inhibitors may be a consequence of the radical trapping ability of the alkoxystyrene, which competes successfully with the inhibitor for the alkyl radicals.

In addition to radical rearrangement, there are two further reactions observed as a consequence of the formation of noncage radicals. Formation of acetophenone from a hydrogen abstraction reaction of $Ar{-}\overset{\overset{\displaystyle O}{\|}}{C}{-}CH_2 \cdot$ and formation of alkane by hydrogen abstraction by an alkyl radical, add evidence for the radical nature of the reaction.

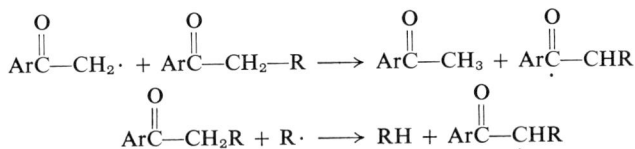

$$Ar\overset{\overset{\displaystyle O}{\|}}{C}{-}CH_2 \cdot + Ar\overset{\overset{\displaystyle O}{\|}}{C}{-}CH_2{-}R \longrightarrow Ar\overset{\overset{\displaystyle O}{\|}}{C}{-}CH_3 + Ar\overset{\overset{\displaystyle O}{\|}}{C}{-}\underset{\cdot}{C}HR$$

$$Ar\overset{\overset{\displaystyle O}{\|}}{C}{-}CH_2R + R \cdot \longrightarrow RH + Ar\overset{\overset{\displaystyle O}{\|}}{C}{-}\underset{\cdot}{C}HR$$

By-product from both abstraction processes is a 1,4-diketone (23), which arises either from a crossed radical termination reaction A or from a chain reaction B that involves addition of the radical to the vinyl ether, followed by loss of an alkyl radical.

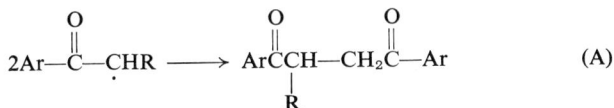

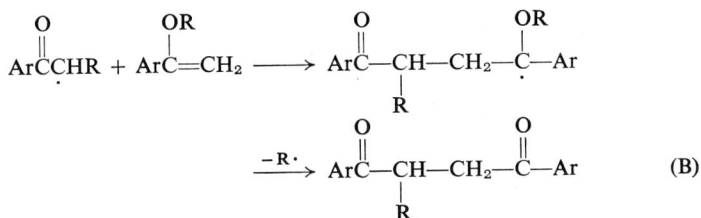

$$2Ar{-}\overset{\overset{\displaystyle O}{\|}}{C}{-}\underset{\cdot}{C}HR \longrightarrow Ar\overset{\overset{\displaystyle O}{\|}}{C}\underset{\underset{\displaystyle R}{|}}{C}H{-}CH_2\overset{\overset{\displaystyle O}{\|}}{C}{-}Ar \qquad (A)$$

$$Ar\overset{\overset{\displaystyle O}{\|}}{C}\underset{\cdot}{C}HR + Ar\overset{\overset{\displaystyle OR}{|}}{C}{=}CH_2 \longrightarrow Ar\overset{\overset{\displaystyle O}{\|}}{C}{-}\underset{\underset{\displaystyle R}{|}}{C}H{-}CH_2{-}\overset{\overset{\displaystyle OR}{|}}{\underset{\cdot}{C}}{-}Ar$$

$$\overset{-R\cdot}{\longrightarrow} Ar\overset{\overset{\displaystyle O}{\|}}{C}{-}\underset{\underset{\displaystyle R}{|}}{C}H{-}CH_2{-}\overset{\overset{\displaystyle O}{\|}}{C}{-}Ar \qquad (B)$$

These secondary hydrogen abstraction processes only become important at high conversions and do not interfere with kinetic studies at 10–20% conversion levels.

The intermolecular nature of the 1,3-alkyl shift in the alkyl styryl system is supported by second-order kinetics, by incorporation of ^{13}C-labeled alkyl group into product from unlabeled alkoxystyrene (15), and by formation of crossed products from rearrangement of mixtures of different alkoxystyrenes.

Rearrangement kinetics are easily followed by infrared spectroscopy. Nuclear magnetic resonance can also be used but is less sensitive to small changes in concentration of reactant or product. The formation of the carbonyl band at 5.88 to 5.95 μ, and the disappearance of bands characteristic of the alkyl styryl ethers (singlet at 8.88–8.94 μ, triplet at 7.65–7.75 μ) are most convenient for analytical purposes. Only aromatic solvents such as diphenylether can be used in these experiments, since hydrocarbons such as heptane or methylbenzenes undergo a secondary radical chain reaction. Spectra and kinetic results for a typical rearrangement of α-benzyloxystyrene are given in Figures 1, 2, and 3.

Kinetic data on several comparative series of styryl ethers are presented in Tables 1, 2, and 3. It is apparent from the data that radical stabilization is an important factor in controlling the rate of rearrangement. Thus, α-isopropoxy- and α-ethoxy styrene rearrange 1.2–1.5 times

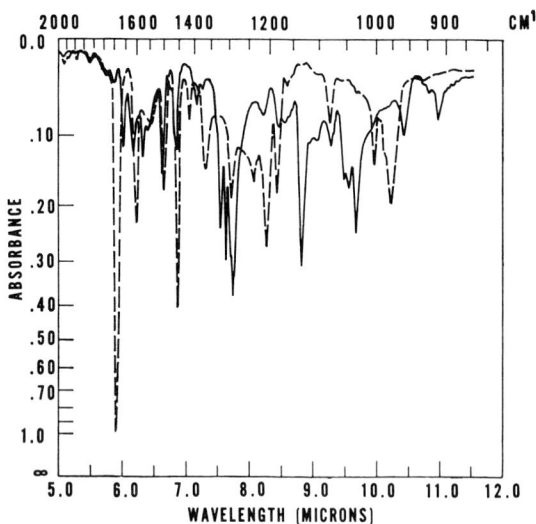

Fig. 1. 10% solutions of (——) α-benzyloxystyrene and (- - - - -) ω-phenylaceto-phenone in CCl_4.

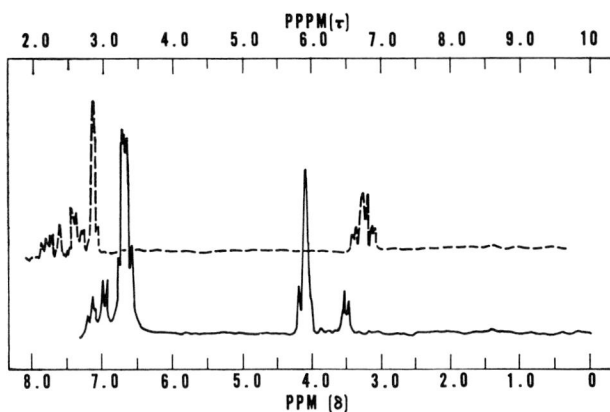

Fig. 2. NMR spectra of (———) α-benzyloxystyrene and its rearrangement product (- - - -) ω-benzylacetophenone.

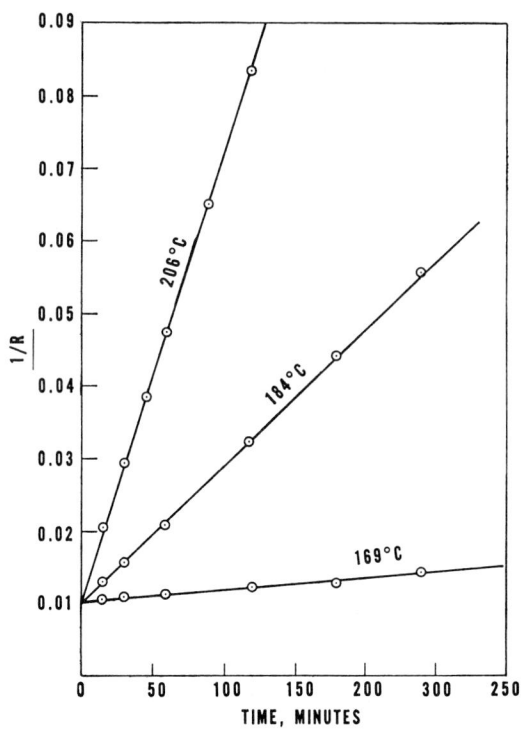

Fig. 3. Rearrangement of 2-benzyloxystyrene.

TABLE 1

Substituent Effects in Radical Rearrangements
of Aryl Vinyl Ethers

$$\begin{array}{c} OCH_3 \\ | \\ R-Ph-C=CH_2 \end{array}$$

R	Relative reactivity
H	1.0
p-Cl	1.35
m-Cl	1.47
p-CN	3.60
p-CH$_3$	1.01

TABLE 2

Rates of Rearrangement for Simple Alkyl Derivatives

$$\begin{array}{c} O-R \\ | \\ Ph-C=CH_2 \end{array}$$

R	k_2 at 236°	Relative rate
CH$_3$	11.1×10^{-4}	1.0
C$_2$H$_5$	12.6×10^{-4}	1.2
CH(CH$_3$)$_2$	16.4×10^{-4}	1.5
n-C$_4$H$_9$	13.1×10^{-4}	1.2

TABLE 3

Rates of Rearrangement for Some Secondary
Alkoxystyrenes

$$\begin{array}{c} O-R \\ | \\ Ph-C=CH_2 \end{array}$$

R	$k_2 \times 10^5$ at 206°
Cyclopentyl	4.6
Cyclohexyl	2.8
Cycloheptyl	3.2
Norbornyl	2.6
sec-Butyl	5.7
Methylcyclopropylcarbinyl	5.9

faster than does α-methoxystyrene. Activation energies of 27–34 kcal were observed. Activation entropy was negative in all measured cases but was more negative with the benzyl derivative than with alkyl derivatives (see Table 4). Stabilization of the alkyl group by a phenyl group, i.e., α-benzyloxystyrene, accelerates the rearrangement by a factor of about 10, and substitution of a second phenyl group doubles this rate. These observations are in accord with resonance energies (16) of the radicals formed by cleavage of the C—O bond.

Data on substituent effects on the aryl group for radical addition to arylvinyl ethers give a rectilinear plot of log k/k_0 against sigma. The positive slope ($\rho = 0.4$) indicates that the radical adding to the arylvinyl ether is acting as an electron donor and that attack on the double bond is encouraged by electron-withdrawing groups. Electron-donating groups have a slight decelerating influence on the reaction rate.

Stabilization of the radical **24** by substituents at X probably has little effect on the overall reaction kinetics because of the overriding driving force for formation of the carbonyl group.

TABLE 4
Energy and Entropy Terms for Alkoxystyrene Rearrangements

	T, °C	$k_2 \times 10^4$	E_a, kcal	$\Delta S\ddagger$, eu
α-Benzyloxystyrene	169	0.537	27 ± 1	−17 ± 2
	184	1.28		
	204	5.91		
α-Methoxystyrene	236	11.1	34 ± 2	−8 ± 1
	250	23.4		
	260	47.3		
α-n-Butoxystyrene	207	1.5	33 ± 1	−9 ± 1
	229	6.6		
	238	13.1		

In view of the second-order kinetics, a cyclic transition state (25) has been proposed for the rearrangement reaction (5). A four-membered cyclic transition state (26) is precluded by the observed second-order kinetics so that six- and eight-membered rings seem most probable. Larger ring size transition states appear unlikely because of the smaller incidence of ternary or higher collisions that would require more complex kinetics.

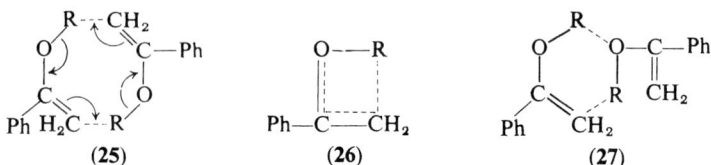

(25)   (26)   (27)

The stereochemical studies of Wiberg and Roland (6) demonstrated that the optically active secondary butyl group in α-sec-butyoxystyrene was 95–100% racemized during rearrangement and that the product ketone had not racemized after being formed. These observations rule out transition states 26 and 27 since retention of configuration should be observed in a four-centered cyclic reaction; in a six-membered cyclic transition state some inversion in the ketone and racemization of the ether should be observed. Indeed, any concerted mechanism seems unlikely in view of the stereochemical results and product distributions. The formation of caged intermediates seems a more attractive possibility. Racemization of the optically active sec-butyl and phenylethyl groups supports the view that the alkyl group is a true free radical at some time during the rearrangement. Such racemization of free radicals, whether planar or tetrahedral, is well established (17).

The intermolecularity of the rearrangement is further demonstrated by the isolation of crossed products from the rearrangement of a mixture of two styryl ethers (5). For satisfactory determinations from this kind of experiment, it is necessary to use two compounds that react at similar rates and the migrating groups must have similar reactivity toward either of the two reactants.

Experiments with α-ethoxy-p-chlorostyrene (28) and with α-n-butoxy-styrene (29) demonstrate that these two ethers rearrange at relatively similar rates. When a mixture of the two ethers was subjected to rearrangement for 2 hr at 250°, a mixture of four ketones was produced in addition to acetophenone and p-chloroacetophenone. The four ketones (30–33) were separated by vapor phase chromatography and identified by infrared spectroscopy and by conversion to oxime derivatives of known melting points.

$$\underset{\substack{\text{0.5 mole }\% \\ \textbf{(29)}}}{\overset{\overset{\displaystyle O-n\text{-}C_4H_9}{|}}{Ph-C=CH_2}} + \underset{\substack{\text{0.5 mole }\% \\ \textbf{(28)}}}{\overset{\overset{\displaystyle O-C_2H_5}{|}}{p\text{-}Cl-Ph-C=CH_2}} \longrightarrow \underset{\textbf{(30)}}{\overset{\overset{\displaystyle O}{\|}}{Ph-C(CH_2)_4CH_3}} \quad 27\%$$

$$\underset{\textbf{(31)}}{\overset{\overset{\displaystyle O}{\|}}{Ph-C-(CH_2)_2CH_3}} \quad 9\%$$

$$\underset{\textbf{(32)}}{\overset{\overset{\displaystyle O}{\|}}{p\text{-}Cl-Ph-C-(CH_2)_2CH_3}} \quad 31\%$$

$$\underset{\textbf{(33)}}{\overset{\overset{\displaystyle O}{\|}}{p\text{-}Cl-Ph-C(CH_2)_4CH_3}} \quad 12\%$$

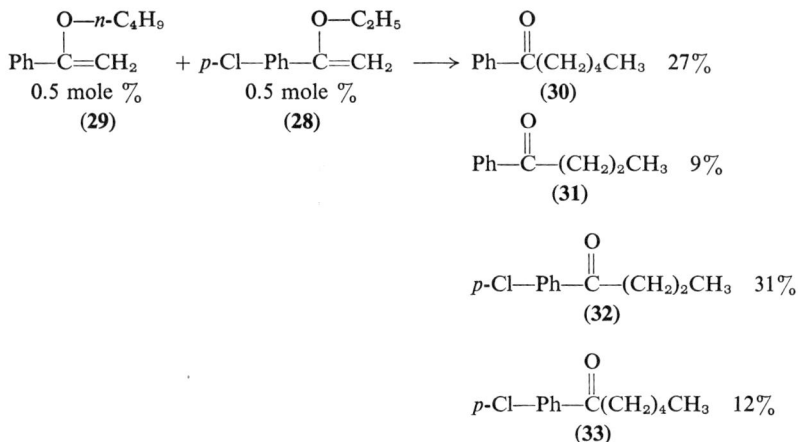

Wiberg's work (15) with a mixture of α-methoxy-^{13}C-p-methylstyrene and α-methoxy-p-ethylstyrene, in which the labeled compound contained 17.7% excess ^{13}C over normal abundance, resulted in the production of p-ethylpropiophenone containing 7.9% excess ^{13}C. For an intermolecular reaction with starting materials that have equal rates of rearrangement, the product should contain 8.9% excess ^{13}C, since the ^{13}C should be equally distributed between the mixed products.

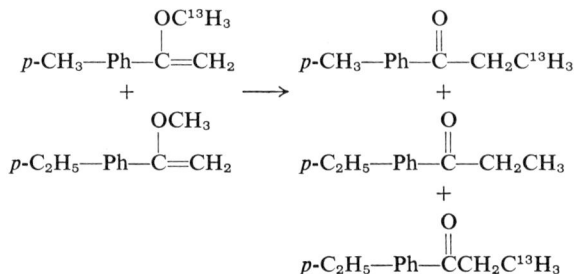

$$\underset{+}{\overset{\overset{\displaystyle OC^{13}H_3}{|}}{p\text{-}CH_3-Ph-C=CH_2}} \qquad \underset{+}{\overset{\overset{\displaystyle O}{\|}}{p\text{-}CH_3-Ph-C-CH_2C^{13}H_3}}$$

$$\overset{\overset{\displaystyle OCH_3}{|}}{p\text{-}C_2H_5-Ph-C=CH_2} \longrightarrow \overset{\overset{\displaystyle O}{\|}}{p\text{-}C_2H_5-Ph-C-CH_2CH_3}$$

$$+$$

$$\overset{\overset{\displaystyle O}{\|}}{p\text{-}C_2H_5-Ph-CCH_2C^{13}H_3}$$

Additional evidence for the presence of radical intermediates in this rearrangement accrues from observations of hydrogen abstraction reactions observed when rearrangements are carried out in the presence of an excess of a wide range of hydrocarbons. Toluene and its derivatives provide 9–49% yields of ω-benzylacetophenones (Table 5) when reacted for

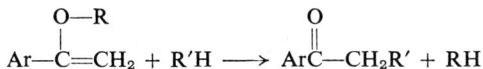

$$\overset{\overset{\displaystyle O-R}{|}}{Ar-C=CH_2} + R'H \longrightarrow \overset{\overset{\displaystyle O}{\|}}{ArC-CH_2R'} + RH$$

15 hr at 200° with α-methoxystyrene. Methane gas is simultaneously formed and provides a convenient measuring stick for following the kinetics of the

TABLE 5

Reactions of α-Methoxystyrene with Hydrocarbons[a]

Hydrocarbon	Yield, wt %	Product[b]
Toluene	37	β-Phenylpropiophenone
p-Chlorotoluene	9	β-p-Chlorophenylpropiophenone
p-Xylene	49	β-p-Methylphenylpropiophenone
p-Methoxytoluene	26	β-p-Anisylpropiophenone
Diphenylmethane	25	β-β-Diphenylpropiophenone
Cyclohexane	44	ω-Cyclohexylacetophenone
Benzylnitrile	37	β-Phenyl-β-cyano-propiophenone
Tetralin	36	ω-Tetralylacetophenone
Benzyl bromide	42	β-Phenylpropiophenone ·
Dibenzylsulfone	18	β-Phenyl-β-benzylsulfonyl-propiophenone
Hexadecane	42	Mixed ω-C_{16} acetophenones

[a] Ten molar excess of hydrocarbon reacted with α-methoxystyrene for 15–20 hr at 200°.

[b] Only product containing hydrocarbon reactant is included. Unreacted α-methoxystyrene and its rearrangement product, propiophenone, make up the bulk of the remainder. Products were identified by NMR, elemental analyses, and independent syntheses, with the exception of the final examples.

reaction. In this case the reaction follows fractional order kinetics that are consistent with a radical path wherein the major termination reaction is dimerization of radicals derived from the hydrocarbon.

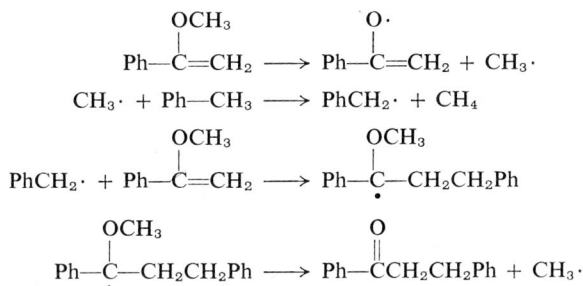

$$\underset{\underset{Ph—C=CH_2}{|}}{OCH_3} \longrightarrow \underset{\underset{Ph—C=CH_2}{|}}{O·} + CH_3·$$

$$CH_3· + Ph—CH_3 \longrightarrow PhCH_2· + CH_4$$

$$PhCH_2· + \underset{\underset{Ph—C=CH_2}{|}}{OCH_3} \longrightarrow \underset{\underset{Ph—\overset{\bullet}{C}—CH_2CH_2Ph}{|}}{OCH_3}$$

$$\underset{\underset{Ph—\overset{\bullet}{C}—CH_2CH_2Ph}{|}}{OCH_3} \longrightarrow \underset{\underset{Ph—CCH_2CH_2Ph}{||}}{O} + CH_3·$$

This reaction is also inhibited by radical scavengers and accelerated by di-t-butylperoxide.

II. 1,3-MIGRATIONS FROM OXYGEN TO NITROGEN

The Chapman rearrangement involves the conversion of aryl N-aryl-benzimidates to N-aroyldiphenylamines. This 1,3-rearrangement of aryl groups, which proceeds by a four-membered transition state, has been reviewed (32).

The thermal rearrangement of alkyl imidates to amides has been reported but seems to be limited to methyl and benzyl derivatives. When the alkyl group can undergo facile elimination to form olefin, this path, rather than isomerization, is favored. Temperatures required for the rearrangement of methyl imidates to amides (15,33), e.g., **34** to **35**, are higher than those for benzyl imidates (34,35) and yields are higher in the latter cases. Furthermore, the reaction has been demonstrated to be intermolecular (15)—in contrast to the intramolecular transition state for the Chapman reaction. Thus, a mixture of methyl-^{13}C-N-(p-tolyl)-formimidate (**36**) and methyl N-(p-ethylphenyl)-formimidate (**37**) was rearranged:

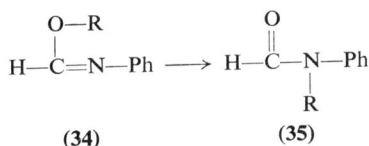

$$
\begin{array}{ccc}
\overset{\displaystyle O-R}{\underset{\displaystyle |}{}} & & \overset{\displaystyle O}{\underset{\displaystyle \|}{}} \\
H-C=N-Ph & \longrightarrow & H-C-N-Ph \\
& & \overset{\displaystyle |}{R}
\end{array}
$$

$$
\text{(34)} \qquad\qquad \text{(35)}
$$

$R = CH_3$, 40% yield of amide, 4 hr at 330°
$R = PhCH_2$, 70% yield of amide, 2 hr at 300°

After reduction to N,N-dimethyl-p-ethylaniline, the product was found to contain an amount of excess ^{13}C in close agreement with the theoretical value for crossed mixing. These results point to the presence of radical intermediates, although inhibition and radical trapping experiments have not been reported.

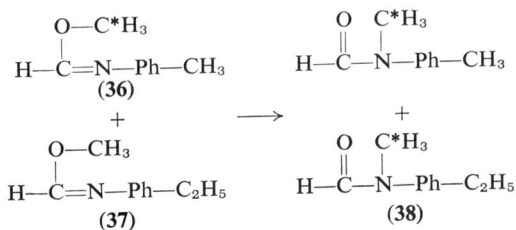

$$
\begin{array}{ccc}
O-C^{*}H_3 & & O\quad C^{*}H_3 \\
| & & \|\quad | \\
H-C=N-Ph-CH_3 & & H-C-N-Ph-CH_3 \\
\text{(36)} & & \\
+ & \longrightarrow & + \\
O-CH_3 & & O\quad C^{*}H_3 \\
| & & \|\quad | \\
H-C=N-Ph-C_2H_5 & & H-C-N-Ph-C_2H_5 \\
\text{(37)} & & \text{(38)}
\end{array}
$$

Early investigators reported the thermal rearrangement of alkyl imidates to amides (36,37). This reaction was subsequently found to be catalyzed by alkyl halides and alkyl sulfates (38,39). Such catalytic reactions are now referred to as the Lander rearrangement, which has also been demonstrated to be intermolecular. Arbuzov and Shishkin (40) have utilized this intermolecularity to intercept the rearranging intermediate and to incorporate a new, more stable, alkyl group into the molecule, e.g., **39** to **40**. Roberts and Vogt (41) have also demonstrated intermolecularity in the sulfuric acid-catalyzed rearrangement of O-ethyl-N-phenylformimi-

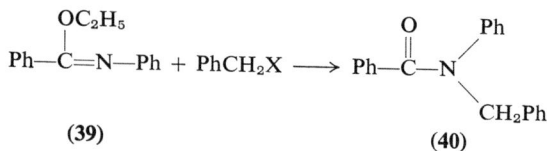

$$\underset{\textbf{(39)}}{\text{Ph}-\overset{\overset{\displaystyle OC_2H_5}{|}}{C}=N-\text{Ph}} + \text{PhCH}_2X \longrightarrow \underset{\textbf{(40)}}{\text{Ph}-\overset{\overset{\displaystyle O}{||}}{C}-N\overset{\displaystyle Ph}{\underset{\displaystyle CH_2Ph}{}}}$$

date by carrying out the reaction in the presence of triisoamyl ortho-formate and isolating a mixture of the N-ethyl and N-isoamyl amides. Presumably, sulfuric acid generates an alkylating species related to the alkyl halide catalyst. Boron trifluoride is also a catalyst for this rearrangement (42).

The cyclic benzyl imidate **41** undergoes C—O fission at 300° (35) with recyclization in a 1,3 manner to produce the isoindole derivative **42**. Steric factors preclude the four-centered transition state of the Chapman rearrangement, and a radical intermediate seems more likely.

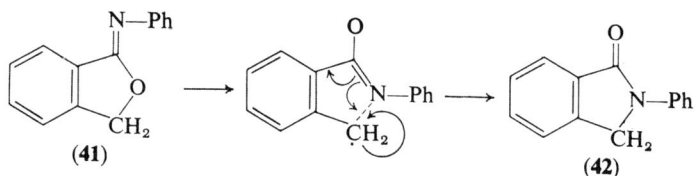

In heterocyclic systems the rearrangement of alkyl groups from oxygen to nitrogen was recognized as early as 1885. Early reported examples included the thermal rearrangement of 2- and 4-methoxypyridines and 2- and 4-methoxyquinolines to the corresponding N-methylpyridones and quinolones (43–45). 9-Methoxyacridine (**43**) yields 10-methylacridone (**44**) on heating at 200°. This reaction is also catalyzed by methyliodide (46,47) and probably proceeds by formation of a quaternary salt, followed by

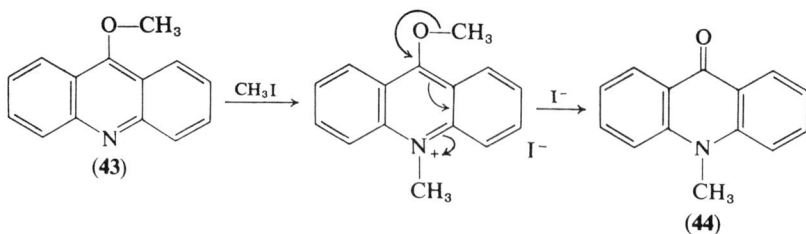

nucleophilic displacement of the O-alkyl group to produce methyl iodide and the rearrangement product.

Alkoxypyrimidines (47), lactim ethers (37,48), quinazoline ethers (49), and 5-alkoxy-1,2,4-oxadiazoles (50) undergo related 1,3-alkyl migrations.

The 2-methoxypyridine rearrangement to *N*-methyl-2-pyridone has been established as an intermolecular reaction by detection of crossed products when a mixture of 2-methoxy-^{13}C-4-methylpyridine (**45**) and 2-methoxy-4-ethylpyridine (**46**) was subjected to quantitative rearrangement (15). The reaction is catalyzed by peroxide initiators and oxygen,

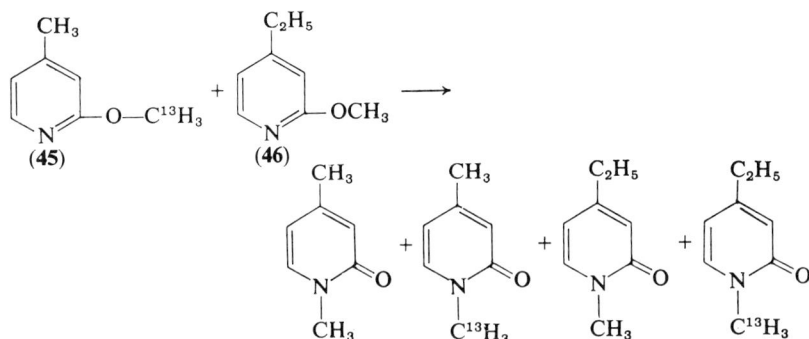

which suggests a free radical chain mechanism where the driving force for termination is the formation of the carbonyl group.

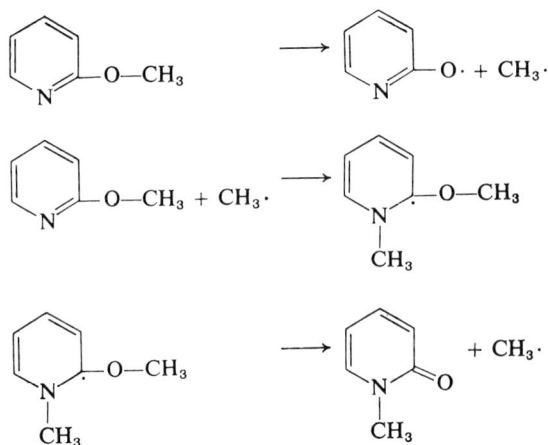

Beak (51) recently examined the 2-methoxy-*N*-methylpyridinium catalyzed equilibration of each of the isomer pairs, 2-methoxypyridine: *N*-methylpyrid-2-one and 4-methoxypyridine: *N*-methylpyrid-4-one. The standard free energies for the isomerization of the ether to the ketone was < -6 and < -2, indicating that *N*-methylpyrid-2-one is 8 kcal/mole more stable than 2-methoxypyridine and that *N*-methylpyrid-4-one is only 1 kcal/mole more stable than 4-methoxypyridine.

Rearrangement of 2-methylthiopyridine (**47**) to *N*-methyl-2-pyrid-thione (**48**) is more sluggish than with the oxygen analog. This observation

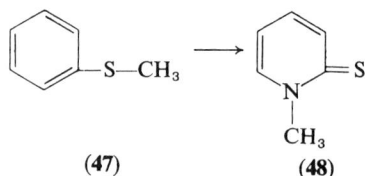

(**47**)   (**48**)

must be associated with the differences in driving forces for the formation of the carbonyl group and those for the thiocarbonyl group.

III. 1,3-MIGRATIONS FROM OXYGEN TO OXYGEN

The thermal rearrangement of methyl benzoate has been observed at 360 and 400° using ^{18}O as a tracer (15,18).

5% rearrangement, 3 hr at 360°
66% rearrangement, 3 hr at 400°

Although no verification of the radical character of this high activation energy rearrangement has been made, there is a formal resemblance between this rearrangement and that of vinyl ethers except that the ester rearrangement involves 1,3-alkyl migration from an oxygen atom to another oxygen atom. The intermolecularity of the rearrangement of methyl benzoate was demonstrated using a ^{13}C-labeled methyl group as a tracer. Rearrangement of a mixture of methyl-^{13}C-benzoate and methyl toluate provided product methyl toluate with 8.9% excess ^{13}C.

Equilibration of 2-methoxy-6-methyl-4-pyrone (**49**) and 4-methoxy-6-methyl-2-pyrone (19) (**50**) may involve a related 1,5-*O* to *O* rearrangement. In this system the 2-pyrone is the more stable isomer despite traditional predic-

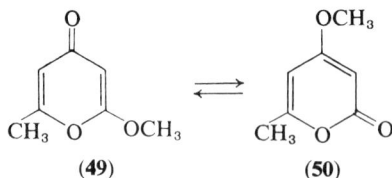

(**49**)   (**50**)

tions that 4-pyrones would be aromatic and thus of lower ground state energy than the nonaromatic 2-pyrones (20). The rearrangement is catalyzed by the fluoborate salt of **49** and probably proceeds via an intermolecular process.

IV. 1,3-MIGRATIONS FROM SULFUR TO NITROGEN

The isomerization of 2-methylthiobenzothiazole (**51**) to 3-methyl-2-benzothiazolinethione (**52**) has been studied as a thermal reaction and as an iodine-catalyzed reaction (21–28). Various mechanisms for the rearrangement have been suggested, including (*1*) the formation of 3-alkyl-

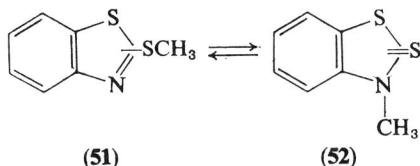

(**51**)   (**52**)

thio-3-alkylbenzothiazolium salts as intermediates (22,23); (*2*) heterolytic fission that produces the thiobenzothiazolyl anion and methyl carbonium ion (24); and (*3*) decomposition via a sulfonium salt (27,28). From most recent studies, an ion pair intermediate has been proposed, with the intermediate isomerizing by a four-center mechanism. Among the *S*-alkyl derivatives of **51**, benzyl, methyl, and neopentyl derivatives undergo rearrangement and alkyl groups with beta hydrogen atoms yield olefins by pyrolytic elimination. It is of interest to note that although the rearrangement of **51** to **52** is not affected by strong acids, the rearrangement of 2,2'-thiobis-(benzothiazole) (**53**) to 3-(2-benzothiazolyl)-2-benzothiazolinethione (**54**) is catalyzed by acids. Four-center reaction in such systems should not require acid catalysis but may be subject to such catalysis (29).

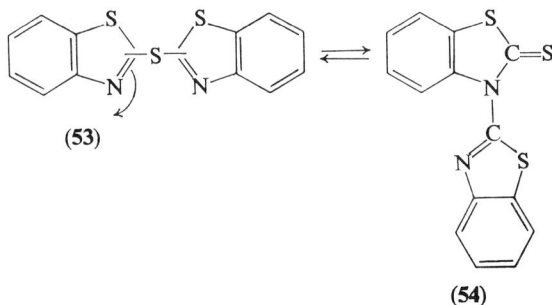

(**53**)   (**54**)

V. 1,3-MIGRATIONS FROM NITROGEN TO CARBON

The radiation-induced isomerization of *N*-alkyl-*N*-vinylsulfonamides (**55**) to *N*-alkyl-2-sulfonylvinylamines (**56**) has been proposed as a 1,3-radical rearrangement (30). The radical character of the reaction is supported by observations that (*1*) the reaction is inhibited by amines and mercaptans, (2) acid or base do not catalyze the rearrangement, (3) the rearrangement is facilitated by radical initiators, and (4) the rate of reaction decreases with increasing dose rate—thereby fitting a curve similar to that for the radical induced polymerization of acrylonitrile (31). The following mechanism is in accord with all of the experimental observations.

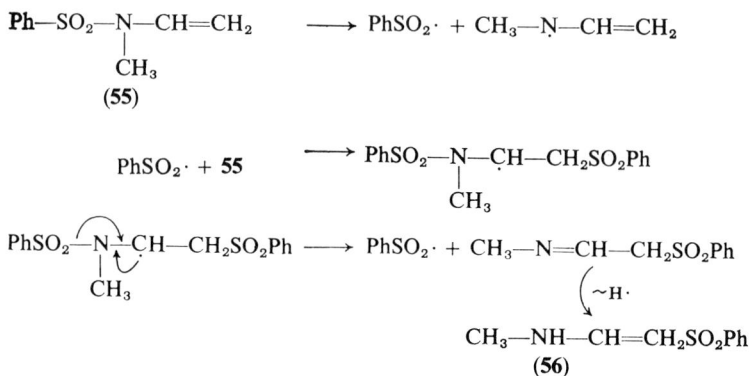

$$Ph—SO_2—\underset{\underset{CH_3}{|}}{N}—CH=CH_2 \longrightarrow PhSO_2\cdot + CH_3—\overset{..}{N}—CH=CH_2$$
$$(55)$$

$$PhSO_2\cdot + 55 \longrightarrow PhSO_2—\underset{\underset{CH_3}{|}}{N}—\overset{..}{C}H—CH_2SO_2Ph$$

$$PhSO_2—\underset{\underset{CH_3}{|}}{N}—CH—CH_2SO_2Ph \longrightarrow PhSO_2\cdot + CH_3—N=CH—CH_2SO_2Ph$$

$$\left(\underset{\searrow}{\sim H\cdot} \right.$$

$$CH_3—NH—CH=CH_2SO_2Ph$$
$$(56)$$

VI. RELATED REARRANGEMENTS

The thermal rearrangement of 2-alkoxypyridine-1-oxides to 1-alkoxy-2-pyridones involves 1,4-migration of an alkyl group from oxygen to oxygen. This reaction occurs readily at 100°, with the methoxy derivative rearranging more readily than the ethoxy derivative (52). The mild conditions required for this rearrangement and the lack of inhibition by radical scavengers indicate that homolytic cleavage of the ether bond does not take place.

Nucleophilic attack of the 1-oxygen atom on the alkyl group by either intra- (57) or intermolecular (58) reaction is consistent with experimental observations.

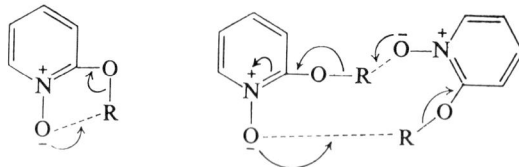

Intramolecular nucleophilic substitution would require a transition state that involves an unlikely front side displacement of the alkyl group. Intermolecular rearrangement via ion pair formation with internal return to yield product has been suggested as the probable mechanism for the transformation (32).

Another related transformation involves a longer range migration of alkyl groups from nitrogen to oxygen in the conversion of betaines to methyl esters. Such rearrangements are illustrated by the rearrangement of the dimethylbetaine of α-pyrrolidine-carboxylic acid (59) to methyl N-methylhygringate (60).

(59)   (60)

Both α- and β-betaines undergo this thermal rearrangement, and Willstatter has demonstrated the interconvertibility of the betaine and ester (53). The methyl group preferentially migrates from nitrogen to oxygen when betaines with two different alkyl groups are subjected to rearrangement.

This observation is in agreement with the pyrolysis of tetraalkylammonium salts wherein the methyl group is lost more readily than is the ethyl group (54,59).

When the zwitterions of the betaine are separated by four or five carbon atoms, a competing elimination of the trialkylamino group occurs and, in addition to the formation of the isomeric aminoacid ester, a cyclic lactone (55) is produced.

Long chain betaines are converted in quantitative yields to the ester (56), an observation that suggests a mechanism involving intermolecular nucleophilic attack of oxygen on carbon.

Thionocarbamates (61) rearrange thermally into thiolcarbamates (62) and a cyclic four-membered transition state based on intramolecularity has been proposed (57).

(61)   (62)

Kinoshita and co-workers (58) have observed acid catalysis of this rearrangement using BF_3-etherate or p-toluenesulfonic acid. The general order of isomerization reactivity for various O-alkylthionocarbamates was

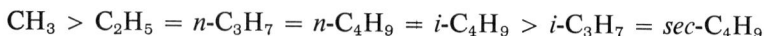

$$CH_3 > C_2H_5 = n\text{-}C_3H_7 = n\text{-}C_4H_9 = i\text{-}C_4H_9 > i\text{-}C_3H_7 = sec\text{-}C_4H_9$$

An intermolecular S-alkylation (**63**) was proposed and supported by evidence against a four-centered reaction, i.e., a four-membered cyclic

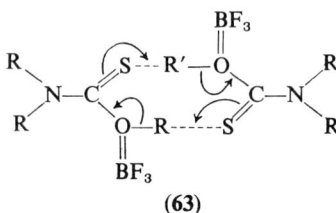

(**63**)

mechanism (*1*) should not be affected by steric hindrance, and (*2*) nucleophilic substitution of oxygen by sulfur should be insensitive to external nucleophiles.

References

1. D. S. Tarbell, *Organic Reactions*, Vol. 2, R. Adams, Ed., Wiley, New York, 1944, p. 1; S. J. Rhoads, *Molecular Rearrangements*, P. de Mayo, Ed., Wiley, New York, 1963, p. 655; B. S. Thyagarajan, *Advances in Heterocyclic Chemistry*, Vol. 8, Academic Press, New York, 1967.
2. (a) L. Claisen, *Chem. Ber.*, **29**, 2931 (1896); (b) L. Claisen and E. Hasse, *ibid.*, **33**, 3778 (1900); **45**, 3157 (1912).
3. H. Staudinger and L. Ruzicka, *Helv. Chim. Acta*, **7**, 386 (1924).
4. W. Wislecenus and R. Schrotter, *Ann. Chem.*, **424**, 215 (1921).
5. E. H. MacDougall, W. M. Lauer, and M. A. Spielman, *J. Am. Chem. Soc.*, **55**, 4089 (1933); W. M. Lauer and M. A. Spielman, *ibid.*, **55**, 4923 (1933); M. A. Spielman and C. W. Mortenson, *ibid.*, **61**, 666 (1939); **62**, 1609 (1940).
6. K. B. Wiberg and B. I. Rowland, *J. Am. Chem. Soc.*, **77**, 1159 (1955).
7. A. W. Burgstahler, L. K. Gibbons, and I. C. Nordin, *J. Chem. Soc.*, **1963**, 4986.
8. A. T. Blades and G. W. Murphy, *J. Am. Chem. Soc.*, **74**, 1039 (1952).
9. C. S. Wang and C. A. Wenkler, *Can. J. Res.*, **21B**, 97 (1943).
10. R. L. Hasche and B. Thompson, U.S. Pat. 2,294,402; *Chem. Abstr.*, **37**, 891 (1943).
11. R. N. Obolentser, *J. Gen. Chem. (USSR)*, **16**, 1459 (1946).
12. W. J. Hickenbottom, *Nature*, **142**, 830 (1938); **143**, 520 (1939).
13. F. Arndt and L. Loewe, *Chem. Ber.*, **71**, 1631 (1938).
14. A. F. Trotman-Dickenson, *Quart. Rev.*, **7**, 208 (1953); W. A. Waters, *Physical Aspects of Organic Chemistry*, Van Nostrand, New York, 1950, p. 164.
15. K. B. Wiberg, T. M. Shryne, and R. R. Kintner, *J. Am. Chem. Soc.*, **79**, 3160 (1957).
16. W. A. Waters, *The Chemistry of Free Radicals*, Oxford University Press, Oxford, 1948, p. 58.
17. W. von E. Doering, M. Farber, M. Spracher, and K. B. Wiberg, *J. Am. Chem. Soc.*, **74**, 3000 (1952); G. Karagunis and G. Drikos, *Z. Physik. Chem.*, **26B**, 428 (1934); G. Karagunis and T. Jannakopoulus, *ibid.*, **47B**, 343 (1940).

18. K. B. Wiberg, *J. Am. Chem. Soc.*, **75**, 2665 (1953).
19. P. Beak, *Tetrahedron Letters*, **1963**, No. 13, 863.
20. G. M. Badger, *The Chemistry of Heterocyclic Compounds*, Academic Press, New York, 1961, pp. 428–429.
21. J. J. D'Amico, S. T. Webster, R. H. Campbell, and C. E. Twine, *J. Org. Chem.*, **30**, 3625, 3628 (1965).
22. K. J. Morgan, *J. Chem. Soc.*, **1958**, 854.
23. D. J. Fry and J. D. Kendall, *J. Chem. Soc.*, **1951**, 1716.
24. C. G. Moore and C. S. Waight, *J. Chem. Soc.*, **1952**, 4237.
25. W. A. Sexton, *J. Chem. Soc.*, **1939**, 471.
26. F. P. Reed, A. Robertson, and W. A. Sexton, *J. Chem. Soc.*, **1939**, 473.
27. W. H. Davies and W. A. Sexton, *J. Chem. Soc.*, **1942**, 309.
28. F. G. Mann and J. Watson, *J. Org. Chem.*, **13**, 502 (1948).
29. J. Hine, *Physical Organic Chemistry*, McGraw-Hill, New York, 1962, p. 505.
30. F. W. Stacey, J. C. Sauer, and B. C. McKusick, *J. Am. Chem. Soc.*, **81**, 987 (1959).
31. I. A. Bernstein, E. C. Farmer, W. G. Rothschild, and F. S. Spalding, *J. Chem. Phys.*, **21**, 1303 (1953).
32. J. W. Schulenberg and S. Arcker, *Organic Reactions*, Vol. 14, A. C. Cope, Ed., Wiley, New York, 1965, p. 1.
33. A. W. Chapman, *J. Chem. Soc.*, **1927**, 1743.
34. F. Cramer, K. Pawelzik, and J. Kupper, *Angew. Chem.*, **68**, 649 (1956).
35. C. J. M. Stirling, *J. Chem. Soc.*, **1960**, 255.
36. W. Wislicenus and M. Goldschmidt, *Chem. Ber.*, **33**, 1467 (1900).
37. R. E. Benson and T. L. Cairns, *J. Am. Chem. Soc.*, **70**, 2115 (1948).
38. G. D. Lander, *J. Chem. Soc.*, **83**, 406 (1903).
39. J. W. Ralls and C. A. Elliger, *Chem. Ind. (London)*, **1961**, 20.
40. A. E. Arbuzov and V. E. Shishkin, *Dokl. Akad. Nauk. SSSR*, **141**, 349, 611 (1961).
41. R. M. Roberts and P. J. Vogt, *J. Am. Chem. Soc.*, **78**, 4778 (1956).
42. F. Cramer and N. Hennrich, *Chem. Ber.*, **94**, 976 (1961).
43. L. Knorr, *Ann. Chem.*, **236**, 107 (1886); **293**, 5 (1896); *Chem. Ber.*, **30**, 922, 927, 937 (1897).
44. A. Lieben and L. Haitinger, *Monatsch.*, **6**, 315 (1885).
45. H. Meyer and R. Baer, *Monatsch.*, **27**, 255 (1906); **34**, 1173 (1913).
46. K. Glen and S. Nitzsche, *J. Poakt. Chem.*, **153**, 200 (1939).
47. G. E. Hilbert and B. Johnson, *J. Am. Chem. Soc.*, **52**, 2001 (1930).
48. S. Petersen and E. Tietze, *Chem. Ber.*, **90**, 909 (1957).
49. R. J. Grout and M. W. Partridge, *J. Chem. Soc.*, **1960**, 3546.
50. V. L. Narayanan and J. Bernstein, *J. Heterocyclic Chem.*, **3**, 714 (1966).
51. P. Beak and J. Bonham, *Chem. Commun.*, **1966**, 631.
52. F. J. Dinan and H. Tieckelmann, *J. Am. Chem. Soc.*, **86**, 1650 (1964).
53. R. Willstatter, *Chem. Ber.*, **35**, 504 (1902).
54. W. Lossen, *Ann. Chem.*, **181**, 377 (1876).
55. R. Willstatter and W. Kahn, *Chem. Ber.*, **37**, 1853 (1904).
56. R. Kuhn and F. Giral, *Chem. Ber.*, **68**, 387 (1935).
57. J. D. Edwards and M. Pianka, *J. Chem. Soc.*, **1965**, 7338; and references therein.
58. Y. Kinoshita, S. Uchiumi, S. Chokai, and Y. Oshima, *Agr. Biol. Chem.*, **30**, 710 (1966).
59. S. Petersen and E. Tretze, *Chem. Ber.*, **90**, 909 (1957).

Oxidative Rearrangements of Vinylic Derivatives

ROBERT J. STELTENKAMP* AND WILLIAM E. TRUCE

Purdue University, Lafayette, Indiana

The reaction of oxygen with olefins generally leads to hydroperoxides (and products formed therefrom) by attack at the allyl position, e.g.

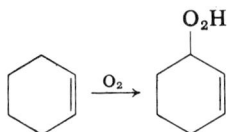

or in some cases epoxides formed by direct attack on the double bond, e.g.

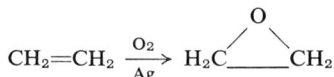

However, with certain substituted olefins, autoxidation leads to products resulting from not only oxidation but also rearrangement. Oxidative rearrangement concerns the general oxygen-induced conversion of olefins to acyl derivatives

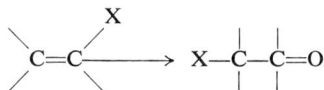

where X may be either a halide or a thiyl radical.

I. VINYL HALIDES

Rearrangements during the oxidation of olefins with molecular oxygen were first reported for brominated ethylenes by Demole in 1878 (1).

* Present address: Colgate-Palmolive Company, Piscataway, New Jersey.

The brominated olefins, by absorbing oxygen from the atmosphere, were converted to the α-bromo acyl bromides, e.g.

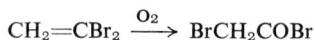

$$CH_2{=}CBr_2 \xrightarrow{O_2} BrCH_2COBr$$

This autoxidation, in which a shift of a halogen atom occurs to the vicinal olefinic carbon atom, has been extended to a variety of halogenated ethylenes and halogenated vinyl ethers (Table 1). The examples shown involve migrations of fluorine, chlorine, and bromine atoms, but no reports involving iodine migrations have been found. The ease of migration appears to be Br > Cl > F as judged by the nature of the products formed from mixed halides, e.g.

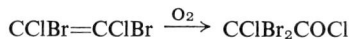

$$CClBr{=}CClBr \xrightarrow{O_2} CClBr_2COCl$$

This chlorodibromoacetyl chloride is formed by the shift of the bromine atom rather than the chlorine. These rearrangements are typically exothermic and are accompanied by the formation of several side products.

The reaction has been catalyzed by the addition of a halogen. Thus, tetrachloroethylene gave 87% trichloroacetyl chloride by the addition of chlorine in carbon tetrachloride solution (7). Similar results were obtained with trichloroethylene, chlorine, and oxygen in the vapor phase in which

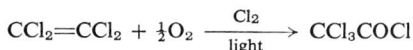

$$CCl_2{=}CCl_2 + \tfrac{1}{2}O_2 \xrightarrow[\text{light}]{Cl_2} CCl_3COCl$$

80% dichloroacetyl chloride was formed along with small amounts of carbonyl dichloride, carbon dioxide, and hydrogen chloride (8). The reaction of these chloroethylenes with oxygen in the absence of a halogen catalyst is negligible under these conditions.

Bromine and fluorine have also been used to promote the reaction of oxygen with halogenated olefins (12,13). The addition of fluorine to liquid tetrachloroethylene at 0°C is inhibited in the presence of oxygen, and the oxidative products, dichlorofluoroacetyl chloride and trichloroacetyl chloride, are formed.

This rearrangement has assumed utility in synthesis as in the preparation of fluoro compounds containing functional groups. Thus, several comparatively inaccessible fluoroalkane carboxylic acids were obtained through oxidative rearrangement of the respective fluoroolefin. For example, 2,3,3-trifluoro-1,1,3-trichloro-1-propene on oxidative-bromination gave a mixture of the bromo and chloroacyl chlorides, which were used in preparing the corresponding uncommon unsaturated acid. The trifluoroacrylic acid was then converted to the fluorinated olefin(13).

$$CF_2ClCF{=}CCl_2 \xrightarrow[Br_2]{O_2} \begin{array}{c} CF_2ClCFBrCOCl \\ + \\ CF_2ClCFClCOCl \end{array} \longrightarrow CF_2{=}CFCO_2H$$

TABLE 1

Oxidative Rearrangements of Halogenated Ethylenes and Vinyl Ethers[a]

Ethylene	Major product	References
$CH_2{=}CBr_2$	$BrCH_2COBr$	1,2
$CHBr{=}CBr_2$	$CHBr_2COBr$ (52%)	1,3
$CHBr{=}CHBr$	$CHBr_2COOH + CHBr_2CHO$	1,4
	$+ BrCH_2COBr$	
$CH_3CH{=}CBr_2$	$CH_3CHBrCOBr$ (31%)	2
$C_6H_5CBr{=}CH_2$	$C_6H_5COCH_2Br$	5
$CBr_2{=}CBr_2$	CBr_3COBr	4
$CBr_2{=}CF_2$	$CBrF_2COBr$ (53%)	3
	$+ CBr_2FCOF$	
$CFBr{=}CFBr$	$CFBr_2COF$	4
$CFBr{=}CBr_2$	$CFBr_2COBr$ (CBr_3COF)	4
$CHF{=} CBr_2$	$CHFBrCOBr$ (49%)	4,6
$CHBr{=}CFBr$	$CHBr_2COF$	4
$CHF{=}CFBr$	$CHBrFCOF$	4
$CClBr{=}CClBr$	$CClBr_2COCl$	4
$CCl_2{=}CCl_2 + Cl_2$	CCl_3COCl (87%)	4,7
$CHCl{=}CCl_2 + Cl_2$	$CHCl_2COCl$ (80%)	8
$CCl_2{=}CCl(OR)$	$CCl_2(OR)COCl$	9
$CCl_2{=}CH(OC_2H_5)$	$CHCl(OC_2H_5)COCl$	10
$CF(OCH_3){=}CFCl$	$FCOCOCl$	11
$CCl_2{=}CCl_2 + F_2$	$CFCl_2COCl + CCl_3COCl$	12
$CFCl{=}CF_2$	CF_2ClCOF (77%)	14
$CF_2ClCF{=}CCl_2 + Br_2$	$CF_2ClCFBrCOCl$ (23%)	15
	$CF_2ClCFClCOCl$ (19%)	
$CF_2ClCCl{=}CCl_2 + Cl_2$	CF_2ClCCl_2COCl	14,15
$CF_2XCX{=}CClX + Cl_2$	$CF_2XCClXCOCl$	16
(where X is Cl or F)		

[a] Yields and catalysts if any are shown when reported.

Oxidation of chlorotrifluoroethylene in the vapor phase gave a 77% yield of chlorodifluoroacetyl fluoride after 5 days (14). Ultraviolet light is needed to accelerate the reaction since only traces of product are formed after six months in the absence of light. This photochemical reaction became

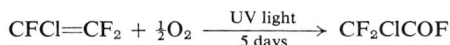

$$CFCl{=}CF_2 + \tfrac{1}{2}O_2 \xrightarrow[\text{5 days}]{\text{UV light}} CF_2ClCOF$$

very vigorous with the addition of halogen to the vapor phase mixture of olefin and oxygen leading to spontaneous pyrolysis at low temperature with chlorine and immediate explosion with bromine. The by-products of this reaction included carbon dioxide, carbonyl difluoride, carbonyl chloride fluoride, and silicon tetrafluoride (reaction was conducted in a pyrex tube). In the liquid phase the acyl fluoride and the volatile breakdown products were again formed, but in addition a liquid peroxide $[C_2F_3ClO]_n$ was produced. The acyl fluoride was formed in a 62% yield on liquid phase oxidation by the addition of an equimolar amount of oxygen to the liquid for 48 hr under a pressure of 12 atm in the dark. The addition of a halogen was not required to catalyze the reaction.

The oxidation of tetrafluoroethylene with molecular oxygen in the dark at low temperature without a halogen catalyst gave an explosive rubberlike polymer with the structure $[CF_2CF_2O_2]_n$ (16). Since no acyl fluoride was reported, a catalyst must be required for the oxidative rearrangement of this olefin.

The oxidation of tetrachloroethylene to trichloroacetyl chloride was recently conducted under nonautoxidative conditions using a solution of nitric and sulfuric acids. The reaction mixture after hydrolysis gave 70% trichloroacetic acid (17).

$$CCl_2{=}CCl_2 + HNO_3 + H_2SO_4 \longrightarrow CCl_3COCl \xrightarrow{H_2O} CCl_3COOH$$

II. VINYL SULFIDES

Oxidative rearrangements were recently extended to a variety of vinyl sulfides (18). As with the brominated ethylenes, the vinyl sulfides also readily absorb oxygen from the atmosphere and undergo conversion to the acyl derivative with migration of the mercapto group. Thus, 1-ethoxy-1-(p-tolylmercapto) ethene readily absorbed oxygen to give as the major product ethyl-p-tolymercapto acetate. By-products of this autoxidation

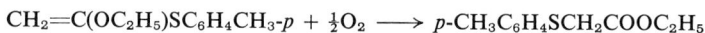

$$CH_2{=}C(OC_2H_5)SC_6H_4CH_3\text{-}p + \tfrac{1}{2}O_2 \longrightarrow p\text{-}CH_3C_6H_4SCH_2COOC_2H_5$$

included p-toluenethiol, p-tolyldisulfide, 1-ethoxy-1,2-bis(p-tolylmercapto) ethene, and ethoxyacetylene. The yields of this autoxidation are increased by the addition of a thiol to serve as a radical initiator and by the introduction of dry oxygen. Cooling was also required with several of the more exothermic vinyl sulfides.

In this fashion the oxidative rearrangements were observed readily with the 1-ethoxy-1-arylmercapto or alkylmercapto ethenes in 47–54% yields. Ketene mercaptals autoxidize to thiol esters but less readily and in lower yields (31–38%).

$$CH_2{=}C(SC_6H_4CH_3\text{-}p)_2 + \tfrac{1}{2}O_2 \longrightarrow p\text{-}CH_3C_6H_4SCH_2COSC_6H_4CH_3\text{-}p$$

As with the halogenated ethylenes, an exchange of thiol groups occurs when a different thiol is introduced during the autoxidation. Thus, when an equimolar amount of benzenethiol is introduced to 1-ethoxy-1-phenyl-mercapto ethene in the presence of oxygen, a mixture of esters is obtained with the phenylmercapto derivative predominating. In a similar manner t-butyl-mercaptan was exchanged with the phenylmercapto group in 1-ethoxy-1-(phenylmercapto) ethene. That the phenylmercapto derivative

$$CH{=}_2C(OC_2H_5)SC_4H_9\text{-}t + C_6H_5SH \xrightarrow{O_2} \underset{42\%}{C_6H_5SCH_2COOC_2H_5} + \underset{4\%}{t\text{-}C_4H_9SCH_2COOC_2H_5}$$

$$CH_2{=}C(OC_2H_5)SC_6H_5 + t\text{-}C_4H_9SH \xrightarrow{O_2} \qquad 30\% \qquad\qquad 19\%$$

predominates over the t-butylmercapto derivative can be rationalized by the relative stabilities of the two thiyl radicals. The t-butylthiyl radical being less stable than the resonance stabilized benzenethiyl may exchange with the benzenethiol producing benzenethiyl, e.g.

$$RS\cdot + PhSH \longrightarrow PhS\cdot + RSH$$

A list of the investigated vinylic sulfides is found in Table 2.

III. MECHANISM OF OXIDATIVE REARRANGEMENTS

The mechanism for these rearrangements appears to involve a radical chain as suggested by Walling (19). Thus, for tetrachloroethylene, the following steps are proposed:

A. $CCl_2{=}CCl_2 + Cl\cdot \longrightarrow CCl_3\overset{\cdot}{C}Cl_2$

B. $CCl_3\overset{\cdot}{C}Cl_2 + O_2 \longrightarrow CCl_3CCl_2O_2\cdot$

C. $2CCl_3CCl_2O_2\cdot \longrightarrow 2CCl_3CCl_2O\cdot + O_2$

D. $CCl_3CCl_2O\cdot \longrightarrow CCl_3COCl + Cl\cdot$

Each of these steps is a common one in free radical chemistry.

Step A has been demonstrated by the radical addition of halogens and thiols to olefins. Step B is plausible since oxygen is a diradical able to couple with other radicals. It is well known that alkyl radicals can rapidly add oxygen to give peroxy radicals. Hydroperoxide intermediates have been isolated by the cooxidation of mercaptans and olefins (20), e.g.,

$$RSH + R'CH{=}CR_2'' + O_2 \longrightarrow RSCHR'CR_2''O_2H$$

The often proposed bimolecular oxygen elimination (step C) may occur through formation of the tetroxide either as a sequence or in a concerted process with subsequent breakdown to oxygen and the oxy radical. This

TABLE 2

Oxidative Rearrangements of Vinylic Sulfides (18)

Vinylic sulfide	Major product	Yield, %
$CH_2{=}C(OC_2H_5)SC_6H_5$	$C_6H_5SCH_2COOC_2H_5$	54
$CH_2{=}C(OC_2H_5)SC_6H_4CH_3\text{-}p$	$p\text{-}CH_3C_6H_4SCH_2COOC_2H_5$	47
$CH_2{=}C(OC_2H_5)SC_4H_9\text{-}t$	$t\text{-}C_4H_9SCH_2COOC_2H_5$	53
$CH_3CH{=}C(OC_2H_5)SC_6H_5$	$C_6H_5SCH(CH_3)COOC_2H_5$	51
$CH_2{=}C(SC_6H_4CH_3\text{-}p)_2$	$p\text{-}CH_3C_6H_4SCH_2CO\cdot$ $(SC_6H_4CH_3\text{-}p)$	31
$CH_2{=}C(SC_3H_7\text{-}i)_2$	$i\text{-}C_3H_7SCH_2CO(SC_3H_7\text{-}i)$	38
$CH_2{=}CHSC_6H_4CH_3\text{-}p$	$p\text{-}CH_3C_6H_4SCH_2CHO$	33
$p\text{-}CH_3C_6H_4SCH{=}CHSC_6H_4CH_3\text{-}p$	No reaction	
$CCl_2{=}C(SC_6H_4CH_3\text{-}p)_2$	No reaction	
$p\text{-}CH_3C_6H_4SCH{=}C(SC_6H_4CH_3\text{-}p)_2$	No reaction	

type of process has been shown to occur in the autoxidation of cumene where the cumylperoxy radicals interact to give cumyloxy radicals and oxygen (21). The cleavage of the oxy radical (step D) produces the product and a halogen radical.

Since in many cases the oxidative rearrangement proceeds without the addition of a radical catalyst, oxygen must partially degrade the olefin producing a trace of halogen or thiol which then initiates the chain reaction through step A. The mechanism proposed is thus consistent with the catalysis observed with radical initiators and light. This mechanism is also supported by the exchange of halogens (12,13) or thiol groups (18) when a different radical is introduced during the autoxidation, i.e., exchange precludes an intramolecular process.

The oxidation of saturated alkyl halides with molecular oxygen is also consistent with this mechanism (19). Pentachloroethane on treatment with oxygen in the presence of chlorine and light gives trichloroacetyl chloride (8). The abstraction of hydrogen from the pentachloroethane produces a

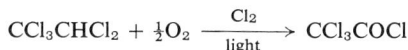

$$CCl_3CHCl_2 + \tfrac{1}{2}O_2 \xrightarrow[\text{light}]{Cl_2} CCl_3COCl$$

radical identical with that formed by addition of the chlorine radical to tetrachloroethylene (step A), thus accounting for the same oxidation product.

While the above mechanism fits the available experimental evidence well, other possibilities can also accommodate the data. One possibility involves the formation of an epoxide with subsequent rearrangement to the acyl derivative. Thus, for tetrachloroethylene

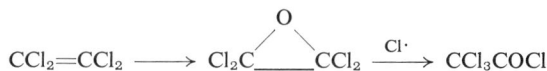

$$CCl_2{=}CCl_2 \longrightarrow Cl_2C\underset{\quad}{\overset{O}{\triangle}}CCl_2 \xrightarrow{Cl\cdot} CCl_3COCl$$

This alternate scheme is supported by the identification of epoxides from the reaction between certain halogenated ethylenes and oxygen. Tetrafluoroethylene oxide has been formed as a product from tetrafluoroethylene and oxygen on treatment with ultraviolet light (22), while chlorotrifluoroethylene oxide has been reported as a probable by-product in the oxidation of chlorotrifluoroethylene (14). It has also been shown that tetrafluoroethylene oxide on decomposition produces trifluoroacetyl fluoride which supports the second stage of this scheme (22). Further studies need to be conducted before any conclusions can be drawn concerning this mechanism.

While both halide and thiyl radicals have been shown to migrate, no examples exist of a corresponding rearrangement with alkoxy or aroxy radicals. Vinyl ethers such as α-alkoxystyrenes undergo a radical-catalyzed or thermal rearrangement which does not involve the uptake of oxygen (23).* Thus α-methoxystyrene on heating is converted to propiophenone. A free radical chain process

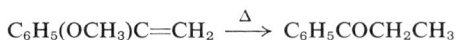

$$C_6H_5(OCH_3)C=CH_2 \xrightarrow{\Delta} C_6H_5COCH_2CH_3$$

has been postulated with the following propagation steps (24).

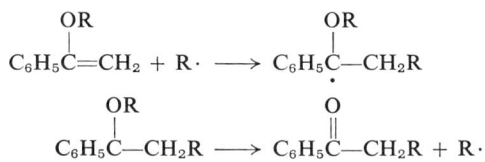

$$\underset{\overset{|}{C_6H_5\overset{|}{C}=CH_2}}{\overset{OR}{}} + R\cdot \longrightarrow \underset{\overset{|}{C_6H_5\overset{|}{\underset{\bullet}{C}}-CH_2R}}{\overset{OR}{}}$$

$$\underset{\overset{|}{C_6H_5\overset{|}{\underset{\bullet}{C}}-CH_2R}}{\overset{OR}{}} \longrightarrow \underset{C_6H_5\overset{O}{\overset{||}{C}}-CH_2R}{} + R\cdot$$

This radical-catalyzed 1,3-shift has been shown to occur also with several ketene acetals (25).

References

1. E. Demole, *Chem. Ber.*, **11**, 315, 1307, 1710 (1878); **12**, 2245 (1879); *Bull. Soc. Chim. France* [ii], **34**, 201 (1880); E. Demole and H. Durr, *Chem. Ber.*, **11**, 1302 (1878).
2. G. B. Bachman, *J. Am. Chem. Soc.*, **55**, 4279 (1933); **57**, 1088 (1935).
3. H. Cohn and E. D. Bergmann, *Israel J. Chem.*, **2** [6], 355 (1965); through *Chem. Abstr.*, **62**, 14488 (1965).
4. F. Swarts, *Bull. Acad. Roy. Belg.*, **33**, 439 (1897); **34** [3], 307 (1897); **35** [3], 849 (1898); **36** [3], 532 (1898); *Rec. Trav. Chim.*, **17**, 231 (1898).
5. C. Dufraisse, *Compt. Rend.*, **172**, 162 (1921).

* The mechanisms of such 1,3-alkyl migrations are discussed elsewhere in this volume.

Editor

6. E. T. McBee, O. R. Pierce, and D. L. Christman, *J. Am. Chem. Soc.*, **77**, 1581 (1955).

7. R. A. Dickinson and J. A. Leemakers, *J. Am. Chem. Soc.*, **54**, 3852, 4648 (1932); M. A. Besson, *Compt. Rend.*, **121**, 125 (1895).

8. K. L. Muller and H. J. Schumacker, *Z. Physik. Chem.*, **B37**, 365 (1937); H. J. Schumacker, *ibid.*, **A189**, 183 (1941); W. A. Alexander and H. J. Schumacker, *ibid.*, **B44**, 313 (1939).

9. L. Henry, *Bull. Acad. Roy. Belg.*, **36** [3], 497 (1899); *Chem. Ber.*, **12**, 1839 (1897).

10. J. Foster, *J. Am. Chem. Soc.*, **31**, 596 (1909).

11. R. S. Corley, J. Lal, and M. W. Kane, *J. Am. Chem. Soc.*, **78**, 3489 (1956).

12. W. T. Miller, Jr., and A. L. Dittman, *J. Am. Chem. Soc.*, **78**, 2793 (1956).

13. A. L. Henne and C. J. Fox, *J. Am. Chem. Soc.*, **76**, 479 (1954).

14. R. N. Haszeldine and F. Nyman, *J. Chem. Soc.*, **1959**, 1084.

15. D. W. Chaney, U.S. Pat. 2,439,505 (1948); through *Chem. Abstr.*, **42**, 7315 (1948); U.S. Pat. 2,456,768 (1948); through *Chem. Abstr.*, **43**, 4683 (1949); U.S. Pat. 2,514,743 (1950); through *Chem. Abstr.*, **44**, 9474 (1950).

16. F. Gozzo and G. Camaggi, *Tetrahedron*, **22**, 1765 (1966).

17. I. G. Khaskin, Y. A. Serguchev, A. A. Proshkin, G. I. Vishevskaya, and D. F. Yavorski, *Med. Prom. SSSR*, **15** [1], 39 (1961); through *Chem. Abstr.*, **55**, 22122 (1961).

18. W. E. Truce and R. J. Steltenkamp, *J. Org. Chem.*, **27**, 2816 (1962).

19. C. Walling, *Free Radicals in Solution*, Wiley, New York, 1957, pp. 447–450.

20. A. A. Oswald and F. Noel, *J. Org. Chem.*, **26**, 3948 (1961); A. A. Oswald, *ibid.*, **26**, 842 (1961); **24**, 443 (1959).

21. P. D. Bartlett and T. G. Traylor, *J. Am. Chem. Soc.*, **85**, 2407 (1963).

22. F. Gozzo and G. Camaggi, *Tetrahedron*, **22**, 2181 (1966).

23. L. Claisen, *Chem. Ber.*, **29**, 2931 (1896); L. Claisen and E. Haase, *ibid.*, **33**, 3778 (1900).

24. K. B. Wiberg, R. R. Kintner, and E. L. Motell, *J. Am. Chem. Soc.*, **85**, 450 (1963).

25. S. M. McElvain and C. L. Stevens, *J. Am. Chem. Soc.*, **68**, 1917 (1946); E. S. Huyser, R. M. Kellogg, and D. T. Want, *J. Org. Chem.*, **30**, 4377 (1965).

Base-Catalyzed Rearrangements of Acetylenic Derivatives

ISSEI IWAI

Central Research Laboratories, Sankyo Co., Ltd., Tokyo, Japan

I. INTRODUCTION

Base-catalyzed reactions and rearrangements are ionic reactions formally involving an attack by a nucleophilic reagent on an electron-deficient center in the reactant molecule or an attack by an electrophilic reagent at a nucleophilic center. In some cases, this reaction occurs within a molecule having both functions of the reagent and reactant resulting in migration of a functional group or modification of the molecular skeleton. Such a reaction constitutes a base-catalyzed "rearrangement."

In general, intramolecular rearrangements can be summarized in a formal sense by the following equation

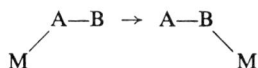

$$A\!-\!B \;\rightarrow\; A\!-\!B$$
$$\diagup \qquad\qquad \diagdown$$
$$M \qquad\qquad\qquad M$$

in which for purposes of discussion M will be referred to as the migrating group, A as the migration origin, and B as the migration terminus. Rearrangements fall into three general mechanistic categories depending on the nature of the cleavage and formation of the bond at M—A and M—B, respectively. The most common type is the nucleophilic rearrangement in which M departs from A with the bonding electrons and acts as a nucleophile. The reaction is initiated by B becoming deficient in electrons, usually by the loss of an anionic leaving group. A second, less common, type is the electrophilic rearrangement in which M departs from A without the bonding electrons and acts as an electrophile. The reaction is initiated by B becoming rich in electrons. The third type is a homolytic rearrangement in which the reaction is initiated by B becoming a radical, and M forming bonds with B by donating one electron to the incipient covalent link.

Base-catalyzed rearrangements discussed in this chapter arise from the formation of a carbanion which is initiated by those basic reagents which remove a group or a hydrogen atom without the bonding electrons. These reactions are therefore a type of electrophilic rearrangement.

It would be convenient to touch upon the characteristics of a triple bond before opening discussion on the title subject.

A triple bond is essentially different from a double bond and its chemical behavior cannot be correctly understood by simply considering it as a double bond with an additional unit of unsaturation. On bromination of an en–yne compound, for instance, bromine predominantly adds to the double bond (1) while hydration occurs predominantly at the triple bond (2). Actually, determination of the relative rates (second-order constants) of bromine addition to the following pairs shows distinctly the stronger reactivity of a double bond (3) in the reaction as compared with that of a comparably situated triple bond: styrene to phenylacetylene ca. 3000, stilbene to diphenylacetylene 250, ethyl fumarate to ethyl acetylenedicarboxylate 60, and 10-undecenonic acid to 10-undencynoic acid 9000. On the other hand, the fact that hex-2-en-4-yne (1) is hydrated to hex-4-en-2-one (2) shows the higher reactivity of the triple bond toward hydration; it has been experimentally shown that, in general, a triple bond is rather

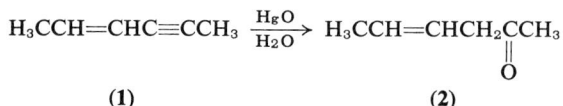

$$H_3CCH{=}CHC{\equiv}CCH_3 \xrightarrow[\text{H}_2\text{O}]{\text{Hg\,O}} H_3CCH{=}CHCH_2CCH_3$$
$$\overset{\|}{\underset{O}{}}$$

(1)   (2)

reactive toward nucleophilic reagents (e.g., C_2H_5OH, RNH_2, etc.) while it is less reactive toward electrophilic reagents [e.g., halogen, peracid (4), ozone (5), etc.]. At first sight it may be surprising that the triple bond is less susceptible to attack by electrophiles than the double bond and more reactive to nucleophilic reagents in spite of the higher π-electron density involved in the triple bond. The distributions of π-electrons involved in the two systems are quite different and this explains the above difference in reactivities. The double bond has an sp^2 hybrid orbital in which the π-molecular orbitals are distributed above and below the plane of the σ bond, thus causing a hindrance to free rotation of the carbon atoms around the σ bond and giving an unsymmetrical character to the double bond. On the other hand, the four atoms of acetylene are bonded together in a straight

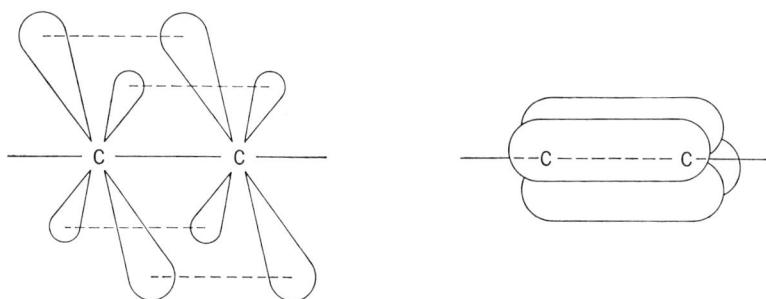

Figure 1

line by the *sp* hybrid orbitals of the carbon atoms forming the σ bond. Each carbon atom still has two *p*-orbitals perpendicular to each other and overlap of the four *p*-orbitals affords two π-molecular orbitals which overlap and have cylindrical symmetry around the σ bond (Fig. 1).

Accordingly the *s* component contained in a triple bond increases to greater degree. Since the π-electrons of a triple bond are held much more tightly and concentrated at the center of the bond to a greater extent than those in an ethylenic bond, the electrons should be resistant to polarization and the bond length of a triple bond may be rather short. Actually, it has been shown that the triple bond is significantly shorter than the double bond. Further, this assumption is supported by dipole moment data and other physical measurements. In particular, the tightly bound nature of

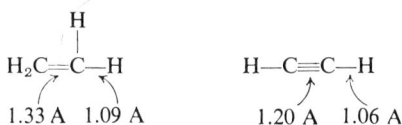

$$H_2C{=}C{-}H \qquad\qquad H{-}C{\equiv}C{-}H$$

$$\overset{H}{\underset{\text{1.33 A} \quad \text{1.09 A}}{}} \qquad\qquad \underset{\text{1.20 A} \quad \text{1.06 A}}{}$$

the π-electrons in a triple bond is apparent from a comparison of the far ultraviolet absorption spectra of acetylene and ethylene which give values of 11.41 and 10.50 eV, respectively, for the first ionization potentials (6). A high concentration of π-electrons at the center of the triple bond makes the carbon atoms electron deficient. Accordingly, a triple bond is more reactive than a comparably situated double bond toward nucleophilic reagents while the condition for electrophilic reagents is quite the reverse. Furthermore, the fact that the hydrogen atom of an ethynyl group (—C≡CH) exhibits strong acidity and is easily substituted by metals to form acetylides and Grignard compounds is also well rationalized on this basis. In addition, the formation of a Mannich base by the reaction of ethynyl compounds with an aldehyde in the presence of amines, just as in the case of active methylene compounds, also shows the deficiency of electrons at the carbon atoms of the triple linkage (**3,4**).

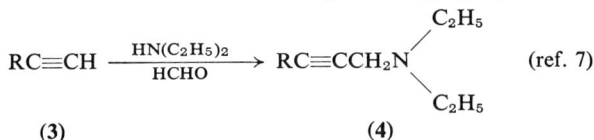

$$RC\equiv CH \xrightarrow[\text{HCHO}]{\text{HN(C}_2\text{H}_5)_2} RC\equiv CCH_2N\begin{array}{c} C_2H_5 \\ \\ C_2H_5 \end{array} \quad \text{(ref. 7)}$$

(**3**)   (**4**)

In our laboratory, comparative studies on the chemical behavior of a propargylic methylene group and a methylene group adjacent to a carbonyl group have been made. Azole compounds, which are usually synthesized from α-halogenated carbonyl compounds, can also be synthesized using α-substituted acetylenic derivatives instead of α-haloketones. A new method for synthesizing azole compounds was thus established (Scheme 1) (8,9).

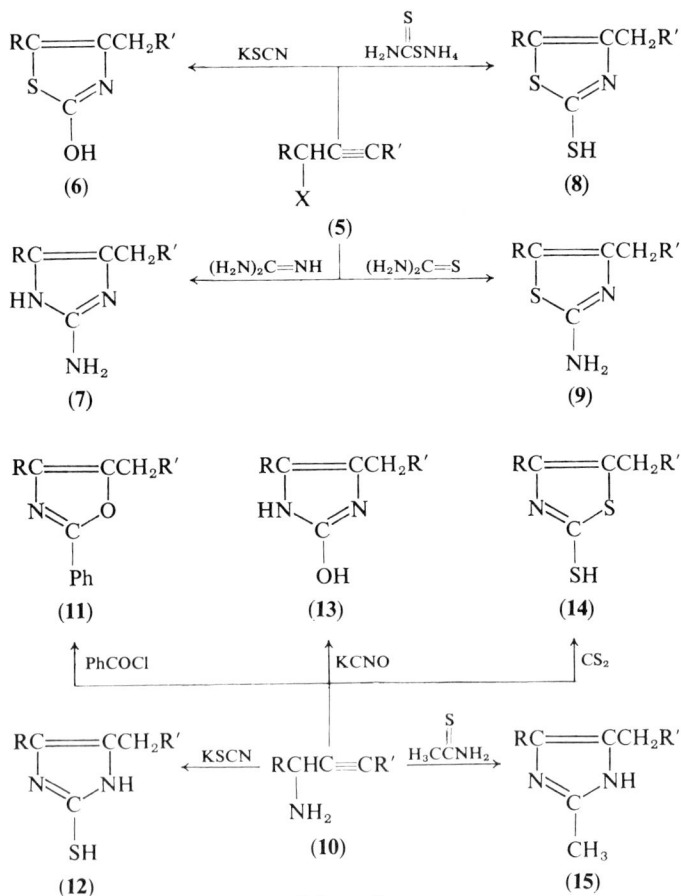

Scheme 1

In addition, acetylenic Mannich bases reacted with sodio derivatives of an active methylene compound to give acetylene derivatives which gave rise to a new C—C linkage by the loss of the base just as in ordinary Mannich bases [aryl-CH_2—$\overset{\oplus}{N}(R_1R_2R_3)X^{\ominus}$] (10) (Scheme 2). In the reaction of trialkylarylmethyleneammonium salt [aryl-CH_2—$\overset{\oplus}{N}(R_1R_2R_3)X^{\ominus}$], with active methylene compounds, the C—N bond of the Mannich base is easily cleaved; the rather stable resonance type, aryl-$\overset{\oplus}{C}H_2$, appears to be an intermediate, and indicates an essential structural requirement for this reaction.

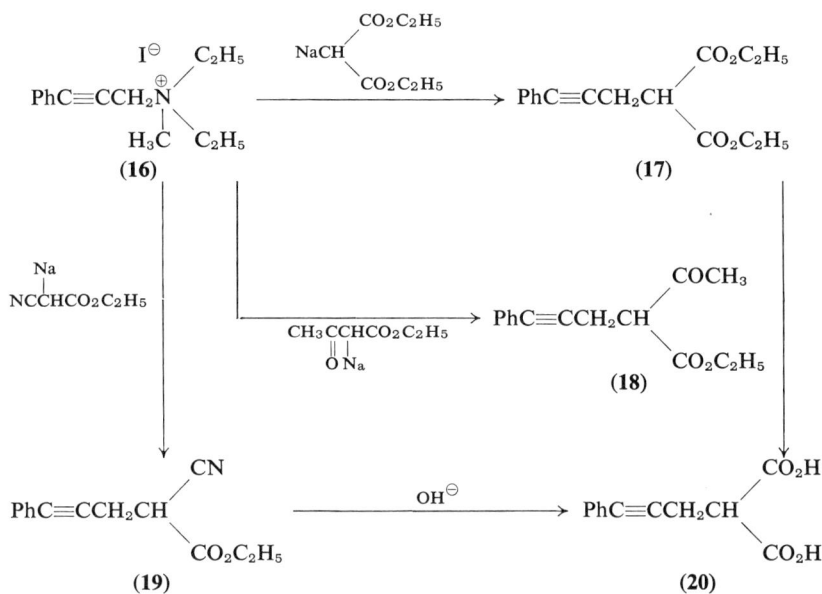

Scheme 2

In the case of the acetylenic Mannich base, formation of phenylproparygyl cation (PhC≡C—$\overset{\oplus}{C}H_2$) as intermediate appears to be essential for the reaction. This also shows one of the characteristics of a triple bond.

The neighboring triple linkage has been shown to cause the propargylic methylene group to exhibit increased acidity and to behave like a methylene group adjacent to a carbonyl group.

With these characteristics of a triple bond in mind, base-catalyzed rearrangements of acetylenic compounds, including prototropy, will be discussed in the following section.

II. BASE-CATALYZED PROTOTROPIC REARRANGEMENTS

A. Acetylene → Allene Isomerization

On treatment of acetylenic compounds with a base, the hydrogen from the propargylic methylene group should be easily abstracted without the bonding electrons to afford a carbanion because of the acidity of the propargylic methylene group. The base-catalyzed rearrangement of an acetylenic compound affords a mixture of products including allene derivatives. The reaction is initiated by abstraction of a proton from the activated position to give an acetylenic carbanion in resonance with an allenic carbanion. The process for the alkoxide-catalyzed rearrangement of ethylacetylene (21) to dimethylacetylene (27) is described as a prototropic rearrangement (11).

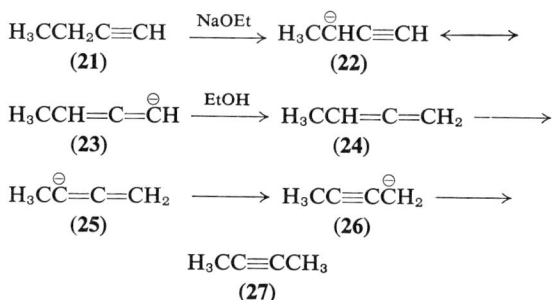

$$H_3CCH_2C\equiv CH \xrightarrow{\text{NaOEt}} H_3C\overset{\ominus}{C}HC\equiv CH \longleftrightarrow$$
$$(21) \qquad\qquad\qquad (22)$$

$$H_3CCH=C=\overset{\ominus}{C}H \xrightarrow{\text{EtOH}} H_3CCH=C=CH_2 \dashrightarrow$$
$$(23) \qquad\qquad\qquad (24)$$

$$H_3C\overset{\ominus}{C}=C=CH_2 \longrightarrow H_3CC\equiv C\overset{\ominus}{C}H_2 \longrightarrow$$
$$(25) \qquad\qquad\qquad (26)$$

$$H_3CC\equiv CCH_3$$
$$(27)$$

The postulation of an allenic intermediate in this process is supported by the rearrangement of isopropylacetylene (28) to 3-methylbuta-1,2-diene (29), the subsequent formation of 2-alkyne being impossible in this case.

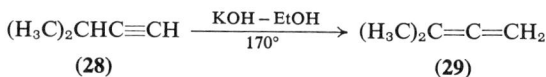

$$(H_3C)_2CHC\equiv CH \xrightarrow[170°]{\text{KOH – EtOH}} (H_3C)_2C=C=CH_2$$
$$(28) \qquad\qquad\qquad\qquad (29)$$

The fact that t-butylacetylene is unchanged under comparable conditions also provides confirmation of this postulation (12).

For clarification of these transformations, Jacobs (11) made careful studies on the isomerizations of 1-pentyne (30), 1,2-pentadiene (31), and 2-pentyne (32). Each of the three isomers yields the same equilibrium mixture which was analyzed by a combination of infrared spectroscopy and analytical distillation with the following results:

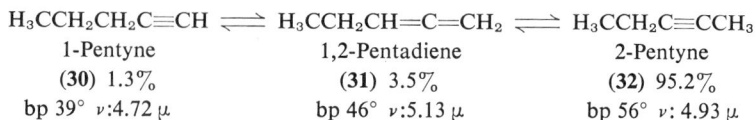

$$H_3CCH_2CH_2C\equiv CH \rightleftharpoons H_3CCH_2CH=C=CH_2 \rightleftharpoons H_3CCH_2C\equiv CCH_3$$

1-Pentyne	1,2-Pentadiene	2-Pentyne
(30) 1.3%	(31) 3.5%	(32) 95.2%
bp 39° ν:4.72 μ	bp 46° ν:5.13 μ	bp 56° ν: 4.93 μ

The other possible isomers, 1,3 and 2,3-pentadiene, were shown not to be formed. The predominance of 2-alkyne (32) in the equilibrium mixture shows the greater thermodynamic stability of this isomer as compared with 1-alkyne (30). This is in good agreement with the results of thermodynamic considerations on propyne and but-2-yne. Each methyl group has been shown to increase progressively the stability by about 5 kcal/mole. The thermodynamic stability of an acetylenic compound is highly affected by hyperconjugation effects. This is more significant in acetylenic compounds than in the comparable ethylenic derivatives. In some cases, the hyperconjugation effect surpasses the conjugation effect (13). It has been logically elucidated that the axially symmetrical π-orbital of the triple bond is convenient for hyperconjugation of the α-methylenic hydrogen. Actually, 2-pentynoic acid (33) is converted into nonconjugated 3-pentyne-carboxylic acid (34) by treatment with potassium hydroxide.

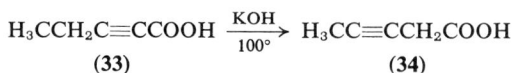

$$\text{H}_3\text{CCH}_2\text{C}\equiv\text{CCOOH} \xrightarrow[100°]{\text{KOH}} \text{H}_3\text{CC}\equiv\text{CCH}_2\text{COOH}$$
$$\text{(33)} \qquad\qquad\qquad\qquad \text{(34)}$$

From the temperature dependence of the equilibrium constants the enthalpies of isomerization for the acetylene–allene transformation have been illustrated in Scheme 3 which interrelates the energies of isomeric acetylenes and dienes (14).

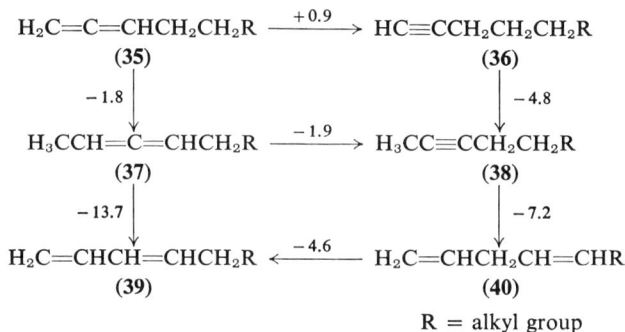

$$\text{H}_2\text{C}=\text{C}=\text{CHCH}_2\text{CH}_2\text{R} \xrightarrow{+0.9} \text{HC}\equiv\text{CCH}_2\text{CH}_2\text{CH}_2\text{R}$$
$$\text{(35)} \qquad\qquad\qquad\qquad\qquad \text{(36)}$$

$$\downarrow -1.8 \qquad\qquad\qquad\qquad\qquad\qquad \downarrow -4.8$$

$$\text{H}_3\text{CCH}=\text{C}=\text{CHCH}_2\text{R} \xrightarrow{-1.9} \text{H}_3\text{CC}\equiv\text{CCH}_2\text{CH}_2\text{R}$$
$$\text{(37)} \qquad\qquad\qquad\qquad\qquad \text{(38)}$$

$$\downarrow -13.7 \qquad\qquad\qquad\qquad\qquad\qquad \downarrow -7.2$$

$$\text{H}_2\text{C}=\text{CHCH}=\text{CHCH}_2\text{R} \xleftarrow{-4.6} \text{H}_2\text{C}=\text{CHCH}_2\text{CH}=\text{CHR}$$
$$\text{(39)} \qquad\qquad\qquad\qquad\qquad \text{(40)}$$

R = alkyl group

Approximate Standard Enthalpies in Kilocalories per Mole of Isomerization of Gaseous Acetylenes and Dienes at 25°(14).

Scheme 3

These data indicate that a terminal allene is of slightly lower energy than an isomeric terminal acetylene but that an internal acetylene should be significantly lower in energy than in isomeric internal allene (2,3-diene). All allenes and acetylenes have much higher energies than isomeric unconjugated dienes, which, as well known, are rich in their energies as compared with the conjugated dienes. The experimental results of isomerization of 1-pentyne and 2-pentyne obtained by Jacobs (11) are in at least qualitative agreement with the thermodynamic data shown in Scheme 3. Furthermore, conversion of mycomycin (**41**) to isomycomycin (**42**) is also readily rationalized on this basis (15). Besides these, another

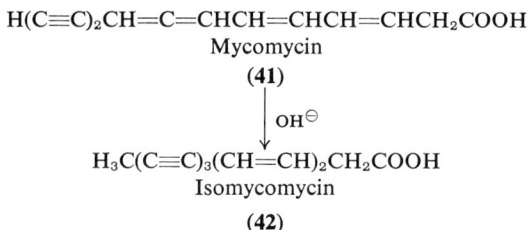

$$H(C\equiv C)_2CH=C=CHCH=CHCH=CHCH_2COOH$$

Mycomycin

(**41**)

$$\downarrow OH^{\ominus}$$

$$H_3C(C\equiv C)_3(CH=CH)_2CH_2COOH$$

Isomycomycin

(**42**)

example has been reported by Prinzbach (16). The terminal allene compound (**43**) isomerized to the methylacetylenic compound (**44**) by treatment with a base.

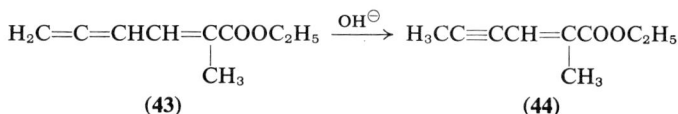

$$\underset{\underset{CH_3}{|}}{H_2C=C=CHCH=CCOOC_2H_5} \xrightarrow{OH^{\ominus}} \underset{\underset{CH_3}{|}}{H_3CC\equiv CCH=CCOOC_2H_5}$$

(**43**)   (**44**)

The intra- versus intermolecular character of a base-catalyzed 1,3-proton transfer in an acetylene–allene system has been investigated by Cram and co-workers (17). In the isomerization of triphenylpropyne-3-*d* (**45**) to triphenyl–allene (**46**), in the presence of proton donors and bases, the intramolecularity varies in a range from 88% in dimethylsulfoxide–

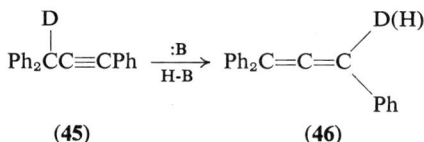

$$\underset{}{\overset{\overset{D}{|}}{Ph_2CC\equiv CPh}} \xrightarrow[H-B]{:B} Ph_2C=C=C\overset{D(H)}{\underset{Ph}{\diagdown}}$$

(**45**)   (**46**)

methanol–triethylenediamine to 19% in methanol–potassium methoxide. They suggested the following mechanism for the rearrangement: The intramolecular rearrangement of acetylene to allene involves migration of a proton attached to a base across the face of a π-electron cloud containing a negative charge. Migration of the proton from the front face of the π-electron cloud to the rear face would involve complete breakage of the hydrogen bond, and at least partial dissociation of the ion pair. These processes are probably slower than those of proton migration and capture in solvents that exhibit high intramolecularity.

If a stronger base such as sodium or sodamide is used in this protatropic rearrangement, the formation of an acetylide with the base disturbs the equilibrium. Thus conversion of 2-pentyne to the less stable 1-pentyne occurs because of the irreversible removal of 1-pentyne from the equilibrium system. A similar rearrangement has been reported also in the case of an acetylenic ether (47) (18). This isomerization reaction can be applied

$$H_3CC\equiv COR \xrightarrow{NaNH_2} HC\equiv CCH_2OR \quad (ref. 18)$$
$$(47) \qquad\qquad\qquad (48)$$

even to those compounds in which the triple bond is located at a position far from the terminal of the molecule (19). Treatment of *cis*-1-chlorohex-2-en-4-yne (51) with phenyllithium gives a mixture of equal amounts of *cis*-

$$H_3C(CH_2)_4C\equiv C(CH_2)_4CH_3 \xrightarrow{NaNH_2} H_3C(CH_2)_9C\equiv CH$$
$$(49) \qquad\qquad\qquad\qquad (50)$$

and *trans*-6-phenylhex-3-en-1-yne (57). Craig and Young (20) postulate a mechanism for the reaction involving the abstraction of a proton by the basic phenyllithium, followed by a double prototropic rearrangement of the vinylacetylene system by way of an intermediate allene (55) or possibly a cumulene (56) as postulated by Petrov and Kormer (21).

The rearrangement of an acetylenic compound to an allenic derivative, which is the first stage of the isomerization of an acetylenic compound described above, is promoted by conjugation of the allenic system with the terminal carboxylic acid group or unsaturated bond. An arylpropargylic compound or 3-yne-carboxylic acid, for example, is rearranged to the allenic derivative in higher yield under milder conditions where no further rearrangement to the isomeric acetylenic compound can proceed and hence the allenic intermediate can be isolated (Scheme 4).

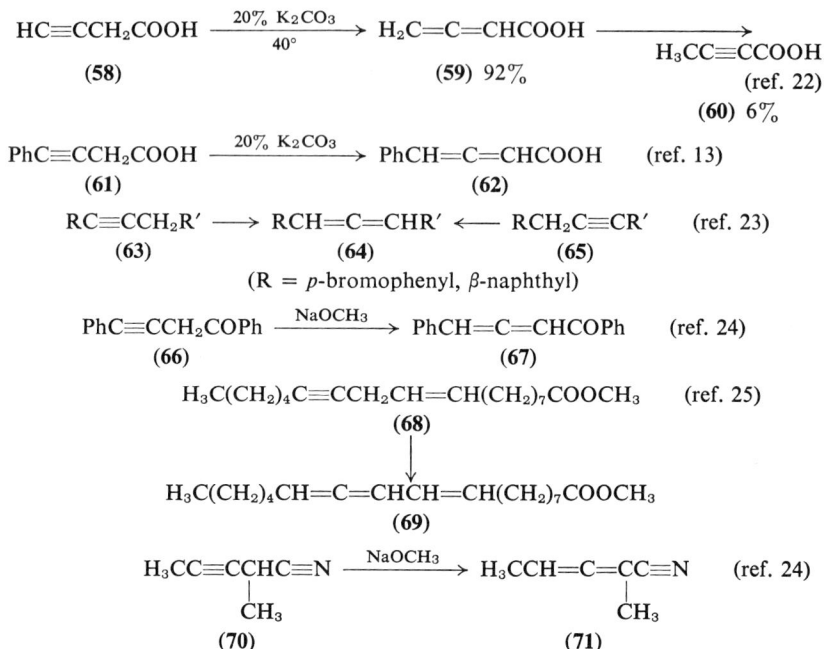

$$HC\equiv CCH_2COOH \xrightarrow[40°]{20\% \ K_2CO_3} H_2C=C=CHCOOH \xrightarrow{\hspace{2cm}} H_3CC\equiv CCOOH$$

(58)   (59) 92%   (ref. 22)

(60) 6%

$$PhC\equiv CCH_2COOH \xrightarrow{20\% \ K_2CO_3} PhCH=C=CHCOOH \quad \text{(ref. 13)}$$

(61)   (62)

$$RC\equiv CCH_2R' \longrightarrow RCH=C=CHR' \longleftarrow RCH_2C\equiv CR' \quad \text{(ref. 23)}$$

(63)   (64)   (65)

(R = p-bromophenyl, β-naphthyl)

$$PhC\equiv CCH_2COPh \xrightarrow{NaOCH_3} PhCH=C=CHCOPh \quad \text{(ref. 24)}$$

(66)   (67)

$$H_3C(CH_2)_4C\equiv CCH_2CH=CH(CH_2)_7COOCH_3 \quad \text{(ref. 25)}$$

(68)

↓

$$H_3C(CH_2)_4CH=C=CHCH=CH(CH_2)_7COOCH_3$$

(69)

$$H_3CC\equiv CCHC\equiv N \xrightarrow{NaOCH_3} H_3CCH=C=CC\equiv N \quad \text{(ref. 24)}$$
$$\qquad\quad |\hspace{6cm}|$$
$$\qquad\quad CH_3 \hspace{5.5cm} CH_3$$

(70)   (71)

Scheme 4

When the allenic rearrangement product has a conjugated system including the aryl group, the isomerization occurs under milder conditions (Scheme 5).

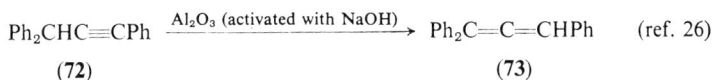

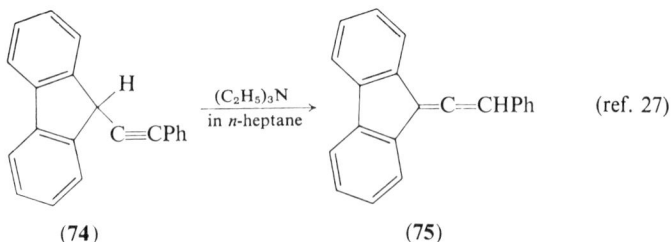

$$Ph_2CHC\equiv CPh \xrightarrow{Al_2O_3 \text{ (activated with NaOH)}} Ph_2C=C=CHPh \quad \text{(ref. 26)}$$

(72)   (73)

(74)   (75)

Scheme 5

Sometimes the basicity of Grignard reagents causes the isomerization:

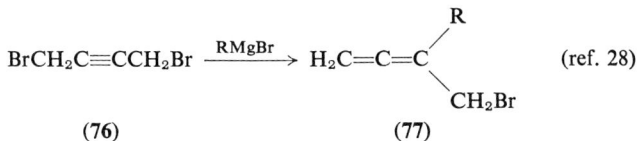

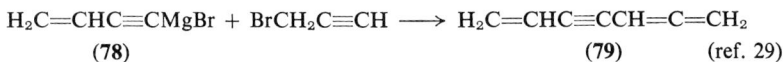

$$BrCH_2C\equiv CCH_2Br \xrightarrow{\ RMgBr\ } H_2C=C=C\begin{smallmatrix}R\\ \\CH_2Br\end{smallmatrix} \qquad \text{(ref. 28)}$$

(76)   (77)

$$H_2C=CHC\equiv CMgBr + BrCH_2C\equiv CH \longrightarrow H_2C=CHC\equiv CCH=C=CH_2$$
(78)   (79)   (ref. 29)

The allenic system in the product which is in conjugation with an atom carrying unshared electrons is also stable.

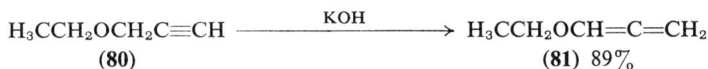

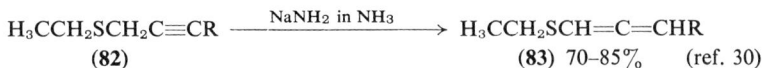

$$H_3CCH_2OCH_2C\equiv CH \xrightarrow{\ KOH\ } H_3CCH_2OCH=C=CH_2$$
(80)   (81) 89%

$$H_3CCH_2SCH_2C\equiv CR \xrightarrow{\ NaNH_2\ in\ NH_3\ } H_3CCH_2SCH=C=CHR$$
(82)   (83) 70–85%   (ref. 30)

$$ClCH_2C\equiv CH \longrightarrow ClCH=C=CH_2 \qquad \text{(ref. 31)}$$
(84)   (85)

Treatment of *t*-butylpropargylether with sodiumamide in liquid ammonia gives *t*-butylacrolein, which is assumed to be derived from the allenic intermediate by hydrolysis (32).

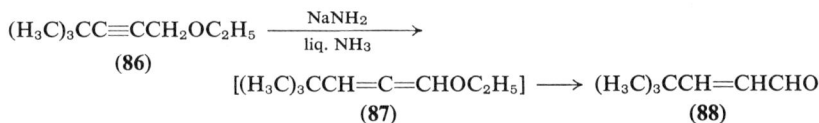

$$(H_3C)_3CC\equiv CCH_2OC_2H_5 \xrightarrow[\text{liq. NH}_3]{\text{NaNH}_2}$$
(86)

$$[(H_3C)_3CCH=C=CHOC_2H_5] \longrightarrow (H_3C)_3CCH=CHCHO$$
(87)   (88)

Some acetylenic ethers and thioethers undergo a similar rearrangement of this type to afford terminal en–yne compounds accompanied by elimination of the ether group.

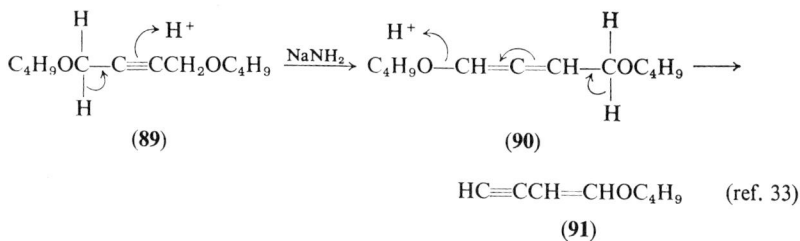

$$C_4H_9OC\overset{H}{\underset{H}{|}}C\equiv CCH_2OC_4H_9 \xrightarrow{\text{NaNH}_2} C_4H_9O-CH=C=CH-COC_4H_9 \longrightarrow$$
(89)   (90)

$$HC\equiv CCH=CHOC_4H_9 \qquad \text{(ref. 33)}$$
(91)

$$RCH_2CH_2C \equiv COR \xrightarrow{NaNH_2} RCH-CH=C=CH-OR \xrightarrow{H^+}$$

$$(92) \hspace{6cm} (93)$$

$$RCH=CHC \equiv CH \hspace{1cm} (ref. 34)$$

$$(94)$$

$$CH_3CH_2C \equiv CSC_2H_5 \longrightarrow CH_2-CH=C=CH-SC_2H_5 \xrightarrow{H^+}$$

$$(96) \hspace{6cm} (97)$$

$$H_2C=CHC \equiv CH \hspace{1cm} (ref. 35)$$

$$(98)$$

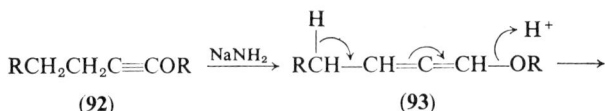

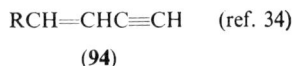

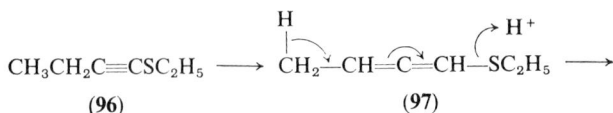

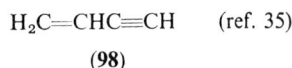

Another example of this rearrangement is illustrated by the conversion of propargyl halide into an allenic compound in the presence of a cuprous salt. In this reaction an anion first dissociates and then recombines at another site of the molecule to yield an allenic derivative. Thus the reaction is described as an anionotropic rearrangement.

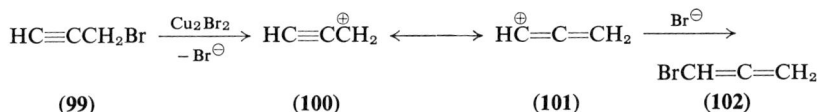

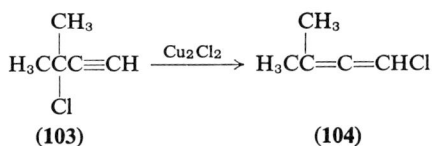

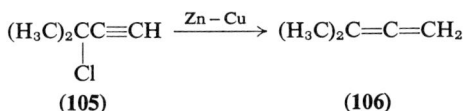

$$HC \equiv CCH_2Br \xrightarrow[-Br^{\ominus}]{Cu_2Br_2} HC \equiv C\overset{\oplus}{C}H_2 \longleftrightarrow H\overset{\oplus}{C}=C=CH_2 \xrightarrow{Br^{\ominus}}$$

$$(99) \hspace{2cm} (100) \hspace{2.5cm} (101)$$

$$BrCH=C=CH_2$$

$$(102)$$

$$\underset{\underset{Cl}{|}}{\overset{\overset{CH_3}{|}}{H_3CCC \equiv CH}} \xrightarrow{Cu_2Cl_2} \overset{\overset{CH_3}{|}}{H_3CC}=C=CHCl$$

$$(103) \hspace{3cm} (104)$$

$$\underset{\underset{Cl}{|}}{(H_3C)_2CC \equiv CH} \xrightarrow{Zn-Cu} (H_3C)_2C=C=CH_2$$

$$(105) \hspace{3cm} (106)$$

B. Acetylene → Conjugated Diene Isomerization

Some acetylenic compounds may rearrange to conjugated dienes by the prototropic rearrangement taking place in alkaline media. A transformation of this type is only practicable, however, when the structure of the compound is such that the diene produced plays a role for completing a more extended conjugated system (36). It should be mentioned that the diene produced in this reaction is always the thermodynamically stable *trans–trans* diene.

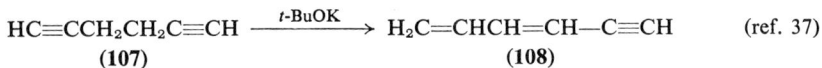

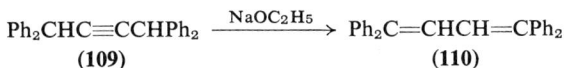

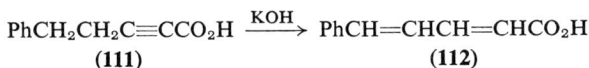

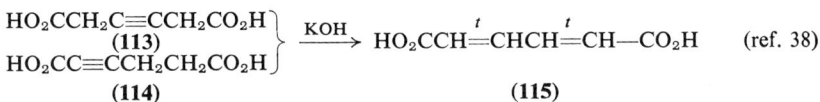

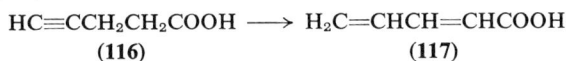

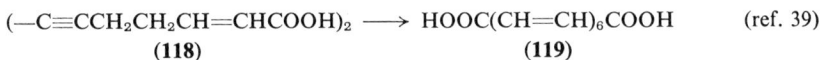

$$HC\equiv CCH_2CH_2C\equiv CH \xrightarrow{\text{t-BuOK}} H_2C=CHCH=CH-C\equiv CH \qquad \text{(ref. 37)}$$
$$\text{(107)} \qquad\qquad\qquad\qquad\qquad \text{(108)}$$

$$Ph_2CHC\equiv CCHPh_2 \xrightarrow{\text{NaOC}_2\text{H}_5} Ph_2C=CHCH=CPh_2$$
$$\text{(109)} \qquad\qquad\qquad\qquad \text{(110)}$$

$$PhCH_2CH_2C\equiv CCO_2H \xrightarrow{\text{KOH}} PhCH=CHCH=CHCO_2H$$
$$\text{(111)} \qquad\qquad\qquad\qquad \text{(112)}$$

$$\left.\begin{array}{l} HO_2CCH_2C\equiv CCH_2CO_2H \\ \text{(113)} \\ HO_2CC\equiv CCH_2CH_2CO_2H \end{array}\right\} \xrightarrow{\text{KOH}} HO_2C\overset{t}{CH}=CHCH\overset{t}{=}CH-CO_2H \qquad \text{(ref. 38)}$$
$$\text{(114)} \qquad\qquad\qquad\qquad\qquad\qquad \text{(115)}$$

$$HC\equiv CCH_2CH_2COOH \longrightarrow H_2C=CHCH=CHCOOH$$
$$\text{(116)} \qquad\qquad\qquad\qquad \text{(117)}$$

$$(-C\equiv CCH_2CH_2CH=CHCOOH)_2 \longrightarrow HOOC(CH=CH)_6COOH \qquad \text{(ref. 39)}$$
$$\text{(118)} \qquad\qquad\qquad\qquad\qquad \text{(119)}$$

By the application of this type of reaction a natural polyene dicarboxylic acid, corticrocin (119), was synthesized (39).

First, in 1959, Sondheimer and Wolovsky (40) accomplished a synthesis of a completely conjugated 18-membered ring cyclic system. They modified the method of Eglinton's oxidative coupling of an ethynyl compound, and cyclized 3 moles of hexa-1,5-diyne (120) to the macroring system having six triple bonds (121). Isomerization of the cyclic acetylene to a completely conjugated en–yne compound cyclooctadeca-1,3,7,9,13,15-hexen-5,11,17-triyne (122) was easily carried out by treatment with potassium *tert*-butoxide under mild conditions (Scheme 6). This synthetic procedure has

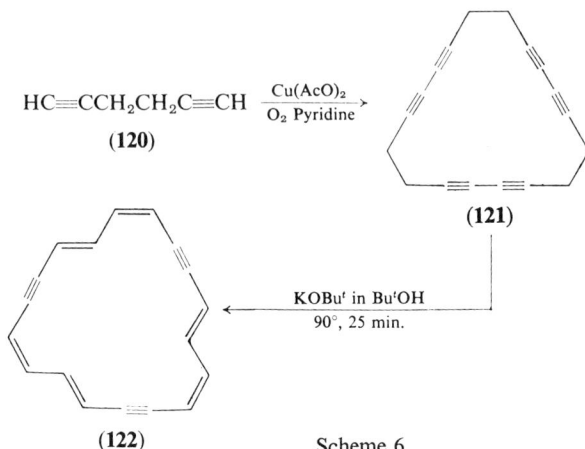

Scheme 6

been extended to a synthesis of much larger ring systems such as 24-(41), 30-, or 50-membered conjugated ring systems (42). Thus a new field of non-benzenoid aromatic chemistry has emerged for the macroring system (43).

III. CYCLIZATIONS INITIATED BY BASE-CATALYZED PROTOTROPIC SHIFTS

It is known that 3 moles of an acetylene afford 1 mole of a benzene compound by pyrolytic condensation. In this section, however, cyclization of acetylenic compounds under basic conditions is discussed. It has also been shown, in the previous section, that a triple bond is easily converted into an allenic or conjugated double bond under basic conditions.

Eglinton et al. (44) found that treatment of hepta-1,6-diyne with potassium t-butoxide gives toluene. This cyclization reaction is assumed to involve isomerization of the triple bond.

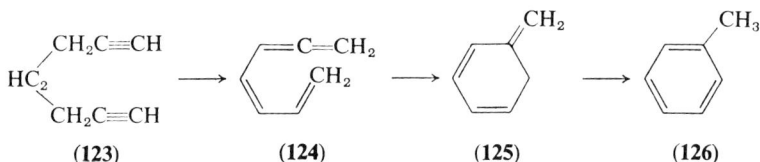

(123)   (124)   (125)   (126)

Further systematic investigation on the cyclization of compounds with the general formula $RC{\equiv}C{-}(CH_2)_n{-}C{\equiv}CR$ has been carried out by this group. Results are summarized in Table 1 (45).

On treatment with potassium t-butoxide cis-dipropargylethylene undergoes allenic isomerization followed by cyclization to give the spiro compound along with a small quantity of dibenzo[a,e]cyclooctadiene (Scheme 7) (46).

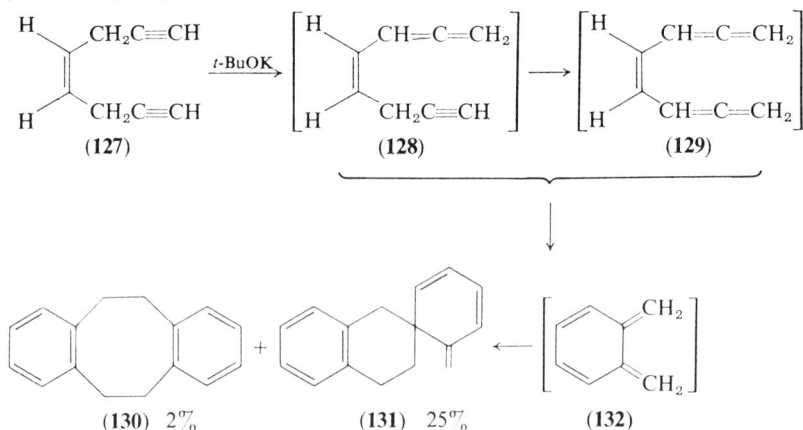

(127)   (128)   (129)

(130) 2%   (131) 25%   (132)

Scheme 7

TABLE 1

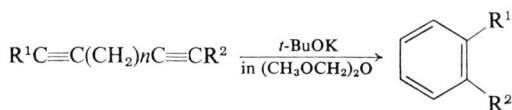

$$R^1C{\equiv}C(CH_2)nC{\equiv}CR^2 \xrightarrow[\text{in } (CH_3OCH_2)_2O]{t\text{-BuOK}}$$

R^1	n	R^2	Products
H	2	H	Vinylether (no benzene)
H	3	H	⟨benzene ring with CH₃⟩
H	4	H	
C_2H_5	0	C_2H_5	⟨benzene ring with ortho-CH₃, CH₃⟩
CH_3	3	CH_3	⟨benzene with ortho-CH₃, C₂H₅⟩ major, ⟨benzene with CH₂CH₂CH₃⟩ minor
H	5	H	
H	6	H	⟨benzene with ortho-C₂H₅, C₂H₅⟩, ⟨benzene with ortho-CH₃, CH₂CH₂CH₃⟩, ⟨benzene with (CH₂)₂CH₃⟩
H	10	H	⟨benzene with R, R⟩ Allenic compound present

The reaction is initiated by proton abstraction from the propargylic methylene group and involves an allenic rearrangement (**128, 129**), followed by cyclization to a six-membered ring bearing two exo-methylene groups. In the case of the *trans*-isomer no cyclization product was obtained.

Iwai and Ide (47) have found that treatment of di(phenylpropargyl)-methane (**133**) with a solution of potassium *tert*-butoxide in *tert*-butyl-alcohol at 62–63° for 4.5 hr gave 4-phenyl-2,3-dihydro-1H-benz[f]indene (**136**).

Since the compound (**133**) has two triple bonds, it would be assumed to afford two kinds of allenic intermediates, mono- (**134**) and di-allenic

X = —CH$_2$—   (**a**)

—S—   (**b**)

—NCH$_3$— (**c**)

—O—   (**d**)

(**133**)

(**134**)

(**137**)

(**135**)

(**138**)

(**136**)

(**139**)

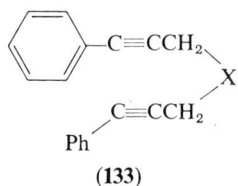

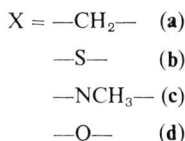

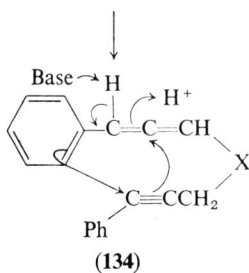

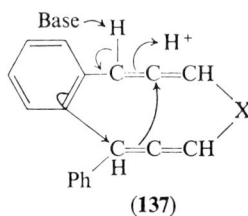

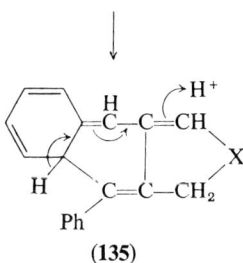

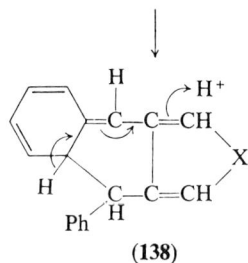

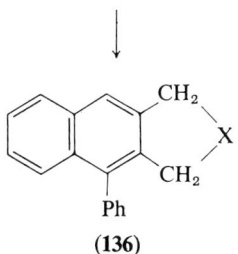

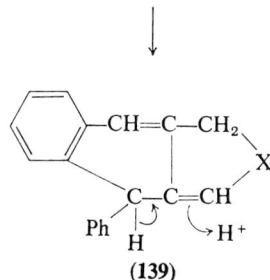

(**137**) compounds. The cyclization would be able to proceed in two different ways to afford phenylnaphthodihydroindene (**136a**) as the final product. In the case of the mono-allene (**134**), a proton is abstracted by the base from the terminal carbon atom of the allenic bond adjacent to the phenyl group and the π-electrons of the phenyl group attack the carbon atom of the other triple bond adjacent to the other phenyl group. Successively, π-electrons of the triple bond attack the central carbon atom of the allenic bond to accomplish the ring formation. The alternative route from **133** to **136** involves diallene which results from simultaneous isomerization of the triple bonds. In this case π-electrons of the phenyl group attack the carbon atoms of the allenic bond and π-electrons of the allenic bond concertedly attack the central carbon atom of the other allenic bond to afford the cyclization products (136).

This cyclization reaction can be extended to other diacetylenic derivatives including sulfur, nitrogen, or oxygen atoms in place of the methylene group. Observation of the reaction times and yields for each case of the reaction shows that the reactions are deeply affected by the electronegativity of the atom which is substituted at the center of the molecule (see Table 2).

TABLE 2
Effect of Electronegativity

	X	Electronegativity (Pauling)	Reaction time, min	Yield, %
136a	—C—	2.5	210	35
136b	—S—	2.5	240	40
136c	—NCH$_3$—	3.0	75	85
136d	—O—	3.5	20	97

The same type of cyclization reaction can also be successfully carried out on dimethyl(2-propynyl)(3-phenyl-2-propynyl)ammonium bromide (140) (48).

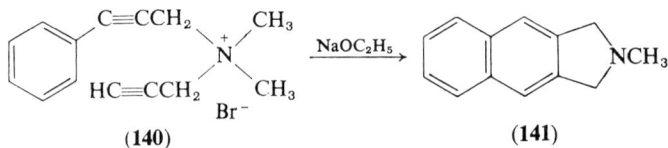

(140)   NaOC$_2$H$_5$ (141)

Contrary to expectation, however, dimethylbis(3-phenyl-2-propynyl)-ammonium bromide (142) did not afford any naphthalene derivative but gave a Stevens type rearrangement product (49) which is discussed in a later section.

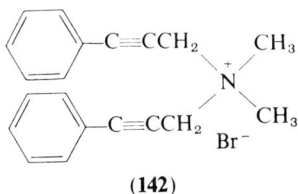

(142)

Transannular cyclizations of cyclic acetylenes have been reported. On treatment of a cyclic thiodiyne compound (143) with the base a di-allenic intermediate is first formed and then the transannular reaction between these two allenic bonds occurs to give the bicyclic sulfur compound (145) (50).

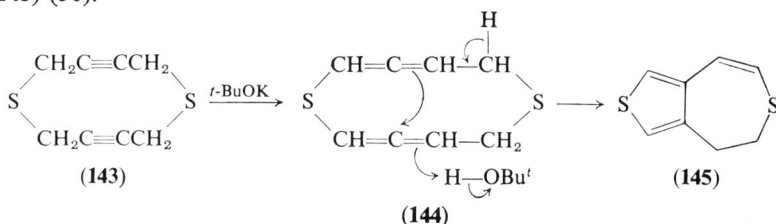

(143)   (144)   (145)

Also, medium size rings with two conjugated diynes also undergo the transannular reaction to form a new ring system (147,149).

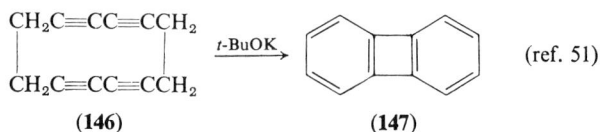

(146)   (147)   (ref. 51)

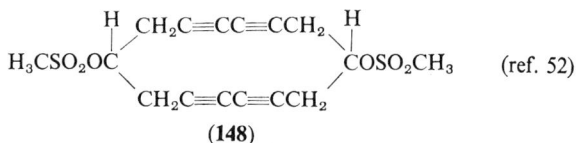

(148)   (ref. 52)

2% KOH in DMSO

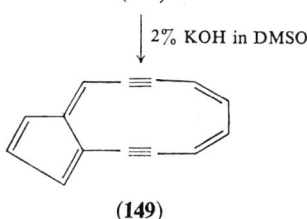

(149)

Iwai and Hiraoka found (48,49) in the course of their study on the chemistry of propargylamines that the triple bond of a propargylammonium halide is much more reactive toward an anionoid reagent compared with the ordinary isolated triple bond. This suggests that the inductive effect of the quaternary amine group is transmitted through the methylene group to the triple bond. A study on the infrared absorption spectra of these compounds supports this assumption: the normal stretching vibration of an ethynyl hydrogen has been reported (53) to appear at around 3300 cm^{-1}, whereas the absorption band due to the ethynyl hydrogen of a propargylammonium halide is observed in the region of $3120-2310 \text{ cm}^{-1}$. This electrophilic character of the triple bond of a propargylammonium group is expected to result in a cyclization reaction thereby neutralizing the positively charged nitrogen atom. The cyclization reaction of propargylphenylpropargyldimethylammonium bromide (140) is considered to proceed on these bases. Furthermore it was shown that 1-propargylpicolinium bromide (150), which has the triple bond of propargylammonium halide and an active methylene group in its molecule, cyclized to 2-methylindolizine under basic conditions (48).

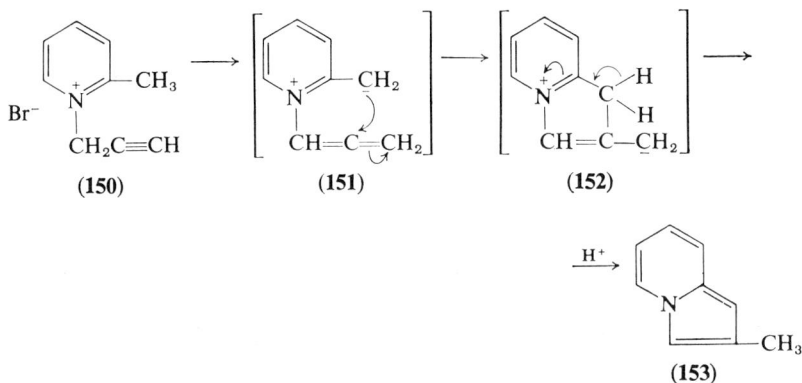

Analogously, 2-amino-1-(2-propynyl)pyridinium bromide (154) gave 2-methylimidazo[1,2-a]pyridine (155) on treatment with aqueous sodium hydroxide solution (48).

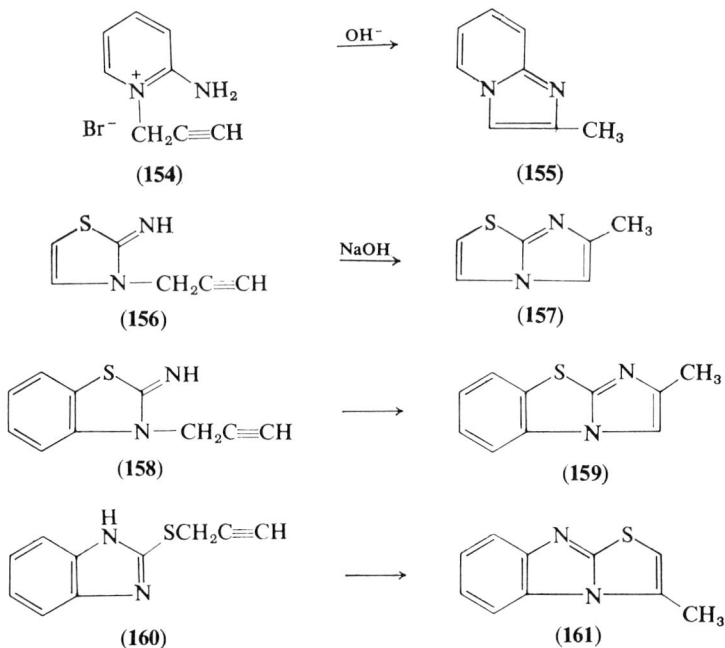

Further, N-propargyl-2-amino-heterocyclic compounds undergo the similar cyclization to fused ring systems (55). A propargylthioether also gives a fused ring compound by the similar procedure (55).

Another example of the base-catalyzed ring formation reaction of propargylamines has been reported. An N-alkyl-N-propargylethanolamine (162) as the alkoxide in ether, or on treatment with sodium hydroxide in dimethyl sulfoxide or on treatment with potassium hydroxide in toluene or xylene, is converted into the corresponding 3-alkyl-2-vinyloxazolidine (164) (54). Formation of 164 is well understood as occurring via an intramolecular nucleophilic addition at the α-carbon atom of the allene moiety of the allenic amino alcohol (163) formed by the base-catalyzed prototropic rearrangement of 162.

In the case of propargylamine, the proton α to the acetylenic function and α to the amino group is sufficiently acidic to be removed by the base to give an allenic intermediate. Intramolecular addition of the alkoxide ion to the intermediate (163) gives the five-membered ring (164).

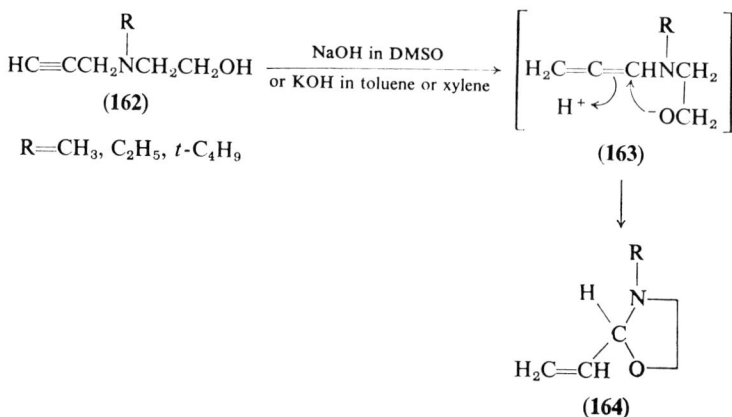

$$HC{\equiv}CCH_2NCH_2CH_2OH \xrightarrow[\text{or KOH in toluene or xylene}]{\text{NaOH in DMSO}}$$

(162)

$$R{=}CH_3,\ C_2H_5,\ t\text{-}C_4H_9$$

(163)

(164)

N-(β-Hydroxyethyl)-4-pyrrolidino-N,1,1-trimethyl-2-butynylamine (165) also gives a cyclized morpholine derivative (167) under similar reaction conditions (56). There are two nitrogen atoms in 165 but the alleneamine formation can proceed only toward the pyrrolidine moiety and the lone pair electrons of the oxygen atom attacks the γ-carbon atom of the allenamine to form the morpholine ring (167).

Under similar conditions, β-hydroxyethylpropargylether (168), in which the nitrogen atom of the propargylamine moiety in the compound

CH$_3$NCH$_2$CH$_2$OH

CH$_3$CC≡CCH$_2$—N⟨⟩

  |
  CH$_3$

(165)

$\xrightarrow[\text{in xylene}]{\text{KOH}}$

⎡ CH$_3$NCH$_2$CH$_2$OH

  CH$_3$CCH=C=CH—N⟨⟩

    |
    CH$_3$ ⎤

(166)

↓

H$_3$C—N⟨ ⟩O
H$_3$C—⟨   ⟩—CH=CH—N⟨⟩
    |
    CH$_3$

(167)

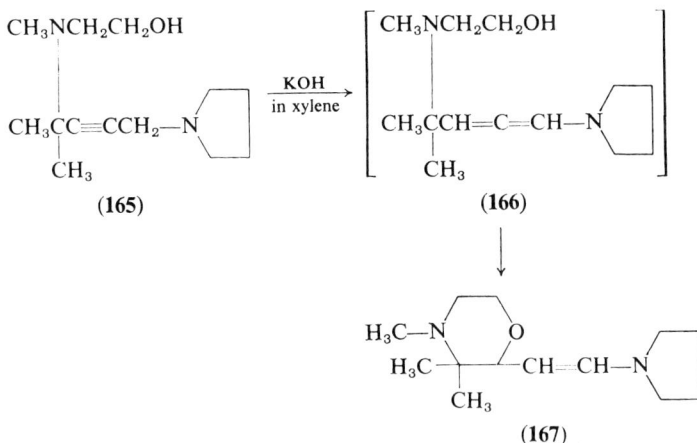

(162) is replaced by an oxygen atom, also gives four kinds of cyclic compounds involving two oxygen atoms (57). It is conceivable that among these compounds, 2-vinyl-1,3-dioxolane (173) and 2-methyl-1,4-dioxene-2 (174) are formed via intermediates which are given by the base-catalyzed re-

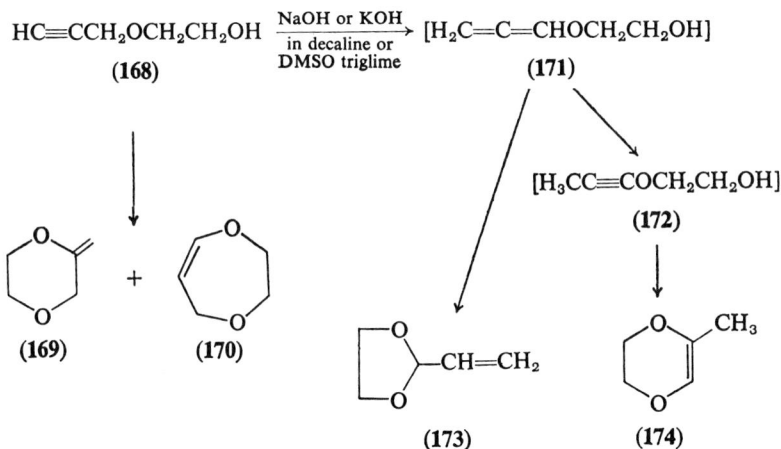

HC≡CCH$_2$OCH$_2$CH$_2$OH $\xrightarrow[\substack{\text{in decaline or} \\ \text{DMSO triglime}}]{\text{NaOH or KOH}}$ [H$_2$C=C=CHOCH$_2$CH$_2$OH]

(168)   (171)

[H$_3$CC≡COCH$_2$CH$_2$OH]

(172)

(169)   +   (170)

(173)   (174)

arrangement of the triple bond of 168. Formation of the other two cyclic products, 169 and 170, should be due to internal nucleophilic additions of the alcohol group to the triple bond. Moreover, it has been confirmed that 2-methyl-1,4-dioxene-2 (174) was not obtained from 2-methylene-1,4-dioxane (169) because 169 was quite stable under the reaction conditions. The transition state for formation of the dioxene is considered to be

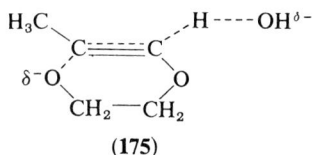

$$H_3C \diagdown C \overline{\overline{\cdots\cdots}} C \diagup \overset{H----OH^{\delta-}}{}$$
$$\delta^- O \diagdown \quad \diagup O$$
$$CH_2 \text{—} CH_2$$

(175)

For a synthesis of trideca-2,10,12-trien-4,6,8-triyne (**177a**) which had been isolated from the Compositae family, trideca-2,10,12-trien-4,7-diyne-6,9-diol (**176a**) was chlorinated with thionylchloride and the product was treated with potassium ethoxide to give **177a** accompanied by an unexpected phenyl derivative, suggesting a new type of cyclization (58). For

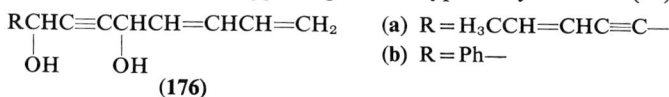

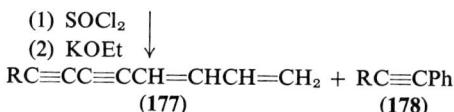

$$RCHC\equiv CCHCH=CHCH=CH_2$$
$$\quad | \qquad |$$
$$\quad OH \quad\; OH$$

(a) $R = H_3CCH=CHC\equiv C\text{—}$
(b) $R = Ph\text{—}$

(176)

(1) SOCl$_2$
(2) KOEt ↓

$$RC\equiv CC\equiv CCH=CHCH=CH_2 + RC\equiv CPh$$
$$\qquad\qquad (177) \qquad\qquad\qquad\qquad (178)$$

confirmation of this interesting cyclization the same procedure was carried out with 1-phenylocta-5,7-dien-2-yne-1,4-diol (**176b**) and diphenylacetylene (**178b**) was obtained along with the expected normal product 1-phenyl-octa-5,7-dien-1,3-diyne (**177b**).

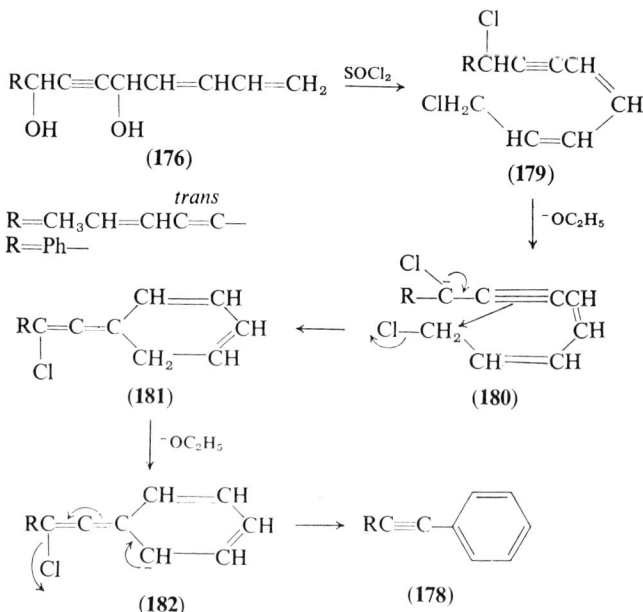

Scheme 8

The mechanism of this cyclization reaction can be visualized as shown by Scheme 8.

The anionotropic rearrangement in the chlorination step would be expected to afford a mixture of *cis* and *trans* isomers. The *cis* isomer is sterically favorable for the cyclization, which would subsequently lead to the formation of a benzene derivative. It should be mentioned that the two compounds (**177a**) and its cyclized derivative (**178a**) have been isolated from the same *Coreopsis* species.

IV. ALLENE CARBENE

Divalent carbon intermediates came to play an important role in synthetic organic chemistry because of their characteristic insertion reactions and the formation of cyclopropanes by reaction with olefins (59).

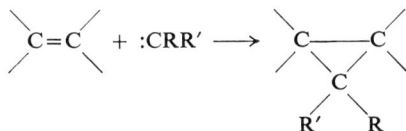

$$\begin{array}{c}\diagdown \\ \diagup\end{array} C = C \begin{array}{c}\diagup \\ \diagdown\end{array} + \;:CRR' \longrightarrow \begin{array}{c}\diagdown \\ \diagup\end{array} C \!\!-\!\! C \begin{array}{c}\diagup \\ \diagdown\end{array}$$

The divalent carbon is linked to the adjacent groups by two covalent bonds and possesses two free electrons. According to the state of the two free electrons, divalent carbons are classified into two groups: (*1*) The first is carbene in the singlet state in which the two free electrons, with antiparallel spins, are located in an sp^2 orbital. The carbene carbon has one vacant p orbital which is vertical to the plane of the sp^2 orbitals. Singlet state carbenes are electron-deficient species, comparable to carbonium ions, with a pair of free electrons comparable to that of carbanions. Therefore, depending on the characters of the neighboring group, they behave as electrophilic or nucleophilic reagents. On addition to an olefin they give a *cis*-addition product with retention of the original stereochemistry. (*2*) The second is a diradical in the triplet state. Each of the two nonbonding electrons, having parallel spins, is located in each of the two p orbitals which are perpendicular to the sp-hybridized orbital of the carbon atom. The characteristic reaction of the triplet state divalent carbon is abstraction of a hydrogen or a halogen atom from a reactant. The carbon atom behaves as a free radical and shows no stereospecificity on addition to an olefin.

Considering the distribution of electrons in a triple bond (see Fig. 2), if a propargyl group affords divalent carbon(propargylene), the linear propargylene having three sp-hybridized carbon atoms and six electrons for distribution in the p orbitals is a cyclindrically symmetrical molecule with two low-lying π-molecular orbitals for four electrons. The next higher

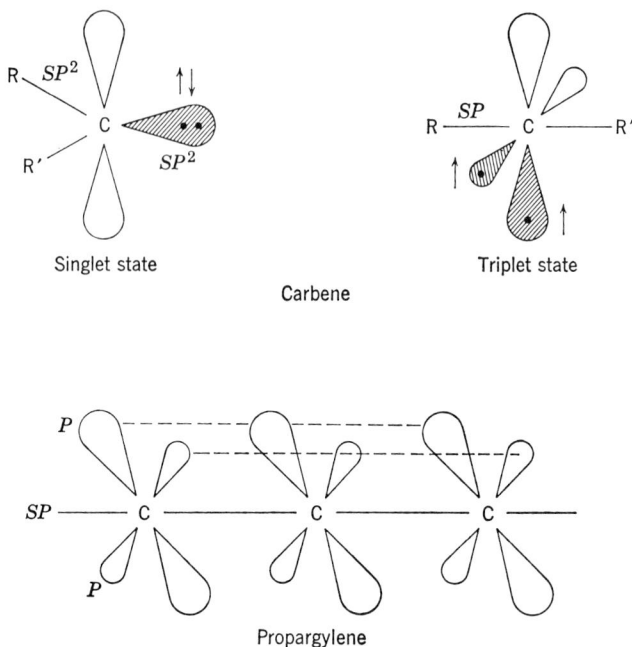

Singlet state   Triplet state

Carbene

Propargylene

Figure 2

two molecular orbitals are nearly equivalent. Therefore, the two remaining nonbonding electrons are distributed singly on each of the orbitals and are effectively stabilized by π-molecular overlap.

The simple Hückel molecular orbital treatment of propargylene gives the orbital energy levels, as seen in Figure 3.

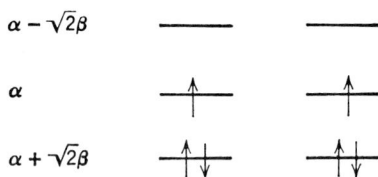

Figure 3

Skell and Klebe (60) and Kirmse (61) have investigated the addition of propargylene generated by photolysis of diazopropyne to *trans*- and *cis*-2-butene. The results are shown in Scheme 9. The product distributions of *cis*- and *trans*-dimethylethynylcycolopropane from *cis*- and *trans*-2-butene show no stereospecificity of the carbene in these reactions. As the occurrence or absence of stereospecificity in the addition of a carbene to an olefin

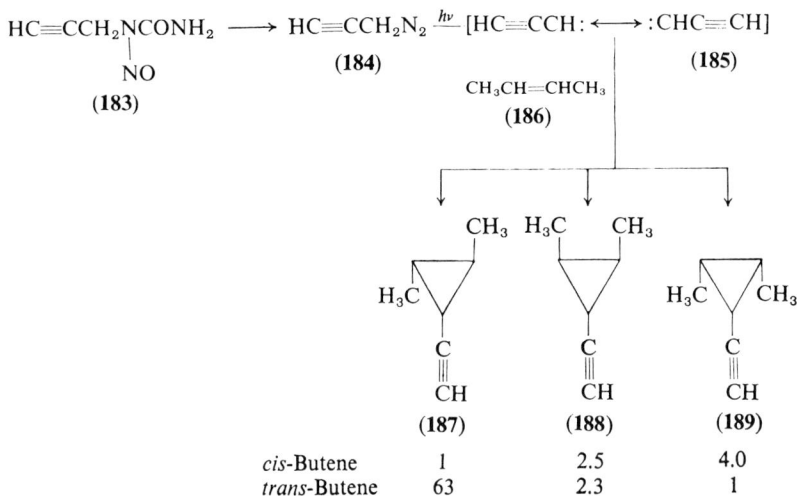

$$HC{\equiv}CCH_2NCONH_2 \longrightarrow HC{\equiv}CCH_2N_2 \overset{h\nu}{\longrightarrow} [HC{\equiv}CCH: \longleftrightarrow :CHC{\equiv}CH]$$

NO
(183)

(184)

(185)

$$CH_3CH{=}CHCH_3$$
(186)

	CH₃ H₃C CH₃ (187)	(188)	H₃C C CH₃ (189)
cis-Butene	1	2.5	4.0
trans-Butene	63	2.3	1

Scheme 9

is the best criterion for distinguishing the singlet or triplet state, the propargylene is assumed to react in a triplet state. This is rationalized on the basis of molecular orbital considerations (Fig. 3).

On treatment with a base, ethynyl compounds having a leaving group, which leaves the molecule with the bonding electrons, yield allene carbenes.

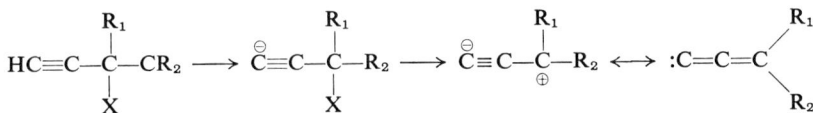

$$HC{\equiv}C{-}\underset{X}{\overset{R_1}{C}}{-}CR_2 \longrightarrow \overset{\ominus}{C}{\equiv}C{-}\underset{X}{\overset{R_1}{C}}{-}R_2 \longrightarrow \overset{\ominus}{C}{\equiv}C{-}\underset{\oplus}{\overset{R_1}{C}}{-}R_2 \longleftrightarrow :C{=}C{=}C\overset{R_1}{\underset{R_2}{}}$$

Skell presented a paper at the 137th Meeting of the American Chemical Society (Cleveland, Ohio, 1960); the evidence for existence of a resonance system of methylpropargylene is provided by the fact that propargylene adds to olefins not only at C-1 but also at C-3 (61) (Scheme 10).

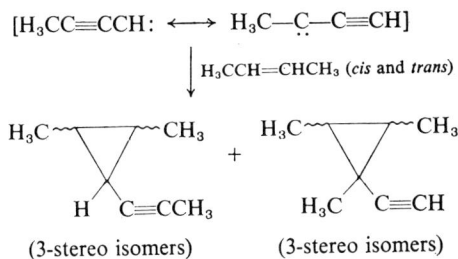

$$[H_3CC{\equiv}CCH: \longleftrightarrow H_3C{-}\overset{..}{C}{-}C{\equiv}CH]$$

$$\downarrow H_3CCH{=}CHCH_3 \ (cis \ and \ trans)$$

(3-stereo isomers)   (3-stereo isomers)

Scheme 10

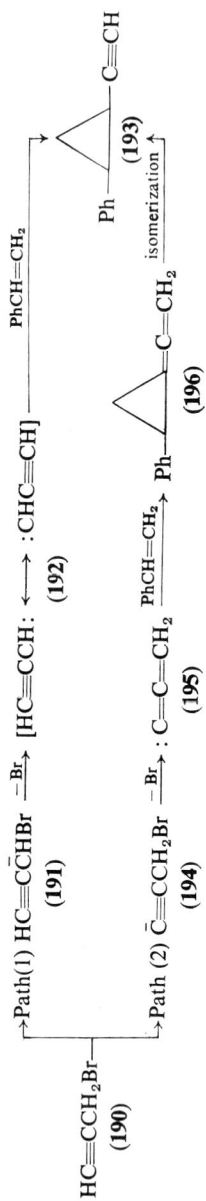

On the other hand an acetylenic compound having the leaving group and at least one hydrogen at the α position to the triple bond may be expected to yield propargylene by α elimination. However, attempts to produce propargylene by α elimination from propargylbromide have led to ambiguous results (61,62). In the presence of styrene, propargylbromide (190) gives only phenylethynyl cyclopropane (193) in 8% yield. For the formation of 193 two possible reaction pathways are considered: (1) α elimination of propargylbromide (190) gives propargylene (192) which adds to styrene to afford 193. (2) Ethenylidene-carbene (195) produced by 1,3-elimination adds to styrene to yield first the allene derivative (196) which isomerizes to the acetylenic compound 193.

For determination of the pathways the experiment was carried out in the presence of cis-2-butene instead of styrene. Unfortunately the results were again ambiguous, there being obtained a mixture of the acetylene (197) and the allene (198) whose stereochemistry was unknown.

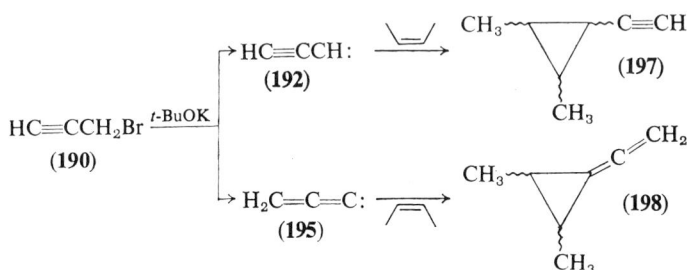

Investigation of base-promoted solvolysis of some tert-ethynyl derivatives has suggested the formation of an allene–carbene intermediate. The solvolysis of tert-ethynyl halides is very slow compared with tert-butyl halides, but is strongly accelerated by a base. On the other hand, base catalysis is not observed when the acetylenic hydrogen is replaced by an alkyl group (63). By solvolyzing 3-bromo-3-methyl-1-butyne (199) in 80% EtOD–20% D_2O mixture it was shown that the base-catalyzed exchange of the acetylenic proton is remarkably faster than base-promoted solvolysis (64). Thus, the formation of the conjugate base (200) would occur preferentially. The conjugate base undergoes S_N1 ionization to yield the zwitterion–carbene intermediate (201). Formation of such an unusual intermediate was first proposed by Hennion (65). Actually, in the presence of tetramethylethylene the tert-ethynyl halide gives allene-cyclopropane (202) by treatment with a base.

The fact that dimethylallenylchloride (203) gives the same cyclopropane derivative (202) under the same conditions (66) also supports the formation of the carbene intermediate (201) in the previous reaction.

$(CH_3)_2CC\equiv CH$ (199), with Br substituent, branches:

- basic solvolysis → $(CH_3)_2CC\equiv \bar{C}$ | Br (200) → $[(CH_3)_2\overset{+}{C}C\equiv \bar{C} \longleftrightarrow (CH_3)_2C=C=C:]$ (201)
- neutral solvolysis → $(CH_3)_2\overset{+}{C}C\equiv CH$ (203)

(201) $\downarrow$ $C=C$

structure (202): $=C=C(CH_3)_2$

$(CH_3)_2C=C=CHCl$ (203) $\underset{B:H}{\overset{B^-}{\rightleftarrows}}$ $(CH_3)_2C=C=\bar{C}-Cl$ (204) $\underset{+Cl^-}{\overset{-Cl}{\rightleftarrows}}$

$[(CH_3)_2\overset{+}{C}-C\equiv \bar{C} \longrightarrow (CH_3)_2C=C=C:]$ (201)

$\downarrow$ $C=C$

structure (202): $=C=C(CH_3)_2$

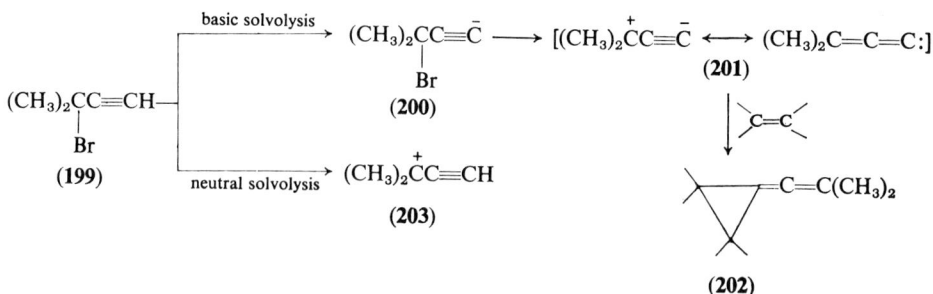

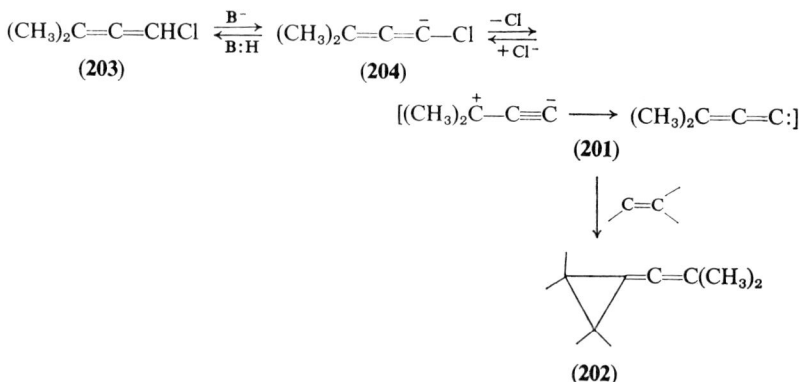

3-Chloro-3-methyl-1-butyne (205) can react with nucleophiles such as the anion of acetoacetate (206), acetylacetone (211), or diethyl sodiomethylmalonate (214) to give products originating from both α and γ attack (67).

In some of these reactions γ attack occurs and leads to rearrangement and deacylation of the initially formed allene, but with diethyl sodiomethylmalonate, the acetylene (215) and the allene compound (216) are isolated in a ratio of 2.54:1. Reaction of 1-chloro-3-methylbuta-1,2-diene with the malonate gives the same pair of compounds 215 and 216 in a ratio of 2.60:1. This close agreement suggests the formation of common intermediate and in both cases the allene-carbene (201) can be trapped as the cyclopropane derivative, $=C=C$, by adding cyclohexene.

Furthermore, sodioethylmalonate reacts with 3-chloro-3-methylpentyne-1 (223) and 1-bromo-3-methyl-penta-1,2-diene (224) to give the compounds, 227 and 228 in yields of 56.4 and 43.6%, respectively, in both cases (68). From the experimental fact that the product ratios in both cases are nearly same, it would appear that the allene-carbene is an intermediate

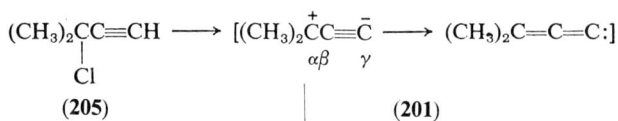

(205)

(201)

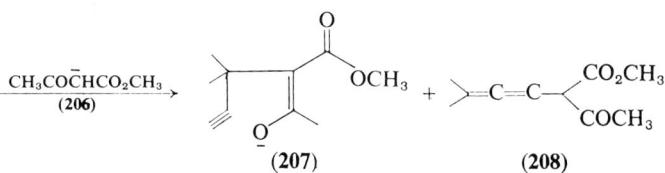

$CH_3CO\bar{C}HCO_2CH_3$
(206)

(207) + (208)

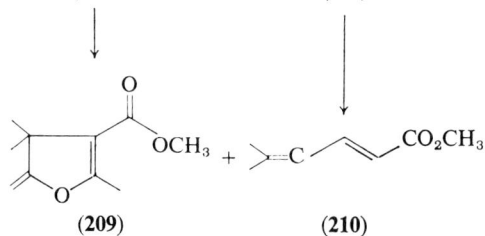

(209) + (210)

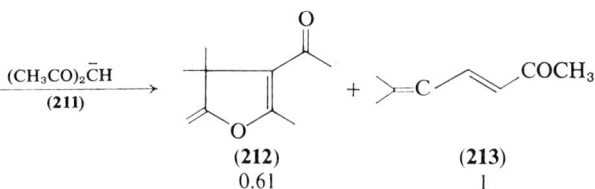

$(CH_3CO)_2\bar{C}H$
(211)

(212)
0.61

(213)
1

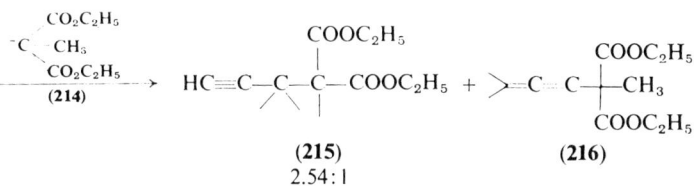

(214)

(215)
2.54 : 1

(216)

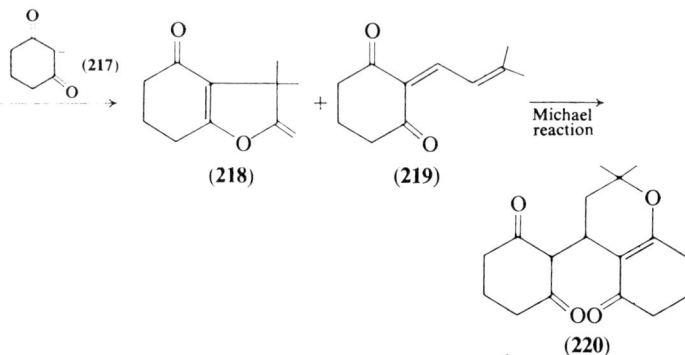

(217)

(218) + (219)

Michael reaction

(220)

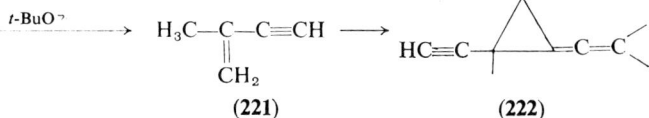

t-BuO⁻

$H_3C-C-C\equiv CH$
CH_2
(221)

$HC\equiv C$ ... $C=C$
(222)

of these reactions, because it is unlikely that the same proportion of products would be obtained by S_N2/S_N2' mechanisms from these different halides, **223** and **224**.

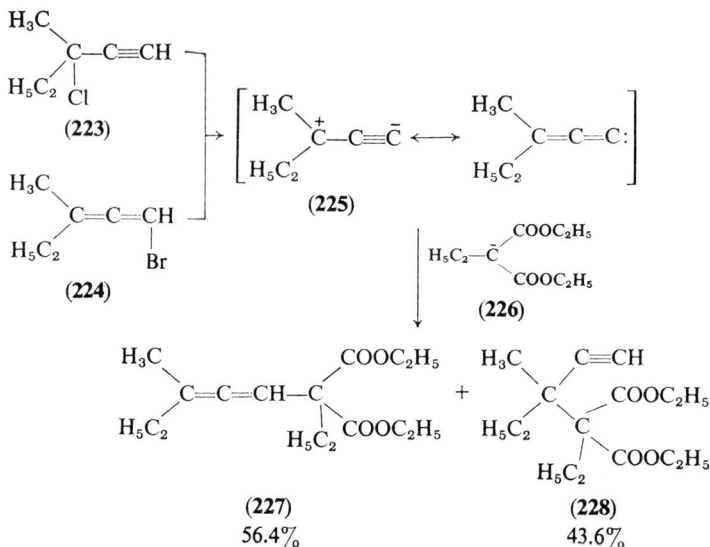

Derivatives of ethynyl carbinol also afford the allene-carbene intermediate by treatment with a base. Cadiot found (69) that α-diphenylethynyl carbinol (**229**) gave tetraphenylhexapentaene (**236**) in a good yield by treatment with potassium hydroxide in the presence of acetic anhydride. On the other hand, treatment of the acetate (**230**) from **229** with potassium butoxide gave the allenyl cyclopropane derivative (**233**) in the presence of styrene. Thus, Hartzler (70) postulated a reaction mechanism for these reactions involving the allene-carbene intermediate (**231**). Formation of **236** may be well explained by assuming an attack of the carbene (**231**) on the conjugate base (**234**) from the acetate (**230**).

It has been shown that formation of the allene carbenes occurs much more favorably in *tert*-acetylenic halides and esters as compared to the corresponding primary compounds because of steric hindrance.

Recently, Hartzler (71) carried out similar reactions on the di-*tert*-butylethynylcarbinol derivative (**237**) and confirmed the mechanism. Treatment of **237** with potassium *tert*-butoxide gives tetra-*tert*-butyl-hexa-1,2,3,4,5-pentaene (**240**) and di-*tert*-butylpropa-1,2-dienyl-*tert*-butylether (**241**) in yields of 20 and 19%, respectively, whereas in the presence of styrene only a cyclopropane derivative (**239**) is obtained. This fact indicates

$Ph_2CC\equiv CH$
   |
  OH
  (229)

$Ph_2CC\equiv CCPh_2$ + $PhCH—C—C=CPh_2$
  | | \C/
 OH   OH   H_2
  (232) 44%
             (233) 25%

$\downarrow$ Ac_2O $\uparrow$ $PhCH=CH_2$

$Ph_2CC\equiv CH$ $\xrightarrow{t\text{-BuOK}}$ $[Ph_2\overset{+}{C}C\equiv \overset{-}{C} \longleftrightarrow Ph_2C=C=C:]$
   | **(231)**
 OAc
 (230)

$\downarrow$

$Ph_2CC\equiv C^-:$ $\longrightarrow$ $Ph_2C=C=C:$
   | **(231)**
 OAc
 (234)

$Ph_2C—C\equiv C—\overset{-}{C}:=C=CPh_2$ $\longrightarrow$ $Ph_2C=C=C=C=C=CPh_2$
       OAc   **(236)**
       (235)

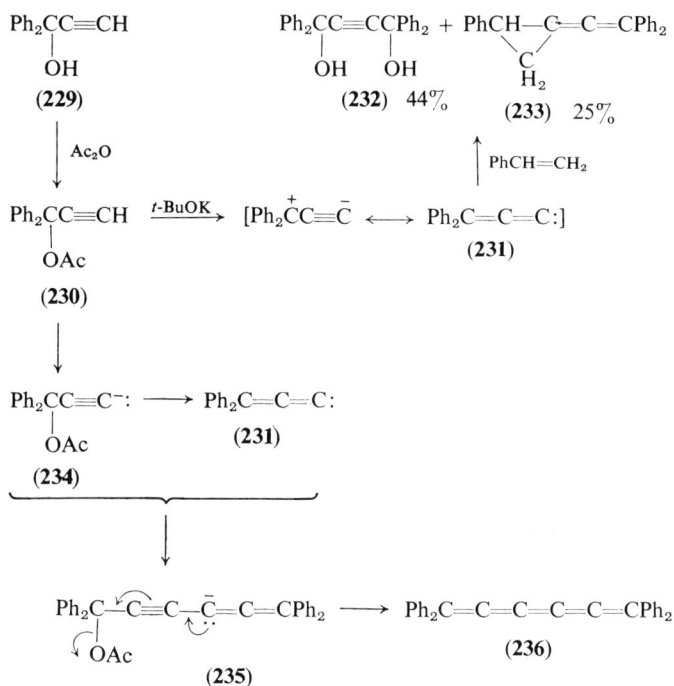

that the reaction should involve the allene carbene (**238**) as an intermediate which reacts predominantly with styrene to form **239**.

The formation of **241** is also explained by attack of the carbene **238** on the *tert*-butoxy anion.

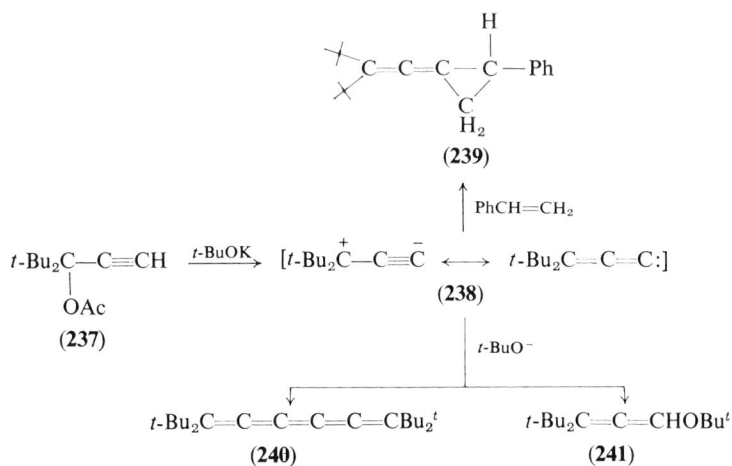

                                  H
                                  |
  \ /C—C=C—C—Ph
  / \ |
                       C
                      H_2
               (239)

              $\uparrow$ $PhCH=CH_2$

$t\text{-Bu}_2C—C\equiv CH$ $\xrightarrow{t\text{-BuOK}}$ $[t\text{-Bu}_2\overset{+}{C}—C\equiv \overset{-}{C} \longleftrightarrow t\text{-Bu}_2C=C=C:]$
   | **(238)**
 OAc
 (237)
                               $\downarrow$ $t\text{-BuO}^-$

$t\text{-Bu}_2C—C=C=C=C=CBu_2^t$ $t\text{-Bu}_2C=C=CHOBu^t$
     (240)   **(241)**

In a broad sense, a Grignard reagent can be considered as a base. Therefore, it is interesting to investigate the Grignard reaction of haloacetylenic compounds in view of the chemistry of a carbene. The reaction of a Grignard reagent with propargyl bromide had been already reported by Prevost et al. (72), but probably incorrectly interpreted in the light of more recent advances in the field of carbene chemistry. Actually, Serratosa (73) has reinvestigated the reaction of Grignard reagents with this primary acetylenic bromide.

If propargyl bromide (190) reacts with Grignard reagents as an acetylene (Scheme 11), 3-bromo-1-propynylmagnesium bromide (242) would be formed, which, upon γ elimination of magnesium bromide, would give the allene carbene (195) (path 1). On the other hand, if 190 reacts as a bromide, the "normal" product, a monosubstituted acetylene (243), should be obtained, according to a metathetical process (path 2).

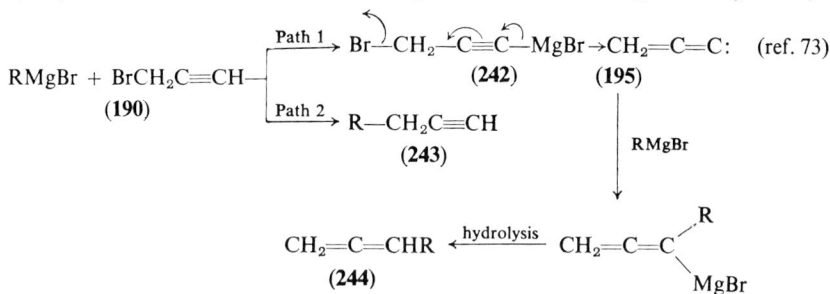

$$\text{RMgBr} + \text{BrCH}_2\text{C}{\equiv}\text{CH} \xrightarrow[\text{Path 2}]{\text{Path 1}}$$
(190)

Path 1: $\text{Br}-\text{CH}_2-\text{C}{\equiv}\text{C}-\text{MgBr} \rightarrow \text{CH}_2{=}\text{C}{=}\text{C}:$ (ref. 73)
(242)   (195)

Path 2: $\text{R}-\text{CH}_2\text{C}{\equiv}\text{CH}$
(243)

$$\text{CH}_2{=}\text{C}{=}\text{CHR} \xleftarrow{\text{hydrolysis}} \text{CH}_2{=}\text{C}{=}\text{C}\begin{smallmatrix}\text{R}\\\text{MgBr}\end{smallmatrix}$$
(244)

$\downarrow$ RMgBr

Scheme 11

The results are summarized in Table 3.

These experimental results can be rationalized by the assumption that Grignard reagents actually react with either one of the two reactive sites in the propargyl bromide molecule depending upon the nature of the radical R, the solvent used, and the reaction temperature: in the order of electron-repelling ability (basicity) of the substituent in the Grignard reagents

TABLE 3

The Effect of the Grignard Reagents (RMgBr) on the Reactive Pathway (73) (Scheme 11)

R	Temp., °C	Solvent	Catalyst	Major product	Suggested mechanism	Refs.
$-\text{C}{\equiv}\text{CH}$	40	Et_2O	Cu_2Cl_2	243	2	74
Aryl	< 0	Et_2O	—	243 + 244	1 + 2	73,75
Alkyl	40	Et_2O	—	243 + 244	1 + 2	73
Alkyl	< 0	Et_2O	—	244	1	73
Alkyl	< 0	THF	—	244	2	

(ethynyl < aryl < alkyl) the carbene formation (path 1) is favored. The lower temperature makes the reaction rate of the metathetical process (path 2) slower. The reaction is strongly affected by the solvent used. Substitution of tetrahydrofuran (THF) for ether makes the metathetical process (path 2) favorable even at low temperature.

V. STEVENS TYPE REARRANGEMENTS

Stevens and co-workers have found that benzylphenacyl dimethyl ammonium bromide undergoes smooth rearrangement with migration of the benzyl group from nitrogen to carbon under influence of strong base to yield α-dimethylamino-β-phenylpropiophenone (237) (76,77).

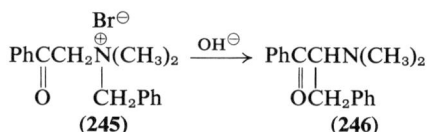

$$\underset{(245)}{\underset{\underset{CH_2Ph}{|}}{\overset{Br^{\ominus}}{PhCCH_2\overset{\oplus}{N}(CH_3)_2}}} \xrightarrow{OH^{\ominus}} \underset{(246)}{\underset{OCH_2Ph}{PhCCHN(CH_3)_2}}$$

The migrating group also can be of the types allyl, benzhydryl (Ph$_2$CH—), or phenacyl (PhCOCH$_2$—). Furthermore, dibenzyldimethyl-ammonium bromide (247), having a benzyl group instead of a phenacyl group in 245, also undergoes rearrangement on treatment with sodium ethoxide to give α-benzyl-N,N-dimethylbenzylamine (248).

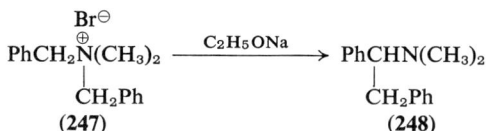

$$\underset{(247)}{\underset{\underset{CH_2Ph}{|}}{\overset{Br^{\ominus}}{PhCH_2\overset{\oplus}{N}(CH_3)_2}}} \xrightarrow{C_2H_5ONa} \underset{(248)}{\underset{\underset{CH_2Ph}{|}}{PhCHN(CH_3)_2}}$$

Stevens demonstrated (77) the intramolecularity of this reaction by applying the reaction simultaneously to two different quaternary ammonium salts in the same medium and demonstrating that no interchange of the migrating group between the two systems occurred.

When various substituents were placed in the *meta* or *para* position of the benzyl group of 245, the reaction rate increased in the order of the electron-attracting ability of the substituent (77–79). In contrast, *para* substituents in the phenacyl group of 245 increase the rate of rearrangement with the order of their electron-releasing ability (80). The rearrangement is retarded by incorporation of electron-attracting substituents in the phenacyl group because of the lower electron density at the negatively charged attacking carbon. Replacement of the benzoyl group by a phenyl or alkyl substituent makes the rate of reaction slower. The reaction then appears to proceed by the formation of a carbanion. The reaction mechanism for the rearrangement is illustrated by Hauser and Kantor (81) as indicated.

$$
\begin{array}{ccc}
\underset{\text{PhCCH}_2}{\overset{\text{O}}{\|}} \quad \text{CH}_2\text{Ph} & \underset{\text{PhCCH}}{\overset{\text{O}}{\|}} \quad \text{CH}_2\text{Ph} & \underset{\text{PhC}}{\overset{\text{O}}{\|}}{-}\text{CHCH}_2\text{Ph} \\
\end{array}
$$

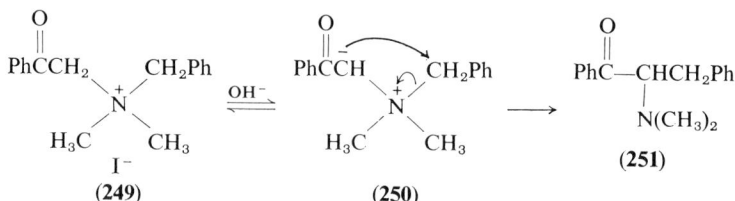

Although the reaction is accelerated by a base, a limit is reached when slightly more than one equivalent is added, at which point virtually all of the substrate has been converted to its conjugated base (**250**). When the rearrangement is carried out on the optically active ammonium ion (**252**), the α-phenylethyl group migrates with retention of configuration (82), indicating that cleavage of the C—N bond and formation of new C—C

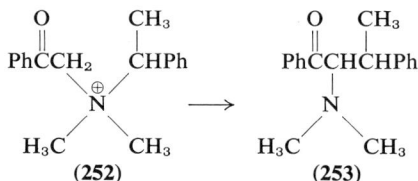

bond should occur on the same side of Cα. Therefore, the reaction is to be considered as an SNi type. In contrast to the more normal nucleophilic rearrangements, in which a group migrates with its pair of bonding electrons to an electron-deficient terminus, the Stevens rearrangement, which can be classified as an electrophilic rearrangement, involves migration of a group without its pair of bonding electrons to an electron-rich carbon atom and the reaction proceeds through a carbanion (it is not a true carbanion but a type of zwitterion in which the negative pole has carbanion character) but an intramolecular nucleophilic displacement process. On this base the Stevens rearrangement is to be indicated first by ylide formation which is followed by C—N bond cleavage.

In the earlier section, it has been shown that the methylene group of a propargyl moiety (RC≡C—CH$_2$—) is similar in chemical behavior to an active methylene group adjacent to a carbonyl group because of the acidity of the α-carbon atom to the acetylenic function.

On treatment of N,N-dimethyl-3-phenyl-2-propynylamine (**245**) with ethylmagnesium bromide, for instance, ethane is liberated.

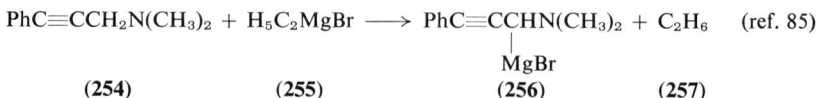

$$
\text{PhC}{\equiv}\text{CCH}_2\text{N(CH}_3)_2 + \text{H}_5\text{C}_2\text{MgBr} \longrightarrow \text{PhC}{\equiv}\text{CCHN(CH}_3)_2 + \text{C}_2\text{H}_6 \quad \text{(ref. 85)}
$$

Therefore, the methylene group of propargylammonium salt would be expected to form a carbanion (ylide) easily, which is required for the first step of a Stevens rearrangement.

On the other hand, it has been known that under basic conditions quaternary ammonium salts of propargylamines react with an active methylene group to form a new C—C bond by liberating a tertiary amine (83). This fact shows that cleavage of the C—N linkage, which is necessary for the second step in a Stevens rearrangement, occurs under basic conditions. The propargyl group has been shown to be capable of acting as both the migrating group and the migration terminus in the Stevens rearrangement, i.e., it forms a carbanion (the first step) and promotes cleavage of the C—N bond. It is interesting to clarify whether a propargyl group plays an active role as migration terminus or as migrating group in the Stevens reaction, depending on the circumstances given.

Treatment of phenacylpropargyldimethylammonium bromide (258) with sodium hydroxide gives the dimethylaminophenacyl propargylic compound (260) (84). In the reaction, abstraction of a proton to form a carbanion occurs predominantly at the methylene group of the phenacyl moiety and cleavage of the C—N linkage takes place at the propargylamine moiety to give the rearranged product (260). In this case, the

phenacyl group acts as a migration terminus and the propargyl group as migrating group.

On treatment of benzyldimethylphenylpropargylammonium iodide (261) with a base, however, a proton was predominantly abstracted from the propargylic methylene to afford a carbanion and the succeeding C—N bond cleavage occurred at the benzylamine moiety to produce a rearranged product 1,4-diphenyl-3-dimethylamino-1-butyne (263) (85). Allyldimethylphenylpropargylammonium bromide (264) underwent the rearrangement in just the same way. However, there is another possibility via 266 having a six-membered transition state.

Independently, Babayan et al. (86) treated N-methyl-N,N-dibenzyl-2-butynylammonium bromide (268) with a base and obtained N-methyl-N-benzyl-1-benzyl-2-butynylamine (269) showing that of the three groups —benzyl, propargyl, and methyl—only the benzyl group acted as the migrating group.

This type of rearrangement of propargylamine can be extended to a cyclic

$$PhC{\equiv}CCH_2\overset{+}{N}CH_2Ph \xrightarrow{OH^-} \left[PhC{\equiv}C\bar{C}H \overset{\frown}{\underset{\underset{H_3C\quad CH_3}{\overset{+}{N}}}{}} CH_2Ph \right] \longrightarrow PhC{\equiv}CCHCH_2Ph$$

$$\underset{\underset{(261)}{H_3C\quad CH_3\ I^-}}{} \qquad \underset{(262)}{} \qquad \underset{\underset{(263)}{H_3C\quad CH_3}}{\overset{|}{N}}$$

$$PhC{\equiv}CCH_2\overset{+}{N}CH_2CH{=}CH_2 \xrightarrow{OH^-} \left[PhC{\equiv}C\bar{C}H \overset{\frown}{\underset{\underset{H_3C\quad CH_3}{\overset{+}{N}}}{}} CH_2CH{=}CH_2 \right] \longrightarrow$$

$$\underset{\underset{(264)}{H_3C\quad CH_3\ Br^-}}{} \qquad \underset{(265)}{}$$

$$PhC{\equiv}CCHCH_2CH{=}CH_2$$
$$\underset{\underset{(267)}{H_3C\quad CH_3}}{\overset{|}{N}}$$

or

$$\left[\begin{array}{c} H_2C \\ \qquad CH \\ PhC{\equiv}C\bar{C}H \quad \overset{\frown}{CH_2} \\ \underset{\underset{H_3C\quad CH_3}{\overset{+}{N}}}{} \end{array} \right]$$
$$\underset{(266)}{}$$

$$\underset{\overset{|}{CH_2C{\equiv}CCH_3}}{\overset{\overset{CH_2Ph}{|}}{H_3C\overset{\oplus}{N}CH_2Ph}} \xrightarrow{OH^{\ominus}} \underset{\overset{|}{CH_2Ph}}{\overset{\overset{CH_2Ph}{|}}{H_3CNCHC{\equiv}CCH_3}}$$
$$\underset{(268)}{} \qquad\qquad\qquad \underset{(269)}{}$$

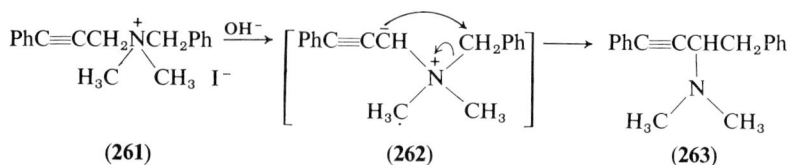

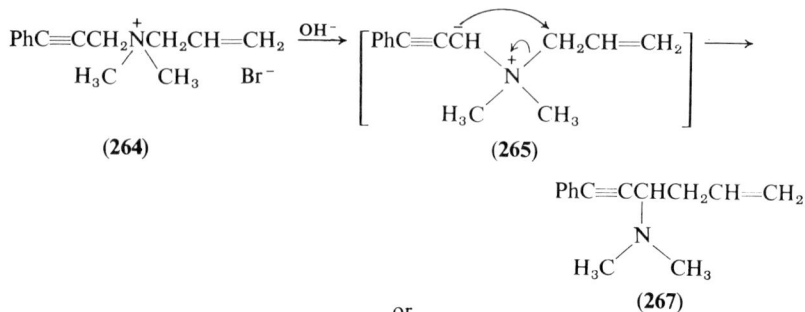

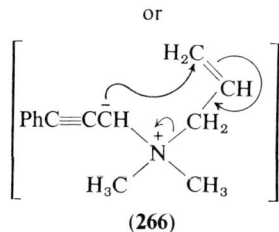

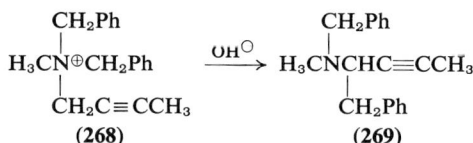

amine to cause a ring expansion (85). Treatment of 2-methyl-2-(3-phenyl-2-propynyl)benzo[f]isoindolinium bromide (270) with aqueous sodium hydroxide gives 2-methyl-3-(2-phenylethynyl)-1,2,3,4-tetrahydrobenzo[g]-isoquinoline (272). This ring expansion reaction can be considered as a Stevens rearrangement involving carbanion formation at the propargylic

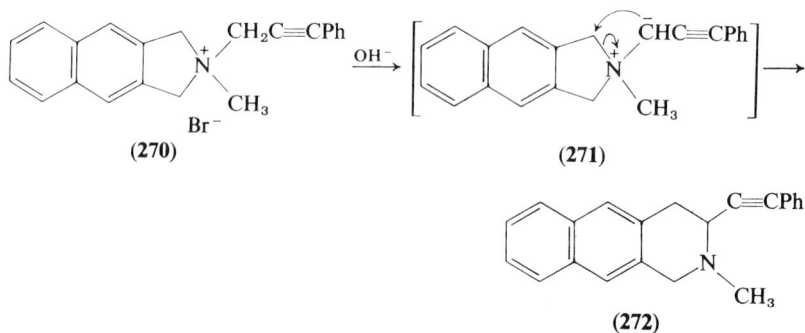

(270)   (271)

(272)

methylene and C—N bond cleavage at the benzylamine. In these cases, the propargylic methylene acts as a migration terminus.

On the basis of the reaction mechanism for these Stevens rearrangements, abstraction of hydrogen should be considered to occur at the phenylpropargylic methylene. Accordingly, it implies a stronger acidity of the methylene group compared to that of a benzylic methylene group. This is in good agreement with the σ^* values which show the stronger electron withdrawing ability of the phenylacetylenic group compared to that of a phenyl substituent:

$$\sigma^*_{ph} = +0.60, \qquad \sigma^*_{PhC\equiv C-} = +1.35 \qquad (87)$$

Treatment of dimethyl-bis-phenylpropargylammonium bromide (273) with aqueous sodium hydroxide or sodium ethoxide gives no rearranged product, while N,N-dimethyl-2-phenyl-1-(2-phenylethynyl)-2,3-butadienyl-amine (275) and N,N-dimethyl-2-phenyl-1-(2-phenylethynyl)-3-butynyl-amine (276) are obtained by treatment with sodium amide in liquid ammonia (85).

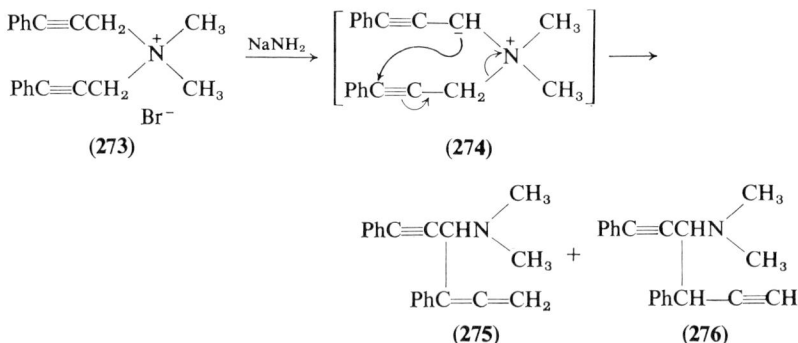

In this molecule, the phenylpropargyl groups act as both migrating group and a migration terminus. Thus more drastic reaction conditions are required for activation at one of these groups because of the uneasiness in the C—N bond cleavage and the balanced structure of the molecule. The reaction mechanism can be described as an SNi′ as shown in the previous formulas. Recently Mark (88)† postulated a similar SNi′ mechanism in the system as illustrated.

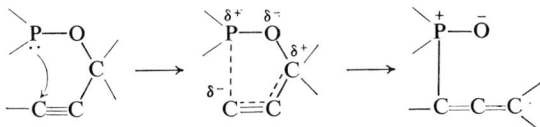

† The phosphite-phosphonate rearrangements are discussed in the chapter by V. Mark in Volume 3 of this series.

Editor

The allenic compound (275) may easily rearrange to the ethynyl compound (276) under the reaction conditions used. Contrarily, benzyldimethylpropargylammonium bromide (277) gave no rearranged product under similar basic conditions, but it afforded N,N-dimethylbenzylamine (278) (85). Thus, it is acceptable that this unexpected liberation of the propargyl group would be due to the formation of carbene under the basic conditions. However, an attempt to trap the carbene as a cyclopropane derivative was fruitless, because of the insolubility of the propargyl ammonium halide in inert solvents.

$$HC\equiv CH_2C \underset{\underset{H_3C}{\diagdown}\overset{\displaystyle I^{\ominus}}{\underset{\displaystyle \overset{\oplus}{N}}{}}\overset{\diagup}{\overset{CH_2Ph}{}} \xrightarrow{OH^{\ominus}} PhCH_2N(CH_3)_2$$

(277)   (278)

$$HC\equiv CCH_2\overset{\oplus}{N}\overset{\diagup}{\diagdown} \xrightarrow{OH^{\ominus}} \overset{\ominus}{C}\equiv CCH_2\overset{\oplus}{N}\overset{\diagup}{\diagdown} \longrightarrow \overset{\ominus}{C}\equiv C\overset{\oplus}{C}H_2 \longrightarrow {:}C\!=\!C\!=\!CH_2$$

When benzhyldryl chloride (279) reacted with piperidyl-N-propargylmagnesium bromide (280), 4,4-diphenyl-3-N-piperidyl-1-butyne (286) was obtained besides the expected normal product (281). Bohlmann and Jurghans (89) postulated a reaction mechanism for the formation of 286 involving a Stevens type rearrangement after ylide formation by reaction of a propargylamine (283) with the carbene formed.

$$Ph_2CHCl + BrMgC\equiv CCH_2N\!\!\!\bigcirc \longrightarrow Ph_2CHC\equiv CCH_2N\!\!\!\bigcirc +$$

(279)   (280)   (281)

$$\left[Ph_2C{:} + HC\equiv CCH_2N\!\!\!\bigcirc \right] \longrightarrow$$

(282)   (283)

$$\left[\underset{\underset{CH_2C\equiv CH}{|}}{Ph_2\overset{-}{C}\!-\!\overset{+}{N}\!\!\!\bigcirc} \right] \longrightarrow \left[\underset{\underset{-CHC\equiv CH}{|}}{Ph_2\overset{H}{C}\!-\!\overset{+}{N}\!\!\!\bigcirc} \right] \longrightarrow Ph_2CHCHC\equiv CH$$

(284)   (285) $$\underset{\underset{\displaystyle \bigcirc}{|}}{N}$$

(286)

From these results, the ease of C—N bond cleavage (under basic conditions), which is an important reaction stage involved in the Stevens rearrangement, can be illustrated by the following order:

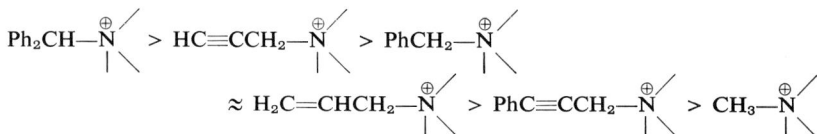

$$Ph_2CH-\overset{\oplus}{N}\diagdown \quad > \quad HC\equiv CCH_2-\overset{\oplus}{N}\diagdown \quad > \quad PhCH_2-\overset{\oplus}{N}\diagdown$$

$$\approx H_2C=CHCH_2-\overset{\oplus}{N}\diagdown \quad > \quad PhC\equiv CCH_2-\overset{\oplus}{N}\diagdown \quad > \quad CH_3-\overset{\oplus}{N}\diagdown$$

In the case of von Braun's reaction, the order of easiness for fission of the C—N linkage is as follows:

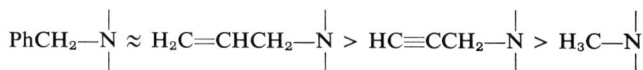

$$PhCH_2-\overset{|}{\underset{|}{N}} \approx H_2C=CHCH_2-\overset{|}{\underset{|}{N}} > HC\equiv CCH_2-\overset{|}{\underset{|}{N}} > H_3C-\overset{|}{\underset{|}{N}}$$

It is reasonable that these two reactions show a similar tendency in the C—N bond cleavage, with the exception of propargylamine which has a strongly acidic ethynyl hydrogen.

The Sommlet-Hauser rearrangement, involving migration of a group without its pair of bonding electrons to an electron-rich carbon atom, is an SNi' type analog of the Stevens rearrangement.

The Sommlet-Hauser rearrangement: Treatment of dibenzyldimethyl-ammonium chloride (287) with sodium amide in liquid ammonia gave (o-methylbenzhydryl) dimethylamine (291) (90). Hauser (91) postulated a mechanism which involves nucleophilic attack of the ylide carbon at the ring position ortho to the benzylammonium moiety. The initial product is then the exomethylene derivative (290) which is readily converted merely by loss and recovery of a proton to an aromatic structure.

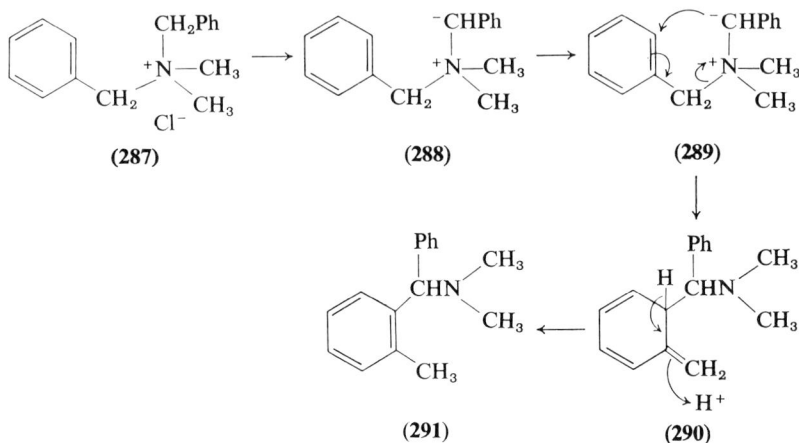

(287)   (288)   (289)

(291)   (290)

The Wittig rearrangement: This rearrangement involves migration of an alkyl group from an oxygen or sulfur to either carbanion or incipient carbanion bonded to the oxygen or sulfur; while the migration from nitrogen to carbanion is involved in the Stevens rearrangement. The product is an alcoholate or mercaptolate anion. In general, stronger bases such as sodium amide or phenyllithium are required for this reaction (92) compared to those in the Stevens rearrangement.

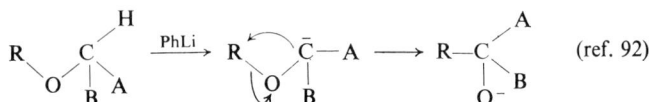

In all the systems studied, one or both of the groups A and B in the migration terminus has been aryl groups, and the migrating group (R) has thus far been limited to methyl, benzyl, and allyl groups. Quite recently, however, Schöllkopf and Rizk (93) found that an acetylenic group can also

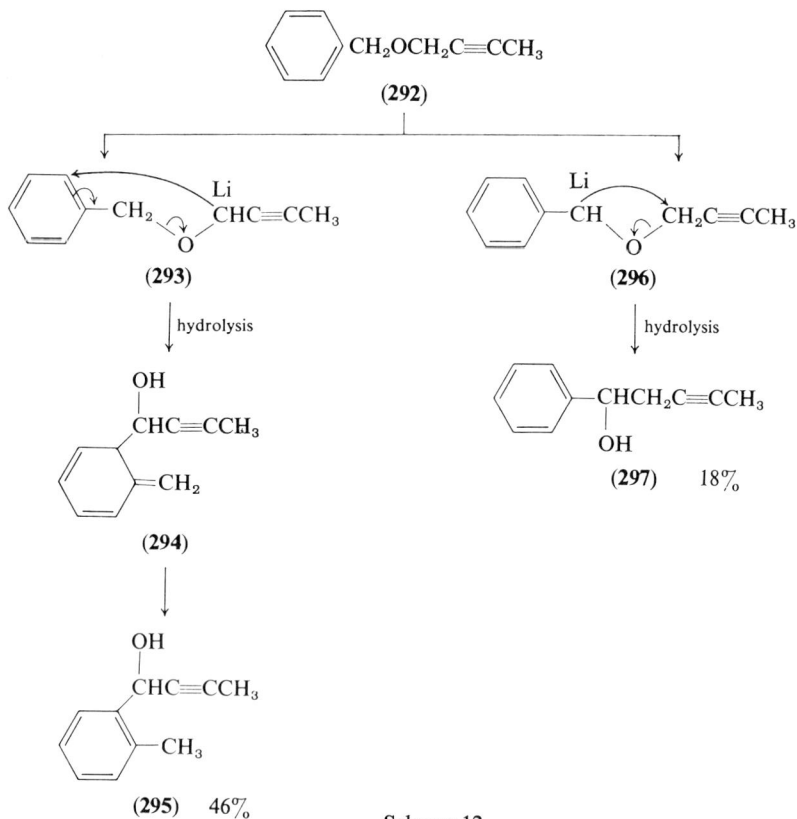

Scheme 12

be a migrating group in the rearrangement. They described the reaction of benzyl-2-butynyl ether (292) with butyllithium in tetrahydrofuran at low temperature. Under these conditions both the Sommelet type and the Wittig rearrangement products 1-(o-methylphenyl)-2-butyne-1-ol (295) and 1-phenyl-3-pentyn-1-ol (297) resulted. They assumed that the rearrangements involve the two methalated ethers, 293 and 296. The reaction mechanism is considered to be that illustrated in Scheme 12.

Furthermore, they have reported that 9-lithio-9-fluorenyl-2-butynyl ether (298), under similar conditions, underwent the Wittig type rearrangement involving allenic isomerization to afford only 9-(1-methyl-1,2-propadienyl)-9-fluorenol (299).

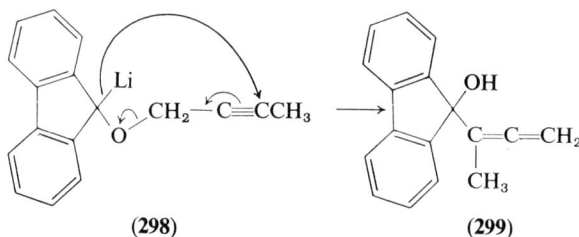

(298)   (299)

References

1. C. Prevost, P. Souchay, and J. Chauvelier, *Bull. Soc. Chim. France*, **18**, 714 (1951).
2. D. B. Killian, G. F. Hennion, and J. A. Nieuwland, *J. Am. Chem. Soc.*, **58**, 892 (1936).
3. P. W. Robertson, W. E. Dasent, R. M. Milburn, and W. H. Oliver, *J. Chem. Soc.*, **1950**, 1628.
4. H. H. Schlubach and V. Franzen, *Ann. Chem.*, **577**, 60 (1952); **578**, 220 (1952).
5. I. N. Nazarov and A. I. Kuznetsova, *Bull. Acad. Sci. URSS, Classe Sci. Chim.*, **1941**, 423; through *Chem. Abstr.*, **36**, 1296[4] (1942); I. N. Nazarov and F. I. Gotman, *Bull. Acad. Sci. URSS, Classe Sci. Chim.*, **1941**, 545; through *Chem. Abstr.*, **37**, 2342 (1943).
6. A. D. Walsh, *Quart. Rev. (London)*, **2**, 73 (1948).
7. C. Mannich and F. Chang, *Chem. Ber.*, **66**, 418 (1933).
8. Y. Yura, *Chem. Pharm. Bull. (Tokyo)*, **10**, 372, 376, 1087, 1094 (1962).
9. I. Iwai and N. Nakamura, *Chem. Pharm. Bull. (Tokyo)*, **14**, 1277 (1966).
10. I. Iwai and T. Hiraoka, *Chem. Pharm. Bull. (Tokyo)*, **10**, 81 (1962).
11. T. L. Jacobs, R. Akawie, and R. G. Cooper, *J. Am. Chem. Soc.*, **73**, 1273 (1951).
12. A. Favorsky, *J. Prakt. Chem.*, **37**, 382 (1888).
13. C. K. Ingold, *Structure and Mechanism in Organic Chemistry*, Cornell University Press, Ithaca, New York, 1953, p. 149.
13a. R. A. Raphael, *Acetylenic Compounds in Organic Synthesis*, Butterworths, London, 1955, p. 135.
14. W. R. Moore and H. R. Ward, *J. Am. Chem. Soc.*, **85**, 86 (1963).
15. F. Bohlmann and W. Sucrow, *Chem. Ber.*, **97**, 1846 (1964).

16. H. Prinzbach and E. Druckrey, *Tetrehedron Letters*, **1965**, 2959.

17. D. J. Cram, F. Willey, H. P. Fischer, H. M. Relles, and D. A. Scott, *J. Am. Chem. Soc.*, **88**, 2759 (1966).

18. J. J. Van Daalen, A. Kraak, and J. F. Arens, *Rec. Trav. Chim.*, **80**, 810 (1961).

19. T. L. Jacobs, R. Akawie, and G. R. Cooper, *J. Am. Chem. Soc.*, **73**, 1273 (1951).

20. J. C. Craig and R. J. Young, *J. Chem. Soc.*, (*C*), **1966**, 578.

21. A. A. Petrov and B. A. Kormer, *Zh. Obschei Khim.*, **34**, 1868 (1964).

22. G. Eglinton, E. R. H. Jones, G. H. Mansfield, and M. C. Whiting, *J. Chem. Soc.*, **1954**, 3197.

23. T. L. Jacobs and S. Singer, *J. Org. Chem.*, **17**, 475 (1952).

24. L. I. Smith and J. S. Swenson, *J. Am. Chem. Soc.*, **79**, 2962 (1957).

25. K. L. Mikolajczak, M. O. Bagby, R. B. Bates, and I. A. Wolff, *J. Org. Chem.*, **30**, 2983 (1965).

26. T. L. Jacobs, D. Dankner, and S. Singer, *Tetrahedron*, **20**, 2177 (1964).

27. C. D. Hurd and F. L. Cohen, *J. Am. Chem. Soc.*, **53**, 1068 (1931).

28. É. Michel and C. Troyanowsky, *Compt. Rend.*, **258**, 3048 (1964).

29. A. A. Petrov and K. A. Molodova, *Zh. Obshchei Khim.*, **32**, 3510 (1962).

30. P. P. Montijn and L. Brandsma, *Rec. Trav. Chim.*, **83**, 456 (1964).

30a. L. Brandsma, H. E. Wijers, and J. F. Arens, *Rec. Trav. Chim.*, **82**, 1040 (1963).

31. T. L. Jacobs and W. F. Brill, *J. Am. Chem. Soc.*, **75**, 1314 (1953).

31a. G. F. Hennion, J. J. Sheehan, and D. E. Maloney, *J. Am. Chem. Soc.*, **72**, 2542 (1950).

32. J. H. van Boom, P. P. Montijn, and J. A. Arens, *Rec. Trav. Chim.*, **84**, 31 (1965).

33. L. Brandsma, P. P. Montijn, and J. A. Arens, *Rec. Trav. Chim.*, **82**, 115 (1963).

34. G. M. Mkryan and S. L. Mandzboyan, *Izv. Akad. Nauk. Arm. SSR*, **18**, 44 (1965); through *Chem. Abstr.*, **63**, 6842e (1965).

35. P. P. Montijn and L. Brandsma, *Rec. Trav. Chim.*, **83**, 456 (1964).

36. K. Brand, *Chem. Ber.*, **54**, 1987 (1921).

37. F. Sondheimer, D. A. Ben-Efraim, and Y. Gaoni, *J. Am. Chem. Soc.*, **83**, 1682 (1961).

38. E. R. H. Jones, G. H. Mansfield, and M. C. Whiting, *J. Chem. Soc.*, **1954**, 3208; E. R. H. Jones, B. L. Shaw, and M. C. Whiting, *ibid.*, **1954**, 3212.

39. E. R. H. Jones, G. H. Whitham, and M. C. Whiting, *J. Chem. Soc.*, **1957**, 4628.

39a. B. L. Shaw and M. C. Whiting, *Chem. Ind.* (*London*), **1953**, 409.

40. F. Sondheimer and R. Wolovsky, *J. Am. Chem. Soc.*, **81**, 1771 (1959).

41. F. Sondheimer and R. Wolovsky, *J. Am. Chem. Soc.*, **81**, 4755 (1959).

42. F. Sondheimer, R. Wolovsky, and Y. Gaoni, *J. Am. Chem. Soc.*, **82**, 754 (1960); F. Sondheimer, R. Wolovsky, and D. A. Ben-Efraim, *ibid.*, **83**, 1686 (1961).

43. F. Sondheimer et al., *J. Am. Chem. Soc.*, **82**, 5765 (1960); *ibid.*, **83**, 1259, 1675, 1682, 4863 (1961); *ibid.*, **84**, 260, 3520 (1962); *ibid.*, **88**, 602 (1966).

44. G. Eglinton, R. A. Raphael, and R. G. Willis, *Proc. Chem. Soc.*, **1960**, 247.

45. G. Eglinton, R. A. Raphael, R. G. Willis, and J. A. Zabkiewicz, *J. Chem. Soc.*, **1964**, 2597.

46. D. A. Ben-Efraim and F. Sondheimer, *Tetrahedron Letters*, **1963**, 313.

47. I. Iwai and J. Ide, *Chem. Pharm. Bull.* (*Tokyo*), **12**, 1094 (1964).

48. I. Iwai and T. Hiraoka, *Chem. Pharm. Bull.* (*Tokyo*), **11**, 1564 (1963).

49. I. Iwai and T. Hiraoka, *Chem. Pharm. Bull.* (*Tokyo*), **10**, 81 (1962); *ibid.*, **11**, 1556 (1963).

50. G. Eglington, I. A. Lardy, R. A. Raphael, and G. A. Sim, *J. Chem. Soc.*, **1964**, 1154.
51. R. Wolovsky and F. Sondheimer, *J. Am. Chem. Soc.*, **87**, 5720 (1965). See also F. Sondheimer, R. Wolovsky, P. J. Garrat, and I. C. Cadler, *ibid.*, **88**, 2610 (1966).
52. J. Mayer and F. Sondheimer, *J. Am. Chem. Soc.*, **88**, 602 (1966).
53. L. J. Bellamy, *The Infrared Spectra of Complex Molecules*, Methuen, London, 1958, p. 58.
54. A. T. Bottini, J. A. Mullikin, and C. J. Morris, *J. Org. Chem.*, **29**, 373 (1964).
54a. W. J. Croxall and J. H. Mellema, US Pat. 2,960,508 (November 15, 1960); through *Chem. Abstr.*, **55**, 14482c (1961).
55. I. Iwai and T. Hiraoka, *Chem. Pharm. Bull. (Tokyo)*, **12**, 813 (1964).
56. R. D. Dillard and N. R. Easton, *J. Org. Chem.*, **31**, 122 (1966).
57. A. T. Bottini, F. P. Corson, and E. F. Böttner, *J. Org. Chem.*, **30**, 2988 (1965).
58. L. Skattebøl and N. A. Sörensen, *Acta Chem. Scand.*, **13**, 2101 (1959).
59. W. von E. Doering and A. K. Hoffmann, *J. Am. Chem. Soc.*, **76**, 6162 (1954).
60. P. S. Skell and J. Klebe, *J. Am. Chem. Soc.*, **82**, 247 (1960).
61. W. Kirmse, *Carbene Chemistry*, Academic Press, New York, 1964, p. 69.
62. H. D. Hartzler, *J. Am. Chem. Soc.*, **81**, 2024 (1959); *ibid.*, **83**, 4990 (1961).
63. A. Burawoy and E. Spinner, *J. Chem. Soc.*, **1954**, 3752.
64. V. J. Shiner, Jr., and J. W. Wilson, *J. Am. Chem. Soc.*, **84**, 2402 (1962).
65. G. F. Hennion and D. E. Maloney, *J. Am. Chem. Soc.*, **73**, 4735 (1951).
65a. G. F. Hennion and K. W. Nelson, *J. Am. Chem. Soc.*, **79**, 2142 (1957).
66. H. D. Hartzler, *J. Org. Chem.*, **29**, 1311 (1964).
67. A. F. Bramwell, L. Crombie, and M. H. Knight, *Chem. Ind. (London)*, **1965**, 1265.
68. S. R. Landor and P. F. Whiter, *J. Chem. Soc.*, **1965**, 5625.
69. P. Cadiot, *Ann. Chim. (Paris)*, **1** [13], 214 (1956).
70. H. D. Hartzler, *J. Am. Chem. Soc.*, **83**, 4990 (1961).
71. H. D. Hartzler, *J. Am. Chem. Soc.*, **88**, 3155 (1966).
72. C. Prevost, M. Gaudemar, and J. Honigberg, *Compt. Rend.*, **230**, 1186 (1950).
72a. M. Gaudemar, *Ann. Chim. (Paris)*, **1**, 160 (1956).
73. F. Serratosa, *Tetrahedron Letters*, **1964**, 895.
74. W. J. Gensler, A. P. Mahadevan, and J. Casella, Jr., *J. Am. Chem. Soc.*, **78**, 163 (1956).
74a. W. J. Gensler and A. P. Mahadevan, *J. Am. Chem. Soc.*, **77**, 3076 (1955).
75. J. C. Craig and M. Moyle, *J. Chem. Soc.*, **1963**, 5356.
76. T. S. Stevens, E. M. Creighton, A. B. Gordon, and M. MacNicol, *J. Chem. Soc.*, **1928**, 3193.
77. T. S. Stevens, *J. Chem. Soc.*, **1930**, 2107.
78. J. L. Dunn and T. S. Stevens, *J. Chem. Soc.*, **1932**, 1926; *ibid.*, **1934**, 279.
79. T. Thompson and T. S. Stevens, *J. Chem. Soc.*, **1932**, 55, 69.
80. J. L. Dunn and T. S. Stevens, *J. Chem. Soc.*, **1932**, 1926; *ibid.*, **1934**, 279.
81. C. R. Hauser and S. W. Kantor, *J. Am. Chem. Soc.*, **73**, 1437 (1951).
82. J. H. Brewster and M. W. Kline, *J. Am. Chem. Soc.*, **74**, 5179 (1952).
83. I. Iwai and T. Hiraoka, *Chem. Pharm. Bull. (Tokyo)*, **10**, 81 (1962).
84. J. L. Dunn and T. S. Stevens, *J. Chem. Soc.*, **1934**, 279.
85. I. Iwai and T. Hiraoka, *Chem. Pharm. Bull. (Tokyo)*, **11**, 1556 (1963).
86. A. T. Babayan, M. S. Indyhikyan, and R. A. Aivazova, *Zh. Obshchei. Khim.*, **33**, 1733 (1963).
87. M. S. Newman, *Steric Effect in Organic Chemistry*, Wiley, New York, 1956, p. 619.

88. V. Mark, *Tetrahedron Letters*, **1962**, 281.
89. F. Bohlmann and K. Junghans, *Tetrahedron Letters*, **1964**, 1701.
90. G. Wittig, H. Tenhaeff, W. Schoch, and G. Koenig, *Ann. Chem.*, **572**, 1 (1951).
91. S. W. Kantor and C. R. Hauser, *J. Am. Chem. Soc.*, **73**, 4122 (1951).
92. C. R. Hauser and S. W. Kantor, *J. Am. Chem. Soc.*, **73**, 1437 (1951).
93. U. Schöllkopf and M. Rizk, *Angew. Chem. Intern. Ed. Engl.*, **4**, 957 (1965).

Orbital Symmetry and Electrocyclic Rearrangements

KENICHI FUKUI AND HIROSHI FUJIMOTO

Department of Hydrocarbon Chemistry
Kyoto University, Kyoto, Japan

I. INTRODUCTION

A. General Properties of Molecular Wave Functions

In order to discuss the properties of a stable molecule in terms of quantum mechanics, we usually employ the Born-Oppenheimer approximation (1), in which the molecular motion is divided into translation, rotation, vibration, and electronic motion. The electronic state of a molecule is given by the solution of the Schrödinger equation for the equilibrium nuclear configuration, which is written as

$$H\Psi_K = W_K\Psi_K \tag{1}$$

$$H = -\frac{h^2}{8\pi^2 m}\sum_i \Delta_i + \sum_{i<j}\frac{e^2}{r_{ij}} - \sum_i\sum_\alpha\frac{Z_\alpha e^2}{r_{i\alpha}} + \sum_{\alpha<\beta}\frac{Z_\alpha Z_\beta e^2}{r_{\alpha\beta}} \tag{2}$$

where Δ_i is the Laplacian operator for ith electron, r_{ij} is the distance between ith and jth electrons, $r_{i\alpha}$ is the distance between ith electron and αth nucleus, $r_{\alpha\beta}$ is the distance between αth and βth nuclei, $-e$ and $Z_\alpha e$ are the electronic charge and the nuclear charge of αth nucleus, respectively, m is the electronic mass, and h is the Planck constant. The last term of the right-hand side of Eq. 2 is a constant for a fixed nuclear configuration. The wave function of Kth electronic eigenstate Ψ_K is a function of the electronic space and spin coordinates $x_1 y_1 z_1 \xi_1, x_2 y_2 z_2 \xi_2, \ldots$, involving also the given nuclear coordinates $X_1 Y_1 Z_1, X_2 Y_2 Z_2, \ldots$ (written en block as $\bar{X}$). The electronic energy W_K, depending upon $\bar{X}$, stands for Kth eigenvalue of the Hamiltonian operator including the nuclear repulsion H.

If we regard the Schrödinger equation (Eq. 1) as for any fixed nuclear configuration, whether it corresponds to the equilibrium configuration of a stable molecule or not, we get a continuous function $W_K(\bar{X})$, which may be called the potential energy function of the system. In this case the equilibrium nuclear configuration for Kth electronic state may be determined as that which yields the absolute minimum of $W_K(\bar{X})$.

The Hamiltonian operator has a certain symmetry with respect to the electronic coordinates. If we write the Hamiltonian operator and the wave function as $H(1, 2, \cdots, N)$ and $\Psi(1, 2, \cdots, N)$, respectively, where the figures i refer to the coordinates of the ith electron x_i, y_i, z_i, and ξ_i, it obviously follows that

$$H(2, 1, \cdots, N) = H(1, 2, \cdots, N)$$

This type of symmetry puts restraint upon the shape of Ψ, requiring that

$$\Psi(2, 1, \cdots, N) = \pm\Psi(1, 2, \cdots, N)$$

The statistical nature of an assembly of electrons as Fermi particles permits only the lower sign. The exact solution Ψ_K may hence be expressed by an infinite term linear combination of determinantal wave functions $D_{K,J}$'s as

$$\Psi_K = \sum_J C_J D_{K,J} \tag{3}$$

Since H does not involve spin operators, it is easy to obtain Ψ_K as possessing a definite total electronic spin. The subscript J represents the "electronic configuration" of the determinantal function $D_{K,J}$, which may be given by an (N,N) determinant as shown by Eq. 4 where $N_{K,J}$ is the nor-

$$D_{K,J} = N_{K,J} \begin{vmatrix} \psi_{j1}(1) & \psi_{j2}(1) & \cdots & \psi_{jN}(1) \\ \psi_{j1}(2) & \psi_{j2}(2) & \cdots & \psi_{jN}(2) \\ \cdots\cdots\cdots\cdots\cdots\cdots\cdots \\ \psi_{j1}(N) & \psi_{j2}(N) & \cdots & \psi_{jN}(N) \end{vmatrix} \tag{4}$$

malizing constant and ψ_{jr} is a one-electron function called a molecular "spin orbital" and J denotes the combination $(j_1, j_2, \cdots, j_N)$. Usually, Ψ_K can be approximated as one or a few terms. In the single-determinant approximation, the "best" function of $D_{K,J}$ is well defined by the Hartree-Fock variation procedure (2). The closed-shell singlet ground state wave function in this approximation is thus determined by Eq. 5 in which ϕ_ν's

$$\Psi_0 = N_0 \begin{vmatrix} \phi_1(1)\alpha(1) & \phi_1(1)\beta(1) & \phi_2(1)\alpha(1) & \cdots & \phi_\nu(1)\alpha(1) & \phi_\nu(1)\beta(1) \\ \phi_1(2)\alpha(2) & \phi_1(2)\beta(2) & \phi_2(2)\alpha(2) & \cdots & \phi_\nu(2)\alpha(2) & \phi_\nu(2)\beta(2) \\ \cdots\cdots\cdots\cdots\cdots\cdots\cdots\cdots\cdots\cdots\cdots\cdots\cdots\cdots \\ \phi_1(2\nu)\alpha(2\nu) \cdots\cdots\cdots\cdots\cdots\cdots\cdots\cdots\phi_\nu(2\nu)\beta(2\nu) \end{vmatrix} \tag{5}$$

are one-electron space functions or "molecular orbitals (MO)," and α and β are usual one-electron spin eigenfunctions.

B. Molecular Symmetry and Molecular Wave Functions

The Hamiltonian operator H in Eq. 2 possesses another kind of symmetry relating to the nuclear coordinates if the molecule bears a symmetry. From Eq. 2 it is easily seen that the first and the second terms of the right side of Eq. 2 are invariant toward any orthogonal transformation and the third term is not changed, provided we do not distinguish the same sort of nuclei, by a transformation of the electronic coordinates representing a rotation of space in which the molecular symmetry is retained.

Namely, such an orthogonal transformation of the electronic coordinates produces no change in the Hamiltonian operator. We are accordingly able to classify the electronic states by means of the behavior of the wave function toward a rotation of space to keep the molecular symmetry unchanged. Such an orthogonal transformation of the electronic coordinates is referred to as a "symmetry operation." Both the kind and the number of symmetry operations belonging to a molecule are dependent on the symmetry of the nuclear configuration.

The group theory serves as an auxiliary to the theoretical treatment, since it can be shown that the whole assembly of such symmetry operations of a molecule makes a group in mathematical sense, called a molecular "symmetry group." Similar to the above-mentioned circumstances in the electron exchange symmetry, the allowable eigenfunction of the Schrödinger equation is subject to a certain limitation, required as the basis of an irreducible representation of the symmetry group corresponding to the symmetry which is possessed by the nuclear configuration. The knowledge of irreducible representation can be supplied, in advance and irrespectively of individual molecular species, from suitable text books (3). Therefore, the degeneracy as well as the behavior toward symmetry operations of allowed electronic states can be predicted by the molecular symmetry.

Sometimes a part of the molecular symmetry is retained during a continuous change of the nuclear configuration, and it happens that the molecular symmetry shifts from one sort to another through such configuration changes. Scheme 1 gives several instances.

In the third example, the initial and the final configurations are different but both belong to the same symmetry. Two different paths are possible through which they are continuously connected, as is illustrated.

To elucidate how the shapes of wave functions are restricted by the molecular symmetry along the path of configuration altering, we take the third as an example. We first consider a molecule of C_2 symmetry. The symmetry operations are identity transformation E and the rotation by π about the symmetry axis C_2. The dependence of the wave function on ψ, the angle of rotation about the symmetry axis, should be

$$\Psi(\psi) \sim \exp\{i\Lambda\psi\}f(\psi) \tag{6}$$

in order to be the basis function of an irreducible representation, where $\Lambda = 0$ or 1 and $f(\psi)$ is a periodic function of ψ with period π, because the operation C_2 signifies the transformation $\psi \to (\psi + \pi)$ and $\Psi(\psi + \pi)$ must be $\Psi(\psi)$ times a constant of which the absolute value is unity. Hence, if we adopt a determinantal form of wave functions, the one-electron function (MO) to appear there must also be of the form $\sim \exp\{i\lambda\psi\}f(\psi)$ ($\lambda = 0$ or 1).

1. Methylene

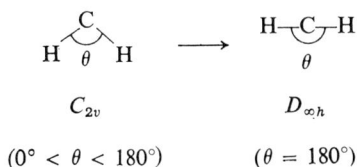

$$C_{2v} \qquad\qquad D_{\infty h}$$

$$(0° < \theta < 180°) \qquad (\theta = 180°)$$

2. Ethylene

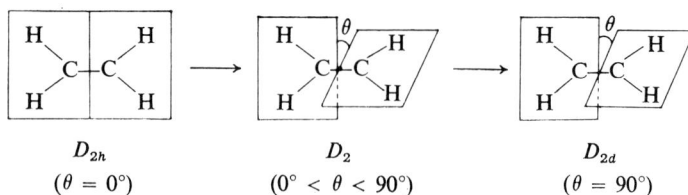

$$D_{2h} \qquad\qquad D_2 \qquad\qquad D_{2d}$$

$$(\theta = 0°) \qquad (0° < \theta < 90°) \qquad (\theta = 90°)$$

3. Allyl → cyclopropyl

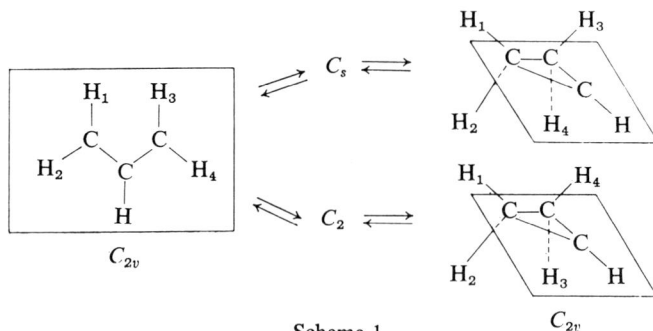

Scheme 1

The state $\Lambda = 0$ is denoted by A, and $\Lambda = 1$ by B. If these refer to MO's, small letters are used: a (for $\lambda = 0$) and b (for $\lambda = 1$). The relation between Λ and λ is given by

$$\Lambda = \sum_j \lambda_j - 2m$$

where m is an integer to be chosen so that Λ and λ_j's are zero or unity. Thus, among the determinantal functions of two-electron systems, the types of $|\phi_a(1)\phi_a(2)|$ and $|\phi_b(1)\phi_b(2)|$ belong to state A, and $|\phi_a(1)\phi_b(2)|$ to B, where $|\cdots\cdots|$ signifies the determinantal wave function like Eq. 5. Similarly, $|\phi_a(1)\phi_a(2)\phi_b(3)\phi_b(4)|$ belongs to A, and $|\phi_a(1)\phi_a(2)\phi_a(3)\phi_b(4)|$ and $|\phi_b(1)\phi_b(2)\phi_a(3)\phi_b(4)|$ belong to B.

The symmetry C_S has one symmetry plane, having two symmetry operations, E and σ_h, and the latter means the reflection with respect to the symmetry plane (say yz plane). The effect of σ_h on the wave function is such that

$$\sigma_h \Psi(x) = \Psi(-x)$$

Therefore, the allowable form of $\Psi(x)$ must be

$$\Psi(x) \sim \begin{cases} g^+(x) : \text{an even function of } x \\ g^-(x) : \text{an odd function of } x \end{cases} \quad (7)$$

so that $\sigma_h g^+(x) = g^+(x)$ and $\sigma_h g^-(x) = -g^-(x)$, satisfying the requirement that $\Psi(x)$ must be the basis of an irreducible representation. These states are denoted by A' and A'', respectively. Thus, $|\phi_{a'}(1)\phi_{a'}(2)|$ and $|\phi_{a''}(1)\phi_{a''}(2)|$ belong to state A', $|\phi_{a'}(1)\phi_{a''}(2)|$ to state A'', and the like, where a' and a'' are employed to indicate the MO symmetry.

The symmetry group C_{2v} possesses E, C_2, σ_v, and $\sigma_{v'}$ as the symmetry operations, the last two being the reflection with respect to the two symmetry planes involving the symmetry axis, and representing the transformation $\psi \rightarrow -\psi$. The allowed wave functions written in terms of ψ are given by Eq. 8 where $f(\psi)$ is a periodic function of ψ with period π. Small letters a_1, a_2, b_1, and b_2 are directed to the classification of one-electron functions.

$$\Lambda = 0 \ \Psi(\psi) \sim \begin{cases} f(\psi) + f(-\psi) : \text{state } A_1 \\ f(\psi) - f(-\psi) : \text{state } A_2 \end{cases}$$

$$\Lambda = 1 \ \Psi(\psi) \sim \begin{cases} \exp\{i\psi\}f(\psi) + \exp\{-i\psi\}f(-\psi) : \text{state } B_1 \\ \exp\{i\psi\}f(\psi) - \exp\{-i\psi\}f(-\psi) : \text{state } B_2 \end{cases} \quad (8)$$

C. Molecular Orbitals and Orbital Symmetry

As described in Section I-A, the best MO's in the single-determinant approximation can be determined by the Hartree-Fock method. In consideration of the difficulty in the calculation for large molecules, however, several methods of approximation in lieu of the Hartree-Fock procedure are available. One such method is Roothaan's in which best MO's are approximated by linear combinations of atomic orbitals (LCAO) (4). The MO's in Eq. 5 are in this approximation represented by

$$\phi_j(1) = \sum_r C_r^{(j)} \chi_r(1) \quad (9)$$

where χ_r is rth atomic orbital (AO), a given, definite basis function, r specifying both the atomic orbital and the atom to which it belongs. The coefficients $C_r^{(j)}$'s are determined so as to give the best functions among this form of MO's.

The requirement with respect to the behavior toward symmetry operations is responsible for the limitation also to the coefficients of LCAO

MO's. Similar to the circumstances mentioned in Section I-B, the MO's for a molecule of C_2 symmetry must be of the form of Eq. 10

$$a - \text{MO} : \phi_a(1) \sim \sum_r c_r\{\chi_r(1) + \chi_r'(1)\}$$

$$b - \text{MO} : \phi_b(1) \sim \sum_r c_r\{\chi_r(1) - \chi_r'(1)\}$$

(10)

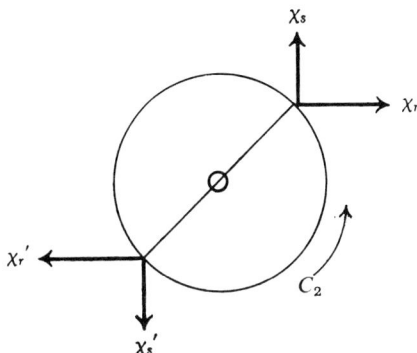

Figure 1

in which χ_r and χ_r' are those AO's which are located symmetrically with respect to the symmetry axis to each other, to be chosen in such a manner that these two can be superimposed by the operation C_2. Figure 1, for the sake of convenience, is drawn in regard to p_x and p_y type AO's. With respect to other types of AO's the principle is also the same.

Similarly, the allowable form of LCAO MO's of a C_S symmetrical molecule is given by Eq. 11 where χ_r and $\bar{\chi}_r$ are those AO's which are symmetric to each other with respect to the symmetry plane (Fig. 2).

$$a'(S) - \text{MO} : \phi^+(1) \sim \sum_r c_r\{\chi_r(1) + \bar{\chi}_r(1)\}$$

$$a''(A) - \text{M\^O} : \phi^-(1) \sim \sum_r c_r\{\chi_r(1) - \bar{\chi}_r(1)\}$$

(11)

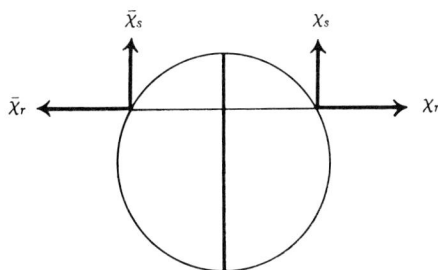

Figure 2

A molecule with C_{2v} symmetry (Fig. 3) thus has MO's of the form of Eq. 12.

$$a_1 - \text{MO} : \phi_{a1}(1) \sim \sum_r c_r \{ \chi_r(1) + \bar{\chi}_r(1) + \chi'_r(1) + \bar{\chi}'_r(1) \}$$

$$a_2 - \text{MO} : \phi_{a2}(1) \sim \sum_r c_r \{ \chi_r(1) - \bar{\chi}_r(1) + \chi'_r(1) - \bar{\chi}'_r(1) \}$$

$$b_1 - \text{MO} : \phi_{b1}(1) \sim \sum_r c_r \{ \chi_r(1) + \bar{\chi}_r(1) - \chi'_r(1) - \bar{\chi}'_r(1) \}$$ (12)

$$b_2 - \text{MO} : \phi_{b2}(1) \sim \sum_r c_r \{ \chi_r(1) - \bar{\chi}_r(1) - \chi'_r(1) + \bar{\chi}'_r(1) \}$$

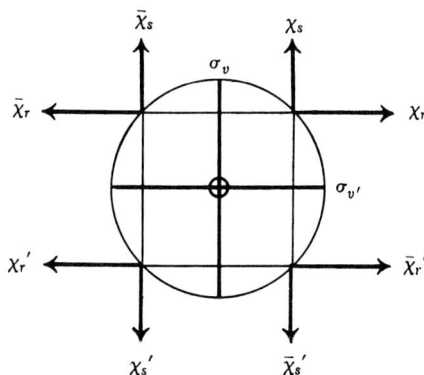

Figure 3

If the change of nuclear configuration is carried out with preservation of the whole or a part of the molecular symmetry, the change of one-electron energy can be correlated with the configuration change (5).

The third example mentioned in Section I-B, the interconversion between allyl and cyclopropyl, may be suitable for the explanation of MO correlation.

The interconversion between allyl and cyclopropyl:

1. C_S course.

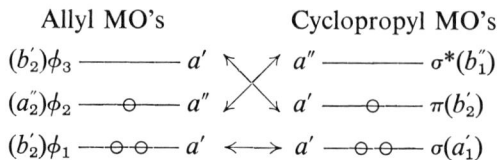

2. C_2 course.

$$
\begin{array}{lcccl}
 & \text{Allyl MO's} & & \text{Cyclopropyl MO's} \\
(b_2')\phi_3 & \underline{\quad\quad} \; b & \longleftrightarrow \; b & \underline{\quad\quad} & \sigma^*(b_1'') \\
(a_2'')\phi_2 & \underline{\;\;\ominus\;\;} \; a & \nwarrow \;\; \nearrow \;\; b & \underline{\;\;\ominus\;\;} & \pi(b_2') \\
(b_2')\phi_1 & \underline{\;\ominus\!\!-\!\!\ominus\;} \; b & \swarrow \;\;\searrow \;\; a & \underline{\;\ominus\!\!-\!\!\ominus\;} & \sigma(a_1')
\end{array}
$$

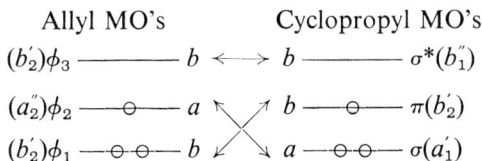

Walsh discussed such a correlation by means of diagrams with respect to the molecules of types AH_2 and AB_2 ($C_{2v} \rightarrow D_{\infty h}$) and other types of molecules (HAB, BAC, and HAAH) (6). In fortunate cases, the stable molecular configuration can be predicted by the Walsh diagram. It should be borne in mind that the energy correlation diagram has to be directed only to the whole molecular energy or to a "separable" part of the molecular energy, in order to discuss the molecular stability. It is not permitted to discuss, e.g., the energy of the sigma or pi part of a conjugated molecule separately, when the configuration change proceeds with hybridization change.

II. THE PRINCIPLE OF ORBITAL INTERACTIONS

A. Intermolecular and Intramolecular Interactions

We consider that two molecules, M and M', draw near to each other so as to enter into interaction. The molecules are exposed to perturbation of each other, giving rise to the change of MO energies. In quantum mechanical terms, the energy of perturbation is composed of the following terms:

1. Zero-order term: When the initial state of the total system involves excited electronic configurations, the zero-order term due to "non-adiabatic quenching" is possible.

2. First-order term: Adiabatic terms appear due to Coulomb and exchange interactions of the two molecules.

3. Second-order term: The adiabatic interaction of two molecules, M and M', causes mixing of polarized states and charge-transfer states (7). Figure 4 is drawn in regard to the ground-state initial configuration.

Among these, the second-order term originating from the orbital overlapping is always responsible for orientation and stereoselection, while the first-order and the zero-order terms are not usually, except in the interaction involving orbital degeneracy.

The charge transfer often makes an important contribution as a first-order term when the adiabatically interacting state and a charge-transfer state possess almost equal energies.

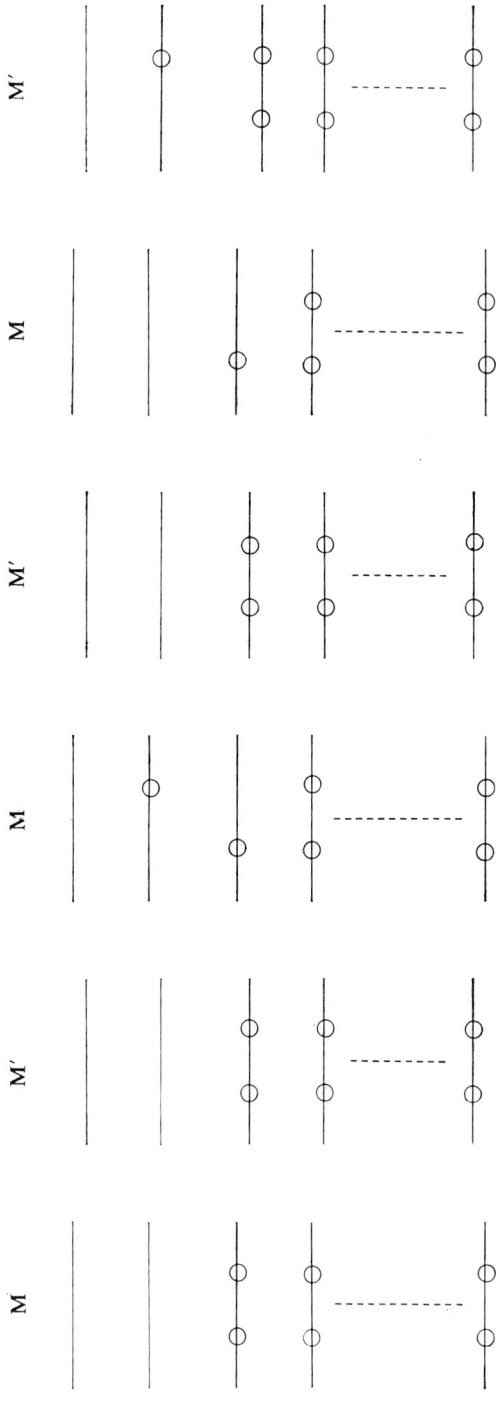

M   M'   M   M'   M   M'

Adiabatic
interaction

Polarization

Charge-transfer

Figure 4

The mixing of the states of different electronic configurations will be mainly responsible for the change of nuclear configuration. The charge-transfer state will cause, in particular in a nearly degenerate case like the aforementioned, a considerable deformation in the shapes of both molecules approaching each other. In some cases the deformation will give rise to increasingly stronger charge-transfer interaction, finally driving both molecules into reaction. This is a possible feature of the intermolecular interaction, in which only one electron plays a conspicuous role.

Most of the rearrangement reactions involve intramolecular interactions. No essential difference may be made between the nature of intermolecular and intramolecular interactions, if we make use of an approximation in which a molecule is partitioned into parts so that each part involves the one-half portion of a reaction center (also compare Section III-D). These parts may be treated as if they were different molecules. Since in ordinary chemical reactions the configurational change takes place only in a limited portion near the reaction center and the remaining part is almost left unchanged, this approximation is usually very effective. Several suitable examples will appear later (Sections V-C and VI-A).

B. The Role of the Highest Occupied and the Lowest Unoccupied Orbitals

As previously described, the importance of the charge-transfer interaction may be anticipated in usual chemical reactions. It is evident that the MO's contributing most to the charge-transfer interaction are the highest occupied (HO) MO and the lowest unoccupied (LU) MO. These two MO's are known to be directly connected to the ionization potential and the electron affinity of a molecule.

The half-occupied MO of a radical or of an odd electron system lies highest and the extension of that MO is responsible for the reactivity. The lone-pair MO's, that is, an MO which is principally localized at the lone-pair AO of an atom and is susceptible to electrophilic attack, also constitute the highest MO levels. Thus, it will be HO MO that plays an essential role in the interaction with an electron acceptor. Similarly, it will be LU MO that is important in the interaction with a donor. Hückel suggested very briefly the role of LU in the reduction of naphthalene and anthracene by alkali (8). Moffitt suggested that the donor reactions of SO_2 to form SO_3 or SO_2Cl_2 are connected to the orbital distribution of the highest occupied electrons which are localized on the S atom (9). Walsh also discussed the reactivity of an excited SO_2 molecule from the distribution of unpaired electron MO's (6).

It was first in planar conjugated molecules that the distribution of HO and LU orbitals attracted attention as displaying a distinguished character in both substitution and addition reactions (10,11), and these orbitals were named "frontier" orbitals. Similar behavior of these particular MO's is noted also in nonplanar saturated molecules (12,13). Recently, the remarkable property of HO and LU in determining the steric course of cyclic reaction of conjugated molecules was pointed out (11,14,15). This will be discussed in detail in a later section.

In view of the conspicuous behavior of these particular MO's, they might collectively be called "frontier" orbitals.

C. Orbital Overlapping and Orbital Symmetry

It was described in Section II-A that the interaction of two ground-state molecules causes mixing of charge-transfer states. This results in a

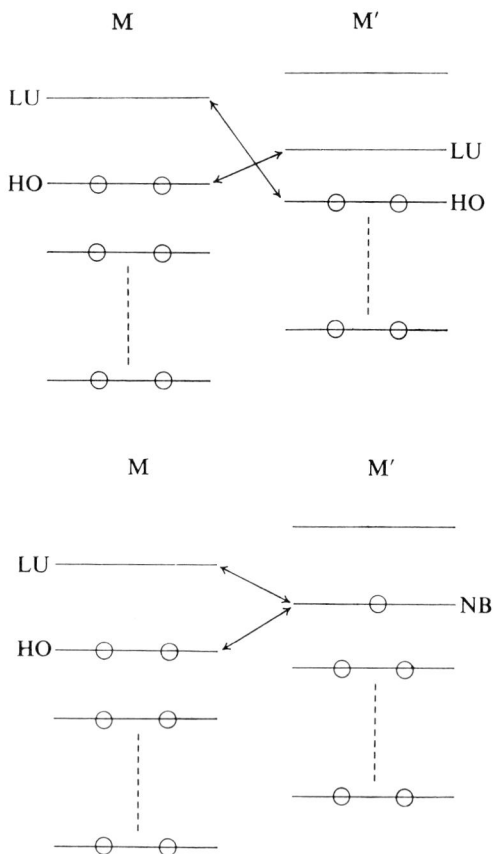

Figure 5

stabilization to decrease the interaction energy to facilitate the occurrence of reaction. The stabilization is shown to parallel the overlap interaction of HO of molecule M and LU of molecule M′, and also of LU of molecule M and HO of molecule M′. Frequently it happens that either one of these predominates and the overlap interaction of HO of the donor molecule and LU of the acceptor is uniquely important. Accordingly, the reaction is expected to take place in and from the direction of the maximum overlapping of these particular MO's (Fig. 5). If a half-occupied MO [nonbonding MO (NB)] exists, this will serve in place of both HO and LU.

Here we discuss the problem by dividing it into two cases: "noncyclic" interaction and "cyclic" interaction. The noncyclic interaction is defined as an interaction with essentially a single overlapping of one AO each, while the cyclic interaction involves a concerted double overlapping. Sometimes triple, and more simultaneous overlappings are also possible.

1. Noncyclic Interactions

Roughly speaking, the stabilization energy due to the mixing of a state produced by the electron transfer from HO of M to LU of M′ by means of a single overlapping may increase with the quantity

$$\sim \sqrt{2} |C_{Mr}^{(HO)} C_{M'r'}^{(LU)} \gamma_{rr'}| \tag{13}$$

where $|G|$ signifies the absolute value of G, $C_{Mr}^{(HO)}$ and $C_{M'r'}^{(LU)}$ are the coefficients in Eq. 9, of rth AO of HO of molecule M and r'th AO of LU of molecule M′, respectively, and $\gamma_{rr'}$ is a "resonance" integral between rth AO of M and r'th AO of M′. The reaction is favored at the AO with the largest coefficient $|C_{Mr}^{(HO)}|$ of the donor molecule and at the AO of the largest $|C_{M'r'}^{(LU)}|$ of the acceptor molecule.

When M is an even-electron molecule and M′ is an odd-electron molecule, the stabilization due to the electron transfer from HO of M to NB of M′ parallels $\sim |C_{Mr}^{(HO)} C_{M'r'}^{(NB)} \gamma_{rr'}|$, and that due to the transfer from NB of M′ to LU of M parallels $\sim |C_{Mr}^{(LU)} C_{M'r'}^{(NB)} \gamma_{rr'}|$. When M and M′ are both odd-electron molecules, the overlap stabilization energy of the first order is represented by $\sqrt{2}|C_{Mr}^{(NB)} C_{M'r'}^{(NB)} \gamma_{rr'}|$.

To illustrate these circumstances, we take a few typical examples. In Figure 6 the shaded and unshaded areas stand for the positive and negative signs of MO wave functions which are chosen to be real.

Example I. Substitution of naphthalene by nitronium ion

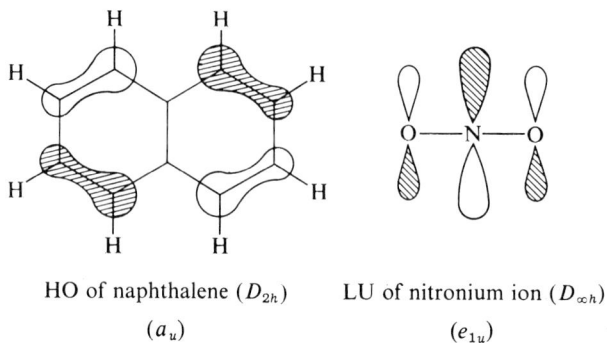

HO of naphthalene (D_{2h}) LU of nitronium ion $(D_{\infty h})$

(a_u) (e_{1u})

Example II. Halogen exchange in alkyl halides (S_N2)

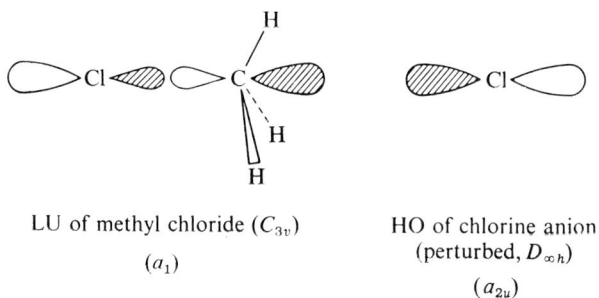

LU of methyl chloride (C_{3v}) HO of chlorine anion
                                      (perturbed, $D_{\infty h}$)

(a_1) (a_{2u})

Example III. Hydrogen abstraction of hydrocarbons by a radical

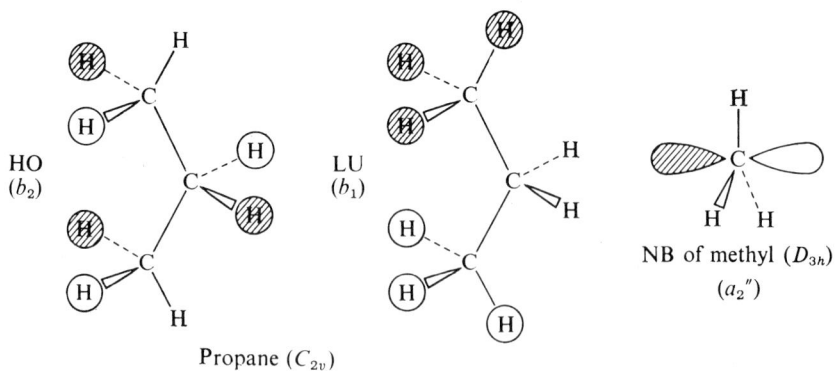

HO
(b_2)

LU
(b_1)

NB of methyl (D_{3h})

(a_2'')

Propane (C_{2v})

Figure 6

2. Cyclic Interactions

According to the perturbation theory, the magnitude of stabilization due to the mixing of the electron transfer from HO of M to LU of M' parallels the quantity.

$$\sqrt{2}\left|C_{Mr}^{(HO)}C_{M'r'}^{(LU)}\gamma_{rr'} + C_{Ms}^{(HO)}C_{M's'}^{(LU)}\gamma_{ss'} + \cdots\right| \tag{14}$$

where (r, r'), (s, s'), etc., represent the centers of overlapping. The characteristic feature of multicentered overlap interactions is the important role played by the sign of MO coefficients. As is well known, a normalized wave function carries an arbitrary factor of which the absolute value is unity. In a real LCAO MO, the sign of AO coefficients is also indefinite by an arbitrary factor, either $+1$ or -1. However, the product of the two AO coefficients in one MO has a definite sign, provided definite signs are given to AO's. On the other hand, the sign of γ's is dependent on the selection of the sign of related AO's.

In order to illustrate the influence of the sign of γ's as well as the sign of AO coefficients, we consider the case of double overlapping. If, for instance, both γ's are negative, the quantity

$$\sqrt{2}\left|C_{Mr}^{(HO)}C_{M'r'}^{(LU)}\gamma_{rr'} + C_{Ms}^{(HO)}C_{M's'}^{(LU)}\gamma_{ss'}\right| \tag{15}$$

will be large when

$$\text{sign}\,(C_{Mr}^{(HO)}C_{M'r'}^{(LU)}) = \text{sign}\,(C_{Ms}^{(HO)}C_{M's'}^{(LU)}) \tag{16}$$

or

$$\text{sign}\,(C_{Mr}^{(HO)}C_{Ms}^{(HO)}) = \text{sign}\,(C_{M'r'}^{(LU)}C_{M's'}^{(LU)}) \tag{17}$$

and will otherwise be small. It is evident that such sign relations are closely connected to the MO symmetry.

Figure 7 will be useful in understanding the relation of reactivity with orbital symmetry.

Example V is an intramolecular reaction involving the interaction of the sigma and pi parts, which are regarded, according to what was mentioned in Section II-A, as if they were different molecules (cf. Section VI-A). The mode of this sigma–pi interaction is understood by the diagram in Figure 7.

In this case the pi part acts as a donor and the sigma part as an acceptor. The sign relation of Eq. 17 is seen to hold.

Example IV. Addition of ethylene with butadiene

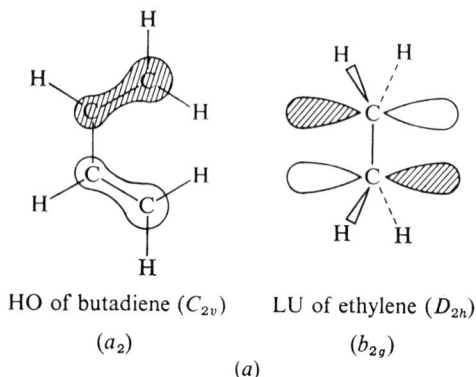

HO of butadiene (C_{2v}) LU of ethylene (D_{2h})

(a_2) (b_{2g})

(a)

Example V. Noncyclo-1,4-addition to butadiene

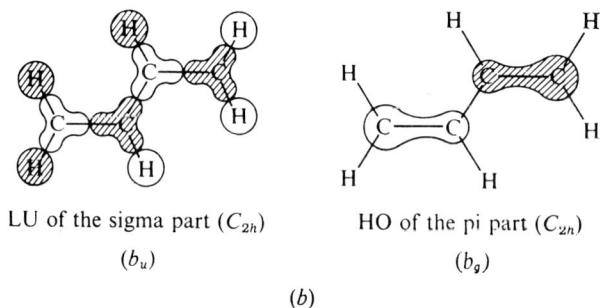

LU of the sigma part (C_{2h}) HO of the pi part (C_{2h})

(b_u) (b_g)

(b)

Figure 7

III. GENERAL STEREOSELECTION RULE FOR
ELECTROCYCLIC INTERACTIONS

A. *Syn* and *Anti* Interactions of Two AO Chains

We consider an AO cycle composed of a chain of AO's in molecule M and a similar chain of M'. The two termini of both chains are assumed to overlap each end of the other chain to form a cycle (Fig. 8). Such a type of interaction may be called an "electrocyclic interaction."

The sign of resonance integrals in Eq. 15 depends on how the sign of AO's is chosen. But, howsoever the sign of AO's is chosen, the mutual

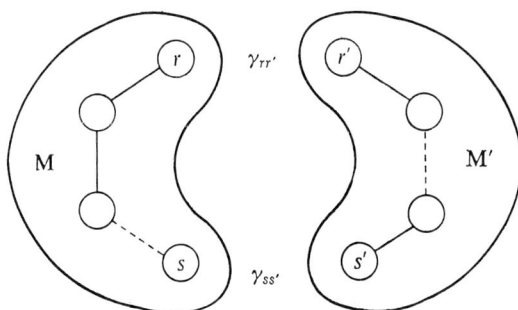

Figure 8

sign relation of each term in Eq. 15 is definite. Therefore, we may choose the sign of AO's in such a way that $\gamma_{ss'}$ as well as all the resonance integrals between the neighboring AO's in the same AO chain become negative. Two cases are then possible. One is the case in which $\gamma_{rr'}$ is negative, and may be referred to as the *syn* interaction, and the other, in which $\gamma_{rr'}$ is positive, is called *anti* interaction. In the former case Eq. 17 should hold in order to favor the reaction to take place, while in the latter case the reaction is facilitated by the relation

$$\text{sign}\,(C_{Mr}^{(HO)}C_{Ms}^{(HO)}) = -\text{sign}\,(C_{M'r'}^{(LU)}C_{M's'}^{(LU)}) \tag{18}$$

When an AO chain contains an odd number of electrons, NB MO acts as both HO and LU, as is already noticed in Section II-C.

B. The Ground State Intermolecular Interaction

We take the pi electron chain of a conjugated polyene as the AO chain mentioned above. The MO in which the AO coefficients at the chain ends possess the same sign is here denoted tentatively by S, and the MO with different signs of C_{Mr} and C_{Ms} as A.

The case in which the electrocycle contains $(4n + 2)$ electrons can be divided into three subcases as can be seen in Figure 9. Since the MO's of linear polyenes are known to be $S, A, S, A, \cdots$ from the lowest level successively, the MO symmetry relation will be given in each case.

From the illustration it is easily understood that in all three subcases the *syn* interaction is favorable for the occurrence of reaction.

The examples taken above are not always limited to the polyene reactions, since others are also treated essentially in a similar manner.

Similarly, the case of $(4n)$ electron cycle is classified into the three subcases shown in Figure 10. We see the *anti* interaction is favorable in all

Example: [Many examples in Sections IV-A, IV-C, VI-A: example V of II-C in which $m = 1$ (π part) and $m' = 4$ (σ part)]

Chain M of   Chain M' of
(4m) electrons   (4m' + 2) electrons

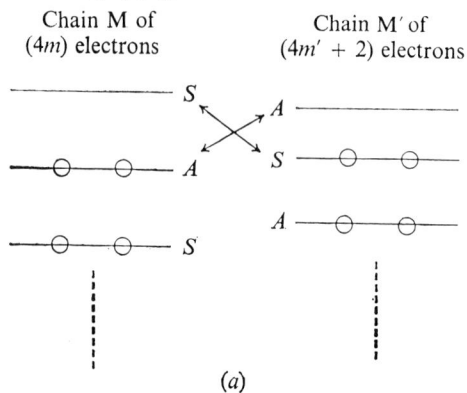

(a)

Example: Vinylogous Cope rearrangements, and 1,5-hydrogen migrations (Sections V-A and B)

Chain M of   Chain M' of
(4m + 1) electrons   (4m' + 1) electrons

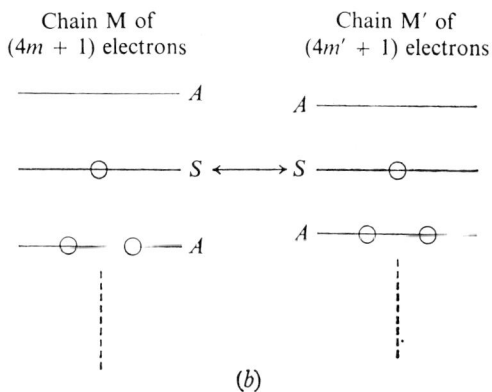

(b)

Example: Cope and Claisen rearrangements (Section V-B)

Chain M of   Chain M' of
(4m + 3) electrons   (4m' + 3) electrons

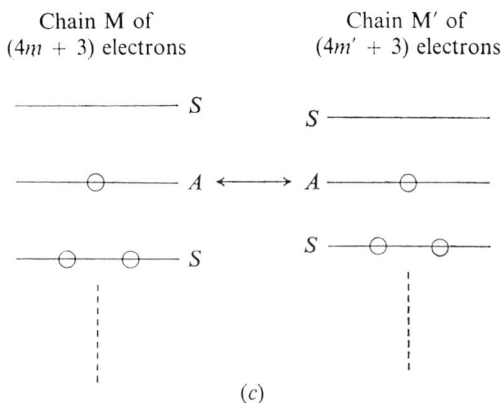

(c)

Figure 9

Example: (so far not known)

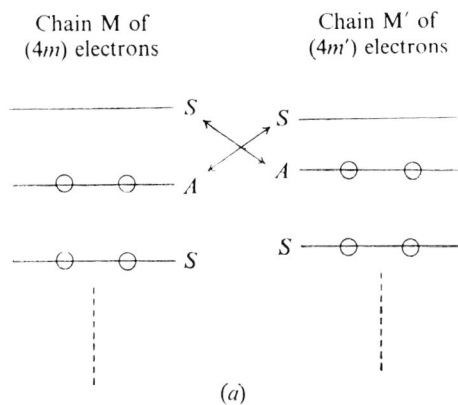

(a)

Example: calciferol–precalciferol rearrangement (Section V-A)

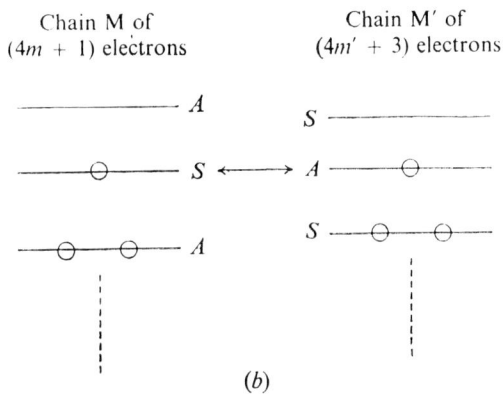

(b)

Example: (so far not known)

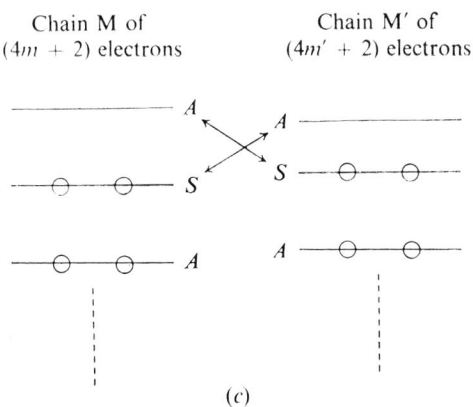

(c)

Figure 10

of these three subcases. Thus, we may conclude for the ground-state inter-molecular reaction that an interaction to form $(4n + 2)$ electron cycle is favored by the *syn* mode and an interaction to form $(4n)$ electron cycle by the *anti* mode (**Rule I**). This rule is also derived more elaborately with regard to the case of general electrocycles (16).

The selection of the two modes of interaction, *syn* and *anti* modes,

1. The *syn* interaction.
Example: Addition of ethylene to butadiene

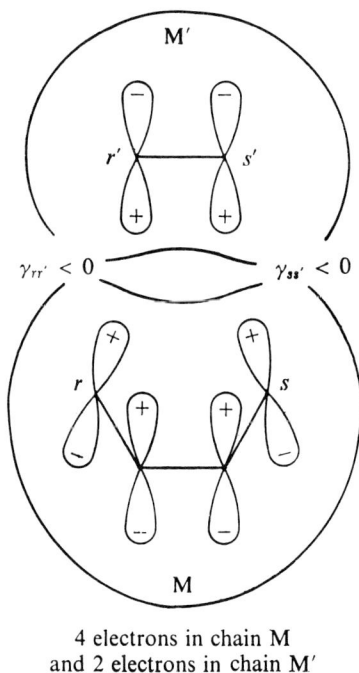

4 electrons in chain M
and 2 electrons in chain M′

Figure 11(*a*)

leads to a striking behavior in the steric course of the reaction, that is, the stereoselection. The circumstances will be illustrated in Figure 11. The signs $+$ and $-$ indicate the way of choosing the sign of AO's.

The electrocyclic reaction other than polyenes can be discussed in a similar manner.

If the geometrical circumstances permit only one mode of the two, Rule I serves as the selection rule of occurrence of the reaction. For instance, the Diels-Alder type additions are required to take place in *cis* mode with respect to both reactants. Accordingly, only the *syn* mode is allowable so that an addition to form a (4*n*)-electron cycle is prohibited.

The orbital symmetry relation was first pointed out by one of the present authors in the case of the Diels-Alder reaction (12). Woodward and Hoffmann treated this problem more comprehensively (14,15, 17,18).

C. The Excited State Intermolecular Interaction

The excited state reaction has aroused considerable interest from recent photochemical studies. The examples of the case in which the *syn* interaction is favorable are shown in Figure 12.

The case in which the *anti* interaction is favorable is exemplified by the Figure 13.

2. The *anti* interaction.
Example: 1,7-Hydrogen migration of 1,3,5-heptatriene

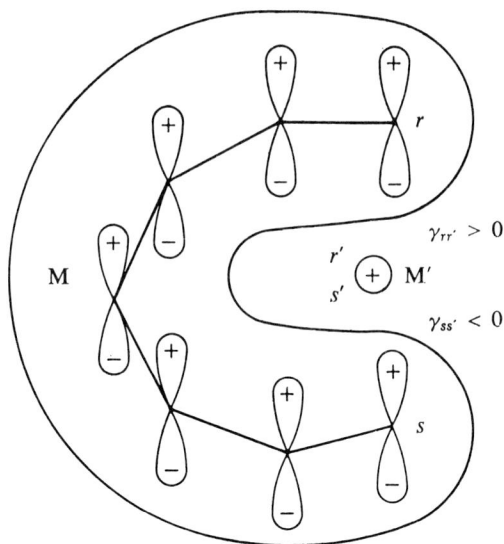

7 electrons in chain M
and one electron in chain M′

Figure 11(*b*)

The stereoselection rule for the photoinduced intermolecular reaction is that an interaction to form (4n) electron cycle is favored by *syn* mode and an interaction to form a (4n + 2) electron cycle by *anti* mode (**Rule II**). The illustrative examples for Rule II will be given later.

Example: Photochemical dimerization of diene (Section IV-B)

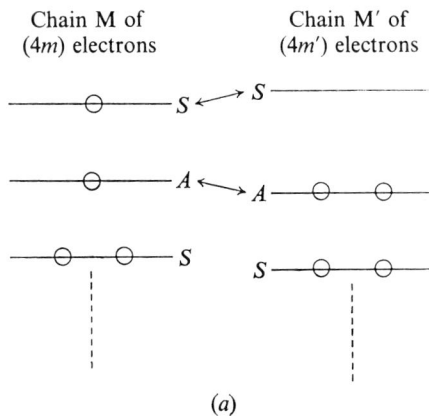

(a)

Example: Photochemical dimerization of olefins, and addition of olefins to enones; photochemical *cis* addition to olefins (Section VI-A)

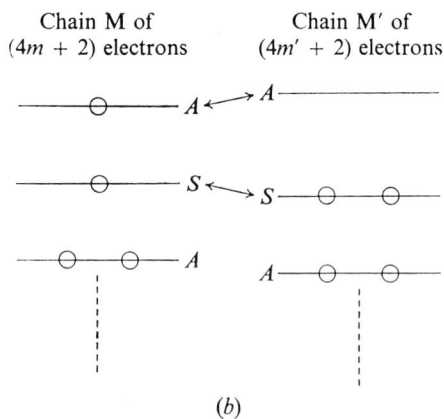

(b)

Figure 12

Example: (so far not known)

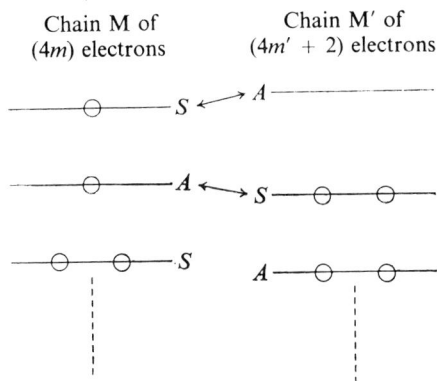

Chain M of
(4*m*) electrons

Chain M' of
(4*m'* + 2) electrons

(or vice versa)
Figure 13

D. The Intramolecular Electrocyclic Interaction

Some kinds of intramolecular reaction like sigma–pi interaction in planar molecules are regarded as if they were an intermolecular reaction, as is discussed in the preceding paragraph, between the sigma AO chain and the pi AO chain. The explanation will be given in Section VI-A.

Example. Hexatriene.

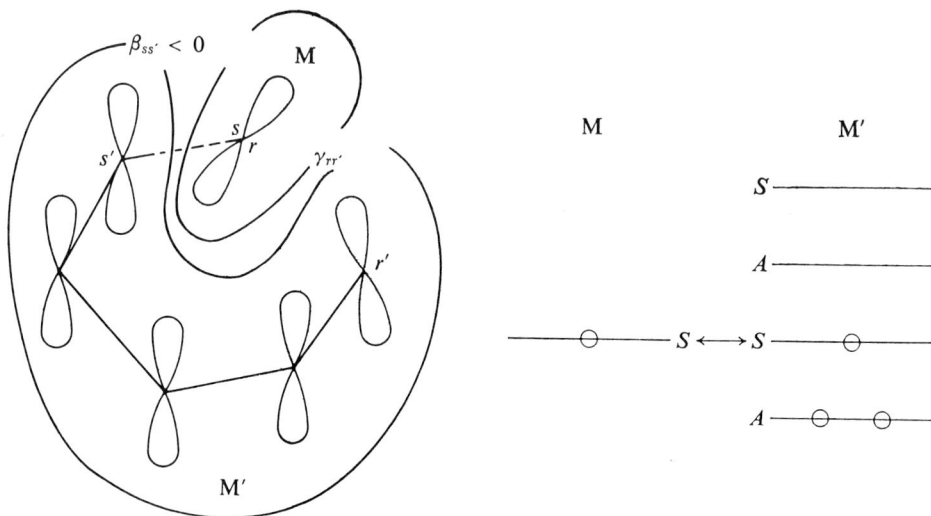

Figure 14. (*a*) The division into one- and five-electron chains.

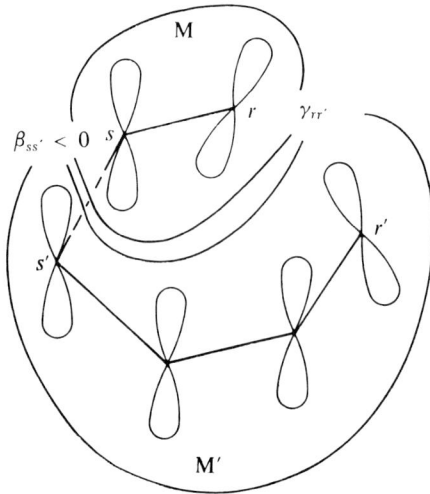

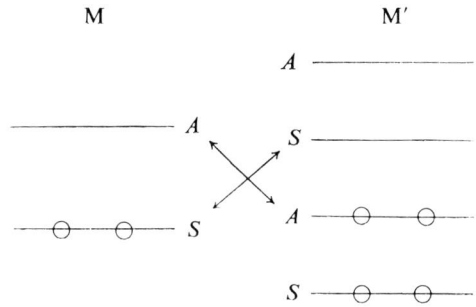

Figure 14. (*b*) The division into two- and four-electron chains.

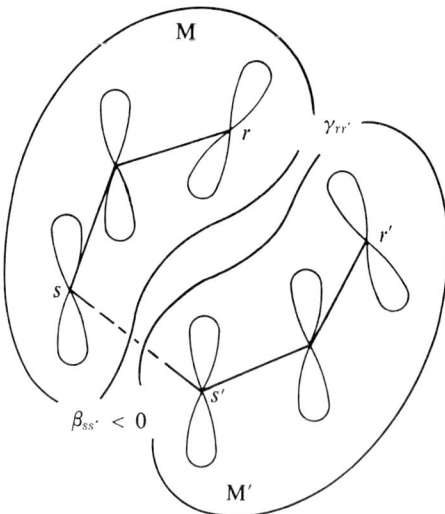

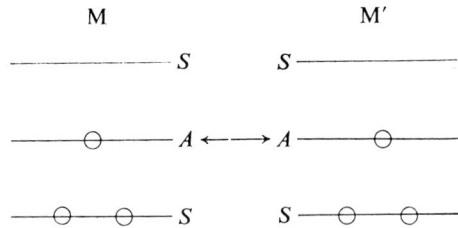

$\beta_{ss'}$ is the resonance integral between two neighboring pi orbitals.

Figure 14. (*c*) The division into three- and three-electron chains.

Another kind of intramolecular electrocycles is formed in the course of cyclization reactions. But if the partitioning technique described in Section II-A is employed, it is evident that the same conclusions as Rules I and II are obtained. For instance, the ground-state cyclization of a linear polyene containing $(4n + 2)$ electrons will follow the *syn* mode, while a polyene of $(4n)$ electrons the *anti* mode. This relation is independent of the way in which the chain is divided (see Fig. 14).

Other kinds of intramolecular reaction are also sometimes discussed by means of the "partitioning technique."

E. Interaction with Odd-Electron Cycles

The interactions so far discussed involve an even-electron cycle. In general, an interaction with the odd-electron cycle does not exhibit a

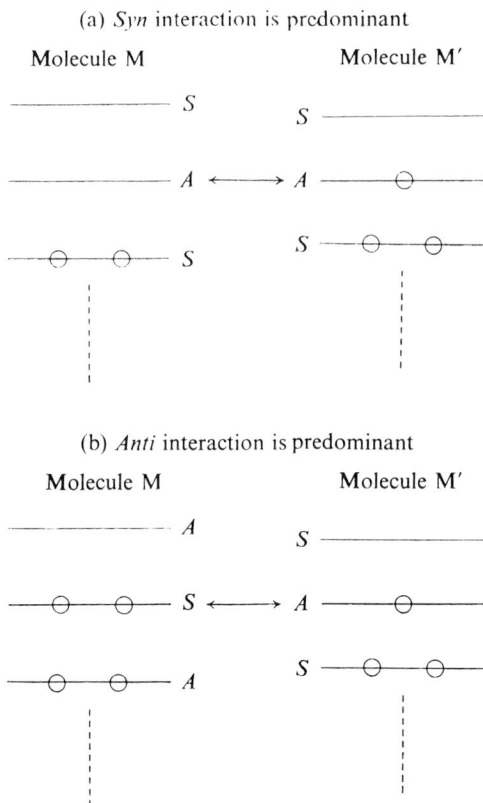

(a) *Syn* interaction is predominant

Molecule M   Molecule M′

Figure 15

distinct selection of *syn* and *anti* modes, since the electron in the half-occupied MO can interact with both S and A MO's of the opponent molecule.
Therefore, an odd-electron cycle is less responsible for the stereodirecting
control than an even electron cycle. This is important in a double electrocycle composed of one odd cycle and one even cycle, both simultaneously
appearing in the transition state. In such a case, the even-electron cycle
would be dominant in determining the steric course. An example will be
given in Section V-A.

However, we have also to take into account some special cases in
which the stereoselection by an odd cycle will be possible. Figure 15 will
serve as an explanation. In case (*a*), NB of molecule M' lies very close to
a MO of molecule M, of the same symmetry as NB, while in case (*b*), it lies
very close to a MO of molecule M of different symmetry from NB.

IV. INTERMOLECULAR CYCLIC REACTIONS

A. Diels-Alder and Dipolar Additions

Before discussing the stereochemical problems involved in molecular
rearrangement processes, it is appropriate to test the applicability of the
general selection rule mentioned in the last section to the intermolecular
cycloadditions, of which the Diels-Alder type is most typical and best
investigated. This reaction is known to occur with a stereospecific pathway
which is *cis* with respect to both diene and dienophile (19,20). The relationship of the orbital energies of diene and dienophile is, in general, as shown
in Figure 16. It is understood that the charge-transfer interaction from HO

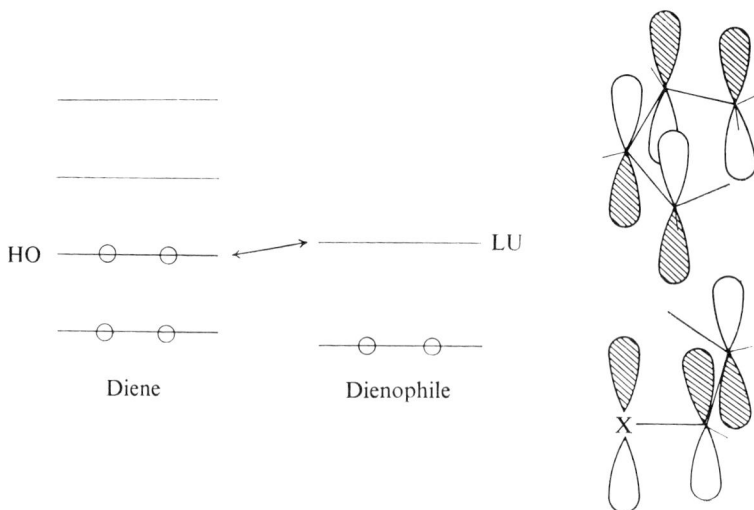

Figure 16

of the diene to LU of the dienophile will play the most dominant role in determining the reaction path. The symmetry properties of the wave functions of these orbitals (frontier orbitals) are shown schematically in Table 1 (11).

From Table 1 it is clear that in any cases which are known to occur

TABLE 1
Symmetry Properties of Diene HO and Dienophile LU

HO of the diene	LU of the dienophile

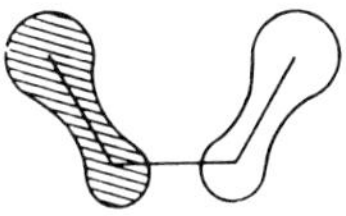

Butadiene

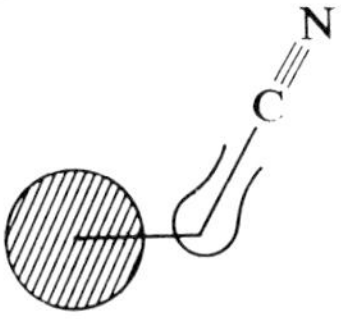

Acrylonitrile

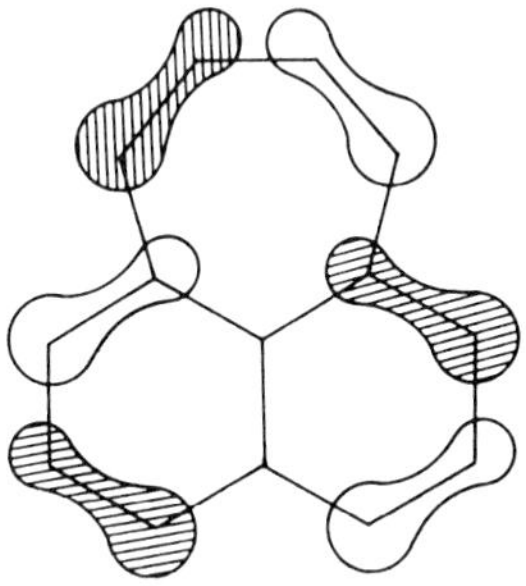

Pleiadiene

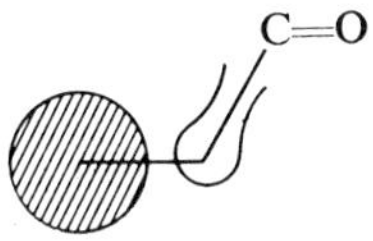

Acrolein

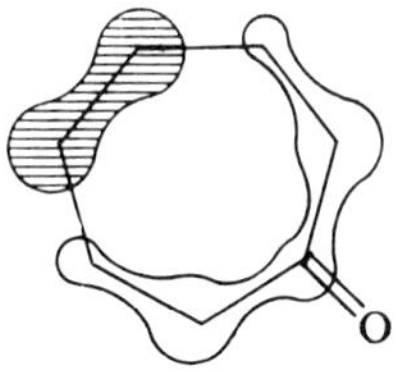

Tropone

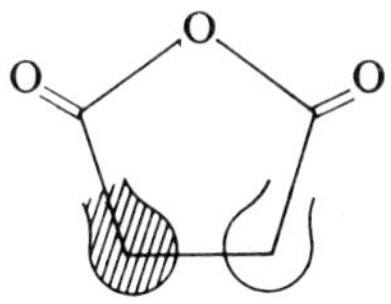

Maleic anhydride

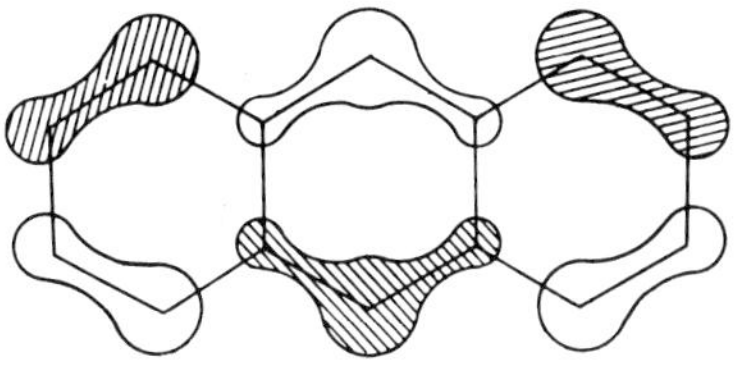

Anthracene

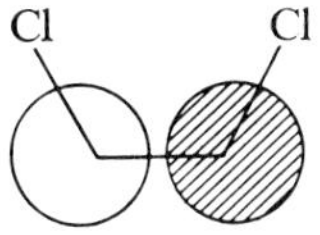

1,2-Dichloroethylene

actually, $C_{Mr}^{(HO)}C_{M'r'}^{(LU)}$ and $C_{Ms}^{(HO)}C_{M's'}^{(LU)}$ have the same sign in conformity with Eq. 16 in favor of *syn* interaction, leading to a *cis* addition with respect to both the diene and the dienophile.

Now, let us consider more generally the addition of ethylene to another conjugated system. The symmetry of the wave functions of HO and LU of ethylene, hexatriene, and naphthalene is shown in Figure 17.

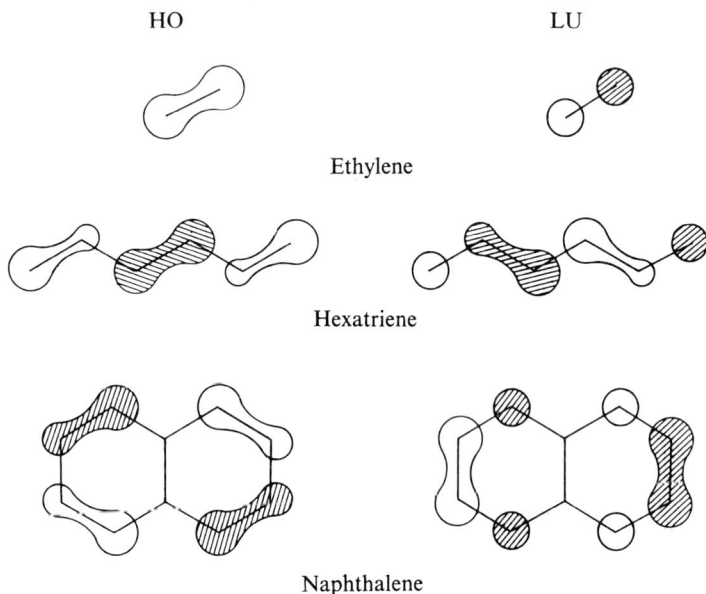

HO   LU

Ethylene

Hexatriene

Naphthalene

Figure 17

From the illustration, it is obvious that the cyclic addition of ethylene to 1,2- or 1,6-positions of another conjugated system will favor the *anti* course, while the *syn* interaction will prevail in the addition to 1,4-positions. These are the examples of Rule I and the cyclic addition of ethylene derivatives to butadiene derivatives is a geometrically favored *syn* case with $4n + 2$ $(n = 1)$ electrons. More rigorous numerical computation for a number of systems substantiates these results (21).

Another example of cyclic additions is the 1,3-dipolar addition (Fig. 18) (22). The number of electrons forming an electrocycle is six. The symmetry (in this case nodal property) of HO of some 1,3-dipoles is shown in Figure 19.

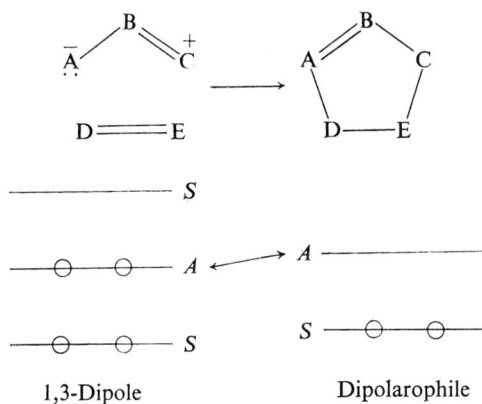

1,3-Dipole   Dipolarophile

Figure 18

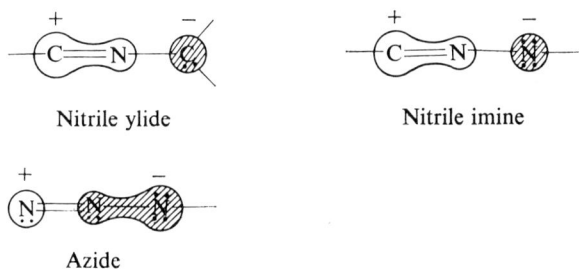

Nitrile ylide   Nitrile imine

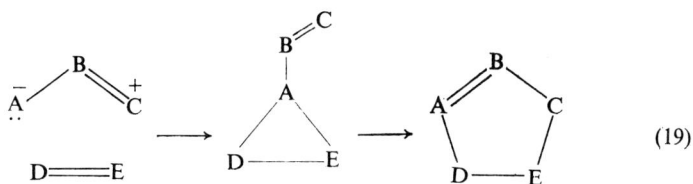

Azide

Figure 19

Two reaction mechanisms have been proposed for 1,3-dipolar additions, i.e., the two-step mechanism via a three-membered cyclic intermediate and the direct formation of a five-membered ring through a simultaneous (or quasi-simultaneous) 1,3-addition (Eq. 19) (23). Rule I

$$\text{(19)}$$

suggests that the latter, the direct two-center addition, might be more favorable, since such a three-membered cyclic intermediate forms less stable electrocycle with $4n$ ($n = 1$) electrons.

Brief mention may be made here of the 1,4-dipolar addition (24) which is also discussed in a similar manner, leading to the conclusion that the *syn* mode interaction will be favorable.

B. Cyclobutane Formation

An interesting problem of electrocyclic interaction is provided by the experimental results on the thermal dimerization of butadiene. The reaction gives *trans*-1,2-divinylcyclobutane and cycloocta-1,5-diene (Eq. 20). Of

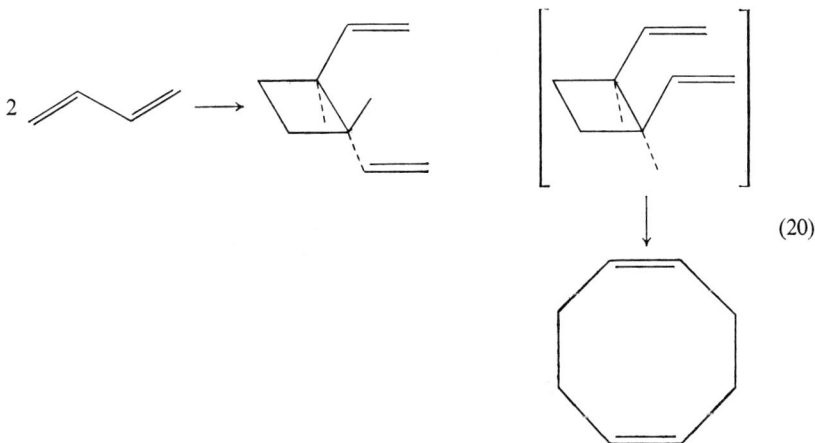

$$(20)$$

these, cyclo-octa-1,5-diene is likely to come not from the direct 1,4-1′,4′-interaction, but from the initially formed *cis*-1,2-divinylcyclobutane through an intramolecular rearrangement of essentially Cope type (25). The disadvantage in direct formation of cycloocta-1,5-diene and 1,3-divinyl-cyclobutane is easily understood from Eq. 15, since in these cases the term

$$|C_{Mr}^{(HO)}C_{M'r'}^{(LU)}\gamma_{rr'} + C_{Ms}^{(HO)}C_{M's'}^{(LU)}\gamma_{ss'}|$$

vanishes with $\gamma_{rr'} = \gamma_{ss'}$ (smaller, higher order energy terms will then appear), while in case of 1,2-divinylcyclobutane, Eq. 15 gives some positive value.

Mention may be made here of the thermal formation of cyclobutanes through cyclic addition of two double bonds. Highly fluorinated olefins undergo thermal dimerization or addition to 1,2-position of other con-jugated systems. Similar cycloadditions are known with regard to allenes, ketenes, and some active olefins such as acrylonitrile (Eq. 21) (26). These examples, at first sight, seem to violate Rule I. However, these reactions are

$$2CF_2{=}CF_2 \xrightarrow{200°C} \begin{array}{c} F_2C{-}CF_2 \\ | \quad\quad | \\ F_2C{-}CF_2 \end{array}$$

$$CF_2{=}CCl_2 + \begin{array}{c} CH_2{=}C{-}C{=}CH_2 \\ | \quad\quad | \\ H_3C \quad CH_3 \end{array} \xrightarrow{100°C} \begin{array}{c} CH_2 \\ CH_2{=}C{-}C \diagup \diagdown CF_2 \\ | \quad | \quad CCl_2 \\ H_3C \quad CH_3 \end{array}$$

$$2CH_2{=}C{=}CH_2 \xrightarrow{400°C} \begin{array}{c} CH_2 \\ H_2C{-}C \diagup \\ | \quad | \\ H_2C{-}C \\ \diagdown CH_2 \end{array} + \begin{array}{c} CH_2 \\ H_2C{-}C \diagup \\ | \quad | \\ H_2C \diagup C{-}CH_2 \end{array}$$

$$2CH_2{=}CH{-}CN \xrightarrow{25°C} \begin{array}{c} CN \\ H_2C{-}CH \diagup \\ | \quad | \\ H_2C{-}CH \\ \diagdown CN \end{array} \qquad (21)$$

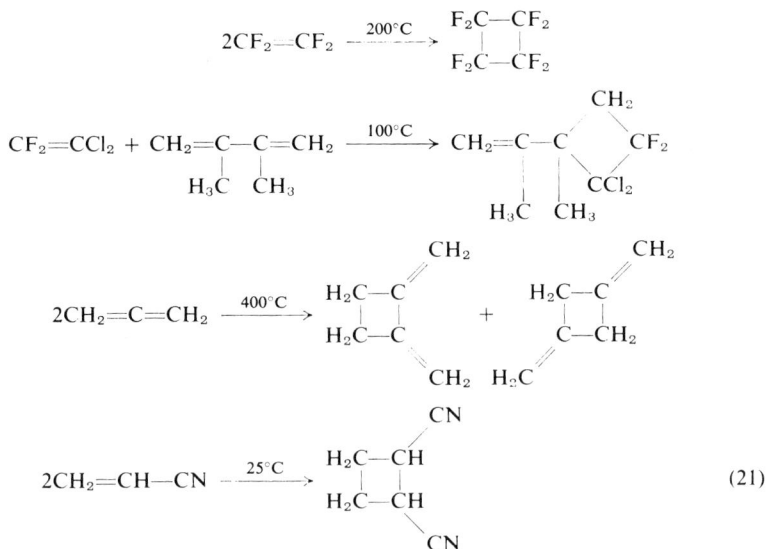

usually considered as belonging to a different kind, i.e., to a two-stage addition via the following stable diradical intermediate or the like:

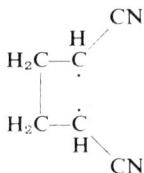

$$\begin{array}{c} CN \\ H \diagup \\ H_2C{-}C \\ | \\ H_2C{-}\overset{\cdot}{C} \\ H \diagdown CN \end{array}$$

The two-stage mechanism via an intermediate has also been proposed for the polar addition of 1,2-bis(trifluoromethyl)-1,2-dicyanoethylene to electron-rich alkenes, giving rise to 1,2-bis(trifluoromethyl)-1,2-dicyano-cyclobutanes at room temperature (Eq. 22) (27). Comparison of Eqs. 13

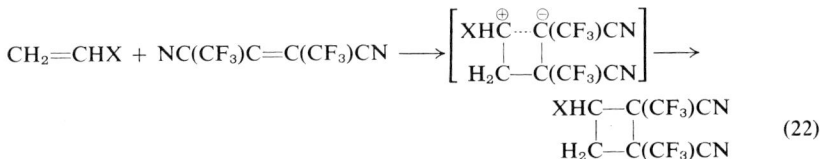

$$CH_2{=}CHX + NC(CF_3)C{=}C(CF_3)CN \longrightarrow \begin{bmatrix} XH\overset{\oplus}{C}\cdots\overset{\ominus}{C}(CF_3)CN \\ | \quad\quad | \\ H_2C{-}C(CF_3)CN \end{bmatrix} \longrightarrow$$

$$\begin{array}{c} XHC{-}C(CF_3)CN \\ | \quad\quad | \\ H_2C{-}C(CF_3)CN \end{array} \qquad (22)$$

and 15 will make one sure that the two-step (or quasi-two-step) mechanism is plausible.

Next we refer to photoinduced cyclic addition reactions. In excited states, the formation of cyclobutanes is favored in contrast with the ground-state additions, as is expected from Rule II. Benzonitrile adds photochemically to trimethylethylene to give a bicyclooctadiene. In the presence of benzophenone, trimethylethylene reacts with benzophenone rather than with the nitrile to form a trimethylene oxide (Eq. 23) (28). Photochemical addition of acetylenes to benzene gives cyclooctatetraenes, which are supposed to be produced through the ring opening of the initially formed bicyclooctatrienes (Eq. 24) (29). Benzophenone-sensitized cyclo-

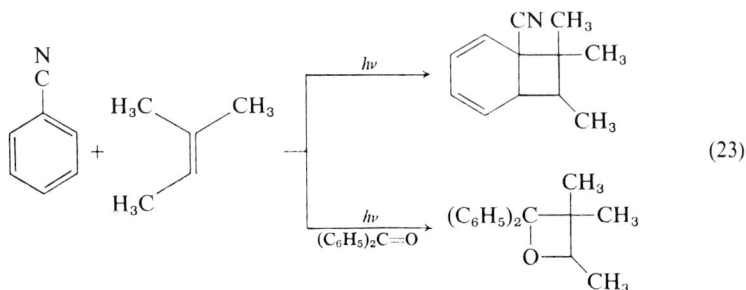

(23)

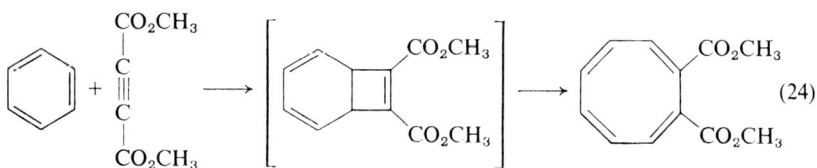

(24)

addition of dimethylmaleic anhydride to furan and thiophene gives cyclobutane derivatives (Eq. 25) (30,31). Dimethylmaleate adds photo-

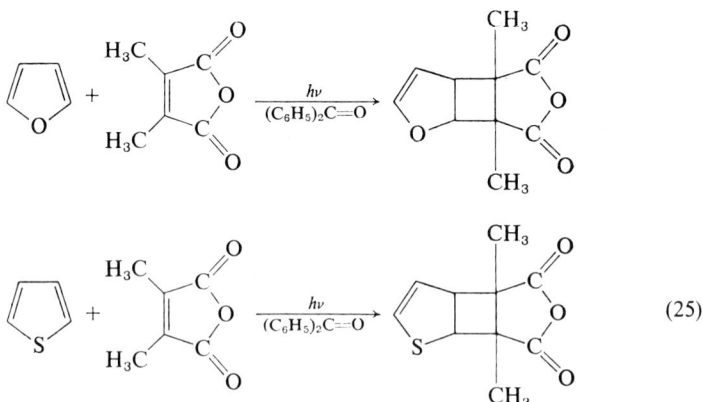

(25)

chemically to norbornene giving rise to *trans*-3,4-dicarbomethoxy-*exo*-tricyclo[4,2,1,0^{2,5}] nonane as the major product along with a lesser amount of *cis,endo*-3,4-dicarbomethoxy-*exo*-tricyclo[4,2,1,0^{2,5}] nonane (Eq. 26) (32).

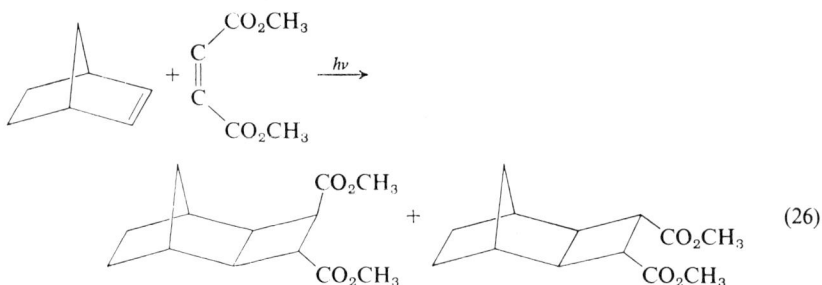

$$(26)$$

Other examples of photoinduced cyclobutane formations are those known in the reaction of α,β-unsaturated ketones. Irradiation of cyclopentenone gives two dimers in high yield (Eq. 27) (33).

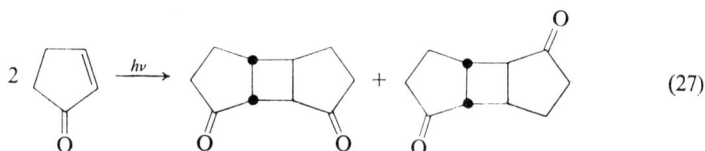

$$(27)$$

Irradiation of α,β-unsaturated ketones in the presence of alkenes and alkynes generally yields cyclobutanes and cyclobutenes. Cyclopentenone reacts with cyclopentene to form a tricyclic ketone (Eq. 28a) (33). Addition of cyclopentenone to but-2-yne gives a cyclobutene, which undergoes an isomerization (Eq. 28b) (34). Cyclohexenone undergoes photochemical

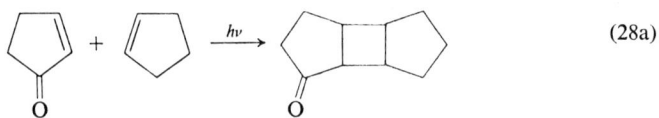

$$(28a)$$

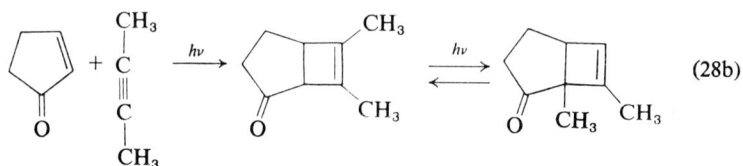

$$(28b)$$

addition to alkenes via a charge-transfer complex (Eq. 29) (35).

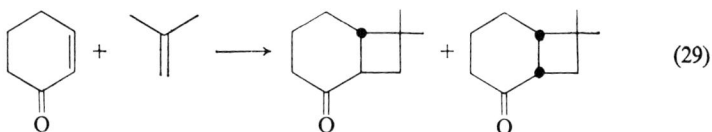

$$(29)$$

(*trans*-fused ring)

The photodimerization of coumarin gives head-to-head *cis* dimer in ethanol, whereas head-to-head *trans* dimer is predominant in benzene or ethanol in the presence of benzophenone as sensitizer (Eq. 30) (36). The

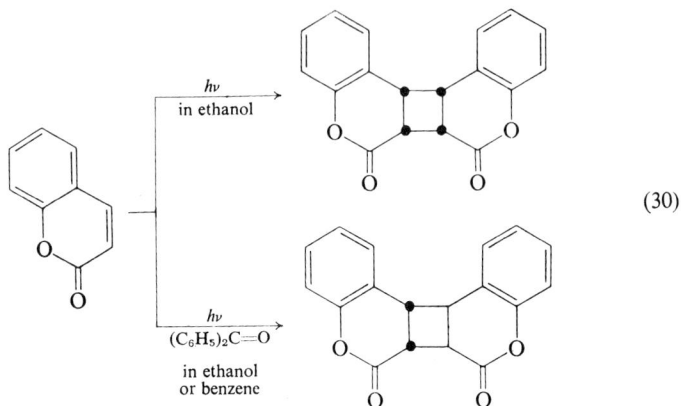

(30)

difference observed in the steric course of these reactions has been considered to be due to the involvement of different excited states.

It is very likely that some of the photoinduced cyclobutane formations are governed by the symmetry properties of those molecular orbitals which would play the most dominant role (*syn* interaction between (A)–(A) and (S)–(S) MO pairs). But experimental results also exist in which some products with *trans*-fused rings are formed (illustrated in the figure of cyclohexenone reaction). This suggests that a two-step mechanism might be operating in these reactions. However, an alternative explanation might be pointed out. If the reactant to be promoted to an excited state by irradiation happens to have a very low lying LU (A), the contribution of the interaction between (S)–(A) MO pair (compare Fig. 20) will cause such *trans*-fused ring through a concerted (or quasi-concerted) *anti*-cyclic interaction.

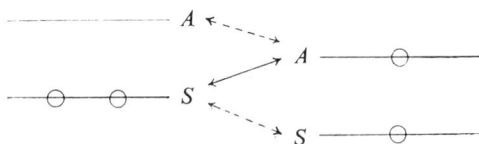

Figure 20

The photochemical addition of alkenes to carbonyl groups is also an example of the formation of a $4n$-membered ring (Eq. 31). These reactions, however, have been understood as a two-step reaction via stable diradical intermediates involving an n,π^* triplet state of carbonyl systems (37).

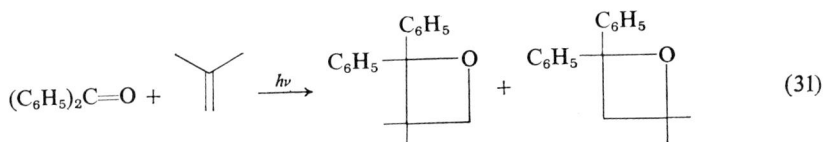

$$(C_6H_5)_2C{=}O \; + \quad \xrightarrow{h\nu} \quad + \tag{31}$$

In the photoaddition of 1,4-naphthoquinone to cyclic olefins, competition between cyclobutane and oxetane formations has been observed (Eq. 32) (38). The photodimerization of tropone in sulfuric acid

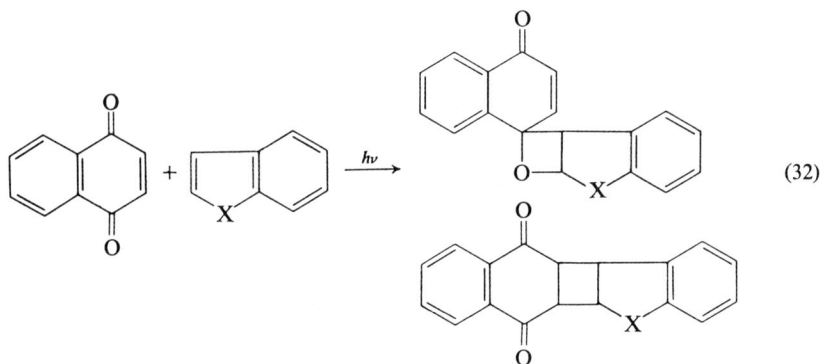

$$\xrightarrow{h\nu} \tag{32}$$

yields tricyclo[6,4,1,1^{2,7}] tetradeca-3,5,9,11-tetraene-13,14-dione, while irradiation of tropone in acetonitrile gives other dimers (Eq. 33) (39,40).

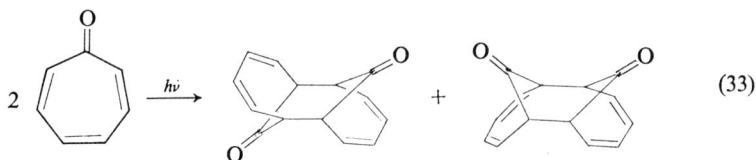

$$2 \quad \xrightarrow{h\nu} \quad + \tag{33}$$

This is an example of cycles with $4n$ ($n = 3$) electrons.

The dimerization of benzoquinone in the solid state gives a cage compound upon further irradiation of initially formed cyclobutane. This reaction is considered to be a successive formation of $4n$ ($n = 1$)-membered rings (Eq. 34) (41).

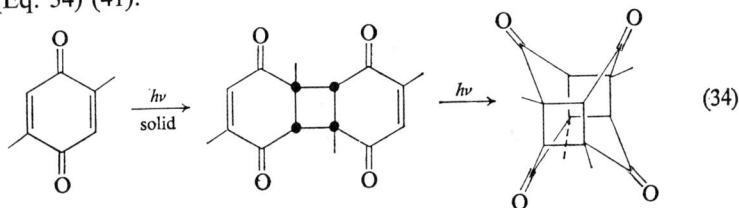

$$\xrightarrow[\text{solid}]{h\nu} \quad \xrightarrow{h\nu} \tag{34}$$

Also we may find verification for Rules I and II in the photochemical reaction of benzene and maleic anhydride (Eq. 35) (42).

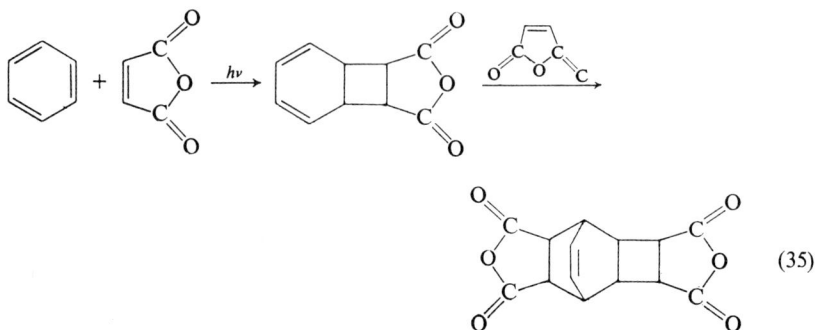

$$(35)$$

There exists another important factor to be taken into account in discussing the course of cyclic addition reactions. The irradiation of butadiene and of cyclohexadiene in the presence of sensitizers leads to the dimerization of these dienes (Eq. 36). The most striking difference between these two dienes observed in their dimerization is that the relative amount of butadiene dimers varies with the variation of sensitizers used, whereas the composition of cyclohexadiene dimers is almost unchanged (43).

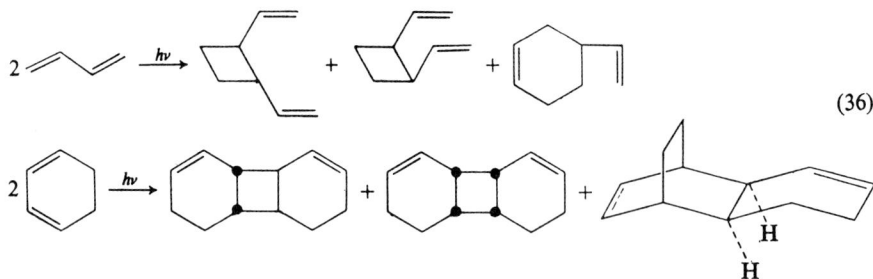

$$(36)$$

An explanation of these phenomena was proposed as follows: In the case of butadiene, the concentration of *trans*-triplet and *cis*-triplet varies with the excitation energy of the sensitizer used, while the skeleton of cyclohexadiene is rigidly fixed to *cis* configuration (44). Such an effect as well as the electrocyclic effect might obviously be one of the influencing factors in determining the course of the cyclic addition reactions. In this connection, the photochemical cycloaddition of butadiene to cyclopentadiene forming a $4n$ ($n = 2$) electrocycle in the process of interaction may be interesting (Eq. 37) (45).

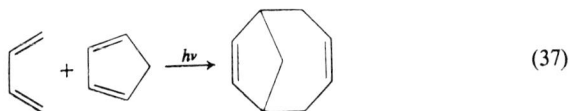

$$(37)$$

Thus, we obtain a selection rule for cyclic additions as summarized in Table 2 (see Eq. 38).

TABLE 2
The Selection Rule for Cyclic Additions

	$m + m' = 4n^{a}$	$m + m' = 4n + 2^{a}$
Thermal	cis–trans	cis–cis
	trans–cis	trans–trans
Photochemical	cis–cis	cis–trans
	trans–trans	trans–cis

[a] The number of electrons forming a cycle is $m + m'$. Here cis–cis and trans–trans correspond to the case of syn and cis–trans and trans–cis to the case of anti interaction mentioned in Section III-A.

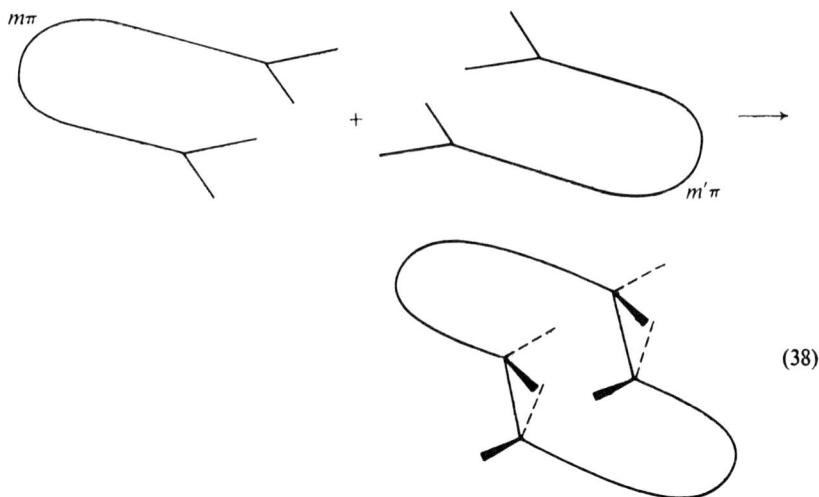

$$(38)$$

C. Other Cyclic Additions

Hydroboration of olefins is known to take place cis with respect to the double bond in an electrophilic fashion (46). The LU of BH_3 molecule is completely localized at $2p\pi$ AO of boron, so that the charge-transfer interaction may be possible with occupied pi MO of the carbon–carbon double

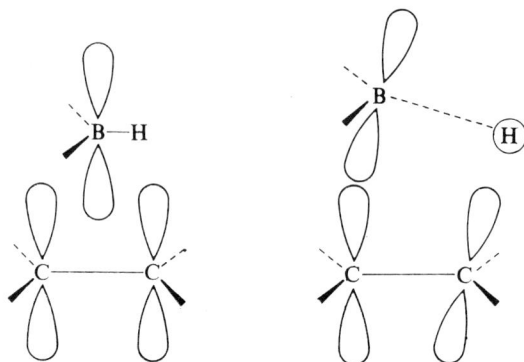

Figure 21

bond (Fig. 21) (47). That the HO is symmetric with respect to the center of the double bond favors the formation of a cyclic intermediate. This is an example of electrocycles with two electrons. As the charge transfer from olefin to the LU of BH_3 proceeds, the boron–hydrogen sigma bond as well as carbon–carbon pi bond is loosened, causing a $p\sigma$ like over-lapping between boron $2p\pi$ AO and one of the carbon $2p\pi$ AO's and simultaneous combination of the hydrogen atom with the other carbon $2p\pi$ AO. A square form interaction is thus performed to give rise to a *cis* addition (48).

In general, *cis* addition to an olefinic double bond may be facilitated when the attacking reagent possesses unoccupied molecular orbitals, most preferably the LU, of the same symmetry as the HO of the reactant double bond. The hydroboration is an example of such cases. Other reactions in a similar condition are the protonation to a double bond, the addition of phenyl cation to a double bond to form phenonium cation (49), the polar halogenation of olefins (50), the addition of singlet carbene and nitrene to olefins (51), the addition of osmium tetroxide, manganate, and per-manganate anions to a double bond (19), etc.

V. INTRAMOLECULAR CYCLIC REARRANGEMENTS

A. Hydrogen, Alkyl, and Aryl Migrations

The intramolecular migration of hydrogen, alkyls, aryls, halogens, and the like in unsaturated systems performs a part in exemplifying the steric control due to the electrocyclic interaction. First we consider the carbonium ion rearrangement. In this case, the number of electrons to form the electrocycle is even and HO of the conjugated part plays the most important role. For instance, the transition state of intramolecular proton migration in ethyl cation may involve a cyclic conjugation similar to that of the protonation to a double bond (Eq. 39). The coefficients of AO's in HO of polyenes at the positions 1,2 or 1,6 have the same sign, in favor of *syn* interaction or suprafacial (15) migration. Those of 1,4-positions have

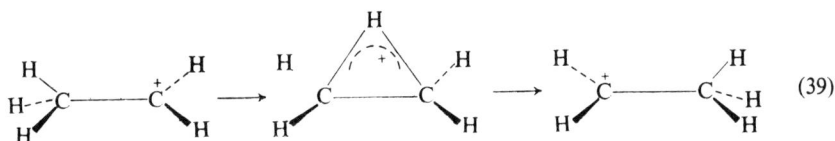

(39)

opposite signs in HO, indicating the 1,4-migration of proton might take place in the *anti* mode or in an antarafacial (15) fashion. The intramolecular migration of alkyl and phenyl cations may be discussed similarly to the proton migration (Fig. 22) (52).

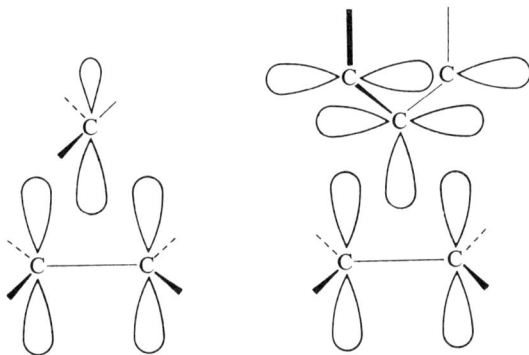

Figure 22

When hydrogen migrates as a radical, as is the case of isomerization of polyenes, the electrocycle is made up of a hydrogen and a conjugated radical chain, so that the MO which will govern the steric course of the migration reaction is the nonbonding unpaired-electron orbital of the residual conjugated part. This case has been comprehensively discussed by Woodward and Hoffmann (15), who showed that 1,5-migration should take place in suprafacial fashion and 1,3- and 1,7-migrations in antarafacial fashion consistent with experimental results (Eq. 40). For example,

$$R_2C=CH-(CH=CH)_k-CHR_2' \rightleftharpoons R_2CH-(CH=CH)_k-CH=CR_2'$$

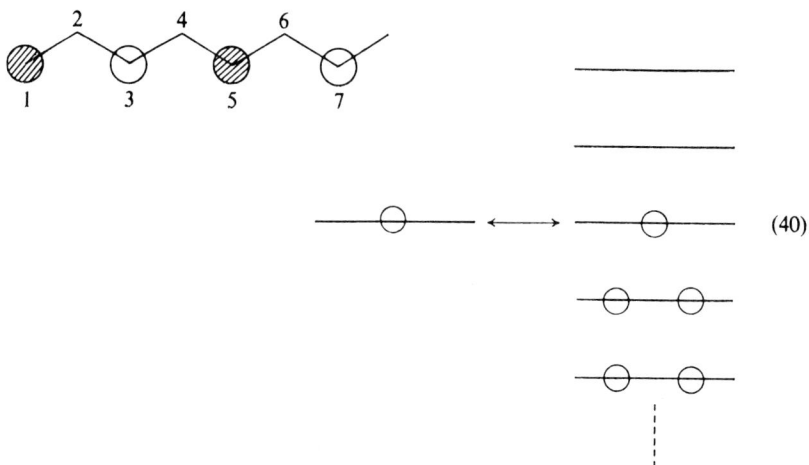

$$(40)$$

Havinga et al. (53) proposed such a cyclic transition state for calciferol–precalciferol rearrangement, indicating hydrogen might shift from the top face of a $2p\pi$ AO to the bottom of another one or vice versa (Eq. 41, see also Fig. 23). A distinction should be made between the migration

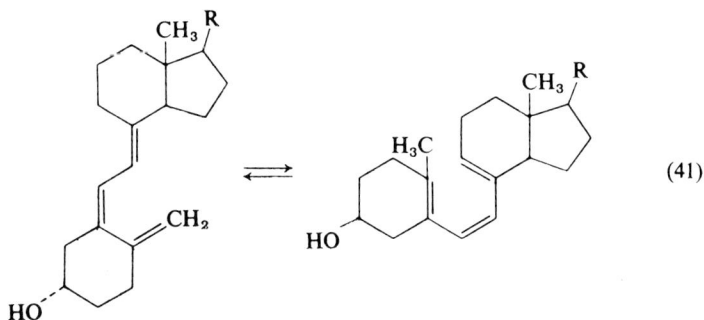

$$(41)$$

reactions in open-chain systems and those in cyclic systems. In open-chain systems, MO calculation gives the nonbonding orbital which possesses the regularity in its symmetry property as has been mentioned above. In cyclic systems, however, a degeneracy originating from their geometrical symmetry occurs in MO levels. For instance, the diagrams of MO energy levels of cyclopentadienyl and cycloheptatrienyl are indicated in Figure 24. Hence, it seems difficult to discuss the steric course of the one-step hydrogen migration in cyclic conjugated systems based on the symmetry property of only one MO. A deeper but simple consideration, however, helps us to understand that thermal 1,5-migration favors the suprafacial course, while 1,3- or 1,7-migrations will take place in the antarafacial mode. It

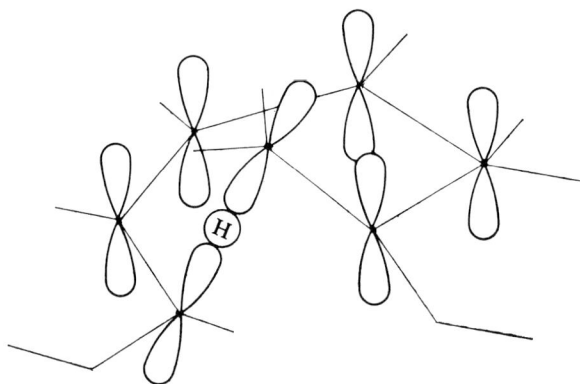

Figure 23

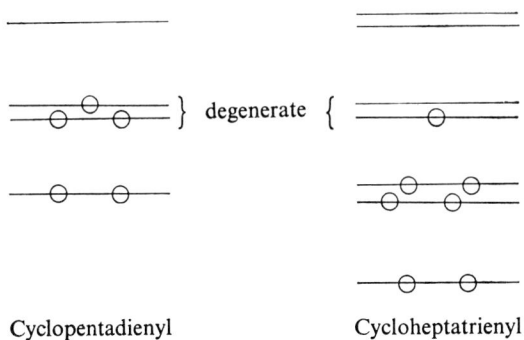

Cyclopentadienyl   Cycloheptatrienyl

Figure 24

should be clear that this reaction belongs to the case which has the transition state with double electrocycles. One is an even-electron cycle and the other an odd-electron cycle. According to the discussion in Section III-E, we may consider the even-electron cyclic interaction as dominant, obtaining at once the conclusion mentioned above. The selection rule thus obtained is the same as that for open-chain systems. Numerical computation can support this result. Thermal 1,5-migrations have been actually observed

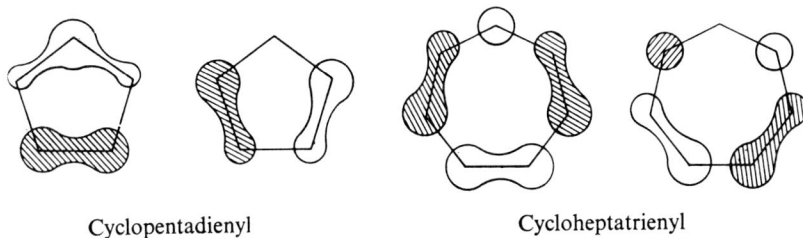

Cyclopentadienyl   Cycloheptatrienyl

Figure 25

158   K. FUKUI AND H. FUJIMOTO

in cyclopentadienes and cycloheptatrienes (Fig. 25) (54). To predict the
steric course of photoinduced isomerization of olefins may be more difficult. The symmetry properties of LU (in the sense of ground state) of allyl,
pentadienyl, and heptatrienyl to which an electron will be promoted upon
irradiation are shown in Figure 26. It may be better to discuss the path of

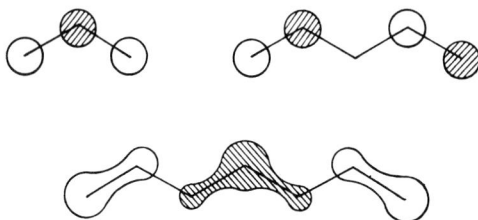

Figure 26

photochemical hydrogen migration reactions separately for each given case
than to give a general selection rule, although we can say, in the roughest
sense, that the favorable steric course might be opposite to that of thermal
ones. The photoinduced isomerization of cyclic olefins is more complicated,
since we should consider more than one electronic configuration for the
excited electronic state of such cyclic systems.

Migration of anions in conjugated anionic systems, accompanied by
carbanion rearrangement, also forms electrocycles with an even number of
electrons in the transition state. Rule I indicates that 1,4-migration will take
place in the suprafacial fashion and 1,2- and 1,6-migrations in the antarafacial fashion (Eq. 42).

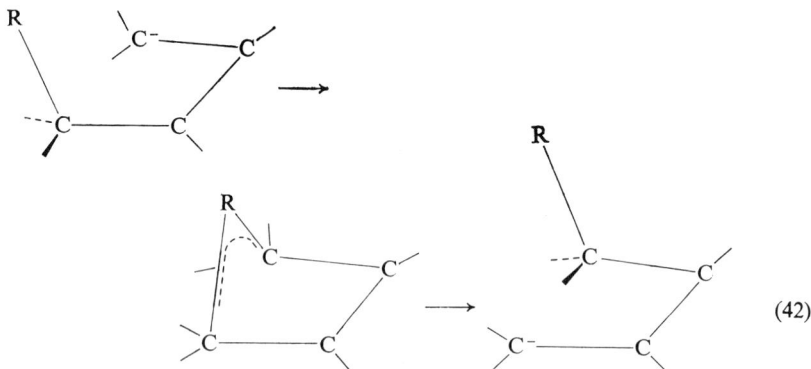

(42)

Finally, we consider migration reactions in odd-electron systems. A
symmetrical radical has been observed in the addition of hydrogen bromide
to symmetrical olefins as but-2-yne (55). Skell et al. (56) showed that the
abstraction of primary hydrogen from isopropyl bromide or *t*-butyl

bromide produced the migration of bromine atom. These findings may present evidence of the mobility of bromine atom through a bridged odd-electron cycle. The unpaired electron in the half-occupied orbital can interact with both HO and LU of the residual skeleton. To predict whether the *syn-* or *anti*-course is favorable, the energy of the half-occupied orbital as well as those of HO and LU must be known (Fig. 27). In general, we cannot expect any distinct selection of *syn* and *anti* modes for such interactions with odd-electron cycles. Speaking with regard to the most popular intra-

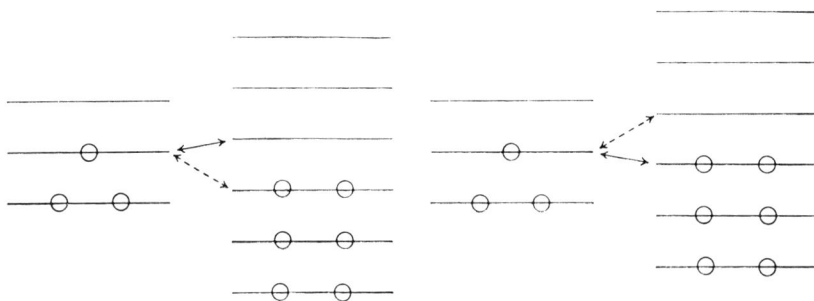

Figure 27

molecular migrations in which the migrating fragment shifts to the adjacent carbon, the reaction through a bridged cyclic intermediate may be less possible in odd-electron systems than in cationic systems, but may be more possible in odd-electron systems than in anionic systems. A similar conclusion has been obtained from more elaborate calculation by Zimmermann et al. (57).

Thus, we obtain selection rules for isomerization of polyenes, and carbonium ion and carbanion rearrangements as are summarized in Tables 3–5.

TABLE 3
The Selection Rule for Intramolecular $(1, 2k + 1)$
Hydrogen Migrations[a]

	Even k	Odd k
Thermal	Suprafacial	Antarafacial
Photochemical	(Antarafacial)[b]	(Suprafacial)[b]

[a] Number of electrons forming a cycle is $2k + 2$. Here suprafacial corresponds to *syn* and antarafacial to *anti* interaction in the sense of Section III-A.

[b] As was mentioned in the text, this rule is not expected to be always valid from a theoretical point of view.

TABLE 4
The Selection Rule for $(1, 2k)$ Carbonium Ion
Rearrangement[a]

	Even k	Odd k
Thermal	Antarafacial	Suprafacial
Photochemical	(Suprafacial)[b]	(Antarafacial)[b]

[a] Number of electrons forming a cycle is $2k$. Here suprafacial corresponds to *syn* and antarafacial to *anti* interaction.

[b] The steric course of photochemical reaction depends on the energy of HO and LU of the migrating species.

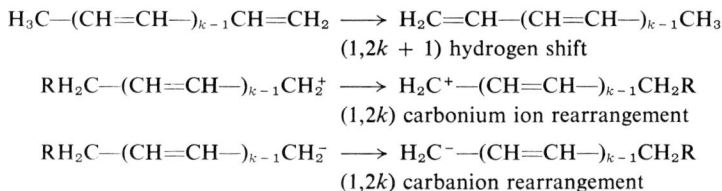

TABLE 5
The Selection Rule for $(1, 2k)$ Carbanion
Rearrangement[a]

	Even k	Odd k
Thermal	Suprafacial	Antarafacial
Photochemical	(Antarafacial)[b]	(Suprafacial)[b]

[a] Number of electrons forming a cycle is $2k + 2$. Here suprafacial corresponds to *syn* and antarafacial to *anti* interaction.

[b] The steric course of photochemical reaction depends on the energy of HO and LU of the migrating species.

$$H_3C-(CH=CH-)_{k-1}CH=CH_2 \longrightarrow H_2C=CH-(CH=CH-)_{k-1}CH_3$$
$$(1,2k + 1) \text{ hydrogen shift}$$

$$RH_2C-(CH=CH-)_{k-1}CH_2^+ \longrightarrow H_2C^+-(CH=CH-)_{k-1}CH_2R$$
$$(1,2k) \text{ carbonium ion rearrangement}$$

$$RH_2C-(CH=CH-)_{k-1}CH_2^- \longrightarrow H_2C^--(CH=CH-)_{k-1}CH_2R$$
$$(1,2k) \text{ carbanion rearrangement}$$

B. Claisen, Cope, and Related Rearrangements

In the Claisen rearrangement, the allyl group of an aryl allyl ether migrates to the position *ortho* in the benzene ring (58). A rearrangement occurring in a similar fashion in 1,5-hexadienes is known as the Cope rearrangement (Fig. 43) (59). The transition state of these reactions is assumed to be a cyclic one composed of two allyls bonding at both ends by $p\sigma$ like overlappings to form an electrocycle with six electrons. We can see

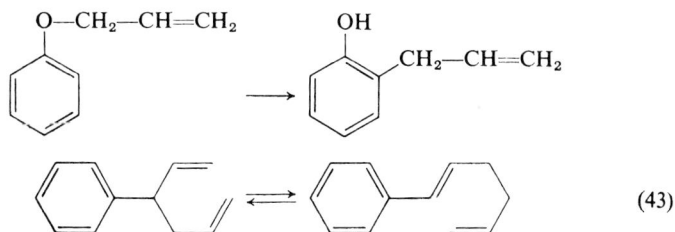

$$(43)$$

that the symmetry property of the two nonbonding MO's favors a *syn* interaction (Fig. 28).

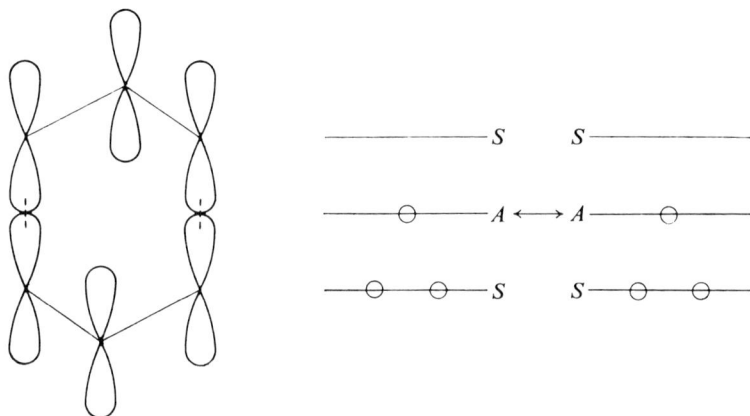

Figure 28

The mechanism of the rearrangement of *trans-α,γ*-dimethylallyl derivatives may be discussed in the same manner (60). For instance,

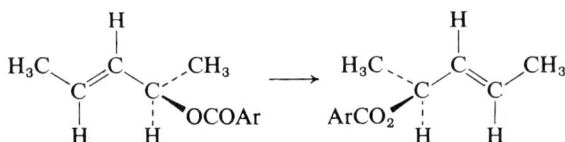

(+)-*trans-α,γ*-dimethylallyl acid phthalate undergoes intramolecular allylic rearrangement to give rise to (−)-α,γ-dimethylallyl acid phthalate (Eq. 44).

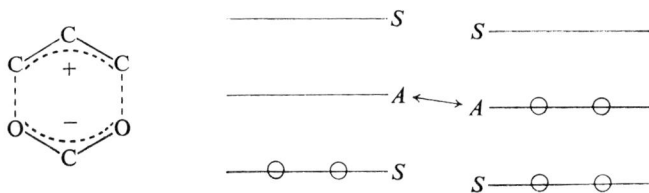

Figure 29

The transition state of this reaction (Fig. 29) is composed of two parts, one bearing two electrons and the other four electrons, from both of which an electrocycle with six electrons is formed. Although electrostatic force acting between the anionic and the cationic parts might be important, Rule I suggests that the electrocyclic interaction will make a considerable contribution in stabilizing such cyclic transition state. An experimental fact that the ether oxygen in the product comes dominantly from the carbonyl oxygen initially existing in the reactant seems to present evidence of the supposition that the transition state involves a conjugated structure.

Another interesting problem relating to the allylic rearrangement mentioned above is *para*-Claisen rearrangement. When an aryl allyl ether has substituents at both *ortho* positions, the migration of the allyl is not to the *ortho* position but to the *para* position. The *para*-Claisen rearrangement (Eq. 45) takes place in two steps, in each of which an electrocycle with

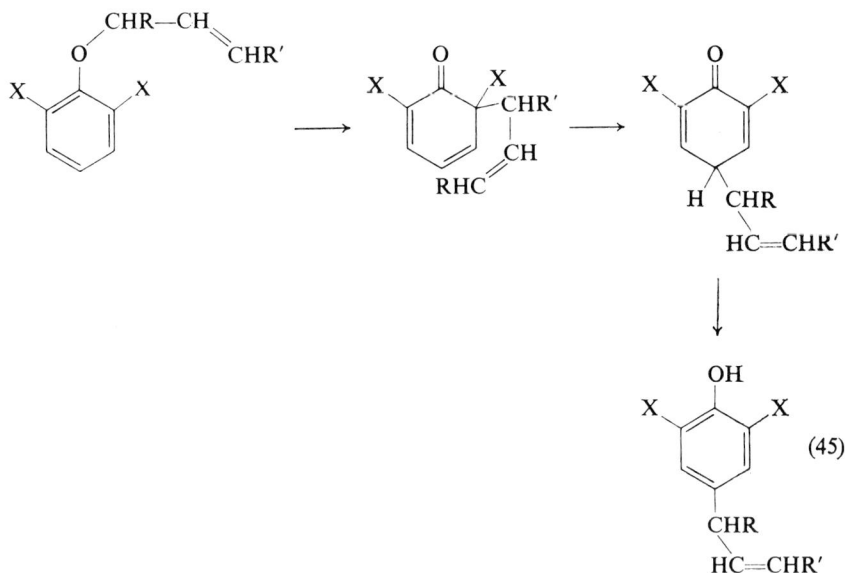

six electrons participates. The clear-cut difference between *ortho*- and *para*-Claisen rearrangements lies in the fact that the allyl group becomes reversed in the former and becomes unreversed (reversed twice) in the latter. This seems to support such a cyclic mechanism (61). A recent study by Thyagarajan and co-workers (61a) reports stereoselectivity in a *para*-Claisen rearrangement for the first time.

Additional evidence for the cyclic mechanism can be found in the thermal isomerization of 4,5-oligomethylene-*cis,cis,trans*-1,4,7-cyclodecatriene (Eq. 46) (62).

$$(46)$$

The transition state of the oxy-Cope rearrangement may also belong to cycles with six electrons (Eq. 47) (63).

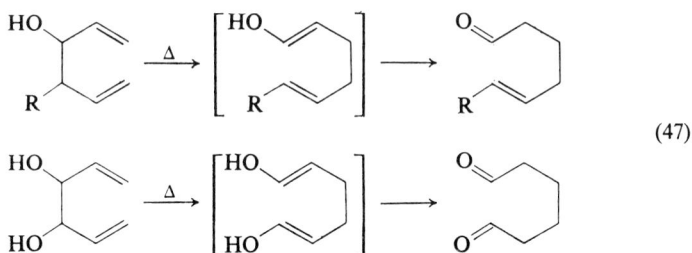

$$(47)$$

Vinylogous Cope rearrangement of *cis,cis*-decatetraene may proceed through a similar cyclic transition state with ten electrons.

The selection rule obtained for such intramolecular rearrangements through a cyclic transition state is summarized in Table 6 (see also Fig. 30).

TABLE 6
The Selection Rule for Intramolecular Rearrangement[a]

	$m + m' = 4n$	$m + m' = 4n + 2$
Thermal	Unfavored	Favored
Photochemical	Favored	Unfavored

[a] Number of electrons forming a cycle is $m + m'$. The selection rule is for the rearrangements through the transition state with *syn*-like cyclic interaction. For larger molecules, rearrangements through a transition state with *anti*-like cyclic interaction might be possible.

m electrons

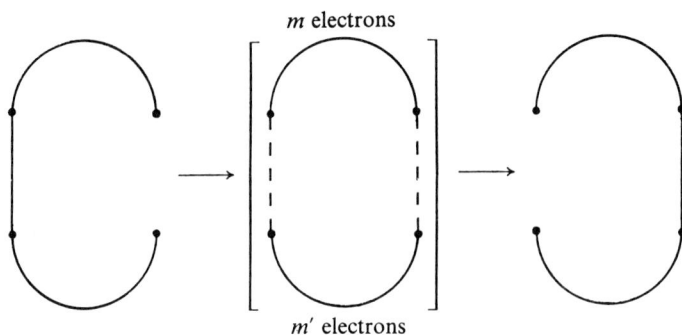

m' electrons
Figure 30

Thus, we can understand why such intramolecular migrations as to form a cycle with $(4n + 2)$ electrons can actually take place through a geometrically favored cyclic transition state.

C. Ring-Closure, Ring-Opening, and Fragmentation Reactions

The ring-closing reaction of some noncyclic conjugated systems and the ring-opening reaction of some cyclic conjugated systems are known to occur highly stereospecifically. Havinga et al. (53) showed that thermal isomerization of precalciferol gave only isopyrocalciferol and pyrocalciferol both having *cis*-configuration, while the photoinduced isomerization gave ergosterol (Eq. 48). Oosterhoff suggested that the difference in the steric course of the thermal and photoinduced reactions might come from the difference in the symmetry property of HO and LU of the conjugated part (64). Woodward and Hoffmann (14) proposed a selection rule for this kind of ring-closure and ring-opening reactions extending Oosterhoff's suggestion. The HO of linear chains with $k\pi$ electrons is antisymmetric when k is $4n$ and symmetric when k is $4n + 2$. To yield a positive sigma like overlapping between two AO's at both termini, the thermal ring closure of $k\pi$ chains to give $(k - 2)\pi$ cyclic systems should occur in conrotatory mode if k is $4n$ and in disrotatory mode if k is $4n + 2$ (Fig. 31). In the case of photoinduced ring closure, an electron is promoted to LU which has the inverse symmetry property to that of HO. Thus, photochemical ring closure of chains with $4n\pi$ electrons will occur in a disrotatory fashion and that of chains with $(4n + 2)\pi$ electrons in a conrotatory fashion. The isomerization of precalciferol offers an example. Thermal isomerization of *trans*-2-*cis*-4-*trans*-6-octatriene is known to take place in the disrotatory mode (65). Bicyclo [4,3,0] nona-2,4-diene is formed from 1,3,5-cyclononatriene thermally in the disrotatory fashion (Eq. 49) (66).

(48)

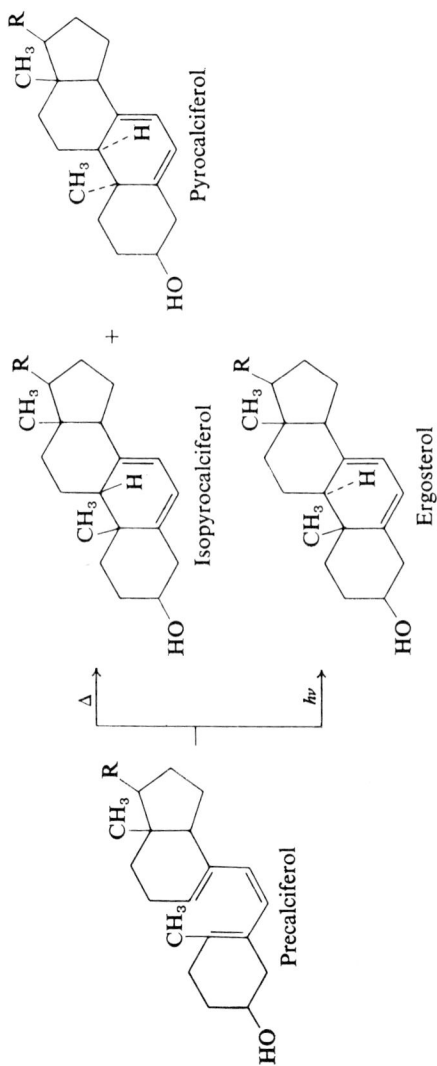

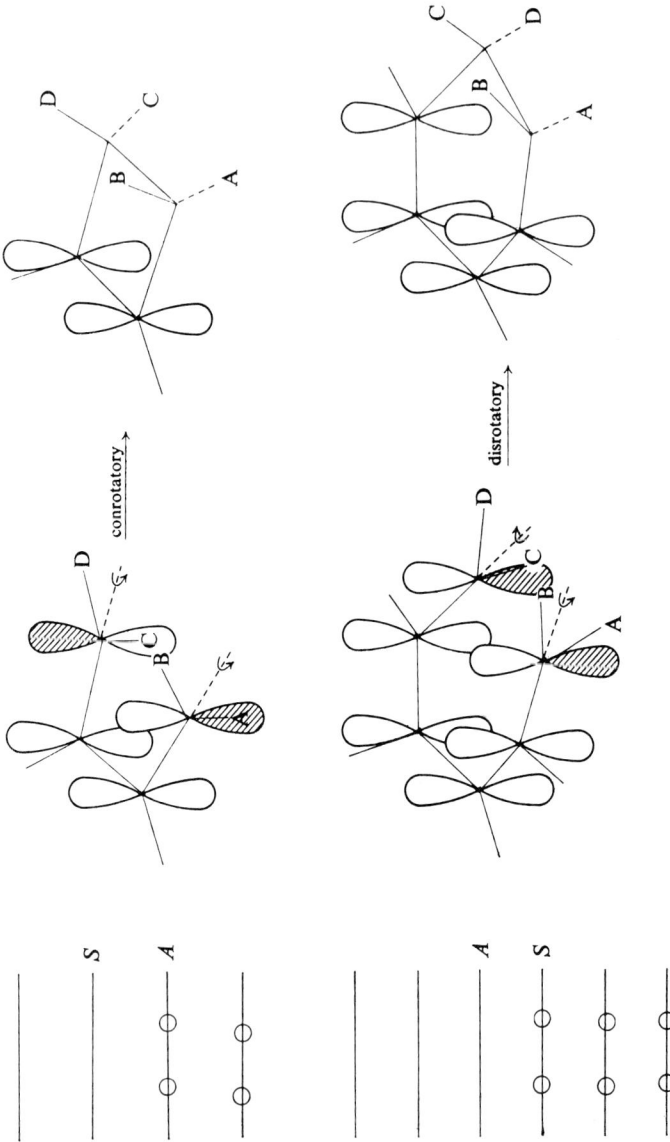

Figure 31

Irradiation of ether solutions of *cis,trans*-1,3-cyclononadiene gives cyclobutenes as major products involving precursory isomerization to *cis,cis*-1,3-
cyclononadiene (Eq. 50) (67). The photosensitized cyclization of *cis,cis-*

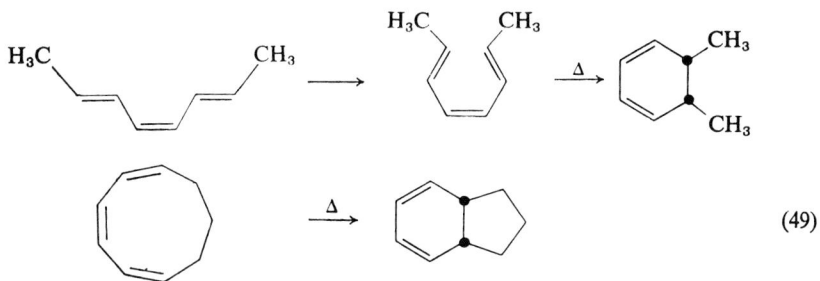

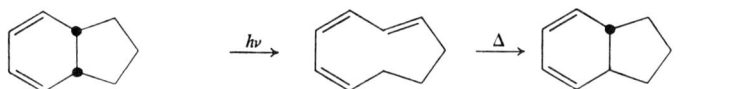

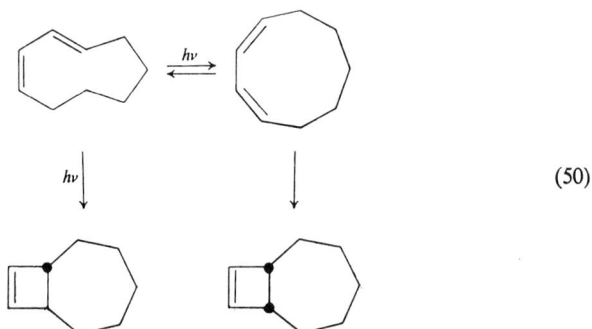

(49)

(50)

1,3-cyclooctadiene to bicyclo [4,2,0] oct-7-ene has been shown to involve
isomerization of diene. However, direct irradiation does not cause such
isomerization (Eq. 51) (68). The photosensitized isomerization of myrcene

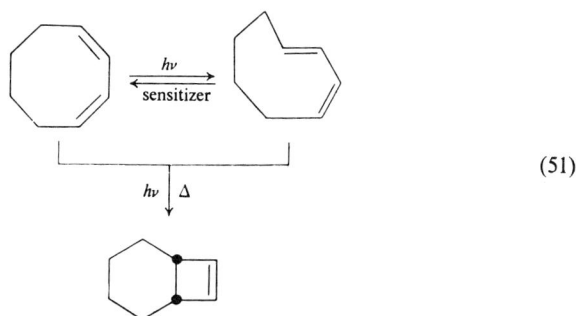

(51)

yields 5,5-dimethyl-1-vinyl-bicyclo [2,1,1] hexane (69). On the other hand, direct irradiation of myrcene gives a cyclobutene (70) (Eq. 52). Both the direct and sensitized reactions of 1,1′-bicyclohexenyl yield a cyclobutene as the major product (Eq. 53) (71). The formation of *cis*-9,10-dihydro-

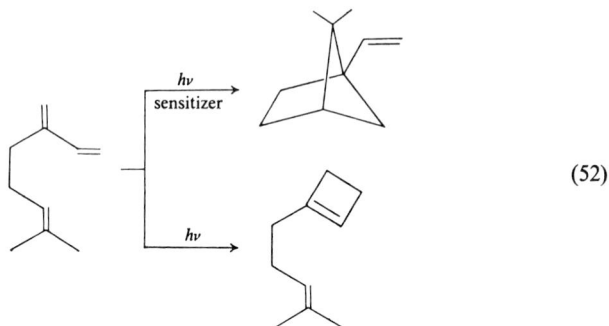

$$(52)$$

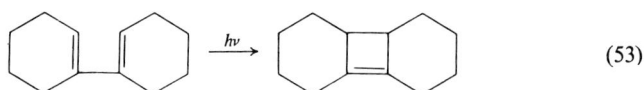

$$(53)$$

naphthalene from *trans*-9,10-dihydronaphthalene through cyclodeca-1,3,5,7,9-pentaene has been proposed (Eq. 54) (72). Isomerization reaction

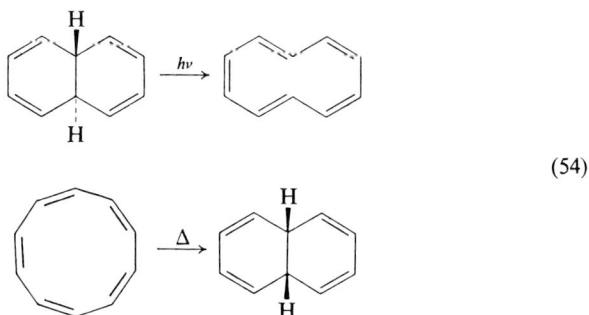

$$(54)$$

via 1,3,5-cyclodecatriene has been reported (73). By the use of this reaction, the preparation of the 1,3,5-cyclodecatriene system has been attempted (Eq. 55) (74).

    The ring opening of cyclic olefins, which is the inverse reaction to the ring closure mentioned above, takes place according to the same selection rule as for the ring closure. The thermal cleavage of cyclic systems involving a $(k - 2) \pi$ electron chain occurs in the conrotatory mode when k is $4n$ and in the disrotatory mode when k is $4n + 2$. The photochemical isomerization takes place in the inverse manner. Thermal ring opening of *cis*-3,4-dicarbomethoxycyclobutene occurs in the conrotatory fashion (Eq. 56) (75).

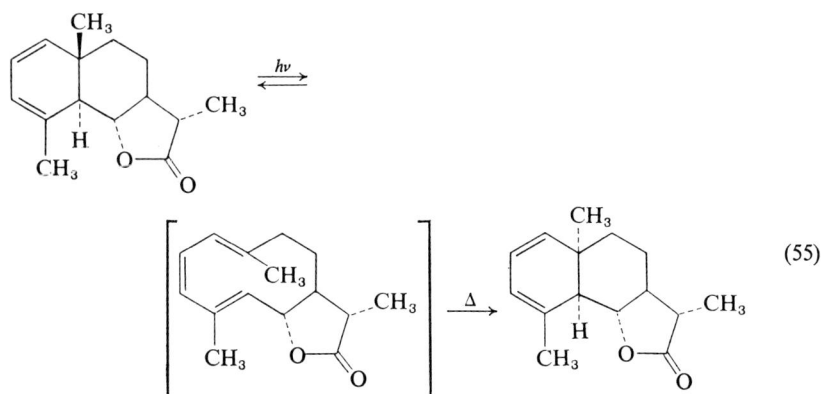

(55)

The isomerization of *cis-* and *trans-*1,2,3,4-tetramethylcyclobut-1-ene yields *cis,trans-*1,2,3,4-tetramethylbutadiene and *cis,cis-*1,2,3,4-tetra-methylbutadiene, respectively (76). Thermal ring opening of *cis-* and *trans-*

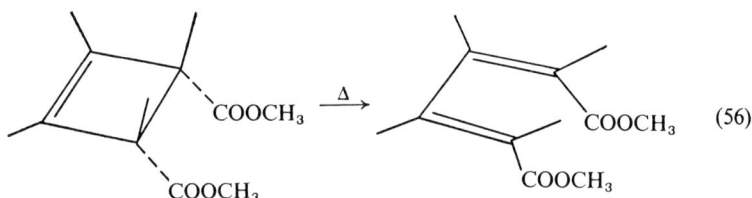

(56)

3,4-dimethylcyclobut-1-ene takes place in the conrotatory mode to give rise to *cis,trans-*2,4-hexadiene and *trans,trans-*2,4-hexadiene, respectively (Eq. 57) (77,78). The thermal isomerization of bicyclo [4,2,0] oct-7-ene gives cycloocta-1,3-diene (Eq. 58) (78). Irradiation of cyclooctatetraene dimer yields [16]-annulene (Eq. 59) (79).

The selection rule proposed by Woodward and Hoffmann is in excellent agreement with the experimental results. However, there are some doubts as to why the steric course of intramolecular cyclization is determined by the symmetry of HO or LU only and why the steric course of a ring-opening reaction is determined by the symmetry of the product (open-chain) MO. The answer has been given by Longuet-Higgins et al. (80), who devised the "correlation diagram," by Fukui (81) who introduced the "overlap-stabilization" (cf. Section VI-C); and by Zimmerman (82), who made an application of MO theory for the "Möbius ring" derived by Heilbronner (83).

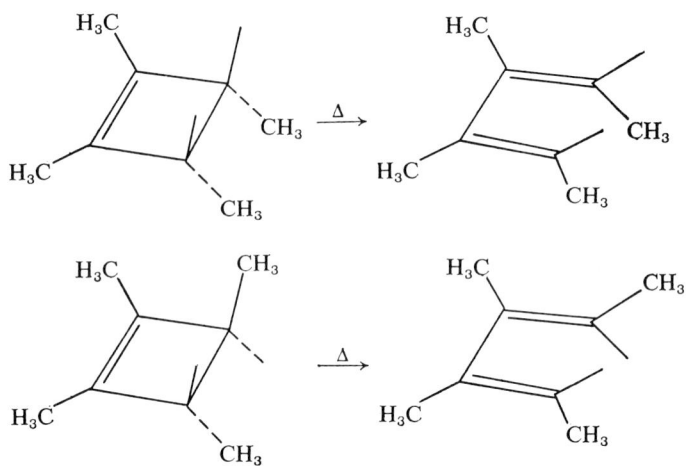

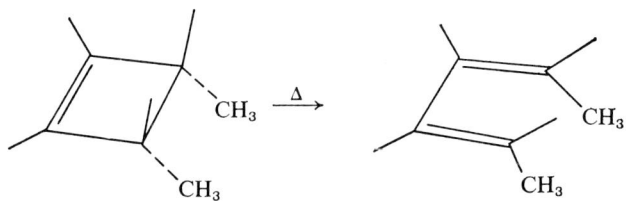

(57)

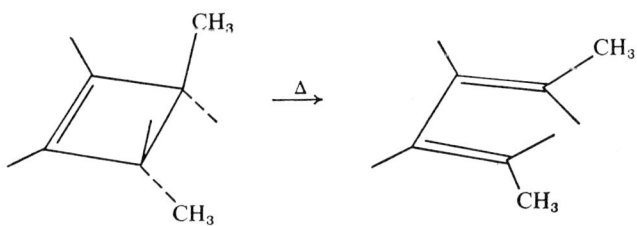

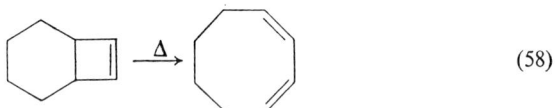

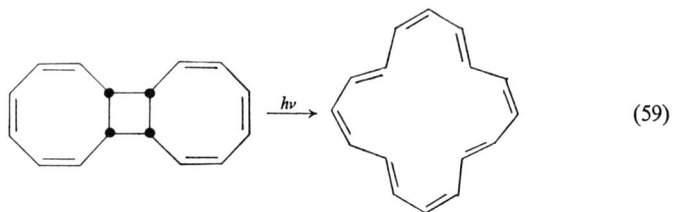

(58)

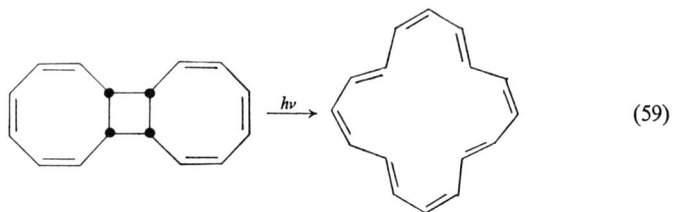

(59)

Aside from these various methods, we attempt here to explain these stereoselective phenomena by employing the "partitioning technique," which was introduced in Section III-D, and permits discussion of the problem morc easily than others and on a unified basis together with the intermolecular cyclic additions and also intramolecular migration reactions mentioned earlier. We try to divide a connected linear molecule into two parts and then recombine them at both ends to form a cyclic isomer (Fig. 32). Here, the interaction at one end is $p\pi$ like and the one at the other end is $p\sigma$ like.

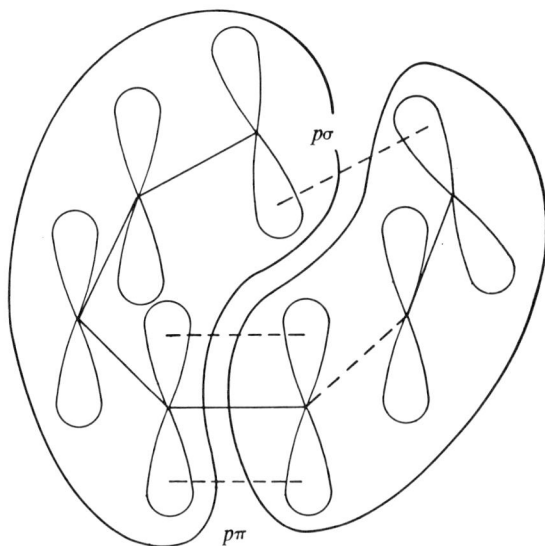

Figure 32

The *syn* interaction clearly corresponds to the disrotatory process and *anti* interaction to the conrotatory process. The cyclization of dienes forms four-electron cycles and that of trienes six-electron cycles. Thus, from Rules I and II, we can obtain the selection rule for intramolecular cyclization reactions exactly the same as the one given by Woodward and Hoffmann (14).

The stereoselection in the ring-opening reaction of cyclic conjugated systems should be discussed in another, but in principle, similar way. The most important term to be considered is the interaction between the pi part and the sigma part of reactant cyclic systems. We consider an electrocyclic

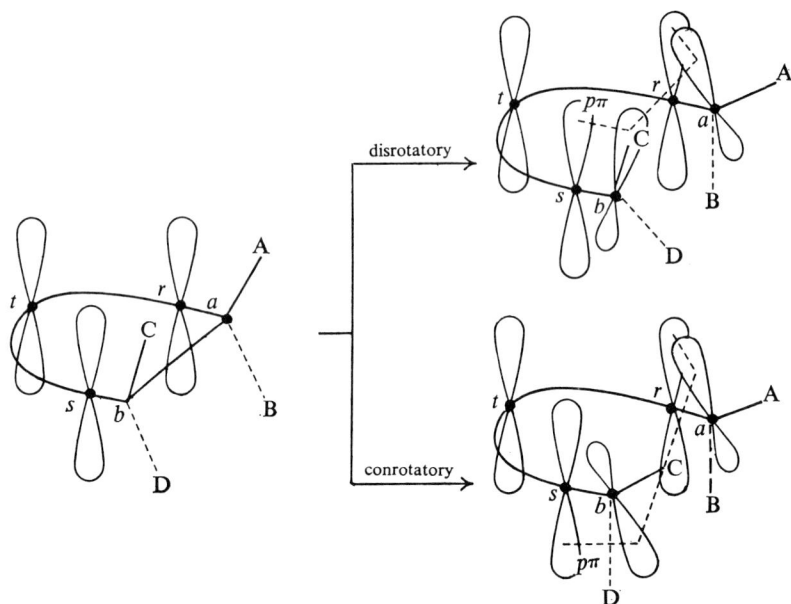

Figure 33

system composed of the $(k - 2)\pi$ conjugated part $r \ldots t \ldots s$ and the sigma bond between carbons a and b to be broken in case of reaction (Fig. 33). As the cleavage of the sigma bond a–b proceeds, a pi-like conjugation arises between each of the two incipient orbitals appearing at carbons a and b and each end of the originally pi-conjugated part $r \ldots t \ldots s$. The components of the two incipient orbitals, perpendicular to the molecular plane, are parallel and antiparallel to each other in the disrotatory and conrotatory interaction, respectively. The symmetry properties of MO's of the initial pi part and the incipient "pi" part are illustrated in Figure 34. Since *syn* interaction clearly corresponds to the disrotatory process and *anti* interaction to the conrotatory process, we can obtain the selection rule for the ring-opening reaction which is entirely the same as that proposed by Woodward and Hoffmann.

Fragmentation of five-membered ring can be discussed in the similar manner. Treatment of *trans*-2,5-dimethyl-3-pyrroline and *cis*-2,5-dimethyl-3-pyrroline with nitrohydroxylamine causes deamination in a sigmasymmetric or disrotatory fashion to give rise to *cis,trans*-2,4-hexadiene and *trans,trans*-2,4-hexadiene, respectively (Eq. 60) (84). Similar stereoselection has been found in thermal fragmentation of other five-membered rings (85).

(i) $k = 4n + 2$

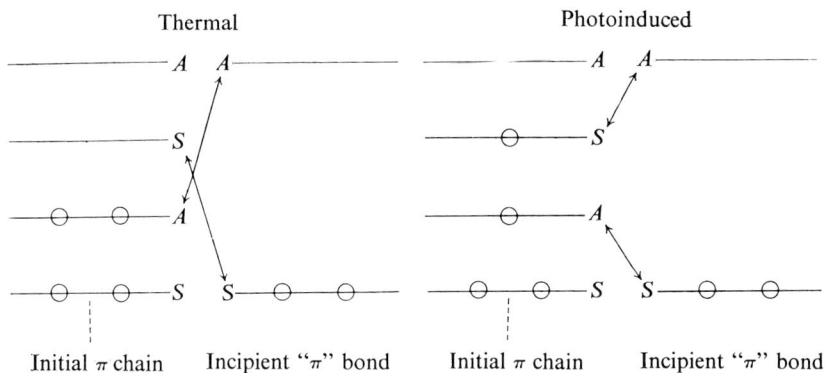

(ii) $k = 4n$

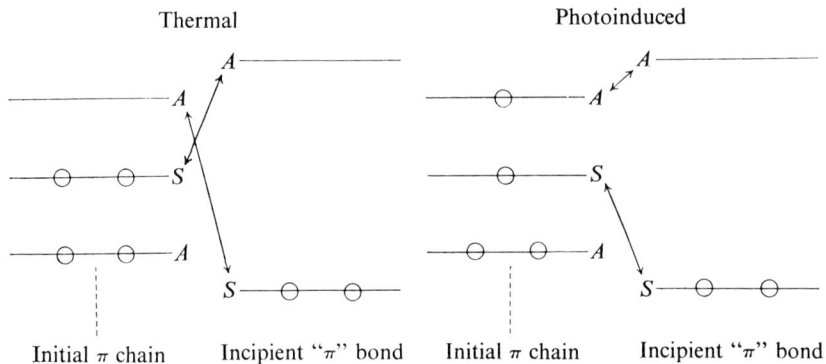

Figure 34

In these cases, two pi electrons and four electrons in four incipient AO's

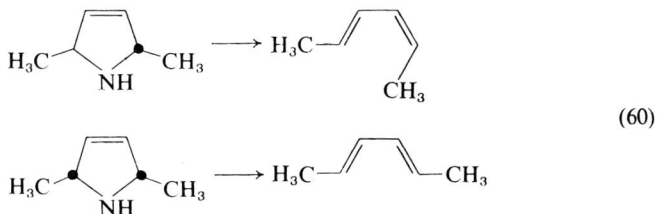

(60)

appearing in the simultaneous fission of the two C—N bonds constitute a cycle with six electrons in the transition state, making disrotatory fragmentation favorable.

The selection rules thus obtained for the ring closures, ring openings, and fragmentations are summarized in Tables 7 and 8 (see Eq. 61).

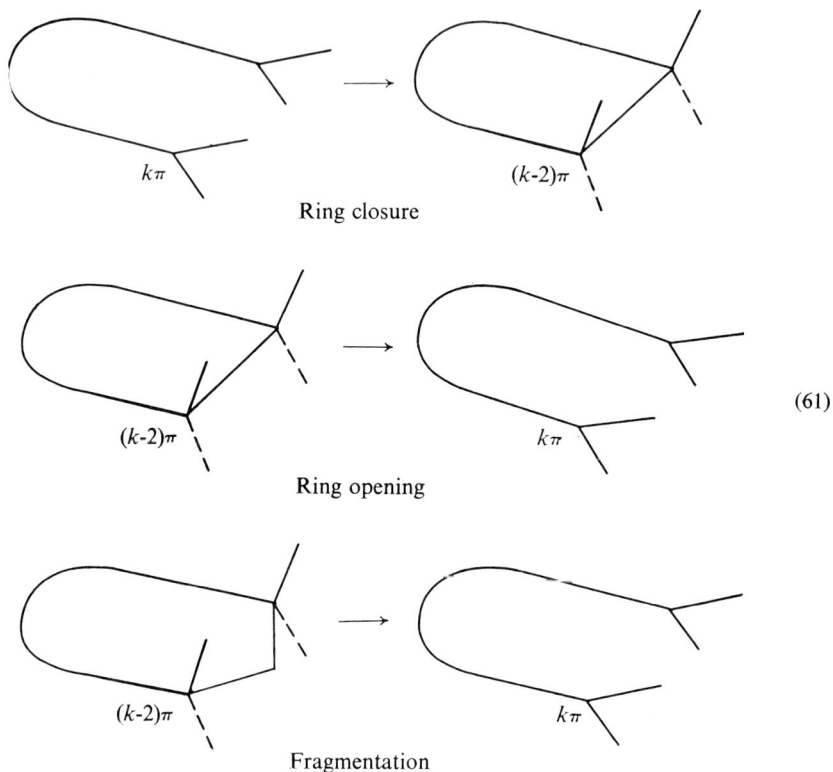

$k\pi$

$(k\text{-}2)\pi$

Ring closure

$(k\text{-}2)\pi$

$k\pi$

Ring opening

(61)

$(k\text{-}2)\pi$

$k\pi$

Fragmentation

TABLE 7

The Selection Rule for Ring-Closure and Ring-Opening
Reactions[a]

	$k = 4n$	$k = 4n + 2$
Thermal	Conrotatory	Disrotatory
Photochemical	Disrotatory	Conrotatory

[a] The number of electrons forming a cycle is k. Here disrotatory corresponds to *syn* and conrotatory to *anti* interaction.

TABLE 8
The Selection Rule for Fragmentation Reactions[a]

	$k = 4n - 2$	$k = 4n$
Thermal	Conrotatory (axisymmetric)	Disrotatory (sigmasymmetric)
Photochemical	Disrotatory (sigmasymmetric)	Conrotatory (axisymmetric)

[a] The number of electrons forming a cycle is $k + 2$. Here disrotatory or sigmasymmetric corresponds to *syn* and conrotatory or axisymmetric to *anti* interaction.

VI. OTHER PROBLEMS

A. Stereoselective Sigma–Pi Interactions

The electronic wave function for planar-conjugated molecules is divided into so-called sigma and pi parts. The sigma part is composed of the MO's which are symmetric with respect to the molecular plane and have the direction of extension on that plane, while the pi part consists of MO's antisymmetric with respect to that plane, to which their direction of maximum extension is perpendicular (Fig. 35).

When such a planar-conjugated system is exposed to a certain chemical interaction, both the sigma and pi parts will be affected, resulting in the hybridization change through sigma–pi interaction. A number of such reactions occurring with stereoselectivity are known. A simple MO treatment to discuss the direction of configuration change in initially planar-conjugated molecules can be obtained, if we regard sigma and pi parts as two separate systems as was done in Section III-D, introducing "resonance" integrals between them at reaction centers (see Figs. 36 and 37). In this way, we are able to apply the general theory of stereoselection disclosed in Section III to the present problem.

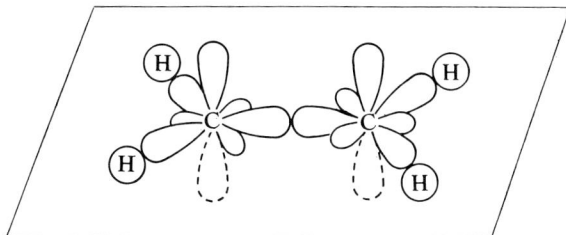

Figure 35

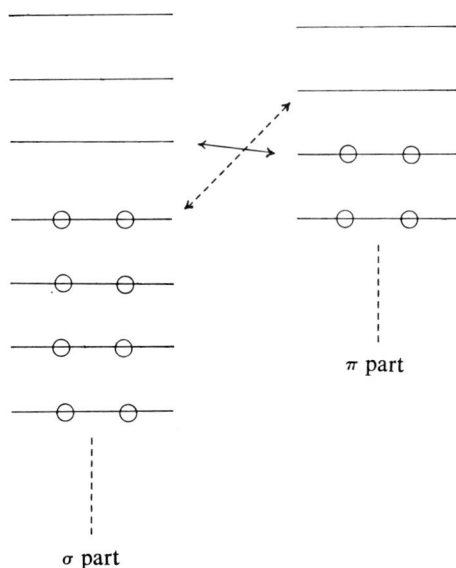

Figure 36

The symmetry property of LU of the sigma part and that of HO of the pi part for some planar conjugated systems are indicated in Table 9. Suppose that a reagent attacks from the direction to which initially p AO has its maximum extension to perform maximum overlapping. Thus, we obtain the selection rule for simultaneous (or quasi-simultaneous) noncyclic two-center interactions as summarized in Table 10. The sigma and pi parts together are regarded to make up an electrocycle ("$\sigma\pi$ cycle" in this table).

The homolytic *trans* addition of halogens and hydrogen halides to alkenes and alkynes has been well established (86). The *trans* E2 reaction may proceed through a transition state resembling the one for 1,2-noncyclic additions. The substitution reaction with allylic rearrangement (S_N2' reaction) which is known to occur in the *cis* mode (87) is an example of allyl cation type sigma–pi interactions (Fig. 38). The addition of Grignard reagents to 10-methyl-1(9),7-hexal-2-one yields 1,6-adducts in which the most predominant isomer bears the newly introduced alkyl group in the axial position (Eq. 62) (88). However, whether this interaction proceeds in the *syn* mode or *anti* mode is not clear. Photoinduced noncyclic addition of N-chlorourethane to cyclic olefins gives *cis* addition product as the major one, while thermal noncyclic addition gives a larger amount of *trans* product (Eq. 63) (89).

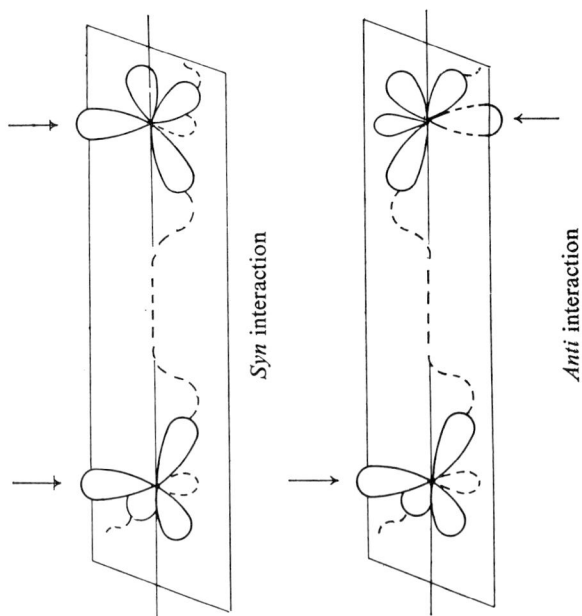

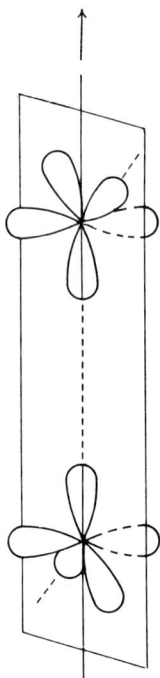

Figure 37

TABLE 9
The Symmetry Property of π HO and σ LU in Conjugated Hydrocarbons

πHO σLU

Ethylene

Butadiene

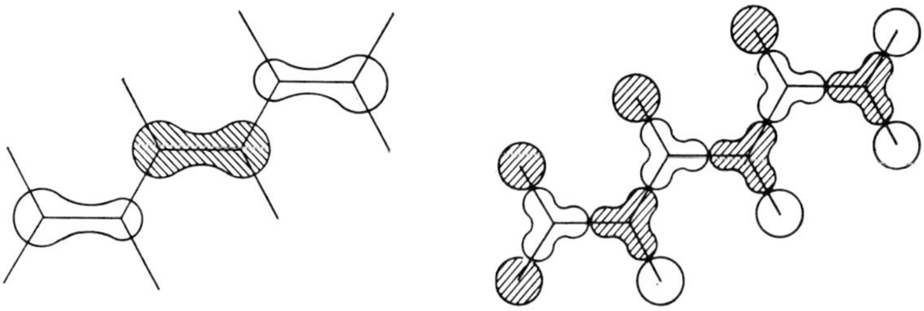

Hexatriene

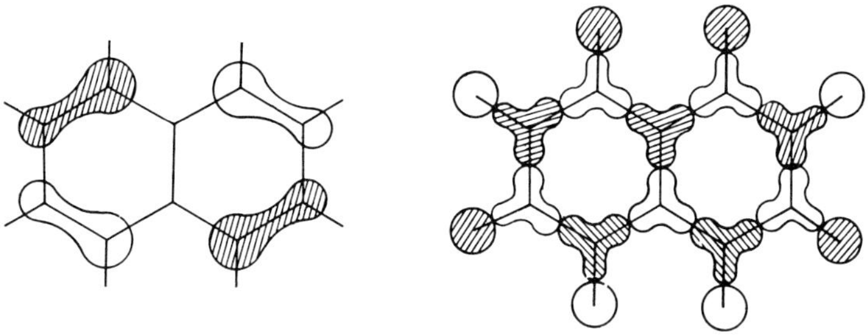

Naphthalene

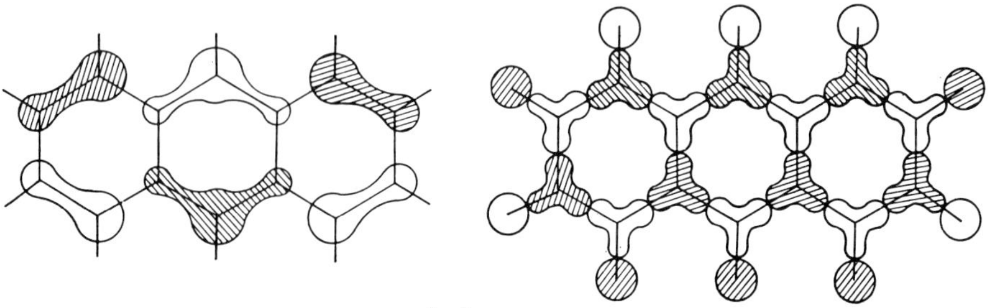

Anthracene

TABLE 10
The Selection Rule for Simultaneous Noncyclic Interactions
at Positions (r, s)

Position of interaction	1,2	1,3		1,4	1,5		1,6
		Cation	Anion		Cation	Anion	
Thermal	anti	syn	anti	syn	anti	syn	anti
Photochemical	syn	anti	syn	anti	syn	anti	syn
Number of electrons in "$\sigma\pi$ cycle"	4	6	8	10	12	14	16

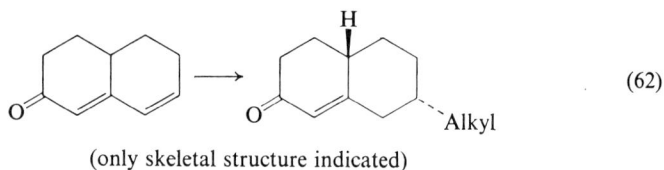

(62)

(only skeletal structure indicated)

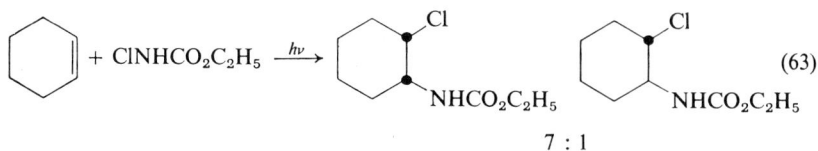

(63)

7 : 1

A similar selection rule for noncyclic interactions was obtained on the basis of the frontier orbital theory (90), and this was also applied to the problem of stereoselection in S_N2' reaction (91).

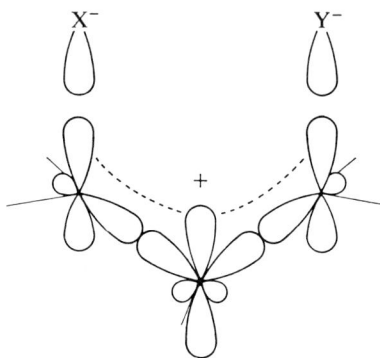

Figure 38

B. Secondary Steric Control in Electrocyclic Processes

The electrocyclic interaction will take place in accord with the selection rules given above, provided no other steric controls exist. In fact, in some cases factors other than the electrocyclic effect happen to play a dominant role. The ring opening of *cis*-1,2,3,4-tetramethylcyclobut-1-ene takes place smoothly at 200°C in the conrotatory fashion to yield *cis,trans*-tetramethylbutadiene, whereas dimethylbicyclo [0,2,3] heptene derivative is hindered from cleaving in the conrotatory mode by the presence of the five-membered ring and undergoes an apparently disrotatory opening at temperatures as high as 400°C (Eq. 64) (92).

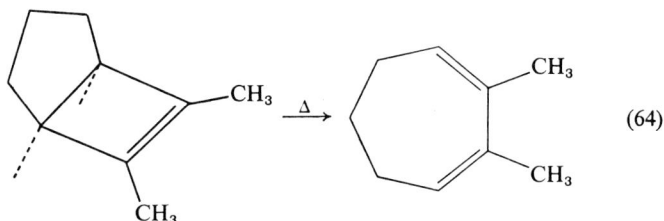

(64)

Treating 3-pyrroline with nitrohydroxylamine yields diene in sigma-symmetric mode. The reaction is supposed to proceed via diazene intermediate and *trans*- and *cis*-2,5-dimethyl-3-pyrrolines give *cis,trans*-2,4-hexadiene and *trans,trans*-2,5-hexadiene, respectively (84). However, *cis,cis*-2,4-hexadiene can also be expected in the disrotatory opening of the *cis*-pyrroline (Eq. 65). Lemal et al. (84) reported that *cis,cis*-hexa-

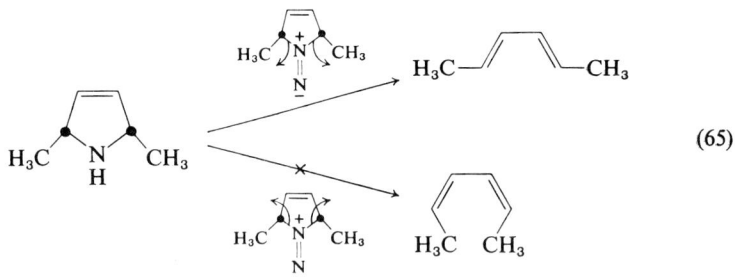

(65)

diene was not found and attributed the result to the steric repulsion between two methyl groups.

Jones et al. (93) showed that the ring opening of cyclopropane to yield allene took place stereospecifically and (−)-*trans*-2,3-diphenyl cyclopropanecarboxylic acid gave (+)-1,3-diphenylallene. In this case, we can expect two types of conrotatory opening. The reaction is supposed to proceed via a combination of concerted collapse of diazocyclopropane and rearrangement of the cyclopropylidene (Scheme 2). Jones et al. pointed out that one of the two conrotatory courses to yield (−)allene might be less favorable than the other due to the steric repulsion between two neighboring phenyl groups. These are the examples in which electrocyclic and

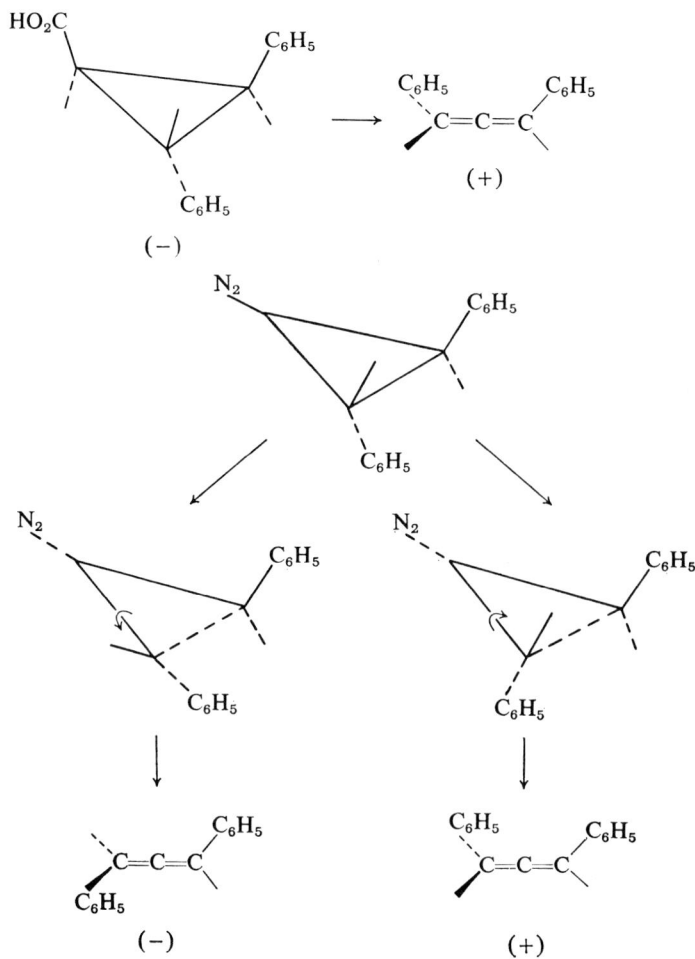

Scheme 2

geometrical requirements competitively or independently demonstrate their effects in controlling the steric courses of the reactions.

It has been reported that *trans*-2-arylcyclopropyl tosylate solvolizes faster than *cis*-2-arylcyclopropyl tosylate (94). The solvolysis of cyclopropyl tosylate is a concerted process, with ring opening occurring in the transition state (Eq. 66). The reaction proceeds in the disrotatory mode, and the

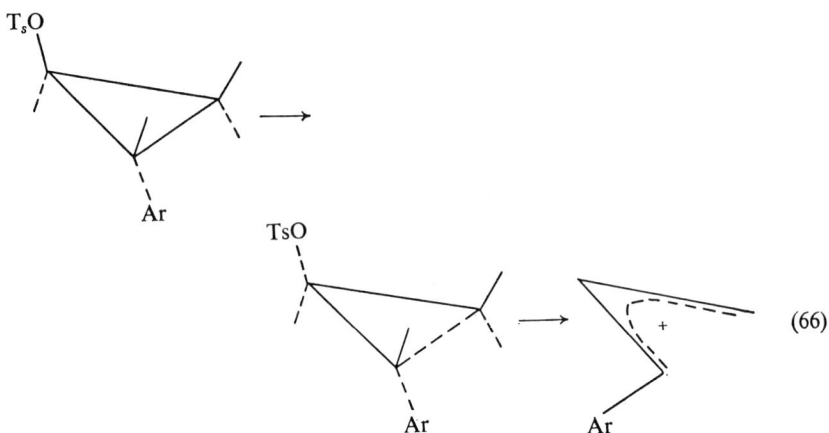

$$(66)$$

aryl group *trans* to the leaving group rotates outward and the *cis* aryl group rotates inward (Fig. 39). The slower rate of solvolysis of *cis*-2-arylcyclopropyl tosylate than *trans*-compound is thus explained since such inward rotation of *cis*-aryl group would lead to sterically hindered allyl

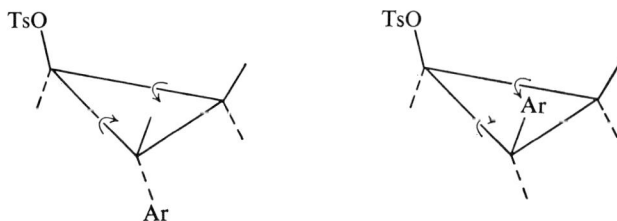

Figure 39

cation. Similar results have been observed in the rate of solvolysis of some cyclopropyl derivatives (95). On the other hand, the direction of rotation in the disrotatory opening of the cyclopropyl methyl cation is inverse to that of cyclopropyl tosylate (Fig. 40) (96). Tanida proposed an interesting explanation about these results; he suggested that cyclopropyl methyl cation

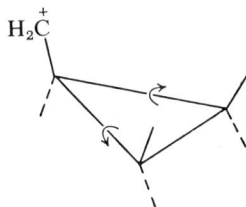

Figure 40

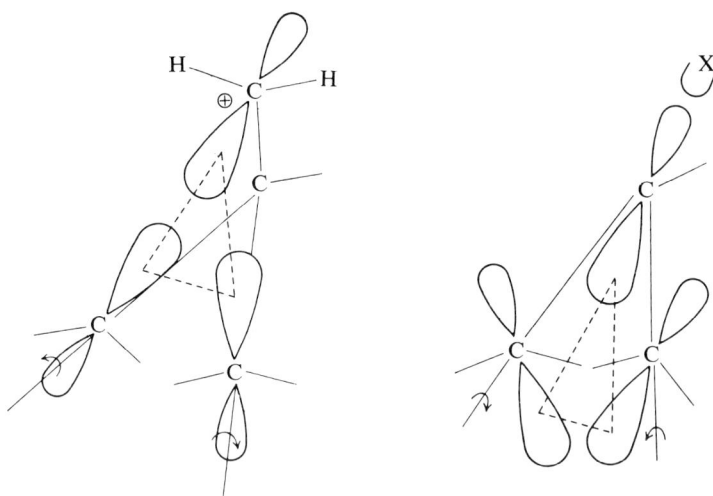

Figure 41

undergoes opening in such a way as to gain larger overlap stabilization at
the transition state between two incipient orbitals appearing through the
breakage of the initial sigma bond and the pi orbital at methylene group,
while, in the case of solvolysis of cyclopropyl tosylate, the bond breakage
itself is the driving force of the reaction to push off the leaving group
(Fig. 41).

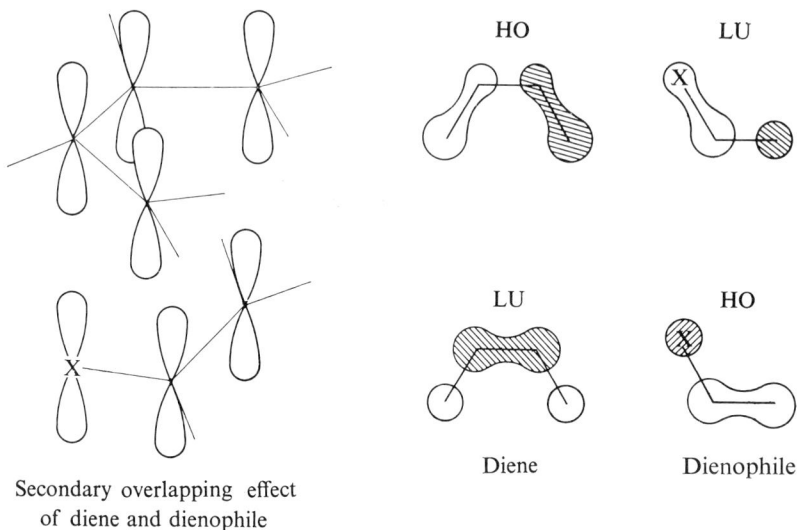

Secondary overlapping effect
of diene and dienophile

Figure 42

The *exo–endo* orientation problem in Diels-Alder reaction was theoretically discussed by Hoffmann et al. (97), extending the idea early employed to discuss the *cis–cis* selection with respect to both diene and dienophile (11). Orbital symmetry relation satisfies the condition for maximum overlap to give rise to the *endo* adduct as the major product (see Fig. 42).

C. Method of Overlap Stabilization

We have introduced in Section V-C the partitioning technique to discuss the stereoselection in the intramolecular cyclization of open-chain systems by assuming it to be an intermolecular interaction between two independent systems. But as far as we consider this reaction as the intramolecular interaction between both ends of a connected chain, as Woodward and Hoffmann early did (98), it is relevant to take the contributions from all of the occupied MO's into consideration in estimating the energy change in the interaction. The molecular orbital perturbation theory shows that the energy change due to the AO overlapping newly introduced into a connected conjugated chain is given by

$$\Delta E \sim 2 \sum_{i}^{occ} \nu_i C_r^{(i)} C_s^{(i)} \gamma_{rs} = 2 p_{rs} \gamma_{rs}$$

where ν_i is the occupation number of ith MO, C_r^i is the AO coefficient in Eq. 9, p_{rs} is the virtual bond order between AO's r and s, γ_{rs} is the resonance integral representing the interaction. Reaction occurs in such a way that ΔE becomes as low as possible. In order to be so, γ_{rs} should be negative for positive p_{rs}, and positive for negative p_{rs}. The bond order between terminal AO's of $k\pi$ open chain bears a sign which is given in Table 11 (see

TABLE 11
The Bond Order between AO's at Both Ends
of $k\pi$ Chain Systems

	$k = 4n$	$k = 4n + 2$
Ground state	−	+
First excited state	+	−

Fig. 43). Since negative γ clearly leads to disrotatory process and positive γ to conrotatory process, we obtain a selection rule for ring-closure reactions which is exactly the same as that summarized in Table 7.

The method of overlap stabilization was successfully applied to discuss the transition state configuration of the Cope rearrangement (99). Two configurations, chair and boat (Fig. 44), may be possible in the tran-

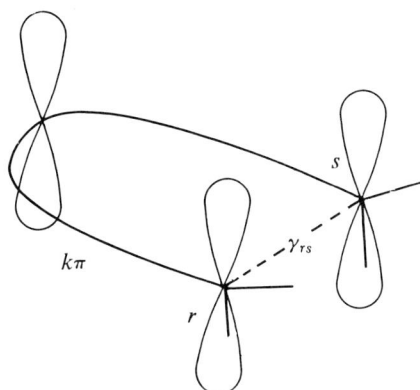

Figure 43

sition state of the Cope rearrangement of 1,5-hexadiene. The bond order between carbon atoms 2 and 2', calculated by, e.g., the Hückel method, is negative. As we take the resonance integrals β' for the sigma like overlapping between two $2p$ AO's 1 and 1' or 3 and 3' as negative, it follows that the introduction of such interaction between carbons 2 and 2' makes

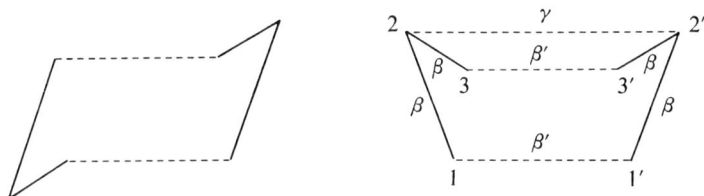

Figure 44

the whole system unstable. Thus we can see that the chair-like transition state comes to possess an energy lower than the boat-like one, in conformity with experimental facts (59).

The change in energy ΔE represented in terms of bond order p_{rs} was called "overlap stabilization" by the present authors (99). The method of overlap stabilization is very useful also in discussing other problems in steric control in complicated systems. For instance, since p_{14} of butadiene is negative, the virtual 1,4-$p\pi$ bond must make the pi electron energy high, so that s-cis-butadiene will be less stable than s-trans-butadiene, provided the sigma part is assumed equal.

VII. CONCLUSION

One of the uses of molecular quantum chemistry is to facilitate our theoretical understanding of complicated chemical facts, enabling us to get novel ideas to promote advances in chemistry. The orbital symmetry criteria recently introduced in discussing the stereochemical phenomena in harmony with such an object exhibit a versatility of molecular orbital consideration in the domain of organic chemistry.

The molecular orbital symmetry is an almost "approximation-invariant" property of a molecule (100). The theoretical conclusion obtained in relation to the orbital symmetry is not appreciably affected by the approximation employed in MO calculation. Furthermore, the orbital symmetry consideration, if we are satisfied with a roughness which would be permissible for the purpose of organic chemical use, is extremely simple and in many cases needs no numerical calculation. The general selection rules expressed in the form of Rules I and II are in principle applied to any sort of concerted electrocyclic interactions to predict the favorable steric course (*syn* or *anti* interaction) of a given reaction only by counting the number of electrons forming the cycle essentially. In some cases, one of the two steric courses is inhibited because of the geometrical requirement. On such occasions the selection rules mentioned above supply the condition of occurrence or nonoccurrence of a given cyclic reaction.

As has been seen in many instances mentioned in the preceding sections, the method introduced in the present chapter employs only the symmetry property of the highest occupied and the lowest unoccupied molecular orbitals throughout. These particular molecular orbitals (frontier orbitals) are already known as those which play a distinct role in governing the orientation in chemical reactions. We are easily able to recognize that, through many instances described in the text, these particular molecular orbitals perform a conspicuous part also in controlling the stereo-selection. Such a result will throw some light upon studying the nature of chemical interactions.

The material treated here covers intermolecular and intramolecular cyclic reactions including additions, dimerizations, eliminations, fragmentations, and substitutions as well as migrations, cyclizations, de-cyclizations, and various other rearrangements. These are discussed on a unified basis from the point of view of electrocyclic interaction in the transition state. The theoretical strategy disclosed above will find more uses which the future accumulation of chemical facts will be able to evolve.

References

1. M. Born and J. R. Oppenheimer, *Ann. Physik*, **84**, 457 (1927).
2. (a) D. R. Hartree, *Proc. Cambridge Phil. Soc.*, **24**, 89, 111 (1928); (b) V. Fock, *Z. Physik*, **61**, 126 (1930).
3. For instance see H. Eyring, J. Walter, and G. E. Kimball, *Quantum Chemistry*, Wiley, New York, 1944, p. 383.

4. C. C. J. Roothaan, *Rev. Mod. Phys.*, **23**, 69 (1951).
5. R. S. Mulliken, *Rev. Mod. Phys.*, **14**, 204 (1942).
6. A. D. Walsh, *J. Chem. Soc.*, **1953**, 2260, 2266, 2288.
7. (a) R. S. Mulliken, *J. Am. Chem. Soc.*, **72**, 600 (1950); (b) **74**, 811 (1952).
8. E. Hückel, *Z. Physik*, **76**, 628 (1932).
9. W. E. Moffitt, *Proc. Roy. Soc. (London)*, **A200**, 414 (1950).
10. (a) K. Fukui, T. Yonezawa, and H. Shingu, *J. Chem. Phys.*, **20**, 722 (1952); (b) K. Fukui, T. Yonezawa, C. Nagata, and H. Shingu, *ibid.*, **22**, 1433 (1954); and many other subsequent papers on the "frontier electron theory."
11. K. Fukui, "A Simple Quantum-Theoretical Interpretation of the Chemical Reactivity of Organic Compounds," in *Molecular Orbitals in Chemistry, Physics, and Biology*, P.-O. Löwdin and B. Pullman, Eds., Academic Press, New York, 1964, p. 513.
12. K. Fueki and K. Hirota, *Nippon Kagaku Zasshi*, **81**, 212 (1960).
13. K. Fukui, "Sigma Molecular Orbital Theory and Chemical Reactivity," in *Modern Quantum Chemistry. Istanbul Lectures*, Part I, O. Sinanoğlu, Ed., Academic Press, New York, 1965, p. 49.
14. R. B. Woodward and R. Hoffmann, *J. Am. Chem. Soc.*, **87**, 395 (1965).
15. R. B. Woodward and R. Hoffmann, *J. Am. Chem. Soc.*, **87**, 2511 (1965).
16. K. Fukui and H. Fujimoto, *Bull. Chem. Soc. Japan*, **40**, 2018 (1967).
17. R. Hoffmann and R. B. Woodward, *J. Am. Chem. Soc.*, **87**, 2046 (1965).
18. R. Hoffmann and R. B. Woodward, *J. Am. Chem. Soc.*, **87**, 4389 (1965).
19. E. S. Gould, *Mechanism and Structure in Organic Chemistry*, Holt, New York, 1960, pp. 514–560.
20. C. K. Ingold, *Structure and Mechanism in Organic Chemistry*, Cornell University Press, Ithaca, New York, 1953, pp. 711–721.
21. K. Fukui and H. Fujimoto, *Bull. Chem. Soc. Japan*, **39**, 2116 (1966).
22. R. Huisgen, *Proc. Chem. Soc.*, **1961**, 357.
23. R. Huisgen, R. Sustmann, and K. Bunge, *Tetrahedron Letters*, **1966**, 3603.
24. R. Huisgen and K. Herbig, *Ann. Chem.*, **688**, 98 (1965).
25. E. Vogel, *Ann. Chem.*, **615**, 1 (1958).
26. J. D. Roberts and C. Sharts, "Cyclobutane Derivatives from Thermal Cycloaddition Reactions," in *Organic Reactions*, A. C. Cope, Ed., Vol. 12, Wiley, New York, 1962, pp. 1–56.
27. S. Proskow, H. E. Simmons, and T. L. Cairns, *J. Am. Chem. Soc.*, **88**, 5254 (1966).
28. J. G. Atkinson, D. E. Ayer, G. Büchi, and E. W. Robb, *J. Am. Chem. Soc.*, **85**, 2257 (1963).
29. (a) D. Bryce-Smith and J. E. Lodge, *J. Chem. Soc.*, **1963**, 695; (b) E. Grovenstein, Jr., and D. V. Rao, *Tetrahedron Letters*, **1961**, 148.
30. G. O. Schenck, W. Hartmann, S-P. Mannsfeld, W. Metznev, and C. H. Krauch, *Chem. Ber.*, **95**, 1642 (1962).
31. G. O. Schenck, W. Hartmann, and R. Steinmetz, *Chem. Ber.*, **96**, 498 (1963).
32. R. L. Cargill and M. R. Willcott, III, *J. Org. Chem.*, **31**, 3938 (1966).
33. (a) P. E. Eaton, *J. Am. Chem. Soc.*, **84**, 2454 (1962); (b) J. L. Ruhlen and P. A. Leermakers, *ibid.*, **88**, 5671 (1966).
34. P. E. Eaton, *Tetrahedron Letters*, **1964**, 3695.
35. E. J. Corey, J. D. Bass, R. LeMahieu, and R. B. Mitra, *Tetrahedron Letters*, **86**, 5570 (1964).
36. (a) R. Anet, *Can. J. Chem.*, **40**, 1249 (1962); (b) G. O. Schenck, I. von Wilucki, and C. H. Krauch, *Chem. Ber.*, **95**, 1409 (1962); (c) G. S. Hammond, C. A.

Stout, and A. A. Lamola, *J. Am. Chem. Soc.*, **86**, 3103 (1964); (d) C. H. Krauch, S. Farid, and G. O. Schenck, *Chem. Ber.*, **99**, 625 (1966); (e) H. Morrison, H. Curtis, and T. McDowell, *J. Am. Chem. Soc.*, **88**, 5415 (1966).

37. (a) D. R. Arnold, R. L. Hinman, and A. H. Glick, *Tetrahedron Letters*, **1964**, 1425; (b) N. C. Yang, M. Nussim, M. J. Jorgenson, and S. Murov, *ibid.*, **1964**, 3657; (c) J. Saltiel, R. M. Coates, and W. G. Dauben, *J. Am. Chem. Soc.*, **88**, 2745 (1966).

38. C. H. Krauch and S. Farid, *Tetrahedron Letters*, **1966**, 4783.

39. T. Mukai, T. Tezuka, and Y. Akasaki, *J. Am. Chem. Soc.*, **88**, 5025 (1966).

40. A. S. Kende, *J. Am. Chem. Soc.*, **88**, 5026 (1966).

41. (a) R. C. Cookson and J. Hudec, *Proc. Chem. Soc.*, **1959**, 11; (b) *J. Chem. Soc.*, **1961**, 4499; (c) D. Bryce-Smith and A. Gilbert, *ibid.*, **1964**, 2428; (d) R. C. Cookson, E. Crundwell, and R. R. Hill, *ibid.*, **1964**, 3062.

42. (a) H. J. F. Angus and D. Bryce-Smith, *Proc. Chem. Soc.*, **1959**, 327; (b) *J. Chem. Soc.*, **1960**, 4791; (c) G. O. Schenck and R. Steinmetz, *Tetrahedron Letters*, **1960**, 1; (d) E. Grovenstein, D. V. Rao, and J. W. Taylor, *J. Am. Chem. Soc.*, **83**, 1705 (1961).

43. (a) G. S. Hammond, N. J. Turro, and A. Fisher, *J. Am. Chem. Soc.*, **83**, 4674 (1961); (b) G. S. Hammond, N. J. Turro, and R. S. H. Liu, *J. Org. Chem.*, **28**, 3297 (1963); (c) G. S. Hammond and R. S. H. Liu, *J. Am. Chem. Soc.*, **85**, 477 (1963); (d) D. Valentine, N. J. Turro, Jr., and G. S. Hammond, *ibid.*, **86**, 5202 (1964); (e) R. S. H. Liu, N. J. Turro, Jr., and G. S. Hammond, *ibid.*, **87**, 3406 (1965).

44. N. J. Turro, *Molecular Photochemistry*, Benjamin, New York, 1965, p. 212.

45. G. Sartori, V. Turba, A. Valvassori, and M. Riva, *Tetrahedron Letters*, **1966**, 4777.

46. H. C. Brown and G. Zweifel, *J. Am. Chem. Soc.*, **81**, 247 (1959).

47. H. Kato, K. Yamaguchi, T. Yonezawa, and K. Fukui, *Bull. Chem. Soc. Japan*, **38**, 2144 (1965).

48. K. Fukui, *Bull. Chem. Soc. Japan*, **39**, 498 (1966).

49. (a) S. Winstein, E. Grunwald, and L. L. Ingraham, *J. Am. Chem. Soc.*, **70**, 821 (1948); (b) D. J. Cram, *ibid.*, **71**, 3863 (1949); (c) K. Fukui, H. Kato, and T. Yonezawa, *Bull. Chem. Soc. Japan*, **35**, 1475 (1962); (d) K. Morokuma, S. Ohnishi, T. Masuda, and K. Fukui, *ibid.*, **36**, 1228 (1963).

50. (a) See for example ref. 19, p. 520; (b) R. C. Fahey, *J. Am. Chem. Soc.*, **88**, 4681 (1966).

51. (a) P. S. Skell and A. Y. Garner, *J. Am. Chem. Soc.*, **78**, 3409, 5430 (1956); (b) H. M. Frey, *ibid.*, **80**, 5005 (1958); (c) T. V. van Auken and K. L. Reinhart, Jr., *ibid.*, **84**, 3736 (1962); (d) G. L. Closs, R. A. Moss, and J. J. Coyle, *ibid.*, **84**, 4985 (1962); (e) G. L. Closs and R. A. Moss, *ibid.*, **86**, 4042 (1964).

52. A. Streitwieser, Jr., *Molecular Orbital Theory for Organic Chemists*, Wiley, New York, 1961, p. 380 and references therein.

53. (a) A. Verloop, A. L. Koevoet, and E. Havinga, *Rec. Trav. Chim.*, **76**, 689 (1957); (b) E. Havinga and J. L. M. A. Schlatmann, *Tetrahedron*, **16**, 146 (1961).

54. (a) W. R. Roth, *Tetrahedron Letters*, **1964**, 1009; (b) S. McLean and R. Haynes, *ibid.*, **1964**, 2385; (c) A. P. ter Borg, H. Kloosterziel, and N. van Meurs, *Rec. Trav. Chim.*, **82**, 717 (1963); (d) A. P. ter Borg and H. Kloosterziel, *ibid.*, **82**, 741 (1963); (e) **84**, 214, 245 (1965); (f) E. Weth and A. S. Dreiding, *Proc. Chem. Soc.*, **1964**, 59; (g) T. Nozoe and K. Takahashi, *Bull. Chem. Soc. Japan*, **38**, 665 (1965); (h) R. W. Murray and M. L. Kaplan, *J. Am. Chem. Soc.*, **88**, 3527 (1966).

55. P. I. Abell and L. H. Piette, *J. Am. Chem. Soc.*, **84**, 916 (1962).
56. P. S. Skell, R. G. Allen, and N. D. Gilmour, *J. Am. Chem. Soc.*, **83**, 504 (1961).
57. (a) H. E. Zimmerman and A. Zweig, *J. Am. Chem. Soc.*, **83**, 1196 (1961); (b) H. E. Zimmerman, "Base-Catalyzed Rearrangements," in *Molecular Rearrangements*, Part I, P. de Mayo, Ed., Interscience, New York, 1963, pp. 345–406.
58. (a) E. N. Marvell, J. L. Stephenson, and J. Ong, *J. Am. Chem. Soc.*, **87**, 1267 (1965); (b) S. J. Rhoads, "Rearrangements Proceeding Through No Mechanism Pathways: The Claisen, Cope and Related Rearrangements," in ref. 57b, pp. 655–706.
59. (a) W. von E. Doering and W. R. Roth, *Tetrahedron*, **18**, 67 (1962); (b) *Angew. Chem.*, **75**, 27 (1963).
60. (a) H. L. Goering and R. W. Greiner, *J. Am. Chem. Soc.*, **79**, 3464 (1957); (b) H. L. Goering and R. R. Jacobson, *ibid.*, **80**, 3277 (1958); (c) H. L. Goering and M. M. Pombo, *ibid.*, **82**, 2515 (1960); (d) H. L. Goering, M. M. Pombo, and K. D. McMichael, *ibid.*, **85**, 965 (1963); (e) H. L. Goering and W. I. Kimoto, *ibid.*, **87**, 1748 (1965).
61. Ref. 19, p. 644.
61a. B. S. Thyagarajan, K. K. Balasubramanian, and R. Bhima Rao, *Chem. Ind. (London)*, **1967**, 401.
62. P. Heimbach and W. Brenner, *Angew. Chem.*, **78**, 983 (1966).
63. F. Brown, P. Leriverend, and J. M. Conia, *Tetrahedron Letters*, **1966**, 6115.
64. Cited in ref. 53.
65. E. N. Marvell, G. Caple, and B. Schatz, *Tetrahedron Letters*, **1965**, 385.
66. (a) D. S. Glass, J. W. H. Whathey, and S. Winstein, *Tetrahedron Letters*, **1965**, 377; (b) E. Vogel, W. Grimme, and E. Dinne, *ibid.*, **1965**, 391.
67. K. M. Schumate and G. J. Fonken, *J. Am. Chem. Soc.*, **88**, 1073 (1966).
68. R. S. H. Liu, *J. Am. Chem. Soc.*, **89**, 112 (1967).
69. R. S. H. Liu and G. S. Hammond, *J. Am. Chem. Soc.*, **86**, 1892 (1964).
70. K. J. Crowley, *Tetrahedron*, **21**, 1001 (1964).
71. W. G. Dauben, R. L. Cargill, R. M. Coates, and J. Saltiel, *J. Am. Chem. Soc.*, **88**, 2742 (1966).
72. E. E. van Tamelen and T. L. Burkoth, *J. Am. Chem. Soc.*, **89**, 151 (1967).
73. E. J. Corey and A. G. Hortmann, *J. Am. Chem. Soc.*, **87**, 5736 (1965).
74. L. A. Paquette and R. W. Begland, *J. Am. Chem. Soc.*, **88**, 4685 (1966).
75. E. Vogel, *Ann. Chem.*, **615**, 14 (1958).
76. R. Criegee and K. Noll, *Ann. Chem.*, **627**, 1 (1959).
77. R. E. K. Winter, *Tetrahedron Letters*, **1965**, 1207.
78. G. R. Branton, H. M. Frey, and R. F. Skinner, *Trans. Faraday Soc.*, **62**, 1546 (1966).
79. G. Schröder and J. F. M. Oth, *Tetrahedron Letters*, **1966**, 4083.
80. H. C. Longuet-Higgins and E. W. Abrahamson, *J. Am. Chem. Soc.*, **87**, 2045 (1965). Woodward and Hoffmann also adopted this method for their further investigation. See ref. 17.
81. K. Fukui, *Tetrahedron Letters*, **1965**, 2009, and ref. 48.
82. H. E. Zimmerman, *J. Am. Chem. Soc.*, **88**, 1564, 1566 (1966).
83. E. Heilbronner, *Tetrahedron Letters*, **1964**, 1923.
84. D. M. Lemal and S. D. McGregor, *J. Am. Chem. Soc.*, **88**, 1335 (1966).
85. (a) W. L. Mock, *J. Am. Chem. Soc.*, **88**, 2857 (1966); (b) S. D. McGregor and D. M. Lemal, *ibid.*, **88**, 2858 (1966).
86. B. A. Bohm and P. I. Abell, *Chem. Rev.*, **62**, 599 (1962).
87. (a) G. Stork and W. N. White, *J. Am. Chem. Soc.*, **75**, 4119 (1953); (b) **78**, 4609

(1956); (c) H. L. Goering, T. D. Nevitt, and E. F. Silversmith, *ibid.*, **77**, 4042 (1955).

88. J. A. Marshall and H. Roebke, *J. Org. Chem.*, **31**, 3109 (1966).
89. K. Schrage, *Tetrahedron Letters*, **1966**, 5795.
90. K. Fukui, *Tetrahedron Letters*, **1965**, 2427.
91. W. Drenth, *Rec. Trav. Chim.*, **86**, 1 (1967).
92. R. Criegee and H. Furrer, *Chem. Ber.*, **97**, 2949 (1964).
93. W. M. Jones and J. W. Wilson, Jr., *Tetrahedron Letters*, **1965**, 1587.
94. C. H. DePuy, L. G. Schnack, J. W. Hausser, and W. Wiedeman, *J. Am. Chem. Soc.*, **87**, 4006 (1965).
95. (a) S. J. Cristol, R. M. Sequeira, and C. H. DePuy, *J. Am. Chem. Soc.*, **87**, 4007 (1965); (b) P. von R. Schleyer and G. W. Van Dine, *ibid.*, **88**, 2868 (1966).
96. H. Tanida, private communication.
97. R. Hoffmann and R. B. Woodward, *J. Am. Chem. Soc.*, **87**, 4388 (1965).
98. (a) Ref. 14; (b) R. Hoffmann and R. A. Olofson, *J. Am. Chem. Soc.*, **88**, 943 (1966).
99. (a) K. Fukui and H. Fujimoto, *Tetrahedron Letters*, **1966**, 251. Also cf. ref. 18 and M. Simonetta and G. Favini, *Tetrahedron Letters*, **1966**, 4837.
100. In some special cases HO (or LU) and the next highest (or lowest) MO are interchanged with each other when the Hückel calculation is replaced by SCF LCAO MO calculation. The case of fluoranthene was discussed by K. Fukui at the Symposium on Atomic and Molecular Quantum Theory, Sanibel Island, 1964.

The Benzidine Rearrangements

H. J. SHINE

Department of Chemistry
Texas Technological College, Lubbock, Texas

I. INTRODUCTION

The name "benzidine rearrangement" ordinarily means the long-known and much-investigated acid-catalyzed rearrangement of aromatic hydrazo compounds. Aromatic hydrazo compounds may also rearrange if heated in neutral solvents such as alcohols, acetonitrile, and benzene. This rearrangement is often called the thermal benzidine rearrangement. The two classes of rearrangement are not unconnected. Rearrangements in neutral alcohol solution are a transition point between the ordinary acid-catalyzed rearrangements and rearrangements in neutral aprotic solvents. The term "benzidine rearrangements" used in the title covers all of the hydrazo-aromatic transformations. It is still convenient, however, to treat the two classes, acid-catalyzed and thermal, separately.

The objective of all modern research in the benzidine rearrangements has been the elucidation of the mechanisms of the rearrangements. The objective has not yet been reached, although we do not seem to be very far from it. The purpose of this review is to describe the benzidine rearrangements and to evaluate the current views on their mechanisms.

Benzidine rearrangements are very often accompanied by a disproportionation reaction. This reaction will also be described, for the point of view will be taken in the following pages that mechanisms of rearrangement are not satisfactory unless they can also explain how concomitant disproportionation occurs. Other reviews and discussions of similar scope have appeared during the last ten years (1–7). In some of these, several of the current theories of the benzidine rearrangements are developed; these are the subject of the present evaluation.

II. ACID-CATALYZED REARRANGEMENT

A. Conditions and Products of Rearrangement

1. Conditions of Rearrangement

The common practice is to treat a solution of the aromatic hydrazo compound with aqueous hydrochloric or sulfuric acid at room temperature or 0°. The solvent is often ethanol or dioxan. Under these conditions hydrazobenzene (1) gives benzidine (2) and diphenyline (3). It is from the first product that the name of the rearrangement is derived. Rearrangement may also occur in solutions of carboxylic acids, such as acetic acid, without

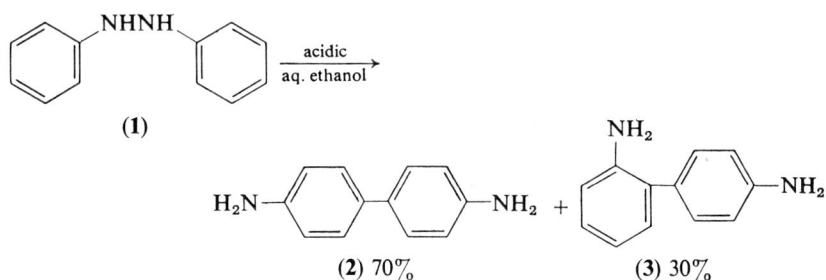

the aid of mineral acid, but in this case rearrangement may be slow (8). Rearrangements have been carried out with hydrogen chloride in hydrocarbon solvents, such as benzene and toluene (9,10), as well as by the action of hydrogen chloride gas on solid hydrazo compounds (11). The action of cold, concentrated hydrochloric acid on the solid hydrazo compound has also been used to achieve particular product distributions (12).

The hydrazo compounds used at present are commonly prepared by the reduction of the corresponding azo compound with zinc and ammonium chloride, or zinc and ammonia, and sometimes with hydrogen over platinum; diimide is also being used successfully in the author's laboratory. Regardless of the method, the hydrazo compound is usually isolated and then rearranged. During the early development of the scope of the rearrangement the hydrazo compound was not always isolated before being rearranged. Instead, the azo compound was reduced with stannous chloride in hydrochloric acid, and the hydrazo compound underwent rearrangement as it was formed. This method was used almost exclusively by Jacobson, and we shall refer to it as Jacobson's method. Many of Jacobson's results (13a) are used in discussions of the benzidine rearrangement, because they are often the only ones available for particular compounds. We shall see that, because of the method of causing rearrangement, some of Jacobson's results play a particularly important part in controversies about the mechanisms of rearrangement.

2. Types of Product

As noted earlier the rearrangement of hydrazobenzene (1) gives benzidine (2) and diphenyline (3). The formation of 2 and 3 from 1 represents two ways of rebonding when the N—N bond of the hydrazobenzene has been broken. In 2 the rebonding between the 4 and 4'-carbon atoms is the benzidine-type bonding, while in 3 the rebonding between the 2 and 4' carbon atoms is the diphenyline-type bonding. Products formed from hydrazoaromatic compounds by these rebonding modes are called benzidines and diphenylines. In principle, there are three other ways in which rebonding can occur to give three other products. They are the 2,2'-, 2,N'-, and 4,N'-bondings, and would lead to *ortho*-benzidine (**4**), *ortho*-semidine (**5**), and *para*-semidine (**6**), respectively. Products formed from hydrazo compounds by these rebonding modes are called *ortho*-benzidines, *ortho*-semidines, and *para*-semidines, respectively. Ordinarily,

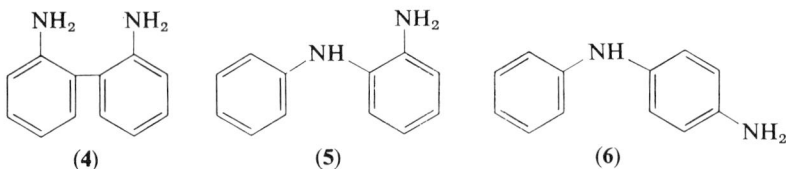

(4)   (5)   (6)

these products are not obtained from the rearrangement of hydrazobenzene. Vecera (14–16) has found, by using chromatography, that **4**, **5**, and **6** are formed from hydrazobenzene in aqueous acid–ethanol solution, but in quantities too small to be isolated. In contrast, isolable amounts of **4**, **5**, and **6** were formed in the ratios shown when solid hydrazobenzene was treated with dry hydrogen chloride (11). Also, *ortho*-benzidine (**4**) is formed in nonpolar solvents (7,17). For example, it has been formed in 7% yield

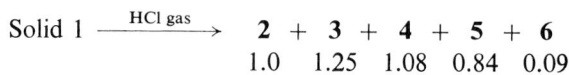

$$\text{Solid 1} \xrightarrow{\text{HCl gas}} \quad 2 \ + \ 3 \ + \ 4 \ + \ 5 \ + \ 6$$
$$\qquad\qquad\qquad\qquad 1.0 \quad 1.25 \quad 1.08 \quad 0.84 \quad 0.09$$

by treating hydrazobenzene with hydrogen chloride in toluene solution (17). The results show, then, that under the ordinary conditions of rearrangement hydrazobenzene will give as major products only two of the possible types, while under certain conditions all of the possible products are obtained. Products with structures analogous to **4**, **5**, and **6** are formed readily from other hydrazo compounds, especially, of course, where the presence of substituents makes formation of the benzidine-type and diphenyline-type product either difficult or impossible.

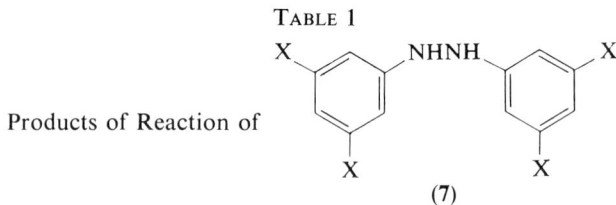

TABLE 1

Products of Reaction of

(7)

Structure	X	% Benzidine	% Diphenyline	*ortho*-Benzidine
7a	Me	26.8	30.3	10.9
7b	Br	18.9	27.2	8.2
7c	Cl	36.4	21.3	16.0

3. ortho-Benzidines

These are not usually obtained from hydrazobenzenes in any more than trace quantities. A notable exception is in the reactions of the 3,3',5,5'-tetrasubstituted hydrazobenzenes (**7a–7c**, Table 1), which give mixtures of the benzidine-, diphenyline-, and *ortho*-benzidine-type products (18). The *ortho*-benzidine-type product (**9** and **12**) is obtained from hydrazonaphthalenes (19,20). The flow diagrams show that the 3,4:5,6- and 1,2:7,8-dibenzocarbazoles (**10** and **13**) are also formed; these also

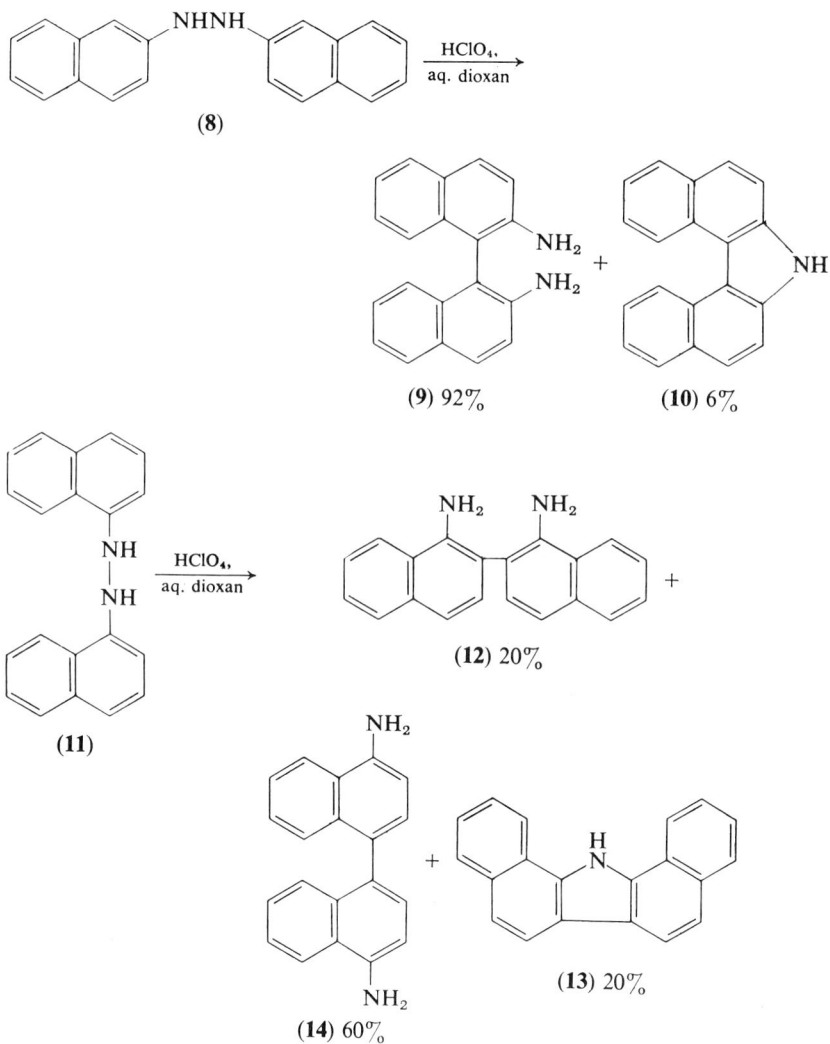

(**8**)

HClO₄, aq. dioxan

(**9**) 92%   (**10**) 6%

(**11**)

HClO₄, aq. dioxan

(**12**) 20% +

(**14**) 60%

(**13**) 20%

represent initial 2,2′-type bonding. The formation of the dibenzocarbazoles is considered again in Sections II-B-2-c and IV-A. The influence of the naphthyl group on product control is so great that even *N*-2-naphthyl-*N*′-phenylhydrazine (**15**) rearranges to the *ortho*-benzidine product (**16**) (21).

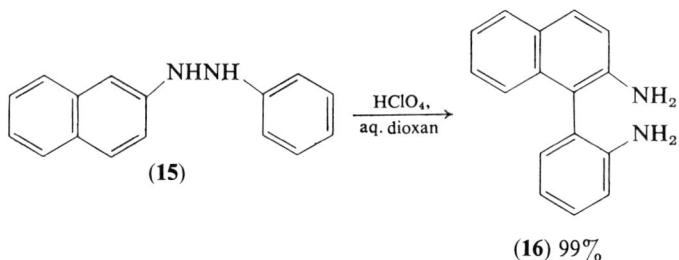

(**15**)

HClO₄, → aq. dioxan

(**16**) 99%

4. ortho-Semidines and Diphenylines

These are obtained from ring-substituted hydrazobenzenes. 4,4′-Disubstituted hydrazobenzenes (**17**) give *ortho*-semidines (**18**). Unsymmetrical 4,4′-disubstituted hydrazobenzenes (**19**) may give two *ortho*-

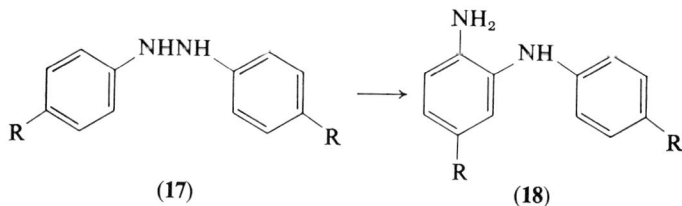

(**17**)   (**18**)

semidines (**20** and **21**), and which one predominates (or is obtained exclusively) depends on the electron-contributing properties of the groups. The better electron donor is found *para* to the unsubstituted amino group

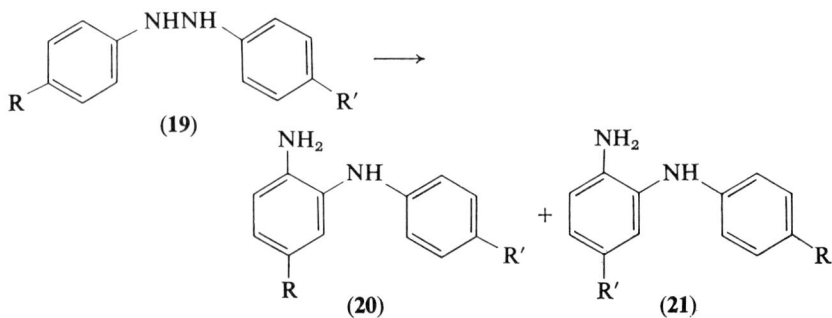

(**19**)

(**20**)   +   (**21**)

in the product. For example, when R = OEt and R′ = Me, the rearrangement product is **20** in 18% yield (13b).

   ortho-Semidines are also formed from hydrazobenzenes that have a single *para*-substituent. Here again a duality in paths exists, because a diphenyline may be formed in preference to, or as well as, an *ortho*-semidine. Thus, the *para*-substituted hydrazobenzene (**22**) will give an *ortho*-semidine (**23**) if R is a strong electron donor, but a diphenyline (**24**) if R is electron attracting. In some cases (R = halogen) both **23** and **24** are obtained. When R is CO_2H or SO_3H, the major product is benzidine,

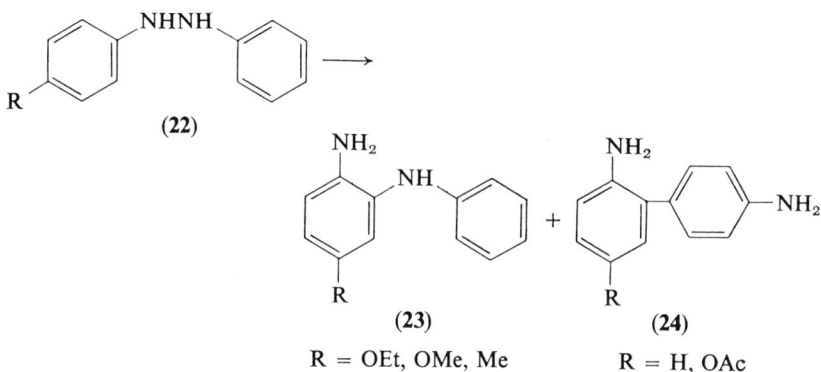

(**22**)

(**23**)   (**24**)

R = OEt, OMe, Me   R = H, OAc

because the substituent is displaced (e.g., as $CO_2 + H^+$) during the rearrangement (13a).

5. *para-Semidines*

   Until recently, opinion was divided on whether or not *para*-semidines are genuine products of intramolecular rearrangement. For this reason, *para*-semidines had a role in the benzidine rearrangements that was more important than at first apparent. How this came about is briefly described.

   Among Jacobson's examples of rearrangement there are many in which a *para*-semidine was obtained. Notable examples are the reactions of the compounds **25–31**. It was the custom, for the most part, to accept *para*-semidines as intramolecular-rearrangement products, just as all the other types of rearrangement products were accepted. But, a *para*-semidine arises from 4,*N′*-bonding, and Hammick and Munro looked upon this as being too long to be able to occur in an intramolecular, concerted process (22). They pointed out (erroneously) that no case had ever been reported in which a *para*-semidine was formed by purely acid catalysis, believing that the only examples of *para*-semidine formation in the literature at that time were those (chiefly Jacobson's) in which Jacobson's method of rearrangement had been used. They proposed, therefore, that the *para*-semidine

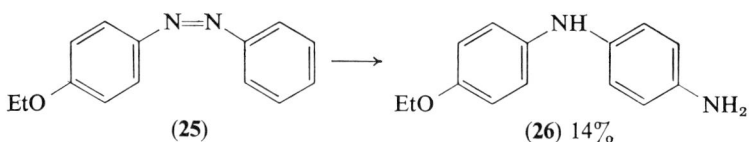

(25)   (26) 14%

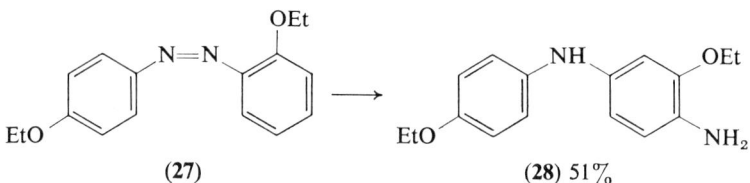

(27)   (28) 51%

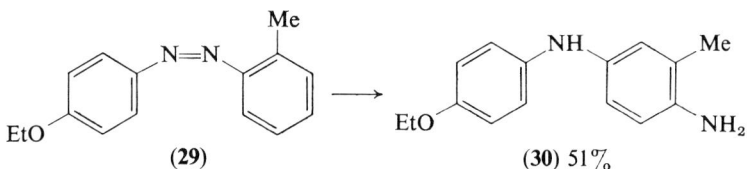

(29)   (30) 51%

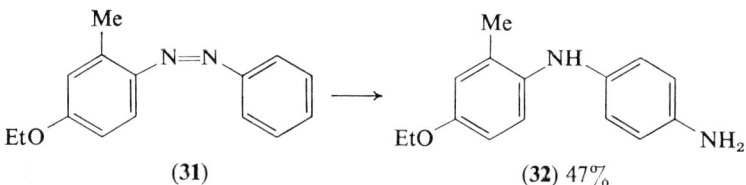

(31)   (32) 47%

rearrangements were not of the ordinary intramolecular kind, but arose from an intermolecular reaction in which the heavy-metal ion played a part. But, there is now no doubt whatever that *para*-semidines are formed in rearrangements free of heavy-metal ions. The formation of *para*-semidine (6) from solid hydrazobenzene and hydrogen chloride has already been noted. 1,2'-Hydrazonaphthalene (33) forms 4-amino-1,2'-dinaphthylamine (34) as well as the expected *ortho*-diamine when stirred with concentrated hydrochloric acid (12). These are examples in which the conditions of rearrangement were unusual. However, *para*-semidine formation from hydrazobenzenes has been observed, by Jacobson and

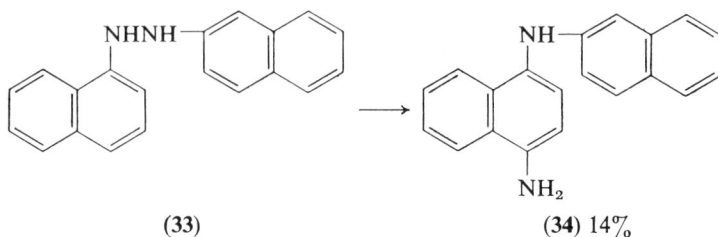

(33)   (34) 14%

TABLE 2

Hydrazobenzenes Which Have Undergone
para-Semidine Formation Under Ordinary Conditions

Substituents[b]	Solvent	Acid	% Yield[a]	Ref.
None	95% ethanol	HCl	+	16
2-Me	95% ethanol	HCl	+	16
4-Me	95% ethanol	HCl	+	16
2-Me; 2'-Me	95% ethanol	HCl	+	16
4-Cl	95% ethanol	HCl	+	23
4-Cl	Methanol	HCl (g)	2.5	13c
4-Cl	60% dioxan	$HClO_4$	24	24
3-Cl; 3'-Cl	95% ethanol	HCl	+	23
4-Br	95% ethanol	H_2SO_4	3	25
4-EtO	95% ethanol	HCl	8	26
4-MeO	95% ethanol	HCl	+	26
4-MeO	60% dioxan	$HClO_4$	20	24
4-NO_2	60% dioxan	$HClO_4$	20	24

[a] The plus sign denotes chromatographic detection.

[b] A *para*-semidine was obtained from N,N'-dimethylhydrazobenzene with
0.01 M HCl in 25% aqueous methanol in 3% yield (26a).

others, under ordinary conditions also, as listed in Table 2. There is no evidence for intermolecularity in these reactions. The *para*-semidine rearrangements belong rightfully in the family of benzidine rearrangements. Nevertheless, we shall see that the formation of *para*-semidines still plays a particular part in considerations of the mechanism of these rearrangements. [It is a remarkable fact that for so many years we have all come to rely upon Jacobson's summary paper (13a) for information, without paying enough attention to what Jacobson said in it and to Jacobson's earlier research papers. We have accepted Hammick and Munro's misleading claim that all of Jacobson's rearrangements were carried out by the Jacobson method, whereas Jacobson says quite clearly that in a few cases he used the hydrazo compound and acid (p. 86 of ref. 13a). It is unfortunate that these cases are not set aside from all of the others in Jacobson's summary paper and will be found only by searching through his earlier papers.]

6. N-Substituted Hydrazo Compounds

Examples that are known include the monosubstituted compounds (**35a–35c**) and N,N'-dimethylhydrazobenzene (**38**). The last compound gives not only the anticipated product (**39**), but also the diphenyline

(20.3%), *ortho*-benzidine (0.9%), *ortho*-semidine (15.5%), and *para*-semidine (3.0%) type products (26a).

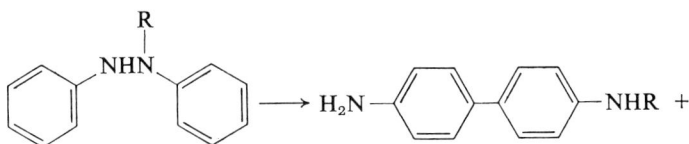

(**35a**) R = Me (27)   (**36a**) R = Me (27), 57%
(**35b**) R = Ac (28)   (**36b**) R = Ac (28)
(**35c**) R = Ph (29)   (**36c**) R = Ph (29)

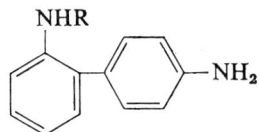

(**37a**) 9%
position of R unproved

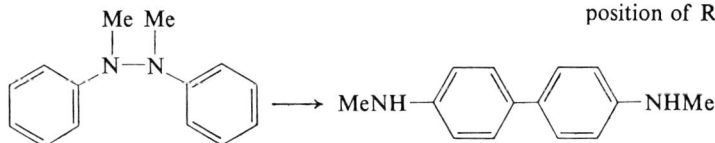

(**38**)

(**39**) 66% (30)
50.7% (26a)

7. *Cyclic Hydrazo Compounds*

A major task in solving the mechanism of the benzidine rearrangement is to explain how the breaking of the N—N bond and the making of a variety of C—C and C—N bonds can occur intramolecularly. The cyclic hydrazo compounds have a bearing on this question, as we shall see later.

2,2'-Hydrazodiphenylmethane (**40**) does not rearrange at all. Instead, it undergoes disproportionation to **41** and **42** (31,32) and other reactions (32) in strongly acidic solution.

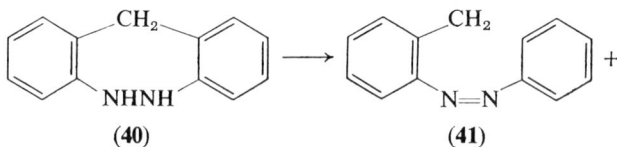

(**40**)   (**41**)

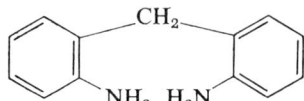

other products

(**42**)

The cyclic hydrazo compounds (43) rearrange if the methylene chain is long enough. In 2N hydrochloric acid the trimethylene compound (43a) did not rearrange, but underwent reduction to 1,3-dianilinopropane (30).

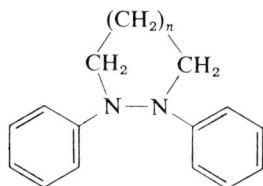

(43)

	43a	43b	43c	43d	43e
$n =$	1	2	3	4	8

The other polymethylene compounds (43b–43e) did rearrange as shown.

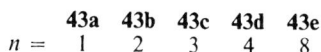

(44) 43%   (45) 20%

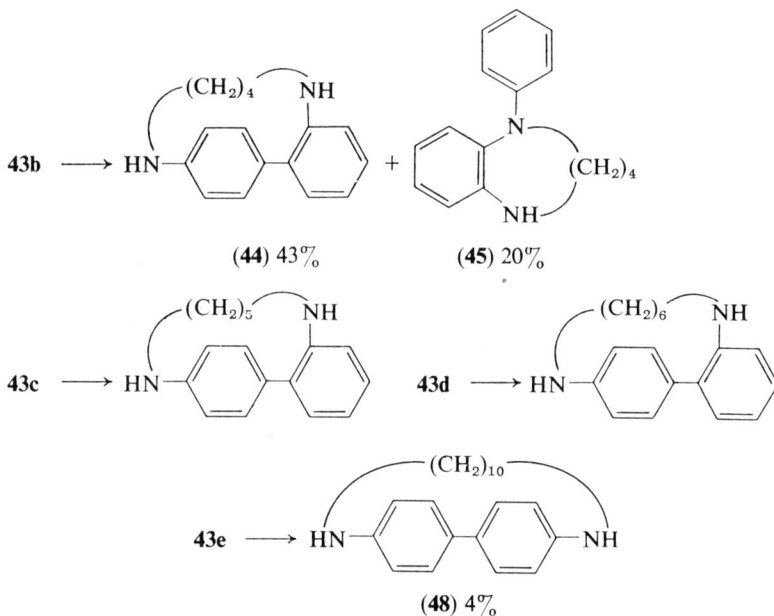

(48) 4%

The strain in these cyclic products must be large, particularly in the diphenylines. A question that must be answered concerns the sort of molecular contortions through which the protonated hydrazo compounds must go in order to allow the bonding for these strained rearrangement products.

8. meta-Rearrangement

In all benzidine rearrangements the new bond formations occur at positions in the rings which were *ortho* or *para* to the hydrazo group.

Rearrangements to a *meta*-position are not known, except for the interesting case of the acidic reduction of 2-ethylaminoazobenzene (49) (33). The product (50) is of a "*meta*-rearrangement." The anomaly is readily

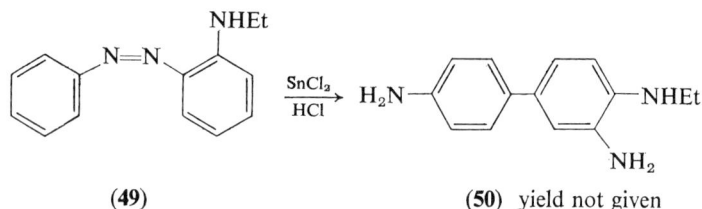

(49)   (50) yield not given

understood if an intermediate is formed during rearrangement in which the ethylamino group becomes equivalent in directing effect to the NH portion of the cleaved hydrazo group. The *meta*-rearrangement anomaly is not so easily understood in terms of concerted rearrangement. These points will be brought out more fully in the discussion of the role of intermediates in the benzidine rearrangements.

9. Disproportionation

In this acid-catalyzed reaction one molecule of hydrazo compound becomes oxidized to the azo compound, while a second is reduced to two molecules of amine (Eq. 1). Few hydrazo compounds rearrange without

$$2ArNHNHAr \longrightarrow ArN=NAr + 2ArNH_2 \qquad (1)$$

also undergoing disproportionation. Neither hydrazobenzene nor the hydrazonaphthalenes disproportionate under the usual conditions of rearrangement. Disproportionation occurs with substituted hydrazo compounds and is particularly marked with 4,4'-disubstituted hydrazobenzenes. When *para*-hydrazotoluene is used, disproportionation accounts for about 40% of the starting material (34,35). Some 4,4'-disubstituted hydrazobenzenes, for example, the dihydroxy and diamino compounds, are reported only to disproportionate and not rearrange at all (13a). *para*-Hydrazobiphenyl, once thought to disproportionate only (36), is now known to disproportionate to the extent of 75–88% and rearrange (to the *ortho*-semidine) to the extent of 12–25% (37).

The disproportionation reaction is a very important part of hydrazoaromatic chemistry. We shall see that a complete description of the mechanism of rearrangement must be able to accommodate concurrent disproportionation.

B. The Mechanism of Rearrangement

1. The Currently Accepted Steps

Briefly the main mechanistic features of the rearrangement are stated here and the equations which describe its course are set out. In later sections the supporting evidence will be described and the current theories of mechanism will be discussed.

The several types of acid-catalyzed benzidine rearrangement are intramolecular. They are specific acid-catalyzed, first order in hydrazo compound, and may be both first and second order in acid. The overall rate law is given by Eq. 2. It tells us about the kinetic orders in reactants.

$$\frac{-d(\text{Hyd})}{dt} = k_2[\text{Hyd}][\text{H}^+] + k_3[\text{Hyd}][\text{H}^+]^2 \tag{2}$$

We know now that some compounds rearrange under first-order acid catalysis, some under second-order, and others under a mixture of both first and second order.

The series of steps leading from reactant to product are described by Eqs. 3–6. They tell us that protonations are rapid and reversible and are followed by the slow steps of the rearrangements. A major unanswered

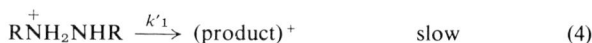

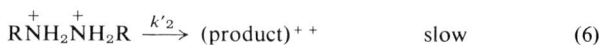

$$\text{RNHNHR} + \text{H}_3\text{O}^+ \overset{K_1}{\rightleftharpoons} \text{R}\overset{+}{\text{N}}\text{H}_2\text{NHR} + \text{H}_2\text{O} \quad \text{fast} \tag{3}$$

$$\text{R}\overset{+}{\text{N}}\text{H}_2\text{NHR} \overset{k'_1}{\longrightarrow} (\text{product})^+ \qquad\qquad \text{slow} \tag{4}$$

$$\text{R}\overset{+}{\text{N}}\text{H}_2\text{NHR} + \text{H}_3\text{O}^+ \overset{K_2}{\rightleftharpoons} \text{R}\overset{+}{\text{N}}\text{H}_2\overset{+}{\text{N}}\text{H}_2\text{R} + \text{H}_2\text{O} \quad \text{fast} \tag{5}$$

$$\text{R}\overset{+}{\text{N}}\text{H}_2\overset{+}{\text{N}}\text{H}_2\text{R} \overset{k'_2}{\longrightarrow} (\text{product})^{++} \qquad\qquad \text{slow} \tag{6}$$

question in the benzidine rearrangements is about the detail of the slow steps, namely, whether they are one-step reactions or two-step reactions involving the formation of an intermediate which is then converted into the product. If this question is ever answered to everyone's satisfaction the mechanism of the benzidine rearrangement will probably be considered settled. If the mechanism of the disproportionation reaction is also so satisfactorily solved, the final stage will have at last been reached in the search for an understanding of these interconnected, acid-catalyzed reactions.

2. The Development of the Currently Accepted Steps

a. Intramolecularity. It was Jacobson's point of view, based on the many rearrangements that he and others carried out, that all rearrangement products were formed intramolecularly (13a). This view prevails now that the doubts about the *para*-semidine rearrangement have been removed. Direct tests confirming the intramolecularity of the formation of benzidines (that is, 2,2'- and 4,4'-bonding) have been made. Direct tests of the formation of diphenylines and the two types of semidine have not been made. But, since these types of product are so often formed along with benzidines, they may also reasonably be expected to be formed intramolecularly. It is fitting to record briefly, as part of the overall story, the tests of intramolecularity that have been made. They amount to searching for "crossed" products from rearrangements of mixtures of symmetrical hydrazo compounds. The first to be carried out was with mixtures of 2,2'-dimethoxy- and 2,2'-diethoxyhydrazobenzene (38). The results were consistent with the formation of 3,3'-dimethoxy- and 3,3'-diethoxybenzidine only, and not with the formation of 3-ethoxy-3'-methoxybenzidine. In a later test, none of the radioactive product (**52**) was formed from the rearrangement of mixtures of *ortho*-hydrazotoluene and 2-methyl-^{14}C-hydrazobenzene (**51**) (39). These tests were in the

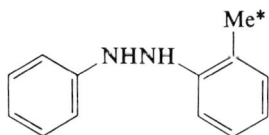

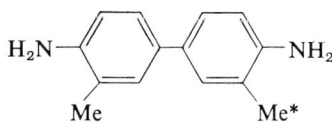

(**51**)   (**52**)

formation of 4,4'-bonded products. The tests of 2,2'-bonded products were made with mixtures of 1,1'- and 2,2'-hydrazonaphthalene. Had rearrangement been wholly or partly intermolecular, some of the products should have been those obtainable from the rearrangement of 1,2'-hydrazonaphthalene, but, these products were not present (40).

b. Kinetic Laws. Attempts to solve the mechanism of the benzidine rearrangement did not come near to success from studies of the products formed. It was only after the kinetics of rearrangement of a variety of hydrazo compounds had been established that the complexity of the benzidine rearrangements was recognizable and some real understanding of their mechanisms was achievable.

There are two turning points in the latter-day history of the benzidine rearrangement. The first of these was the discovery by Hammond and Shine (41) that the rearrangement of hydrazobenzene in aqueous ethanol was first order in hydrazobenzene and second order in acid. An overall rate equation was established (Eq. 7). It was thought then that the end of the

$$\frac{-d(\text{Hyd})}{dt} = k[\text{Hyd}][\text{H}^+]^2 \qquad (7)$$

benzidine problem was in sight. A driving force for the scission of the N—N bond had been found—the repulsion of the two positively charged nitrogen atoms in **53**—and now only the details needed filling in. It was not known then that only the beginning had been reached or, as a matter

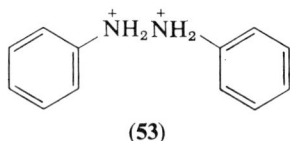

(53)

of fact, only rereached after a lapse of nearly 50 years. Van Loon (42) had found in 1903 that the rate of formation of benzidine from hydrazobenzene was second order in acid. But, van Loon's second-order discovery was overlooked by the later kineticists. This is not the only point of van Loon's work that was overlooked, for he had shown, with dichloroacetic acid, that the rearrangement was catalyzed by hydrogen ion rather than by undissociated acid, a key feature of the rearrangement that has had to be firmly established in recent years.

Van Loon's method of following the rate of rearrangement was to measure the amount of benzidine formed, with time, by precipitating it as the dihydrogen sulfate. The tackling of the kinetics of the benzidine rearrangements was later made easier by Dewar (43) with the use of Bindschedler's green. This green, water-soluble dye, used in the form of its zinc chloride salt, oxidizes hydrazoaromatics almost instantaneously (Eq. 8). Since Bindschedler's green can also be titrated with reducing agents such as titanous chloride, a method was at hand for determining the amount of hydrazo compound in a solution by adding the solution to a solution of

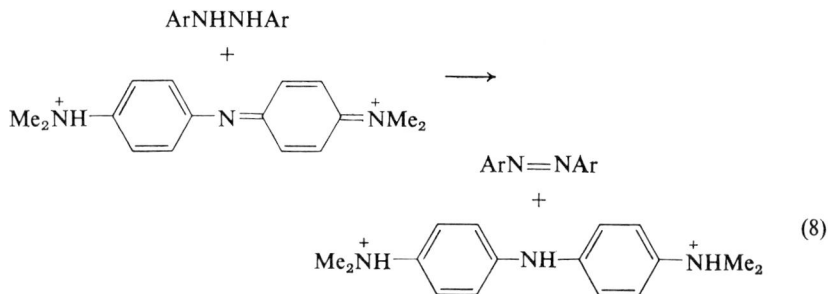

(8)

Bindschedler's green and back-titrating with titanous chloride. This method of analysis, when applied to the rates of the hydrazoaromatic reactions, determines only the rate at which the hydrazo compound is used up. Where more than one product is formed, as in the rearrangement of hydrazobenzene, the analytical method does not tell us that the formation of all products is governed by the same kinetic law. By analyzing rearrangement solutions spectrophotometrically, rather than by using the Bindschedler's green method, Carlin was able to show that not only was the rate of disappearance of hydrazobenzene expressible by Eq. 7, but that the rate law applied to the formation of both products (44). The spectrophotometric method was used to discover also that the rate of formation of the *ortho*-semidine from *para*-hydrazotoluene is also described by Eq. 7 (34). Thus, by the several methods it was established with hydrazobenzene and *para*-hydrazotoluene that the benzidine, diphenyline and *ortho*-semidine rearrangements could all be described by Eq. 7.

The second turning point was the surprising discovery by Carlin and Odioso that Eq. 7 was not applicable to *ortho*-hydrazotoluene. The rearrangement is a clean one, the only product being 3,3'-dimethylbenzidine. The overall rate law governing the disappearance of *ortho*-hydrazotoluene was found to be as in Eq. 9 (45). There is no doubt that this result was the key which finally enabled others to open the door to the

$$\frac{-d(\text{Hyd})}{dt} = k[\text{Hyd}][\text{H}^+]^{1.6} \tag{9}$$

mechanism of the benzidine rearrangement. An explanation was provided by Blackadder and Hinshelwood (46), which remains today. It is that the rearrangement of a hydrazo compound may be both first and second order in acid and follows the rate law given by Eq. 2. It is a very simple explanation that took a long time for discovery and some more time for acceptance,

$$\frac{-d(\text{Hyd})}{dt} = k_2[\text{Hyd}][\text{H}^+] + k_3[\text{Hyd}][\text{H}^+]^2 \tag{2}$$

but has now been fully proved experimentally. The position is that at low acidities a hydrazo compound may rearrange under first-order acid catalysis, while at higher acidities the rearrangement may follow second-order acid catalysis. The rearrangement of some hydrazo compounds is such that, no matter what the acidity, only the former type can be achieved experimentally, while, analogously, the rearrangements of some other compounds fall in the second category. Carlin's result with *ortho*-hydrazotoluene was obtained because, under the conditions used, the *ortho*-

hydrazotoluene was rearranging simultaneously by two paths—one, first order in acid and the other, second order. The overall result was an average of the two, fortuitously near the mean of 1.5. Similar results were obtained with other compounds. With 4-chloro-4′-methylhydrazobenzene the order in acid was 1.6 and with 4-*tert*-butyl-4′-chlorohydrazobenzene it was 1.5 (47). The conditions of rearrangement of these compounds and the range of acidities over which the rearrangements were followed were

TABLE 3

Kinetic Order in Acid for the Rearrangement
of the Compounds RNXNHR′

RNXNHR′			Order in acid		
R	R′	X	Low [H$^+$]	High [H$^+$]	Ref.
para-Styryl	*para*-Styryl	H	1.0	1.0	49
1-Naphthyl	1-Naphthyl	H	1.0	1.0	6
1-Naphthyl	2-Naphthyl	H	1.0	1.0	6
para-Anisyl	Phenyl	H	1.0	1.0	24
para-Acetaminophenyl	Phenyl	H	1.0	1.0	24
ortho-Iodophenyl	*ortho*-Iodophenyl	H	1.0	1.0	24
ortho-Bromophenyl	*ortho*-Bromophenyl	H	1.0	2.0	24
ortho-Anisyl	*ortho*-Anisyl	H	1.0	1.0	24
ortho-Anisyl	Phenyl	H	1.1	2.0	24
2-Naphthyl	2-Naphthyl	H	1.0	1.2	6
1-Naphthyl	Phenyl	H	1.0	2.0	6
2-Naphthyl	Phenyl	H	1.1	2.0	6
ortho-Tolyl	*ortho*-Tolyl	H	1.3	2.0	6
Phenyl	Phenyl	Me	1.0	1.9	48
para-Biphenylyl	Phenyl	H	2.0	2.0	24
para-Biphenylyl	*para*-Biphenylyl	H	1.8	2.0	37
ortho-Biphenylyl	*ortho*-Biphenylyl	H	2.0	2.0	24
Phenyl	Phenyl	H	2.0	2.0	6
para-Tolyl	*para*-Tolyl	H	2.0	2.0	34
para-*tert*-Butylphenyl	*para*-*tert*-Butylphenyl	H	2.0	2.0	50
ortho-Fluorophenyl	*ortho*-Fluorophenyl	H	2.0	2.0	24
para-Chlorophenyl	Phenyl	H	2.0	2.0	24
ortho-Chlorophenyl	*ortho*-Chlorophenyl	H	2.0	2.0	24
para-Chlorophenyl	*para*-Chlorophenyl	H	2.0	2.0	24
para-Bromophenyl	*para*-Bromophenyl	H	2.0	2.0	24
para-Iodophenyl	*para*-Iodophenyl	H	—	2.0	24
para-Nitrophenyl	Phenyl	H	2.0	2.0	24

such that again only the average of the two processes was detectable. The first demonstration of the validity of Eq. 2 came with the use of N-methylhydrazobenzene by White and Preisman (48). Thereafter, the whole range of possibilities was demonstrated by Banthorpe, Hughes, and Ingold. The position today is summarized in Table 3.

The entries in Table 3 show some compounds which rearrange only under first-order acid dependence and some which rearrange only under second order. In the middle of the table are listed those compounds in whose rearrangement the acid dependence changes with acidity. A plot of log k versus log [H$^+$] for these compounds is a curve, the slope of which approaches 1.0 at low acidity and 2.0 at high acidity. In between these ranges the slope of the curve varies continuously, getting larger with increasing acidity. For these compounds the second term in Eq. 2 becomes negligible at low acidities, while the first term becomes negligible at high acidities. Equation 2 can be rewritten as Eq. 10. The constant k_T in Eq. 10

$$\frac{-d(\text{Hyd})}{dt} = k_T[\text{Hyd}] \qquad (10)$$

$$k_T = k_2[\text{H}^+] + k_3[\text{H}^+]^2 \qquad (11)$$

is the rate constant for the overall disappearance of the hydrazo compound and is given by Eq. 11. From Eq. 11 it is seen that a plot of $k_T/[\text{H}^+]$ versus [H$^+$] will be a straight line of intercept k_2 and slope k_3. Thus, for

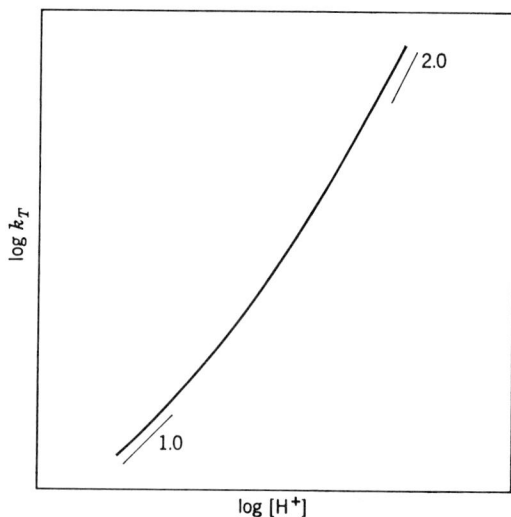

Figure 1

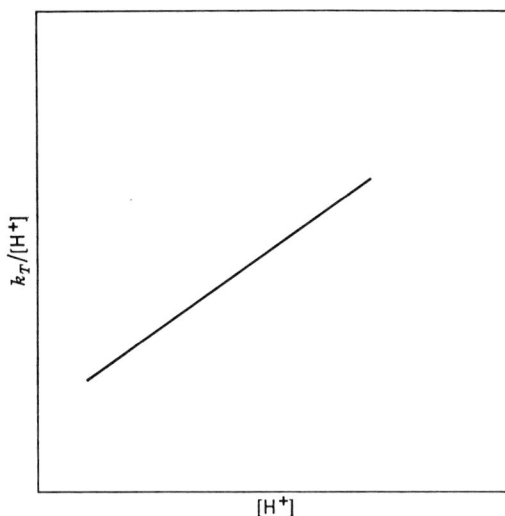

Figure 2

those compounds in whose rates of disappearance the acid dependence changes with acidity, two diagnostic and confirmatory plots should be obtainable; they are shown schematically in Figures 1 and 2. Plots of this kind have been obtained for some of the compounds listed in the middle portion of Table 3. The table does not specify what low and high acidities are, because these vary from one compound to another (they are given in the original publications). Nor does Table 3 list solvent, temperature, and other conditions. The important feature of Table 3 is the duality in acid dependence, predicted by the rate law of Eq. 2 and now fully substantiated.

c. **Isotope Effects and Specific-Acid Catalysis.** The overall process in the rearrangement of a hydrazo compound may be separated into four parts: protonation at one or both of the nitrogen atoms, the breaking of the N—N bond, the making of a new bond (either C—C or C—N), and the loss of either one or two ring protons (one in the semidine rearrangements and two in the benzidine and diphenyline). There is still a difference of opinion as to whether the N—N bond breaking and final bond making are concerted processes. The parts of the rearrangement that are settled are the protonations and deprotonations; these are not slow, rate-determining steps.

If all steps of a rearrangement were fast except for the final loss of ring protons, we should expect that the replacement of the appropriate ring protons in a hydrazo compound by deuterium or tritium would slow down its rate of rearrangement. The effect of ring deuterium on the rate of rearrangement has been tested in two important cases: one, hydrazo-benzene, in which the dependence on acid is second order (6,51) and the other, 1,1'-hydrazonaphthalene, in which it is first order (6). In neither case did ring deuteration affect the rate of rearrangement. The latest and most complete sets of data are given in Tables 4 and 5.

TABLE 4

The Effect of Ring Deuteration on the Rate and Products of
Rearrangement of Hydrazobenzene in 90% Ethanol at 0° (6)

Position of D in substrate	$10^3 k_3$, sec^{-1} mole^{-2} liter^2	Products	
		Benzidine, %	Diphenyline, %
None	2.80	71.8	27.2
All but 4,4'	2.87	71.4	27.9
4,4' only	2.85	72.8	26.2

TABLE 5

The Effect of Ring Deuteration on the Rate and Products of
Rearrangement of 1,1'-Hydrazonaphthalene in 60% Dioxan at 0° (6)

Position of D in substrate	k_2, sec^{-1} mole^{-1} liter	Products		
		4,4'-Diamine, %	1,1' Diamine, %	Dibenzo-carbazole, %
None	1.65	63.6	17.0	16.7
2,2'	1.64	63.1	6.5	29.5
4,4'	1.63	62.3	18.1	18.5

The first column in each of these tables lists the positions in the rings of the hydrazo compound at which protium was replaced by deuterium. The second column lists the appropriate rate constants. The other columns list the products of rearrangement. It is immediately apparent that the rate constants are not affected by the deuterium substitution. This means that the removal of hydrogen ion by either a solvent molecule or an anion, either from an intermediate (e.g., 54) or in a process concerted with C—C bond making, is not part of the rate-determining step. If hydrogen removal were part of a slow step in the rearrangement, the transition state

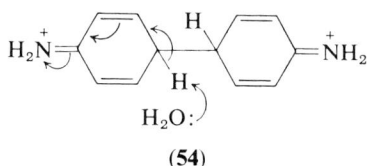

(54)

leading to the product would contain a water molecule (or an anion, X^-) acting as base, and, therefore, the parts of the acid H_3O^+ (or HX), and the rearrangement would be classifiable as general-acid catalyzed (52). It is evident that this is not the case here. It is also evident that the distribution of products from hydrazobenzene is decided before hydrogen is removed from the rings. The whole of the answer in the hydrazobenzene case is that neither the rate of rearrangement nor the product distribution is affected by loss of hydrogen from the rings. This loss must take place well after the main transition state of the rearrangement has been passed.

The same is to be said of the rearrangement of 1,1'-hydrazonaphthalene, except for one feature. The relative *amounts* of 1,1'-diamine and dibenzocarbazole are affected by replacing 2,2'-protium with deuterium. Neither the overall rate of rearrangement nor the relative amounts of 4,4'- and 2,2'-bonded products are affected. Therefore, the competition between 1,1'-diamine and dibenzocarbazole formation takes place after those two features have been decided. The competition, in fact, is at the time of the second (and last) ring-hydrogen removal (Eq. 12). Process *a* leads to dibenzocarbazole and process *b* to 1,1'-diamine. Where process *b*

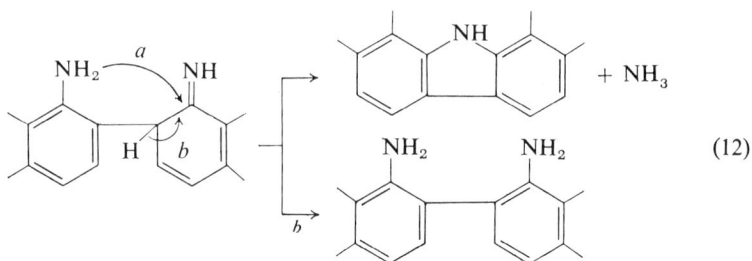

(12)

is made slower by deuterium substitution the formation of dibenzocarbazole is enhanced; but this competition occurs well after the main reaction pathways have been traversed.

These ring-deuteration results showed that proton removal was not part of the slow step in the rearrangements. What about proton addition? There are two diagnostic tests for answering this question. Both have been used and give the same answer: protonation occurs in a rapid equilibration prior to rearrangement, and this happens regardless of whether the rearrangement is first or second order in acid.

If the rate-determining step of an acid-catalyzed reaction is the transfer of a proton from the acid to the substrate, the replacement of protium in the acid by deuterium will cause a retardation in the rate of reaction, the extent of the retardation depending on how far the transfer had proceeded in the transition state (53). This effect can be detected by carrying out the reaction first in H_2O, where the acid will be H_3O^+, and next in D_2O, where the acid will be D_3O^+. If, on the other hand, the rate of the acid-catalyzed reaction depends only on the concentration of the protonated substrate, and this is formed in a rapid equilibration with the acid before the slow step of the reaction occurs, reaction in D_2O will be faster (usually about twofold) than in H_2O. The reason for this is that D_3O^+ in D_2O is a stronger acid than H_3O^+ in H_2O, and, therefore, more of a substrate will be converted, in equilibrium, into its conjugate acid by D_3O^+ than by the same concentration of H_3O^+. The results from benzidine rearrangements are given in Table 6. The values of k_D/k_H in the fifth

TABLE 6

Rearrangements of RNHNHR'. Kinetic Solvent Isotope Effects: Dioxan–H_2O and Dioxan–D_2O^a (6)

R	R'	$[H^+]$ or $[D^+]$	Order in H^+ $(= x)$	k_D/k_H $(= y)$	f_m
1-Naphthyl	1-Naphthyl	0.010	1.0	2.3	2.3
2-Naphthyl	Phenyl	0.020	1.15	2.6	2.2
		0.31	1.75	3.8	2.1
ortho-Tolyl	ortho-Tolyl	0.010	1.25	2.1	1.8
		0.29	1.9	3.5	1.9
Phenyl	Phenyl	0.19	2.0	4.8	2.2

[a] 60 vol. of dioxan and 40 vol. of water at 0° containing $HClO_4$.

column are the experimental values. For those hydrazo compounds whose rates of rearrangement are wholly or partly second order in acid, the values represent the cumulative effects of more than one proton (deuteron) addition. The term f_m in the sixth column is the rate-enhancement factor per added proton (obtained as the positive root of the equation $(x - 1)f_m^2 + (2 - x)f_m - y = 0$; x and y are defined in Table 6). The data show that *all* proton transfers are made in rapidly reached equilibria before the rearrangement step begins.

An acid-catalyzed reaction is said to be general-acid catalyzed if either proton addition (by H_3O^+ or HX) or proton removal (by H_2O or

X^-) is the rate-determining step of the reaction. If neither of these conditions is met, the reaction is said to be specific-acid catalyzed. The latter is the case with the benzidine rearrangements, and so van Loon said it was, with scant evidence—evidence that is now provided by Banthorpe, Hughes, and Ingold in a most elegant fashion.

The second diagnostic test for specific- or general-acid catalysis is based on the Hammett-Zucker hypothesis. The hypothesis is that if a substrate undergoes an acid-catalyzed reaction with a rate that is proportional to the stoichiometric concentration of the acid, the reaction is general-acid catalyzed. If, instead, the rate is proportional to Hammett's term h_0, the reaction is specific-acid catalyzed. A plot of log rate constant versus $\log h_0$ (that is, versus $-H_0$, where H_0 is the Hammett acidity function) would be a straight line. In contrast, if the reaction were proportional to the stoichiometric acid concentration, a plot of log rate constant versus log acid concentration would be a straight line. The slope of either line would tell us the kinetic order of the reaction in acid.

The Hammett-Zucker hypothesis is not always reliable (53) and, therefore, is not of decisive value. In the benzidine rearrangements the diagnosis made from applying the Hammett-Zucker hypothesis is of specific-acid catalysis and is confirmed, of course, by the deuterium solvent results described earlier. For the rearrangement of hydrazobenzene in aqueous dioxan, a plot of $\log k_T$ versus log acid concentration is linear, with a slope of 2.0, up to an acid concentration of $0.25N$. Above this acidity, the plot curves upwards, the rates of rearrangement being faster than expected on the basis of stoichiometric acidity. A plot of $\log k_T$ versus $-H_0$ is linear both below and above $0.25N$ acid and has a slope of 2.1. Similar results are obtained with some other hydrazoaromatics (6).

The kinetic description of the benzidine rearrangement is thus full of detail. The rearrangement is specific-acid catalyzed, first order in hydrazo compound, and may be either separately or simultaneously first and second order in acid. The series of equations that fits this description is given in Section II-B-1. The constants k_2 and k_3 in Eq. 2 represent, then, $k_1'K_1$ and $k_2'K_1K_2$, where K_1 and K_2 are the equilibrium constants in Eqs. 3 and 5.

d. Solvent and Salt Effects. The rates of benzidine rearrangements in aqueous solvents are increased by the addition of salts. The rates also become faster as the solvent is made more polar. That is, for example, the rate of rearrangement of 1,1'-hydrazonaphthalene in a series of aqueous organic solvents was faster the more polar the organic component of the solvent (20). The rate of rearrangement of hydrazobenzene in ethanol–water mixtures (54) and of 2,2'-hydrazonaphthalene in dioxan–water mixtures (19) changes in a more complex way. When the water content of

anhydrous or slightly aqueous solvent is increased the rate of rearrangement falls until a particular water content is reached, whereupon further
increase in water content causes the rate to rise again.

The distribution of products of rearrangement may also be affected
by the solvent. It has already been noted (Section II-A-2) that the
"unusual" products from the rearrangement of hydrazobenzene are
obtained in nonpolar solvents. The distribution of the usual products of
rearrangement of hydrazobenzene is also affected by changes in solvent.
The trend is away from benzidine and toward diphenyline as the solvent
becomes less polar for example, going through the series: water, aqueous
ethanol, aqueous dioxan (55,56).

These salt and solvent effects bespeak, in general, a developing
polarity in the transition state of the rearrangement greater than that of the
protonated molecule about to undergo rearrangement. The decrease in
the rate of rearrangement caused by making an anhydrous solvent
slightly aqueous is thought to be due to a decrease in the equilibrium
concentration of the protonated hydrazo compound in the slightly
aqueous solvent. When the solvent contains sufficient water such that
further addition no longer affects the protonation equilibrium, the addition
affects the rate by changing the polarity of the solvent (6).

C. Theories of Mechanism

1. The Four Contending Theories

Until recently there were only three theories contending to explain
the mechanism of the benzidine rearrangement. These are the polar-
transition-state theory, proposed by Banthorpe, Hughes, and Ingold; the
π-complex theory proposed by Dewar; and the caged-radical theory,
which has no particular advocate but which is often found in discussions
of the benzidine rearrangement. Each of these theories attempts to explain
the characteristics of the benzidine rearrangement which have been
described in earlier sections.

The polar-transition-state theory differs from the π-complex and
caged-radical theories in a special way. The last two theories provide for
the rate-determining formation of an intermediate along a rearrangement
path. The intermediate does not have the bonding of the final product.
Instead the quinonoidlike skeleton of the final product is formed rapidly
from the intermediate and is converted by subsequent fast proton shifts
into the product. The intermediate is called a π complex in the one theory
and a pair of solvent-caged radicals in the other. In the polar-transition-

state theory the quinonoidlike skeleton is formed directly in the rate-determining step.

The fourth theory is that of Lukashevich (2). It differs from all other theories in disregarding practically all the kinetic evidence on which any sound theory must be based. We shall discuss Lukashevich's theory for the purpose of record, but it must be acknowledged now that it is invalid.

2. The Polar-Transition-State Theory

a. The Polar Transition State. This theory derives its name from the description of the transition state which is traversed between the protonated hydrazo compound and the product skeleton. No other theory has stressed so strongly (if at all) the nature of the transition state. Because there are two kinetic paths in benzidine rearrangements there are two types of polar transition state to be described. One of them includes one proton and the other two. In the polar-transition-state theory the salt and solvent effects on rates of rearrangement are considered to be too marked to be attributed to changes in charge distribution in going from solvated protons to protonated hydrazo molecules. Instead the magnitude of these effects is considered to call for the development of a transition state of high polarity in the rate-determining step. This polarity is obtained by the heterolysis of the N—N bond of a protonated molecule. In the transition state for the one-proton mechanism one half of the heterolyzing, protonated molecule has the character of an aryl amine and the other, the character of an arylimino cation. This is shown for 1,1'-hydrazonaphthalene with structure **55**. In the transition state for the two-proton mechanism one half of the

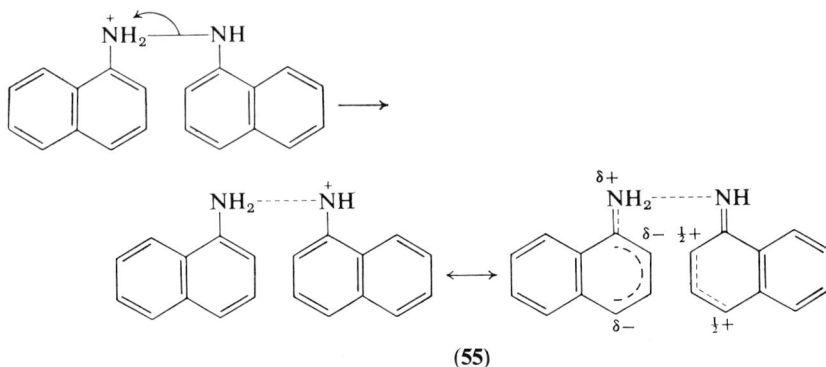

(55)

heterolyzing, diprotonated molecule has the character of an aryl amine and the other, the character of a dication. This is shown for hydrazobenzene with structure **56**.

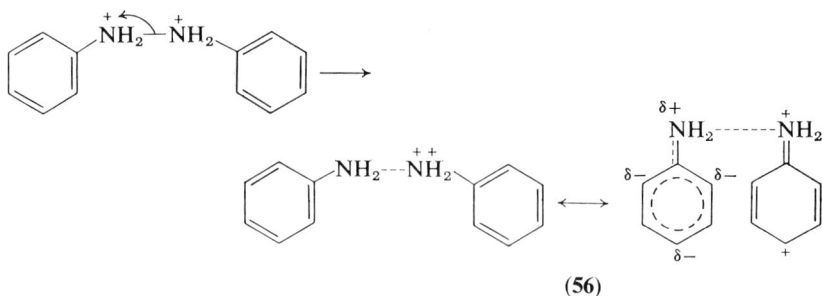

(56)

Each part of each transition state is shown with its most probable charge distribution, and these indicate the most probable bond formations that will occur. They are 4,4′ and 2,2′ in **55**, and 4,4′ and 2,4′ in **56**. The overall process of rearrangement involves, then, the heterolysis of the N—N bond, concerted with the formation of new bonds, the formation going according to the most favorable charge distributions in the transition state. When a hydrazo compound carries a substituent the distribution of charge in the transition state will be affected. Therefore, it is possible to correlate the nature of the substituents with the types of product obtained. Also, the ease of reaching a polar transition state will depend on how well the substituent encourages heterolysis (that is, on how well it can accommodate charge distribution). Therefore, the effect of a substituent on the rate of a rearrangement can be fitted to the polar-transition-state theory.

The addition of the first proton is considered, in the polar-transition-state theory, to be the major step in overcoming the activation barrier to rearrangement. The reason for this is that a monoprotonated hydrazo molecule already has some of the electrical dissymmetry that is to be achieved in the transition state. The addition of the second proton in the two-proton mechanism furnishes a symmetrical molecule, and this is considered to undo the advantage of dissymmetry which was achieved in the monoprotonated state. However, diprotonation also places in the molecule two adjacent positive charges, repulsion between which encourages N—N bond scission. Consequently, where monoprotonation does not provide a sufficiently large driving force for obtaining heterolysis, the addition of a second proton gives assistance, albeit minor, in overcoming the barrier to bond scission.

This particular point of view and also the stress on the polarity of the transition state have been criticized by Sterba and Vecera (57). These workers have found that the increase in the rate of rearrangement of hydrazobenzene, N-1-naphthyl-N′-phenylhydrazine, and ortho-hydrazotoluene (but, for unknown reasons, not 1,1′-hydrazonaphthalene) caused by added salt is attributable mostly to the change in h_0 caused by the salt.

They have also estimated that the addition of the second proton to hydrazobenzene lowers the activation energy for N—N bond scission by a considerable amount. In the opinion of Sterba and Vecera, therefore, the addition of the second proton represents as much of an important contribution to the N—N bond scission as the addition of the first proton. That is, it is not necessary to stress the incipient polarity of the monoprotonated molecule and its relevance to a highly polar transition state. Sterba and Vecera feel that the transition states in the rearrangements are not as polar as proposed by Banthorpe, Hughes, and Ingold. They also feel that a π-complex intermediate is formed in the rate-determining step of a benzidine rearrangement. This and the belief that the transition state is not necessarily as polar as hitherto thought have led them to the opinion that the charge distribution in the intermediate can be more or less symmetrical (e.g., as represented with **57**) or unsymmetrical (e.g., as represented with **58**), depending on the nature of the aryl groups, with the unsymmetrical charge distribution being caused, for example, by the presence of an electron-donating substituent R. It is a departure from the

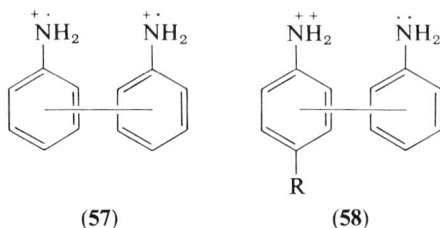

(57)   (58)

polar-transition-state theory to propose that an intermediate is formed (although the theory has been modified recently in this respect; see ref. 24), and this will be discussed in more detail later. The possibility that the transition state may not be as polar as proposed is not firm enough ground for rejecting the theory though. It is useful to examine further the theory's application in explaining many of the facts of the benzidine rearrangement.

b. Product Distribution.   The distributions of charge in the transition-state structures **55** and **56** and the bonding to which they lead have already been pointed out. The polar-transition-state theory envisages that these two transition states differ from each other in the way in which displacement of the aryl rings and their synchronous merging occurs. That is, in **56** the fully positively charged nitrogen atom of the dication portion and the partially positively charged nitrogen atom of the polar aniline portion repel each other and cause a displacement of the rings. As this is occurring, the highly positively charged *para*-position of the dication portion is tilted and attracted toward the electron-rich aniline ring and leads to 4,4'- and 2,4'-bonding. The theory also accommodates the trend toward diphenyline

(2,4'-bonding) in less polar solvents. In these, it is proposed, attraction of the positive *para*-position for the ring and the N—N displacement are increased. Consequently, the rings are better tilted toward 2,4'-bonding.

In contrast with these sorts of displacements, the two portions of the structure **55** in which charge delocalization and electron delocalization are more general and uniform are viewed as moving toward each other without much of the longitudinal displacement caused by N—N charge repulsion. Consequently, both 4,4'- and 2,2'-bonding occur.

How far apart the bonding positions are when bonding begins to occur, and how far apart the nitrogen atoms have been displaced is, of course, unknown. Critics of the theory feel that the distances would be prohibitively long for synchronization.

When an *ortho*-semidine is formed from an unsymmetrical 4,4'-disubstituted hydrazobenzene the better electron-donating substituent is found *para* to the primary amine group. The 4-situated electron-donating group stabilizes the cationic part of the transition state. The polar-transition-state theory provides for synchronous separation of the nitrogen atoms and bonding of the electron-deficient 2-position and electron-rich N'-position. This is represented by structure **59**, assuming that the rearrangement is two-proton catalyzed, and by structure **60**, assuming that it is not. The structure **60** has been written (instead of the structure **61**) without

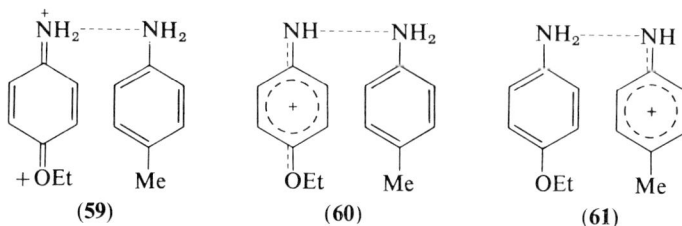

(59)   (60)   (61)

following the practice (58) of placing the single proton on the (anticipated) more basic nitrogen atom. But, the transition-state diagram so obtained is the better suited for charge delocalization. Supposing that protonation of either nitrogen occurs (i.e., as in **60** and **61**), we may propose that rearrangement via the transition state **60** would be the faster. This situation would not be changed if the transition state occurred in a reaction path which gave an intermediate instead of the quinonoidlike product of the polar-transition-state theory.

The products of rearrangement of 4-chlorohydrazobenzene are the diphenyline (**62a**), the *ortho*-semidine (**63a**), and the *para*-semidine (**64a**) (13,24). This rearrangement is second order in acid (24). If it is treated according to the polar-transition-state theory the heterolysis of the N—N bond and the charge character of the transition state may be

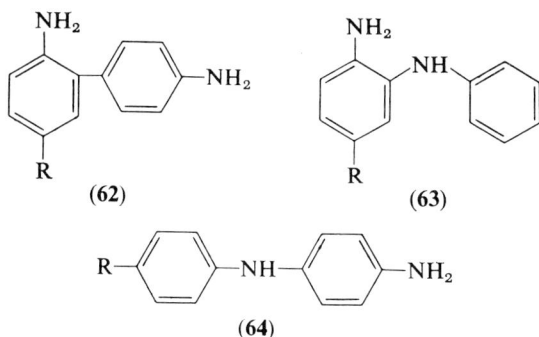

(62)

(63)

(64)

(62a)–(64a) R = Cl; (62b)–(64b) R = OMe

represented as in structure **65**. We must visualize here, though, three transition states in which, synchronous with the parting of the nitrogen atoms, bonding occurs between the 2,N'-positions (*ortho*-semidine), 2,4'-positions (diphenyline), and 4,N'-positions (*para*-semidine).

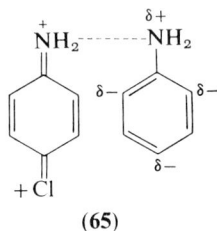

(65)

The difficulty with *para*-semidine formation emerges here. When the polar-transition-state theory was first formulated it incorporated the views of Hammick and Munro (22) that the synchronous bonding process for *para*-semidine formation was stereochemically unreasonable, and therefore, that *para*-semidine formation either was intermolecular or involved a heavy-metal ion. Now that *para*-semidines are known to be genuine benzidine-rearrangement products, the applicability of the polar-transition-state theory to their formation becomes questionable. In the opinion of the author the synchronous breaking of the N—N bond and making of the 4,N' bond requires too great a molecular distortion to be reasonable. A more acceptable approach would be to provide for the rate-determining formation of an intermediate in which reorientation corresponding with *para*-semidine bonding can occur. Again, this is a matter of opinion, and, with further extension of opinion, there seems no reason to exclude intermediate formation from the paths of the other rearrangements.

A similar problem arises with the formation of *para*-semidines from 4-methoxy- and 4-ethoxyhydrazobenzene.

4-Methoxyhydrazobenzene gives the 2,N'-semidine (**63b**) and the 4,N'-semidine (**64b**), but not the *ortho*-benzidine. The polar transition state is represented by structure **66** (rather than **67**). The preferred charge distributions and/or geometries of the transition states must be such as to rule out the 2,2'-bonding which occurs in the somewhat analogous one-

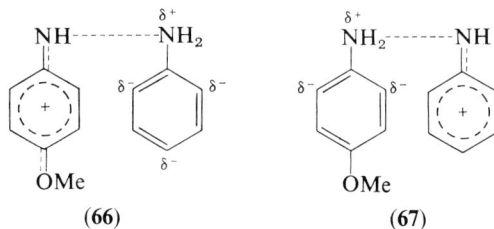

(66)   (67)

proton-catalyzed rearrangement of N-1-naphthyl-N'-phenylhydrazine. In terms of polar-transition-state theory the presence of the methoxyl group must cause displacement of the rings, rather than the congruent merging, which in the naphthalene compound leads to 2,2'-bonding.

c. Rates of Rearrangement. The rates of benzidine rearrangements are enhanced by electron-donating substituents and retarded by electron-withdrawing ones. Strict comparison of rates can be made only among compounds which rearrange by the same kinetic law and in the same circumstances. These conditions are not easily achieved. Some of the most useful data in the literature have been collated by Banthorpe, Hughes, and Ingold and are listed in Table 7. These data can be summarized as sequences of the decreasing effectiveness of R and R' in enhancing the rate of rearrangement as follows:

For the one-proton mechanism:

> 1-naphthyl > 2-naphthyl > *ortho*-tolyl > phenyl

For the two-proton mechanism:

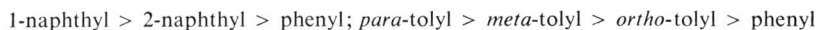

> 1-naphthyl > 2-naphthyl > phenyl; *para*-tolyl > *meta*-tolyl > *ortho*-tolyl > phenyl

One might anticipate that the more basic a hydrazo compound the greater the concentration of its conjugate acid and so the faster its rate of rearrangement. The data show that this is not the rule. The basicities of hydrazoaromatics are not known, but we can assume that the relative basicities of the ArNH portions parallel the relative basicities of the analogous aryl amines. The following comparison can then be made:

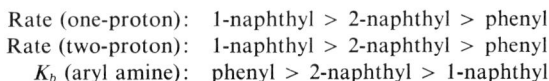

> Rate (one-proton):   1-naphthyl > 2-naphthyl > phenyl
> Rate (two-proton):   1-naphthyl > 2-naphthyl > phenyl
> K_b (aryl amine):   phenyl > 2-naphthyl > 1-naphthyl

TABLE 7

Rate Constants for Rearrangements of RNHNHR' at 0° by the
One-Proton (k_2 in sec^{-1} mole^{-1} liter) and Two-Proton (k_3 in
sec^{-1} mole^{-2} liter^2) Mechanisms (6)[a]

R	R'	$10^3 k_2$	$10^3 k_3$
In 60% aqueous dioxan containing HClO$_4$			
Phenyl	Phenyl	—	1.7
ortho-Tolyl	ortho-Tolyl	0.21	8.5
ortho-Tolyl	para-Tolyl	—	1400
2-Naphthyl	Phenyl	0.50	5.0
1-Naphthyl	Phenyl	20.0	130
2-Naphthyl	2-Naphthyl	460	—
1-Naphthyl	2-Naphthyl	1000	—
1-Naphthyl	1-Naphthyl	1800	—
In 95% ethanol containing HCl[b]			
Phenyl	Phenyl	—	2.4
ortho-Tolyl	ortho-Tolyl	0.25	7.5
meta-Tolyl	meta-Tolyl	—	15
para-Tolyl	para-Tolyl	—	124

[a] Some adjustments have been made for temperature and medium effects.

[b] These data have been collected from the papers of R. B. Carlin and co-workers.

The sequence in effect on rate is exactly the opposite of the sequence in basicities. Thus, although under comparable conditions the concentration of the conjugate acid of hydrazobenzene will be greater than that of 1,1'-hydrazonaphthalene, the latter rearranges faster. The polar transition states, for example, in the two series may be represented by the structures **68–70** and **71–73**. (Structure **70** does not imply that the one-proton rearrangement of hydrazobenzene has been detected.) In each series the ease of delocalizing the positive charge on nitrogen decreases toward the right. Also, in the series **68–70**, the ease of delocalizing the pair of electrons of the amino group decreases toward the right. The overall effect is the raising of the activation barrier to rearrangement in the order **68 → 70** and **71 → 73**. (Any differences in entropies of activation are assumed to be of lesser importance.) The series for the hydrazotoluenes and toluidines are as follows:

Rate (two-proton): *para*-tolyl > *meta*-tolyl > *ortho*-tolyl > phenyl

K_b (aryl amine): *para*-tolyl > *meta*-tolyl > phenyl > *ortho*-tolyl

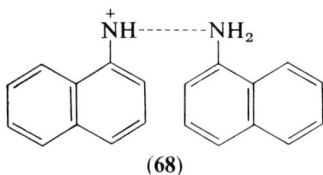

(68)

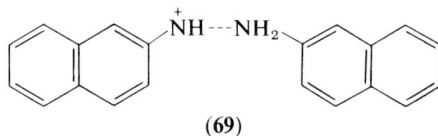

(69)

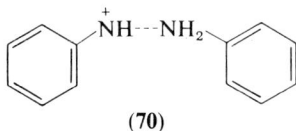

(70)

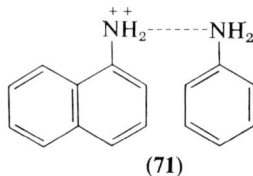

(71)

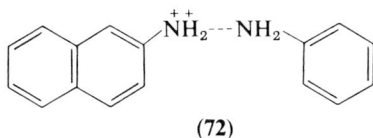

(72)

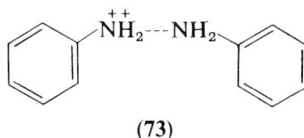

(73)

Here, the order in basicity is similar to the order in rates because the methyl group increases basicity by electron donation and delocalizes a positive charge in the same way. The rate of rearrangement of *ortho*-hydrazotoluene is smaller than that of *meta*-hydrazotoluene because steric inhibition of protonation (or solvation of the cation) makes *ortho*-hydrazotoluene a weaker base than the *meta*-isomer. Stabilization of the transition state by methyl-group hyperconjugation is not sufficient to overcome the difference in the anticipated basicities of the *ortho*- and *meta*-isomers. But, it is sufficient to overcome the difference between the anticipated basicities of *ortho*-hydrazotoluene and hydrazobenzene, for which reason *ortho*-hydrazotoluene rearranges faster than hydrazobenzene.

These examples show how well the polar-transition-state theory can accommodate the rate data. It will be apparent, though, that it is only the polar transition state part of that theory which is involved here. The data would be just as well accommodated by the rate-determining formation of a nonquinonoidlike intermediate via a polar transition state.

d. Orders in Acid. According to the polar-transition-state theory a hydrazo compound ArNHNHAr′ may rearrange by the one-proton mechanism if two conditions are met. They are that, in the monoprotic ion ArNH$_2^+$NHAr′ the unprotonated portion be too weakly basic to readily accept the second proton, yet also be capable of delocalizing the positive charge of the developing transition state. The low basicity of the unprotonated portion may be achieved by electron-pair delocalization, as in the naphthyl compounds, or by steric hindrance to protonation (or cation solvation) as in the *ortho*-substituted compounds. Structural

(74)

(75)

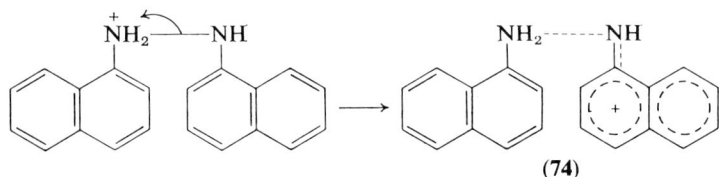

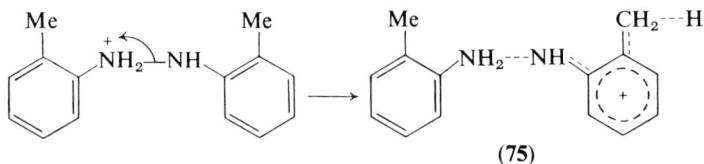

examples are given by **74** and **75**. Where these conditions are not met diprotonation may take place and lead to two-proton-catalyzed rearrangement. This explanation of the dual-order catalysis is based upon the achievement of a polar transition state in the rearrangements. No other satisfactory explanation has been put forward of why some compounds rearrange by a one- and others by a two-proton mechanism.

3. The Caged-Radical Theory

This theory is usually applied to rearrangements by a two-proton mechanism. The idea is that the lowest-energy scission engendered by the repulsion of the two positively charged nitrogen atoms in the dication $ArNH_2^+NH_2^+Ar$ is bond homolysis. Two cation radicals (e.g., **76**) would

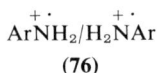

$$\overset{+\,\cdot}{ArNH_2}/\overset{+\,\cdot}{H_2NAr}$$

(76)

be formed in the rate-determining step, each of which is better stabilized by resonance than the fragments of heterolytic scission. The structure **76** should not be confused with structure **57** (Section II-C-2-a). The latter represents charge distribution in a complex, while the former represents two separate radical ions which are prevented momentarily from diffusing away from each other by a "cage" of solvent molecules. Recombination within the solvent cage will take place, according to the theory, to give the various types of rearrangement product.

Caged-radical intermediates are well known in free-radical reactions. The caged radicals are usually neutral radicals. Recombination to give the original molecule has been demonstrated in a number of cases, but the radicals must eventually leave the solvent cage if a free-radical reaction is to occur, and, of course, the neutral radicals do leave the cage readily. Although evidence has been presented for the geminate recombination of cation radicals (amidinium ions, a different type from the present case, and only to the extent of 40–60%) (59) and although theory suggests that two cation radicals would have a strong attraction for each other (60), it is doubtful that, if formed, the proposed caged cation radicals of a benzidine rearrangement would be entirely free of any of the other reactions of caged radicals.

One of the attractive features of the caged-cation-radical theory is that it can be applied to the disproportionation reaction. The reactions of radicals which have escaped from the cage may be formulated as in Eqs. 13 and 14. These represent the reactions of escaped radicals with

$$ArNH_2^{+\cdot} + ArNHNHAr \longrightarrow Ar\overset{+}{N}H_3 + Ar\overset{\cdot}{N}NHAr \qquad (13)$$

$$ArNH_2^{+\cdot} + Ar\overset{\cdot}{N}NHAr \longrightarrow Ar\overset{+}{N}H_3 + ArN{=}NAr \qquad (14)$$

nearby hydrazo molecules. In contrast with these proposed reactions, no one has ever been able to find evidence of reaction of either escaped or caged radicals with the solvent. It may be that aromatic amine cation radicals are not strong enough oxidizing agents to oxidize solvent molecules and so, if they were formed and escaped from the solvent cage, they would oxidize only hydrazo molecules. Attempts to detect radicals by ESR spectroscopy in the disproportionation of *para*-hydrazobiphenyl were unsuccessful, however (37). In some hydrazoaromatic reactions the hydrazo compound undergoes reduction, for example, *para*-hydrazotoluene not only rearranges and disproportionates, but also is reduced to *para*-toluidine (34,35). It is thought that the reducing agent is the solvent (ethanol) and that radical-ion intermediates are reduced. But, no definite confirmatory evidence has been found.

Attempts to detect radicals by ESR spectroscopy in the rearrangement of hydrazobenzene and 1,1′-hydrazonaphthalene have also been unsuccessful (61).

The failure to detect radicals and radical side reactions casts strong doubt on the validity of the caged-radical theory. There are other reasons for doubt, too, most of which have been described by Banthorpe, Hughes, and Ingold (6). For example, homolysis of the diprotonated ion is not the sort of process that would have the salt and solvent effects observed in benzidine rearrangements. Even though Sterba and Vecera have shown that the transition states of the rearrangements may not be as polar as proposed by Banthorpe, Hughes, and Ingold, they must certainly have a fair degree of polarity. The dispersal of two units of positive charge from the ion $ArNH_2^+NH_2^+Ar$ in the formation of the two caged cation radicals does not call for the observed effects of solvent on rates of rearrangement, effects which are suited to a more polar process than homolytic bond dissociation.

If doubts are raised about the caged-radical theory in its most suitable form, the two-proton rearrangement, they become intensified when the theory is applied to the one-proton rearrangement. Homolytic dissociation of the ion $ArNH_2^+NHAr$ into the unsymmetrical radical pair (77) has no

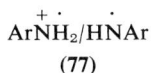

$$\overset{+}{Ar}\overset{\cdot}{NH_2}/\overset{\cdot}{H}\overset{\cdot}{N}Ar$$

(77)

particular virtue. The repulsion between like charges, operating in the dication, and the stability of the two symmetrical radical ions of 76 are absent. The mutual attraction which theory describes for the two cation radicals is also absent, so that diffusion from the solvent cage should occur. We might anticipate also that the orientations of the two recombining radicals in 77 would be different from the orientations of the recombining radicals in 76. Therefore, when a compound is capable of rearranging separately by both first- and second-order acid catalysis we might anticipate, if caged radicals were involved, a different distribution of products in the one-proton from that in the two-proton rearrangement. This is not the observed result.

The caged-radical theory, therefore, in both the one- and two-proton forms, does not appear consistent with observed results.

4. The π-Complex Theory

a. General Considerations. This theory has had its ups and downs since it was first proposed (43). The reason for this is that Dewar built around the core of the theory—the formation of a π complex—a number of predictions and explanations which were subsequently shown to be untenable. The predictions were made in the absence of the kinetic data which later changed the picture completely, and some of the explanations were of experimental results which were misleadingly wrong. Nevertheless, the π-complex theory has been remarkably resilient for the reason that the essential part of it—the π complex—is an attractive and useful concept, which, when removed from the predictions which have encumbered it, can be easily adapted to experimental results.

The theory was first applied to benzidine rearrangements when it was thought that they were all kinetically first order in acid (43). The

monoprotonated hydrazo compound was viewed as undergoing a rate-
determining heterolytic scission to form a π complex, represented by
structure **78a**, rather than the final product. When it became known that
the rearrangement of hydrazobenzene was second order in acid, this view
had to be modified. One of the proposed modifications was that the
diprotonated hydrazobenzene formed the π complex (**78b**), which then

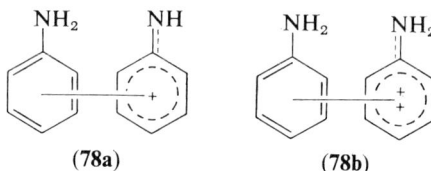

(**78a**)   (**78b**)

collapsed to product. The formation of the dipositive π complex (**78b**)
was considered not to be the best of explanations for second-order acid
kinetics, however (62). Instead, the proposal was made that the first
proton formed the π complex (**78a**), and a rate-determining reaction with
the second proton caused **78a** to unfold into the product.

When examples of mixed-order acid kinetics were discovered and it
became necessary to explain how rearrangements could be both first and
second order in acid, the formation of π complexes and their reaction with
a second proton became the basis of an overall theory for the family of
rearrangements. The position was then (4) that an aromatic hydrazo
compound was converted into a π complex after becoming monoprotonated. This π complex could collapse to product or isomerize to other
π complexes which could collapse to product. The formation and isomerizations of the π complexes were reversible and each type of product
had its own precursor π complex. Rearrangements of this kind were first
order in acid. When a rearrangement was second order in acid, the second
proton was utilized in attacking the particular π complex which corre-
sponded with the product to be formed. In cases of this kind the attack of
the second proton was rate determining. The theory was formulated before
specific-acid catalysis was so firmly established. In this respect the proposed
rate-determining protonation reactions of the π-complex theory became
invalid.

Another prediction of the π-complex theory—that first-order acid
catalysis would prevail at high acidities and second-order catalysis at
low—was also contradicted by later developments.

Other parts of the π-complex theory which had to be abandoned in
the face of accumulated experimental evidence concerned the *ortho*-
semidine rearrangement. This was predicted to be first order in acid (62),
but then Carlin and Wich showed the rearrangement of *para*-hydrazo-

toluene to be second order (34). Later, as part of the mixed-acid-order, π-complex theory, bulky substituents in 4,4′-hydrazobenzenes were designated as promoting first-order in preference to second-order acid catalysis. This proposal was made when 4-*tert*-butyl-4′-chloro- and 4-chloro-4′-methylhydrazobenzene were found to rearrange by fractional-order acid catalysis (Section II-B-2-b). It was not in harmony with the known second-order rearrangement of *para*-hydrazotoluene and became quite untenable when 4,4′-di-*tert*-butylhydrazobenzene was found to be a second-order acid case (50).

One of the examples of hydrazoaromatic behavior that has been used throughout Dewar's reviews of the benzidine rearrangement is that of *para*-hydrazobiphenyl. It illustrates a characteristic of the theory of easily being able to incorporate facts which are wrong, but also illustrates another characteristic of the theory—its flexibility. That is, no matter what fact is removed for being wrong, the theory can be adjusted so as to be still useful.

Until recently *para*-hydrazobiphenyl was thought to disproportionate quantitatively and rearrange not at all. The π-complex theory explanation of this was that the two *para*-phenyl groups prevented the formation of the first-required π complex, from which, by rotation, the next-required π complex (leading to the *ortho*-semidine) would be formed. It is known now that *para*-hydrazobiphenyl does rearrange if, instead of being boiled according to earlier recipes, its acid solution is kept at 0–25°. Curiously, if we were to follow Dewar's arguments on this case to their logical end, we would conclude that the benzidine rearrangement involved a caged-cation-radical intermediate rather than a π complex, for one of Dewar's reasons for ruling out ion-radical formation and criticizing the caged-radical theory was that, if ion radicals were involved we should expect *para*-hydrazobiphenyl to rearrange, since the *para*-phenyl substituent could not possibly hinder the dimerization of the ion radical (**79**) to a semidine. But, following arguments of this kind in the benzidine rearrangement to their logical end is hazardous. The fact that *para*-hydrazobiphenyl

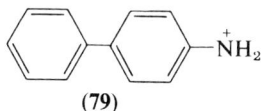
(**79**)

does rearrange may just as well mean that the appropriate π complex is not as hard to form as was thought or that no intermediate is required at all.

Thus, of the original proposals for the π-complex theory and all of its modifications except the most recent (3), only the π complex itself remains.

Dewar and Marchand (3) have pointed out that schemes can be easily written involving π complexes which would be in full accord with the new data. The Eqs. 15–20 were given as an example; π_1 and π_2 represent the

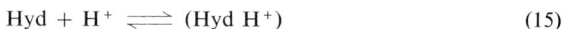

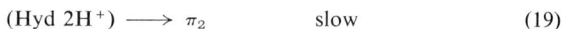

$$\text{Hyd} + \text{H}^+ \rightleftharpoons (\text{Hyd H}^+) \tag{15}$$

$$(\text{Hyd H}^+) \longrightarrow \pi_1 \qquad \text{slow} \tag{16}$$

$$\pi_1 \longrightarrow \text{products} \tag{17}$$

$$(\text{Hyd H}^+) + \text{H}^+ \rightleftharpoons (\text{Hyd 2H}^+) \tag{18}$$

$$(\text{Hyd 2H}^+) \longrightarrow \pi_2 \qquad \text{slow} \tag{19}$$

$$\pi_2 \longrightarrow \text{products} \tag{20}$$

one- and two-proton π complexes. Dewar and Marchand point out that the same schemes can be written with caged radicals serving as the intermediates in place of the π complexes, but arguments against caged-radical formation are given which are to some extent similar to those in Section II-C-3.

b. Transition States and the π-Complex Theory. A notable gap in the π-complex theory, on which Banthorpe, Hughes, and Ingold have commented, is the absence of reference to transition states (6). As a matter of fact, reference to transition states is hard to find in any of the earlier discussions of the benzidine rearrangement. It is this particular aspect of the benzidine rearrangement which has set it apart from most other organic reactions. A recognized practice in applying physical-organic chemistry to reaction mechanisms is to try to obtain a picture of the reaction's transition state at the start. With this picture one attempts to explain all that is known of the course of the reaction—its kinetic, stereo-chemical, and product-forming features, etc. This practice has been avoided in the benzidine rearrangements until Banthorpe, Hughes, and Ingold developed the polar-transition-state theory. The benzidine rearrangement differs from most other organic reactions, for which a picture of a transition state is usually easily developed, since several transition states must be visualized, one per product type, originating from the same source, and probably differing by only small amounts of energy. The π-complex theory deals in intermediates and, in its earlier developments, attempted to account for what was known about the benzidine rearrangements in terms of the intermediates. A better approach would have been to account for experimental evidence in terms of transition states. Since these are absent from the π-complex theory the most logical remedy is to use the polar transition states, that is, to combine the polar-transition-state and π-complex theories. This, at first glance, may appear to be unsuitable, since the same π complex could be formed by homolytic and heterolytic scission of the N—N bond. In the two-proton rearrangements, the homolytic scission might be expected to be preferred. The volume of activation ($\Delta V^{\ddagger}$) for the rearrangement of hydrazobenzene is 1.5 cc/mole (63) and of *ortho*-hydrazotoluene is -7.2 cc/mole (64). It is estimated that the volume of activation for a two-proton rearrangement whose transition state involved homolytic scission of the N—N bond would be nearer 10 cc/mole, and it is concluded that small or negative experimental values are more in accord with a polar transition state (65). Again, in spite of any modification of salt effects for which Sterba and Vecera's results call (Section II-C-2-a), the salt and solvent effects and the many other results are in harmony with a polar transition state. If a π-complex intermediate is to be formed, its transition state is best described as polar.

We arrive at this stage with a feeling of dealing only in semantics. Is there much difference between a theory with a polar transition state and no intermediate and a theory with a polar transition state and an intermediate? In terms of energetics there is not much difference. The π-complex intermediates would represent small dips in the free energy of the system as the reaction proceeded. In terms of geometry or stereochemistry, the π-complex intermediates are useful. In the polar-transition-state theory the type of product is determined not only by the distribution of charge and electron-pair density, but also by the geometry of approach of the two halves of the transition state, that is, with or without some degree of displacement. In the π-complex theory the two halves of the complex lie in parallel planes in which the disposition toward product bonding is determined by the distribution of charge and electron-pair density. If the two theories are to be combined we must allow for N—N bond breaking to be coordinated with the movement of the two halves of the molecule into appropriate π-complex configurations. Further description of this process is difficult. The formation of π-complex intermediates would allow us to dispense with considerations of concerted bond making and breaking over uncomfortably large distances and the molecular distortions they would require. The involvement of the intermediates becomes intuitively attractive. The *proof* of their involvement, however, is either questionable or nonexistent.

c. Evidence For and Against π-Complex Intermediates. (*1*) Very little of anything that has been said for or against π-complex intermediates in the benzidine rearrangements carries the weight of definite evidence. We now exclude further consideration of all of the parts of the old π-complex theory that have been shown to be wrong, but confine the remark to the π-complex idea itself. As has been pointed out in earlier sections and by Dewar and Marchand (3), kinetic data themselves shed no light on this matter. Where the polar-transition-state theory calls for concerted bond making and breaking over long distances and in unconvincing geometrical orientations, the intervention of a π-complex intermediate is intuitively attractive. But, that is all. There are some situations, however, in which an intermediate seems indispensable; yet, there are others in which it seems impossible.

(2) A most interesting case is the rearrangement of 2-ethylamino-hydrazobenzene (80) (Section II-A-8). We are going to assume that the use of Jacobson's method in the work introduced no special problems, such as the possibility of intermolecular reactions or heavy-metal ion participation. The newly clarified *para*-semidine situation gives some assurance on that score. The most reasonable explanation of the rearrangement of 80 is that an intermediate was formed. This is represented as a one-proton π complex (82), although, since 36% hydrochloric acid was used (33), the rearrangement may well have been of the two-proton type. The prediction of the polar-transition-state theory would be that the

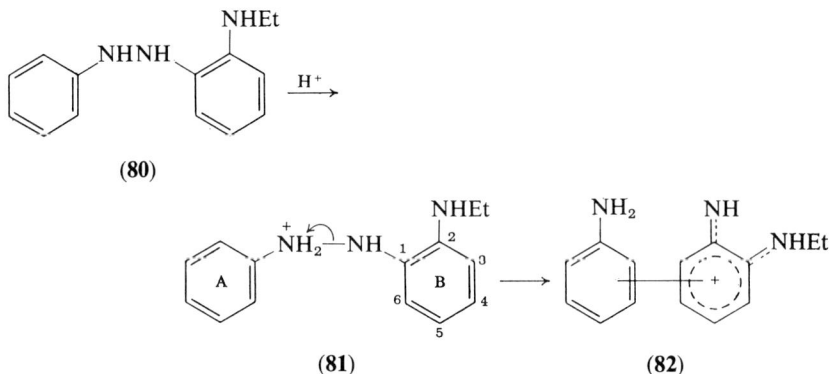

(80)

(81)   (82)

heterolyzing molecule (as in 81) would lead to bonding at the 4- and 6-positions of ring B. The theory would not predict bonding at the 5-position where it actually occurs. At least, no similar case is known, certainly not among the 2-alkyl and 2-alkoxy compounds wherein a possible 5-directing substituent is found. The π-complex representation (82) shows that the ethylimino and imino groups in ring B are positionally equivalent; and the ethylimino group, furthermore, is now the better controller of charge distribution. The argument in favor of a π complex is strong, but, in the absence of quantitative kinetic and product data it is not certain.

(3) The rearrangement of *meta*-hydrazoaniline has been cited by Clovis and Hammond as indicating the involvement of π complexes (66). The rearrangement is inverse first order in acid. Rearrangement of the labeled compound (83) was studied. The product, 2,2'-diaminobenzidine (84), can be formed by three paths: (a) 4,4'-bonding (benzidine type),

(b) 2,2′-bonding (ortho-benzidine type), and (c) 2,4′-bonding (diphenyline type). By determining the amount of ^{15}N in **84** and the diaminocarbazole obtained from it, it was possible to determine the extent of 2,2′-coupling. This increased when the acidity of the rearrangement solution was

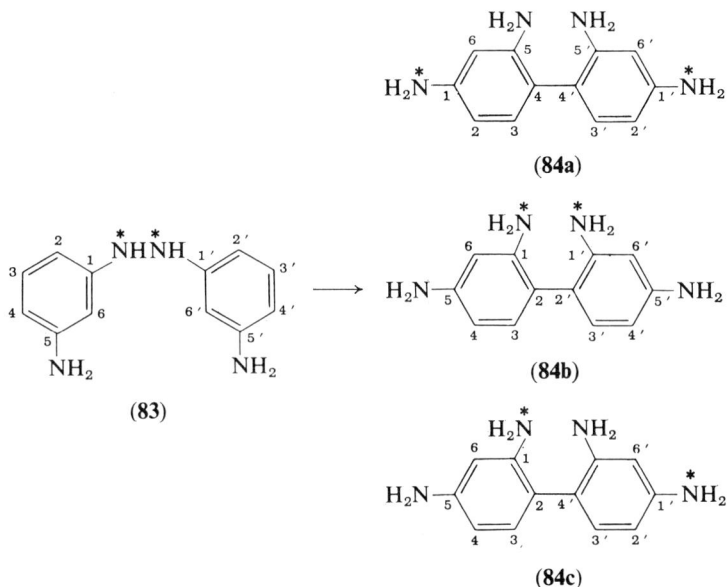

(84a)

(83)

(84b)

(84c)

increased. At an acidity of less than $2 \times 10^{-3}M$ about 34–35% of 2,2′-coupling occurred, while at $3.77 \times 10^{-2}M$ acidity the extent was 44.8%. Over this range of acidities the rearrangement was still first order in acid. This indicates that the rate-determining and product-determining steps are not the same and implies the formation of an intermediate, which was represented as the π complex (**85**). Further, explanation of the increase in 2,2′-coupling with increasing acidity was offered in the possibility that **85** undergoes a rapid reaction with a second proton to give the symmetrical intermediate, represented here as the π complex (**86**). This π complex (which as shown here differs a little, but not materially, from Clovis and Hammond's structure) is able to collapse to product and, being symmetrical, can give equal amounts of 2,2′- and 4,4′-coupling.

Although Clovis and Hammond's proposals are reasonable they are not unquestionable from the point of view of offering definite evidence for the participation of an intermediate. First, the three, one-proton paths to product formation (**84a–84c**) could be presented as polar-transition-state-theory paths, in which an intermediate (i.e., **85**) would not be required. Second, rate constants of duplicate runs varied by about 10%.

Therefore, there is the possibility that small amounts of two-proton catalysis occurred, increasing in importance with increasing acidity, but going undetected in the rate measurements. The two-proton, polar-transition-state-theory rearrangements would also cause an increase in the extent of 2,2'-coupling. These counter-arguments to Clovis and Hammond's proposals, while not strong, make the case for the formation of the intermediate (85) not as good as it appears at first.

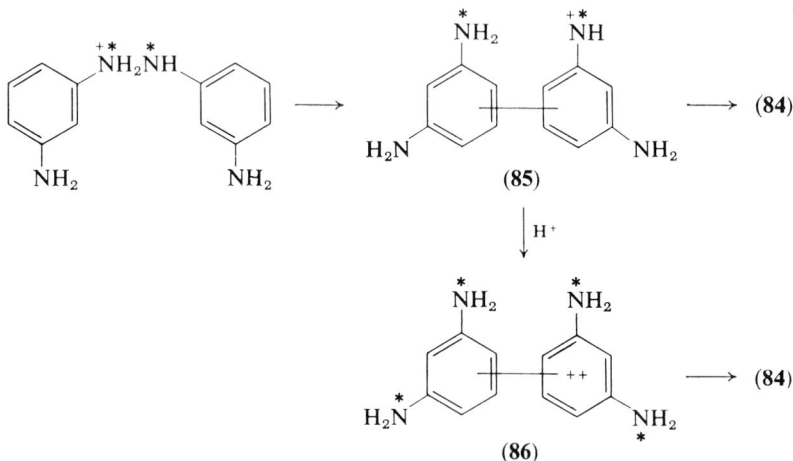

(Clovis and Hammond's results with the ^{15}N-labeled 83 have an interesting bearing on the π-complex theory in its original forms. Unused 3,3'-diaminohydrazobenzene which was recovered had not undergone ^{15}N-scrambling. That is, if a π complex was formed from 83 it cannot have reverted to 83. The reversal of π-complex formation was a feature of the π-complex theory of rearrangement.)

(4) The rearrangements of the cyclic N,N'-polymethylene compounds (Section II-A-7) present problems for the π-complex intermediate theory. Wittig and co-workers have pointed this out (30). It is impossible to make the phenyl rings in models of some of these compounds (in which the nitrogen atoms are quaternary-nitrogen models) line up parallel to each other. In some cases, when the polymethylene chain is long enough, the rings can be brought close to the parallel alignment, but there is no possibility of rotation (because of the restriction of the connecting poly-methylene chain). The use of the models suggests that the rearrangement must occur without the intervening intermediate. This may be so. It may be that we should regard the π-complex intermediate in some cases to be of such high energy that it becomes indistinguishable from a transition state, while in others (generally) of favorable geometry and charge

distribution, the π complex should be regarded definitely as an energy minimum along the reaction coordinate.

5. Lukashevich's Theory

Lukashevich has concluded that aromatic hydrazo compounds can form monoacid salts but are too weakly basic to form diacid salts. This conclusion is apparently based on the failure to obtain diacid salts by treating solutions of hydrazo compounds in ether or benzene and toluene with hydrogen chloride and hydrogen bromide. Under this treatment some hydrazo compounds formed an isolable, insoluble salt, and the salt was always the monoacid one (2). Lukashevich regards these facts as showing that a hydrazoaromatic cannot become diprotonated. The theory which incorporates the steps of Eqs. 5 and 6 (Section II-B-1) is therefore rejected.

The fallacy in this argument is evident. It is not uncommon in chemical reactions that an intermediate is detectable (kinetically or otherwise) but not isolable. The kinetic evidence for diprotonation is so strong that it cannot be refuted by the failure to isolate diacid salts.

It is Lukashevich's view, furthermore, that a monoacid salt can rearrange not spontaneously but only under the continued action of the acid. The basis for this view apparently is that since monoacid salts can be isolated, they obviously cannot rearrange spontaneously. The transition state for the rearrangement under continued action of the acid is represented as **87** (2). Suppose we accept Lukashevich's view that diprotonation

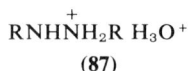

$$\overset{+}{RNHNH_2R} \; H_3O^+$$

(87)

cannot occur and add one of our own that monoprotonation must surely not be a rate-determining process. In that case the transition state (**87**) is for a reaction which is second order in acid. In these circumstances the double protonation would be "illusory," but all rearrangements would be second order in acid. Furthermore, they would all be general-acid catalyzed which, of course, is not correct.

But, the circumstances above may be the wrong ones to prescribe. It is not easy to understand the meaning of some crucial parts of Lukashevich's views. It is pertinent to quote a relevant paragraph:

Hydrazo compounds are not useful for kinetic studies because they only resemble the usual diacid bases. The rate of monoprotonation is dependent on the basicity of the starting hydrazo compound whereas the rate of the subsequent stage is only indirectly related to the basicity of the monoprotonated molecule and is determined by the stability in the presence of the acid agent. With a considerable difference in the rates of the first and second phases there is created an illusion of double protonation in case of compounds which form salts resistant to the further action of acid. In a number of cases monoprotonated hydrazo compounds are, however, extremely sensitive to acids and then the rate of the second phase is very high. It is just this simple fact, substantiated by the kinetic equations that has convinced investigators that these examples prove the existence of a "spontaneous" rearrangement of monoprotonated hydrazo compounds.

The basis for the first statement is quite unclear. As for the second, the rate-controlling protonation which it implies is unsubstantiated. Kinetic equations can be written which fit a competition between first and second "phases" such that a fast second phase causes an apparent first-

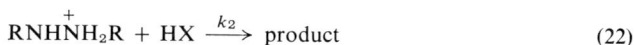

$$\text{RNHNHR} + \text{HX} \underset{k_{-1}}{\overset{k_1}{\rightleftharpoons}} \text{RNH}\overset{+}{\text{N}}\text{H}_2\text{R} + \text{X}^- \tag{21}$$

$$\text{RNH}\overset{+}{\text{N}}\text{H}_2\text{R} + \text{HX} \xrightarrow{k_2} \text{product} \tag{22}$$

$$-d(\text{Hyd})/dt = k_1 k_2[\text{HX}]\{[\text{Hyd}][\text{HX}]/(k_{-1} + k_2[\text{HX}])\} \tag{23}$$

order acid dependence. These are Eqs. 21–22 and Eq. 23 which is obtained by steady-state treatment. Here, if $k_2[\text{HX}] \gg k_{-1}$ the reaction will follow first-order acid kinetics, while if $k_{-1} \gg k_2[\text{HX}]$ the dependence on acid will be second order. But, the equations do not agree with the known, fast proton transfers and isotope effects. The whole of the Lukashevich views, therefore, must be summed up as unacceptable.

6. Summary of the Theories

Of the four theories, we can dismiss Lukashevich's as contradicting experimental evidence and dispose of the caged-radical theory for inadequate supporting evidence. The polar-transition-state theory goes a long way toward accounting for all of the known facts. The synchronous making and breaking of bonds over long distances which the polar-transition-state theory requires is an unattractive feature of the theory. The π-complex theory in its original forms is not in accord with many experimental data. Divorced from the earlier forms of the theory, however, π complexes may serve as intermediates in the rearrangements. A useful overall description of the rearrangements is that π-complex intermediates are formed via polar transition states. No firm evidence exists, however, to *demand* the interposition of intermediates (π complex or otherwise) in the reaction paths. The settling of this point is the remaining major task in the mechanism of the benzidine rearrangement. Provision must be made for intermediate formation in the disproportionation reaction which is discussed in the following section.

III. ACID-CATALYZED DISPROPORTIONATION

When a hydrazoaromatic compound undergoes concurrent rearrangement and disproportionation, the two reactions obey the same kinetic law. This has been reported for *para*-hydrazotoluene (34,35), 4,4'-di-*tert*-butyl-, 4-*tert*-butyl-4'-chloro- (50), 4,4'-dichlorohydrazobenzene (67), and *para*-hydrazobiphenyl (37). Disproportionation accounts for the disappearance of 40% of *para*-hydrazotoluene and at least 75% of *para*-hydrazobiphenyl. Thus, it is not a minor side reaction. It is an important part of hydrazoaromatic chemistry, yet no one knows how it occurs.

The stoichiometry of the disproportionation reaction requires two molecules of hydrazo compound (Eq. 1, Section II-A-9). Since the reaction is first order in hydrazo compound one of these molecules must participate in the rate-determining step of the reaction, while the other must be used up after the rate-determining step has been passed. But the molecule of substrate that participates in the rate-determining step cannot have undergone any type of skeletal change that would prevent its being converted subsequently to either the azoaromatic or the scission amine. For this reason, a hydrazoaromatic molecule which is being taken on its way to rearrangement in a concerted process, as described by the polar-transition-state theory, cannot be involved in disproportionation.

An intermediate must be formed in the rate-determining step of the disproportionation reaction. The simplest way of accounting for this and for concurrent rearrangement is represented in Scheme 1. In this scheme,

$$R\overset{+}{N}H_2\overset{+}{N}H_2R \xrightarrow{\text{slow}} \text{Intermediate-1}^{++} \xrightarrow{a} \text{Rearrangement}$$

$$b \downarrow \quad \text{RNHNHR}$$

Disproportionation

Scheme 1

the diprotonated hydrazo compound is used since most of the reported disproportionations have been second order in acid, and the dication forms an intermediate which rapidly either rearranges (path *a*) or disproportionates (path *b*). This division in paths requires that the relative extents of disproportionation and rearrangement vary with the concentration of the free hydrazo compound. Because the concentration of free hydrazo compound will vary with the acidity of the solution, the product distribution should also vary with acidity. Satisfactory studies of these points have not been made because the changes in substrate and acid concentrations which have been employed have not been very large. The indications so far are that the product distribution does not vary with either acidity or initial substrate concentration (34,37).

If this is to be the case, the division in paths must occur in such a way as to maintain product ratios independent of substrate and acid concentrations. Such division may be represented by Scheme 2. The path *c* here is the polar-transition-state path, and we have already assessed the value of placing an intermediate in it (Section II-C-6). The path *d* to

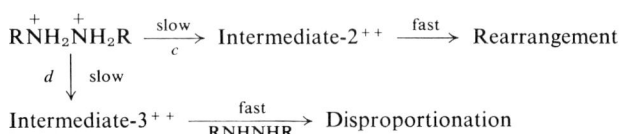

$$\overset{+}{R}NH_2\overset{+}{N}H_2R \xrightarrow[c]{slow} \text{Intermediate-2}^{++} \xrightarrow{fast} \text{Rearrangement}$$

$$d \downarrow slow$$

$$\text{Intermediate-3}^{++} \xrightarrow[RNHNHR]{fast} \text{Disproportionation}$$

Scheme 2

disproportionation must have an intermediate, designated here as Intermediate-3. The nature of this intermediate is quite unknown, although speculations about it have been made.

One suggestion for the nature of Intermediate-3 has already been made—that it is a pair of caged radicals which, on diffusing from the solvent cage, enter the disproportionation reaction (Eqs. 13 and 14, Section II-C-3). The arguments against the participation of radical intermediates have also already been given. To them can be added the point that if Intermediate-3 were a pair of cation radicals, the transition state of path *d* would not require solvation by polar solvents as much as the polar transition state of path *c*. In that event, we should expect a change in product distribution toward more disproportionation on changing to solvents of low polarity, a possibility which has yet to be tested properly.

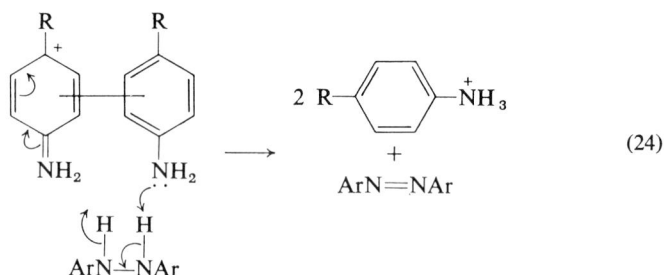

$$(24)$$

The Intermediate-3 can also be a π complex. The disproportionation reaction may then be represented as the bimolecular reaction of Eq. 24. Dewar proposed this type of reaction with the monocationic π complex when the reactions of all hydrazo compounds were thought to be first order in acid (58). Vecera, Synek, and Sterba have considered the two-proton modification (Eq. 24), but have concluded (without any strong experimental basis) that disproportionation may occur by both the π-complex path and the cation-radical path (55).

The π-complex path of Eq. 24 has an interesting analogy in the very rapid oxidation of hydrazo compounds by Bindschedler's green (Eq. 25). Also, one hydrazo compound in acid solution may oxidize another, more stable hydrazo compound. Thus, acidified *para*-hydrazotoluene oxidizes

(25)

hydrazobenzene (35), and acidified *para*-hydrazobiphenyl oxidizes 4,4′-dichlorohydrazobenzene (37). An ESR search for radicals in the reactions of *para*-hydrazobiphenyl was in vain. The formation of a π-complex intermediate, followed by reaction as in Eq. 24, would account for the observations.

The two oxidation reactions which have just been quoted provide room for further thought about intermediates in hydrazoaromatic reactions. A diprotonated hydrazo compound will oxidize another hydrazo compound which is in excess. Yet, evidence for the oxidation of the solvent has never been found. The lack of this evidence is usually cited as an argument against radical intermediates in hydrazoaromatic reactions. The same difficulty would apply, however, if the intermediate in the disproportionation reactions were a π complex. The apparent absence of reaction with the solvent may be due only to the fact that the intermediate (π complex or radicals) is not a strong enough oxidizing agent to oxidize the alcoholic solvents in which the reactions are usually carried out. (There are, of course, other arguments against radical intermediates besides the one of no apparent reaction with solvent.) In continuing the analogy between the π-complex reaction and the Bindschedler's green reaction (Eq. 25), we note that even so fast a hydrazo oxidant as Bindschedler's green reacts only slowly with alcoholic solvents.

The disproportionation reaction, then, is explainable with the use of a π-complex intermediate. This gives an added attraction to including π-complex intermediates in the rearrangement paths, for we may ask: If an intermediate must be formed in the disproportionation reaction is it not likely that similar intermediates are formed in the rearrangements? The implied answer to this question is, of course, yes. Recently, cases of concurrent rearrangement and disproportionation which are first order in acid have been reported. For example, as much as 70% of 4-acetaminohydrazobenzene undergoes disproportionation (24), while 20% of 4-methoxyhydrazobenzene does so too. In these examples we see how closely the several transformations of hydrazoaromatics are connected. Several rearrangement products may be formed and disproportionation may occur, all under the same main kinetic description, whether it is first or second order in acid. It is not at all unexpected, then, that intuition would call for the same sorts of intermediates in the one type of reaction that analysis requires in the other.

In this connection we refer to a very recent and novel description of a class of intermediates which would serve for the disproportionation reaction (24). They are quinonoid, ring-linked, and still-protonated intermediates, somewhat similar to those proposed for rearrangement in the polar-transition-state theory. An intermediate which is proposed for the disproportionation reaction is illustrated by structure **88** in Eq. 26. The proposal assumes that the loss of the groups R in **88** does not compete

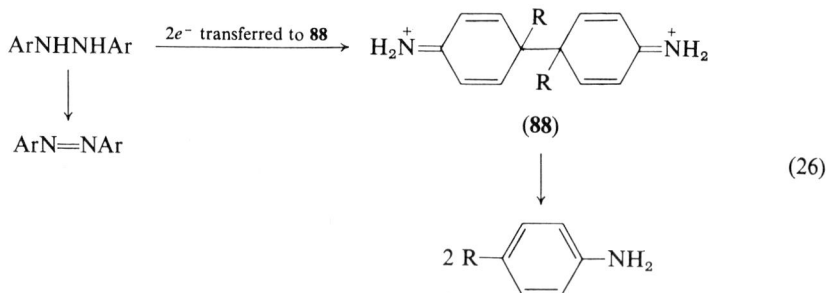

$$\text{ArNHNHAr} \xrightarrow{\ 2e^-\ \text{transferred to}\ \mathbf{88}\ } H_2\overset{+}{N}\!=\!\!\left\langle \begin{array}{c} R \\ \\ R \end{array} \right\rangle\!=\!\overset{+}{N}H_2$$

ArNHNHAr → ArN=NAr

$$2\ R\!-\!\!\left\langle \right\rangle\!-\!NH_2$$

(88)

(26)

with disproportionation. Equation 26 depicts the transfer of two electrons from a hydrazoaromatic molecule to the intermediate, which is thereupon split into two molecules of aryl amine. The novelty of this proposal is the requirement that bonding occurs at the 4,4'-positions of the protonated hydrazo compound while those positions bear substituents which must not be ejected (i.e., in the way that substituent hydrogen is ejected as a proton). The proposal is attractive because disproportionation is observed mostly with hydrazo compounds which *do* bear 4,4'-substituents. Yet, the proposal is also disturbing in that, if it is correct, we might surely expect to have found some cases in which both disproportionation *and* substituent ejection occur. The *tert*-butyl group is an attractive candidate for ejection or solvolysis from an intermediate such as **88**. For example, the boiling of 3,4-di-*tert*-butylaniline in aqueous acid causes the loss of the 4-*tert*-butyl group (68). The loss occurs presumably from the intermediate (**89**). This intermediate is probably not easily formed, while the corresponding

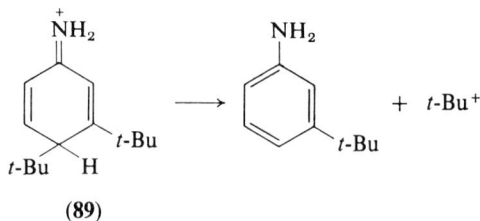

(**89**)

intermediate **88** if it exists is, as it were, ready-made for the ejection of the *tert*-butyl group. However, 4,4'-di-*tert*-butylbenzene disproportionates (50) but does not also undergo group ejection.

There are several recorded cases of a *para*-substituent's ejection accompanying rearrangement (69). It is not possible to say if disproportionation occurred also, because the reactions were carried out with Jacobson's method. 4-Carboxyhydrazobenzene has also been heated with hydrochloric acid under nonreducing conditions (70). The ejection of the carboxyl group was noted and some 4-carboxyazobenzene (about 12%) was obtained. But, whether the formation of the carboxyazobenzene was caused by disproportionation or air oxidation of the hydrazo compound cannot be said.

Thus, the answers in test cases are missing. The acceptance of **88** (R = phenyl) as an intermediate in the very facile disproportionation of *para*-hydrazobiphenyl also engenders some misgiving on account of the crowding of the phenyl groups which would be required.

A final note on the disproportionation reaction—based on the reactions of the solid monoacid salts of some hydrazo compounds Lukashevich has proposed that disproportionation occurs as in Eq. 27 (2).

$$2Ar\overset{+}{N}H_2NHAr \longrightarrow ArN{=}NAr + 2Ar\overset{+}{N}H_3 \qquad (27)$$

When applied to reactions in solution this proposal has no validity. It would require, for example, that disproportionation be second order in hydrazo compound.

IV. THERMAL REARRANGEMENT AND
DISPROPORTIONATION

A. Conditions and Products of Rearrangement

Some aromatic hydrazo compounds rearrange cleanly when heated in solution, while others undergo concurrent (and sometimes predominant) disproportionation. The compounds which rearrange best are those with one or two naphthyl groups, and among these, the ones with the 2-naphthyl group rearrange most cleanly.

The thermal rearrangement of 2,2'-hydrazonaphthalene to 2,2'-diamino-1,1'-binaphthyl was discovered by Meisenheimer and Witte (71) in 1903, but because the hydrazo compound was then heated in aqueous alcoholic sodium hydroxide, these workers thought that the rearrangement was base catalyzed. About 45 years later Krolik and Lukashevich (72) showed that the rearrangement took place in neutral ethanol at 95°, and therefore classified it as thermal. It is interesting to note that during that lapse of time some workers, apparently unaware of the thermal rearrangement of hydrazoaromatics, studied the kinetics of what was thought to be solely the thermal disproportionation of hydrazobenzene, 4-methylhydrazobenzene, and *para*-hydrazotoluene (73). Other workers recognized that these hydrazobenzenes rearranged as well as disproportionated but, being interested in the disproportionation, did not dwell further on the rearrangement (74). Had these several workers chosen to work with 2,2'-hydrazonaphthalene instead of the other compounds the state of benzidine chemistry might now be quite different.

The most recent data on the products of thermal rearrangements are given in Table 8 (75–77). The products of rearrangement of the naphthyl compounds do not differ from those of the acid-catalyzed rearrangement. The distribution of products from the thermal rearrangement of hydrazobenzene is noticeably different from that of acid-catalyzed rearrangement. Diphenyline is the major product obtained from the thermal rearrangement in polar solvents, and the trend is toward the semidines in nonpolar solvents. The table shows how much cleaner the rearrangements of the 2-naphthyl compounds are than the rearrangements of the others. The 1-naphthyl compounds undergo extensive decomposition unless their solutions are rigorously degassed, and even after heating, the degassed solutions which were colorless when sealed, darken on exposure to air and form tarry materials (75,78). For these reasons and others the entries for the last three compounds in Table 8 show results only of a semi-quantitative nature. The + sign means that a product was detected, and

TABLE 8

Products[a] of Thermal Rearrangement at 110° (75–77)

Products	Solvent				
	EtOH	MeCN	Me$_2$CO	C$_6$H$_6$	None
Rearrangement of 2,2′-hydrazonaphthalene					
2,2′-Diamine	78.0	75.0	70.9	80.1	74.8
Carbazole	20.1	20.3	22.0	10.0	23.6
Azo	0.2	1.8	3.9	3.1	0.5
Rearrangement of N-2-naphthyl-N′-phenylhydrazine					
2,2′-Diamine	90.7	89.0	90.0	92.3	68.3
Carbazole	6.7	9.1	5.1	9.0	7.4
Azo	0.2	1.5	2.5	0.8	12.1
Rearrangement of 1,1′-hydrazonaphthalene					
4,4′-Diamine	20[b]	4[b]	0[b]	0	3
1,1′-Diamine	+ + +	+ + +	+ + +	+ + +	+ +
Carbazole	30	10	10	30	0
Azo	17	30	60	25	60
1-Naphthylamine	+ + +	+ + +	+ + +	+ + +	+ + +
Rearrangement of N-1-naphthyl-N′-phenylhydrazine					
4,4′-Diamine	+ +	+ + +	+ +	+ +	+ + +
1,1′-Diamine	+ + +	+	+ + +	+ + +	+ + +
Carbazole	+	+	+	+ (?)	+ (?)
Azo	−	−	−	+ + +	+ + +
Amines (two)	−	−	−	+ +	+ +
Rearrangement of hydrazobenzene					
Benzidine	+	+	+	+	+[c]
Diphenyline	+ + +	+ + +	+ +	+	+
ortho-Semidine	−	+	+ + +	+ + +	+ + +
para-Semidine	−	−	−	+ +	+ +
Azobenzene	+	+ +	+ +	+	+
Aniline	+	+ +	+ +	+	+

[a] Mole %.
[b] At 80°.
[c] At 130°.

the number of signs gives some idea of the relative amounts of products. The − sign means that a product was not detected.

4-Methyl-, 2,2′-dimethyl-, 4,4′-dimethyl-, and 2,2′-dimethoxyhydrazobenzene rearrange when heated alone. The *ortho-* and *para-*semidines are the major rearrangement products, but the major reaction is disproportionation (79,80).

The rearrangement of 2,2'-hydrazonaphthalene (**8**) gives 3,4:5,6-dibenzocarbazole (**10**) as well as 2,2'-diamino-1,1'-binaphthyl (**9**). These products are also obtained from the acid-catalyzed rearrangement (Section II-A-3). The formation of **10** from **9** does not occur under either the conditions of acid-catalyzed or thermal rearrangement of **8**. This shows that in the rearrangement the two amino groups of product **9** are not formed simultaneously. One of them is formed first as in **90**, while the formation of the other (giving **9**) competes with the cyclization reaction that leads to **10**.

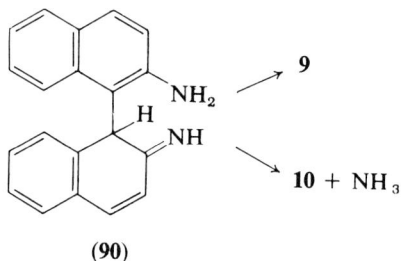

(**90**)

B. Mechanism of Rearrangement

1. Intramolecularity

The rearrangements of N-1-naphthyl-, N-2-naphthyl-N'-phenylhydrazine, 1,1'-, and 2,2'-hydrazonaphthalene have been shown to be intramolecular in the solvents ethanol, acetonitrile, acetone, and benzene. The last case is truly surprising because if a solvent were to be chosen in which intermolecular, free-radical reactions should be favored, it is benzene. We might have anticipated that, in analogy with the formation of radicals from the dissociation of tetraarylhydrazines, the diarylhydrazines would also undergo free-radical reactions to some extent. The disproportionation reactions of the hydrazobenzenes may be radical reactions, analogous to those of Eqs. 13 and 14 (Section II-C-3), but involving neutral phenylimino radicals. Curme's work showed that the disappearance of hydrazobenzene and its ring-methyl derivatives was a first-order reaction (73). Although we now know that rearrangement as well as disproportionation was occurring, we can still accept the major reaction—disproportionation—to have been first order in substrate. In that case one may wonder whether the rate-determining step leads to arylimino radicals, as Curme proposed, or to a neutral π complex, as Dewar has proposed (3). One would have thought that if arylimino radicals were involved in disproportionation they would also combine intermolecularly to form rearrangement products. No sign of intermolecular rearrangement has been found with mixtures of 1,1'- and 2,2'-hydrazonaphthalene, however, and as far as the author is aware, no evidence for intermolecular rearrangement has been reported anywhere. The results show so far, then, that rearrangement is intramolecular and suggest that even disproportionation may not involve free radicals. As a final comment on the last point we note that radicals could not be detected by ESR spectroscopy during the reactions (rearrangement and disproportionation; see Table 8) of 1,1'-hydrazonaphthalene in benzene at 100° (61). The failure to detect radicals by this method is not a certain demonstration that radicals are absent since they may have had too short a life time for detection. A number of monomers failed to polymerize when included in the reaction solution, but this also is not a certain demonstration of the absence of naphthylimino radicals. On the whole though the tests do not encourage us to consider radical pathways in either the disproportionation or the rearrangement reaction.

2. Kinetics, Solvent Effects, and Transition States

The thermal rearrangements are first order in hydrazo compound. The rates are larger in polar solvents than in nonpolar and are largest in hydroxylic solvents. The kinetics of rearrangement in some solvents, such as benzene, are not simple and an answer to them has not been found.

Rate constants for the rearrangement of 2,2'-hydrazonaphthalene are given in Tables 9 and 10 and illustrate the solvent effects.

TABLE 9

First-Order Rate Constants (10^5k, min^{-1}) for the Rearrangement of 2,2'-Hydrazonaphthalene at 80° in Degassed Solutions (81)

EtOH	Acetone	Dioxan	Pyridine	THF[a]
690	11	7	4.5	4.7

[a] Tetrahydrofuran.

TABLE 10

First-Order Rate Constants (10^3k, min^{-1}) for the Rearrangement of 2,2'-Hydrazonaphthalene in Alcohols at 80° under Nitrogen (82)

MeOH	n-PrOH	EtOH	i-PrOH	t-BuOH
13.3	9.21	7.63	5.28	4.37

The exceptional rate in ethanol is seen in Table 9. From Table 10 it is seen that the rates decrease with decreasing acidity of the alcohol. It was also found in this work that the rate of rearrangement of 2,2'-hydrazonaphthalene in ethanol was increased by adding water. A plot of log rate constant versus the Grunwald-Winstein Y value for the solvent was linear, indicating that the rate of rearrangement was related to the ionizing power of the solvent. With these data as a basis Shine and Trisler proposed that the thermal rearrangements in hydroxylic solvents were of the acid-catalyzed type, the alcohol acting as a general acid via hydrogen bonding, and that the transition states were polar (82). This proposal fits in well with the overall polar-transition-state theory developed later by Banthorpe, Hughes, and Ingold for the acid-catalyzed rearrangement and extended by them to the thermal rearrangement.

Banthorpe, Hughes, and Ingold view a thermal rearrangement in a nonhydroxylic, polar solvent as having a polar transition state, one half of which is cationic and the other half, anionic (6). This view is based mainly upon solvent effects and the effect of aryl groups on relative rates (1-naphthyl > 2-naphthyl > phenyl). In a hydroxylic solvent the dispersal of charge occurs from the anionic half of the transition state into a solvent molecule via hydrogen bonding. In general characteristics the transition state for a thermal rearrangement (in all polar solvents) is regarded as similar to one for a one-proton rearrangement, and the two types of rearrangement are expected to give similar products. The reason for the difference in products from the thermal and acid-catalyzed rearrangements of hydrazobenzene is attributed to the difference in transition states (the thermal being more like a one-proton type) and the mode of approach of the two halves of these states caused by the difference in charge and electron-pair distribution therein.

Dewar and Marchand (3) look upon a thermal rearrangement as involving a neutral π complex. This π complex has not been described in any detail. Presumably, it may be represented as having the same sort of relationship to an unprotonated transition state as the protonated π complexes have to the one- and two-proton transition states. A choice between the two theories—with or without a π-complex intermediate—is again likely to be based more on opinion than on experimental fact.

The mechanisms of thermal rearrangement may have wider scope than as described above. The polar-transition-state theory, for example, is not applied to thermal rearrangements in nonpolar solvents (6). Rearrangements in these solvents (e.g., benzene) are kinetically not straightforward. The reason for this is not known. Ascribing the difficulties to free-radical reactions is tempting, but we do not know if these reactions do or do not occur. Not much of a quantitative nature is known about the rearrangement of hydrazobenzenes. Rearrangement is accompanied by disproportionation. It is evident that the free energy of activation for rearrangement is so high with these compounds that an alternate reaction path is found. The mechanism of the alternate path—disproportionation—is not known, particularly as to whether or not free radicals are involved. The comparative ease of thermal rearrangement of the naphthyl hydrazo compounds brings to mind the easy Claisen rearrangement of N-allyl-1-naphthylamine as compared with the thermal decomposition of N-allylaniline (83). The evidence in Claisen rearrangements points clearly to cyclic transition states, and perhaps the thermal benzidine rearrangements have more of Claisen-type characteristics than is at present known.

Acknowledgments

Much of the author's work in hydrazoaromatic rearrangements has been supported by the Robert A. Welch Foundation. To this foundation, and to the National Science Foundation, for earlier support under Grant No. G14551, he is much indebted. The many fruitful discussions with W. J. Meikle, Sandia Corporation, are gratefully acknowledged. Permission granted by the Elsevier Publishing Company to use material from the author's book *Aromatic Rearrangements* is acknowledged with thanks.

References

1. H. J. Shine, *Aromatic Rearrangements*, Elsevier, Amsterdam, 1967.
2. V. O. Lukashevich, *Tetrahedron*, **23**, 1317 (1967).
3. M. J. S. Dewar and A. P. Marchand, *Ann. Rev. Phys. Chem.*, **16**, 338 (1965).
4. M. J. S. Dewar, in *Molecular Rearrangements*, Vol. 1, P. de Mayo, Ed., Interscience, New York, 1963, p. 323.
5. M. J. S. Dewar, in *Theoretical Organic Chemistry (Kekulé Symposium)*, Butterworths, London, 1959, p. 204.
6. D. V. Banthorpe, E. D. Hughes, and C. K. Ingold, *J. Chem. Soc.*, **1964**, 2864.
7. M. Vecera, *Chem. Listy*, **52**, 1373 (1958).
8. V. O. Lukashevich and L. G. Krolik, *Dokl. Akad. Nauk SSSR*, **120**, 316 (1958); *Engl. Transl.*, **120**, 357 (1958).
9. V. O. Lukashevich and L. G. Krolik, *Dokl. Akad. Nauk SSSR*, **129**, 117 (1959); *Engl. Transl.*, **129**, 947 (1959).
10. V. O. Lukashevich, *Dokl. Akad. Nauk SSSR*, **159**, 1095 (1964); *Engl. Transl.*, **159**, 1333 (1964).
11. M. Vecera, J. Gasparic, and J. Petranek, *Collection Czech. Chem. Commun.*, **23**, 249 (1958).
12. L. G. Krolik and V. O. Lukashevich, *Dokl. Akad. Nauk SSSR*, **135**, 1139 (1960); *Engl. Transl.*, **135**, 1411 (1960).
13. (a) P. Jacobson, *Ann. Chem.*, **428**, 76 (1922); (b) **427**, 142 (1922); (c) **367**, 304 (1909).
14. J. Gasparic, J. Petranek, and M. Vecera, *Mikrochim. Acta*, **1955**, 1026.
15. M. Vecera, J. Petranek, and J. Gasparic, *Chem. Ind. (London)*, **1956**, 99.

16. M. Vecera, J. Petranek, and J. Gasparic, *Collection Czech. Chem. Commun.*, **22**, 1603 (1957).

17. V. O. Lukashevich and L. G. Krolik, *Dokl. Akad. Nauk SSSR*, **63**, 543 (1948).

18. R. B. Carlin and W. O. Forshey, Jr., *J. Am. Chem. Soc.*, **72**, 793 (1950).

19. D. V. Banthorpe, *J. Chem. Soc.*, **1962**, 2407.

20. D. V. Banthorpe, E. D. Hughes, and C. K. Ingold, *J. Chem. Soc.*, **1962**, 2386.

21. D. V. Banthorpe, *J. Chem. Soc.*, **1962**, 2429.

22. D. L. Hammick and D. C. Munro, *J. Chem. Soc.*, **1950**, 2049.

23. M. Vecera and J. Petranek, *Collection Czech. Chem. Commun.*, **25**, 2005 (1960).

24. C. K. Ingold, personal communication in advance of publication; D. V. Banthorpe, A. Cooper, and C. K. Ingold, *Nature*, **216**, 232 (1967).

25. J. R. Peffer, Ph.D. Thesis, Carnegie Institute of Technology (1958).

26. H. J. Shine, C. M. Baldwin, and J. H. Harris, *Tetrahedron Letters*, **1968**, 977.

26a. W. N. White and E. E. Moore, personal communication.

27. B. Rassow and K. Berger, *J. Prakt. Chem.*, **84**, 260 (1911).

28. D. W. Davis and D. L. Hammick, *J. Chem. Soc.*, **1954**, 475.

29. P. F. Holt and B. P. Hughes, *J. Chem. Soc.*, **1954**, 764.

30. G. Wittig, W. Joos, and P. Rathfelder, *Ann. Chem.*, **610**, 180 (1957); G. Wittig and J. E. Grolig, *Chem. Ber.*, **94**, 2148 (1961).

31. W. Theilacker and O. Korndörfer, *Tetrahedron Letters*, **1959**, 5.

32. L. D. Hartung and H. J. Shine, unpublished work.

33. J. Rakusan and Z. J. Allan, *Tetrahedron Letters*, **1966**, 4955.

34. R. B. Carlin and G. S. Wich, *J. Am. Chem. Soc.*, **80**, 4023 (1958).

35. G. S. Hammond and J. S. Clovis, *J. Org. Chem.*, **28**, 3283 (1963).

36. G. Friebel and B. Rassow, *J. Prakt. Chem.*, **63**, 444 (1901).

37. H. J. Shine and J. P. Stanley, *J. Org. Chem.*, **32**, 905 (1967).

38. C. K. Ingold and H. V. Kidd, *J. Chem. Soc.*, **1933**, 984.

39. D. H. Smith, J. R. Schwartz, and G. W. Wheland, *J. Am. Chem. Soc.*, **74**, 2282 (1952).

40. D. V. Banthorpe, *J. Chem. Soc.*, **1962**, 2413.

41. G. S. Hammond and H. J. Shine, *J. Am. Chem. Soc.*, **72**, 220 (1950).

42. J. P. van Loon, *Rec. Trav. Chim.*, **23**, 62 (1904).

43. M. J. S. Dewar, *J. Chem. Soc.*, **1946**, 777.

44. R. B. Carlin, R. G. Nelb, and R. C. Odioso, *J. Am. Chem. Soc.*, **73**, 1002 (1951).

45. R. B. Carlin and R. C. Odioso, *J. Am. Chem. Soc.*, **76**, 100 (1954).

46. D. A. Blackadder and C. Hinshelwood, *J. Chem. Soc.*, **1957**, 2898.

47. M. J. S. Dewar and H. McNicoll, *Tetrahedron Letters*, **1959**, 22.

48. W. N. White and R. Preisman, *Chem. Ind. (London)*, **1961**, 1952.

49. H. J. Shine and J. T. Chamness, *J. Org. Chem.*, **28**, 1232 (1963).

50. H. J. Shine and J. T. Chamness, *J. Org. Chem.*, **32**, 901 (1967).

51. G. S. Hammond and W. Grundemeier, *J. Am. Chem. Soc.*, **77**, 2444 (1955).

52. K. B. Wiberg, *Physical Organic Chemistry*, Wiley, New York, 1964, p. 397.

53. J. Hine, *Physical Organic Chemistry*, 2nd ed., McGraw-Hill, New York, 1962, pp. 71, 121.

54. L. J. Croce and J. D. Gettler, *J. Am. Chem. Soc.*, **75**, 874 (1953).

55. M. Vecera, L. Synek, and V. Sterba, *Collection Czech. Chem. Commun.*, **25**, 1992 (1960).

56. D. V. Banthorpe, *J. Chem. Soc.*, **1962**, 3308.

57. V. Sterba and M. Vecera, *Collection Czech. Chem. Commun.*, **31**, 3486 (1966).

58. M. J. S. Dewar, *The Electronic Theory of Organic Chemistry*, Oxford University Press, Oxford, 1949, p. 234.

59. G. S. Hammond and R. C. Neuman, Jr., *J. Am. Chem. Soc.*, **85**, 1501 (1963).
60. K. H. Hausser and J. N. Murrell, *J. Chem. Phys.*, **27**, 500 (1957).
61. D. V. Banthorpe, R. Bramley, and J. A. Thomas, *J. Chem. Soc.*, **1964**, 2900.
62. M. J. S. Dewar, *Ann. Rept. Progr. Chem. (Chem. Soc. London)*, **48**, 126 (1951).
63. J. Osugi and T. Hitouji, *Rev. Phys. Chem. Japan*, **34**, 88 (1964).
64. J. Osugi, M. Sasaki, and I. Onishi, *Rev. Phys. Chem. Japan*, **36**, 100 (1966).
65. J. Osugi, personal communication.
66. J. S. Clovis and G. S. Hammond, *J. Org. Chem.*, **28**, 3290 (1963).
67. J. T. Chamness, unpublished work.
68. A. W. Burgstahler, P.-L. Chien, and M. O. Abdel-Rahman, *J. Am. Chem. Soc.*, **86**, 5281 (1964).
69. P. Jacobson, *Ann. Chem.*, **303**, 290 (1898).
70. G. J. Bloink and K. H. Pausacker, *J. Chem. Soc.*, **1950**, 1950.
71. J. Meisenheimer and K. Witte, *Chem. Ber.*, **36**, 4153 (1903).
72. L. G. Krolik and V. O. Lukashevich, *Dokl. Akad. Nauk SSSR*, **65**, 37 (1949).
73. G. O. Curme, Jr., *J. Am. Chem. Soc.*, **35**, 1143 (1913); J. Stieglitz and G. O. Curme, *Chem. Ber.*, **46**, 911 (1913); J. Stieglitz and H. T. Graham, *J. Am. Chem. Soc.*, **38**, 1736 (1916).
74. H. Wieland, *Chem. Ber.*, **48**, 1098 (1915).
75. D. V. Banthorpe and E. D. Hughes, *J. Chem. Soc.*, **1964**, 2849.
76. D. V. Banthorpe, *J. Chem. Soc.*, **1964**, 2854.
77. D. V. Banthorpe and E. D. Hughes, *J. Chem. Soc.*, **1964**, 2860.
78. H. J. Shine, F.-T. Huang, and R. L. Small, *J. Org. Chem.*, **26**, 380 (1961).
79. M. Vecera, J. Gasparic, and J. Petranek, *Chem. Ind. (London)*, **1957**, 299.
80. L. G. Krolik and V. O. Lukashevich, *Dokl. Akad. Nauk SSSR*, **139**, 110 (1961); *Engl. Trans.*, **139**, 649 (1961).
81. H. J. Shine, *J. Am. Chem. Soc.*, **78**, 4807 (1956).
82. H. J. Shine and J. C. Trisler, *J. Am. Chem. Soc.*, **82**, 4054 (1960).
83. S. Marcinkiewicz, J. Green, and P. Mamalis, *Tetrahedron*, **1961**, 14; *Chem. Ind. (London)*, **1961**, 438.

The Meisenheimer Rearrangement of Tertiary Amine Oxides

R. A. W. JOHNSTONE

Department of Organic Chemistry
The University of Liverpool, Liverpool, England

The isomerization discussed here as the Meisenheimer rearrangement is the thermal conversion of a tertiary amine oxide (**1**) to a substituted hydroxylamine (**2**).

$$R^1R^2R^3\overset{+}{N}-\overset{-}{O} \xrightarrow{\Delta} R^1R^2NOR^3$$
$$\text{(1)} \qquad\qquad \text{(2)}$$

I. HISTORICAL INTRODUCTION

In 1895, Pinner (1) reported investigations on the reactions of nicotine-1'-oxide (**3**) and described the formation of a new substance, nicotone, on heating the oxide. Pinner assigned to nicotone a structure (**4**) containing a tetrahydrofuran ring, but many years later, in 1950, Rayburn et al. (2) showed that nicotone was in fact 2-methyl-6-3'-pyridyltetrahydro-1,2-oxazine (**5**) formed by rearrangement of nicotine-1'-oxide. Thus, although Pinner had unknowingly described the rearrangement of a tertiary amine oxide to a substituted hydroxylamine, it was some 20 years later before Meisenheimer (3) first correctly recognized such a reaction as a rearrangement. Meisenheimer found that heating *N*-methyl-*N*-allylaniline oxide (**6**) in strongly alkaline solution afforded the isomeric *O*-allyl-*N*-methyl-*N*-phenylhydroxylamine (**7**) in good yield. A little later, Meisenheimer et al. (4) reported similar rearrangements of *N*-methyl- and *N*-benzyl-*N*-allylaniline oxide to the corresponding hydroxylamines but they were unable to effect a similar transformation of dialkylallylamine oxides. The reaction became known as the Meisenheimer rearrangement.

Meisenheimer and co-workers had carried out the isomerizations in aqueous alkaline solution and thought these basic conditions were necessary for reaction, but some 25 years afterward Kleinschmidt and Cope (5), while confirming the nature of the reaction, found that alkali was unnecessary except to liberate the amine oxides from their salts, a form in which they are often prepared. More significantly, they found that rearrangement of N-crotyl-N-methylaniline oxide (8) yielded the "inverted" product O-2-but-3-enyl-N-methyl-N-phenylhydroxylamine (9) and not O-crotyl-N-methyl-N-phenylhydroxylamine (10), and they compared

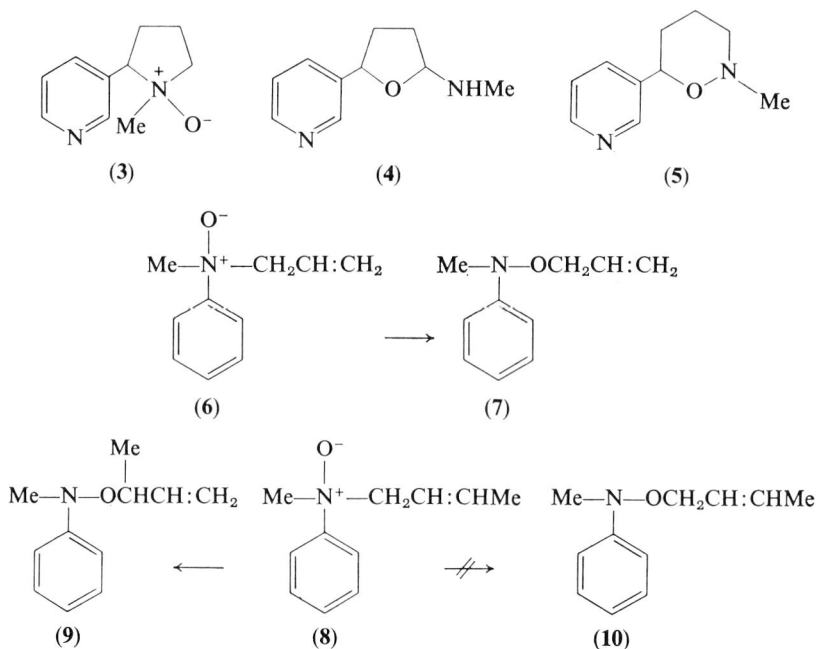

(3)   (4)   (5)

(6)   (7)

(9)   (8)   (10)

the reaction with the well-known Claisen rearrangement of O-allylphenols (6). From this point, later investigations of the Meisenheimer rearrangement have been directed to determining its scope and to understanding its mechanism. Analogies have been sought with other 1,2-isomerizations and a discussion of the rearrangement of tertiary amine oxides must take cognizance to some extent of investigations into the mechanisms of similar transformations.

II. SCOPE OF THE REACTION

Cope and Towle (7) suggested that in aqueous solution hydration of the amine oxide would reduce the effective charge at oxygen and so decrease the rate of rearrangement. In fact they found that heating the fairly dry amine oxides alone at 85–165° effected a smooth rearrangement and, in contrast to Meisenheimer's earlier failure, they were able to isomerize dialkylallylamine oxides (alkyl = Me, Et, n-Pr, iso-Pr, n-Hexyl) to O-allyl-N-dialkylhydroxylamines under these anhydrous conditions. Recently, evidence has appeared of strong complex formation at the charged oxygen atom of amine oxides in polar solvents (8).

During their examination of the scope of the Meisenheimer rearrangement, Cope et al. (9) found that with hydrogen atoms present on the carbon beta to nitrogen, an elimination reaction took place to yield an olefin. Whereas N,N-dimethylbenzylamine oxide (11), on heating, rearranged to give O-benzyl-N-dimethylhydroxylamine (12), its homolog, N,N-dimethyl-α-phenethylamine oxide (13) gave styrene and N,N-dimethyl-

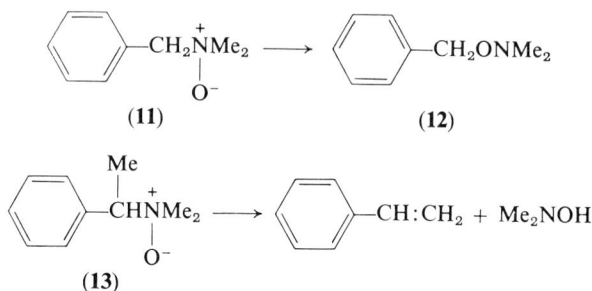

hydroxylamine. The latter type of reaction, a β-elimination often referred to as the Cope elimination, had actually been reported many years earlier by Mamlock and Wolffenstein (10) but they did not extend their work and it remained for Cope and co-workers to explore the scope of the reaction (11). In fact the very wide scope of the β-elimination process is a limiting factor to the scope of the Meisenheimer rearrangement. For compounds in which either elimination or isomerization might occur, these

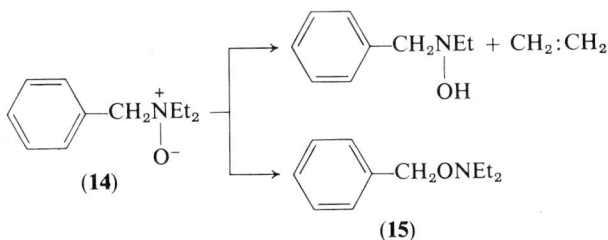

reactions are often found to be competitive, and N,N-diethylbenzylamine oxide (14), for example, on heating, afforded both N-ethyl-N-benzyl-hydroxylamine and ethylene, and O-benzyl-N,N-diethylhydroxylamine (15).

Apart from the restrictive effect of elimination on the rearrangement of N-oxides, Cope found also that the type of group which could migrate was fairly closely defined. Even when β-elimination is impossible, as in the pyrolysis of N,N-dimethyl-β,β-dimethyl-β-phenethylamine oxide (16), which has no beta hydrogen atoms, mainly exothermic decomposition was observed at moderate temperatures to give largely the amine (17) produced by simple deoxygenation together with about 5% of the expected rearrangement product (18) and also some of the aldehyde (19). Subsequently, it was found that other amine oxides, expected to suffer β-elimination, as for example those of cycloöcten-3-yldimethylamine (12), exo-5-dimethylamino-2-norbornene, and exo-5-dimethylamino-2-norbornane (13), appear to have given small amounts of the corresponding rearrangement products on pyrolysis as well as the normal products of elimination. It is evident from this and accumulated later work that for successful rearrangement, the migrating group should be able to delocalize effectively electron density at the migration center, and there should be no hydrogen atoms beta to the nitrogen of the amine oxide and conformationally capable of taking part in the five-membered transition state required for elimination.

As has been mentioned already, Rayburn et al. (2) were able to show that Pinner's nicotone was a Meisenheimer rearrangement product of nicotine-1'-oxide, but not until 1962 was further use made of this ring enlargement reaction. Then, Quin and Roof (14), in experiments to determine the general utility of the reaction, pyrolyzed a number of pyrrolidine-N-oxides (20) to obtain the corresponding 1,2-oxazines (21) in good

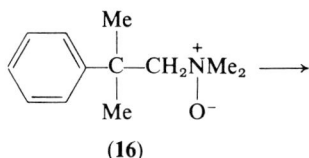

(16)

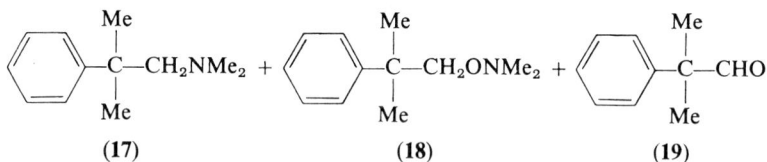

(17)   (18)   (19)

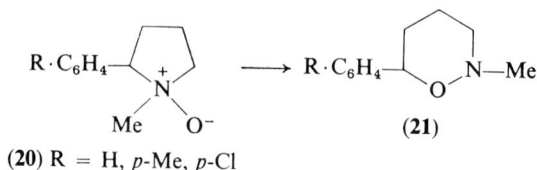

(20) R = H, p-Me, p-Cl

yields. In keeping with earlier experience, they found that 2-ethylpyrroli-
dine oxide did not rearrange and only a ring-opened product, formed by
β-elimination, could be isolated. Further to their work on the stereochemistry of the Meisenheimer rearrangement of nicotine-1'-oxide,
Carruthers and Johnstone (15) effected this ring enlargement reaction with
larger ring amine oxides. Thus, N-methyl-anabasine oxide (22) afforded the
seven-membered 1,2-oxazepine (23) in good yield, while 1-methyl-2-phenyl-
hexahydroazepine oxide (24) gave the eight-membered 1,2-oxazocine (25)
in moderate yield. In all rearrangements of N-oxides some starting amine
is recovered after pyrolysis and in these experiments it was noticed that
increasing deoxygenation occurred as ring size increased. Allowing for
recovered amine from these reactions, the yields of ring-enlarged products
are very good. Almost concurrently, Quin and Shelburne (16) reported the
preparation of some 1,2-oxazepines (26) in yields of about 50% by a
similar ring enlargement of the corresponding piperidyl oxides.

Henry and Leete (17) found that gramine-N'-oxide (27) gave only a
poor yield of rearranged material on heating alone at 125°, but that
in refluxing acetonitrile containing a trace of pyridine a 61% yield could
be obtained. Other solvents such as toluene, dimethylformamide, and
dioxan were not so useful. Quin and Shelburne (16) extended this range
of solvents and found dimethylacetamide at 170° was most effective

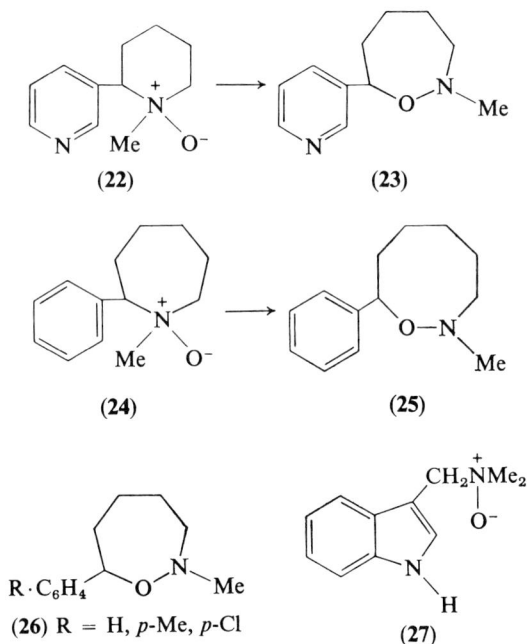

(22)   (23)

(24)   (25)

(26) R = H, p-Me, p-Cl   (27)

for the rearrangements studied by them. Also, they observed that in these solvents, at temperatures of up to 177° for periods up to 1 hr, the 1,2-oxazepines produced were quite stable. In contrast, earlier reports (2,15) mention the elimination of oxygen from the cyclic oxaza compounds which reverted to the initial amines on refluxing. However, it has been reported (15) that this type of deoxygenation possibly proceeds through radical formation on the surface of the containing vessel so that in solution, especially at temperatures well below those necessary for deoxygenation, this reaction might well not be expected to take place.

The β-elimination reaction of N-oxides to form olefins finds a parallel in a similar β-elimination of sulfoxides. Several reports have appeared (18) of this type of elimination, as with the sulfoxide (28), and it was natural that an analogy to the Meisenheimer rearrangement should have been sought with sulfoxides. Indeed, Cope et al. (19) attempted such a rearrangement with allyl phenyl sulfoxide but achieved no success, and it was not until 1966 when the thermal reactions of some benzylic sulfoxides were reported (20) that a rearrangement seems to have been accomplished. A number of substituted benzyl methyl sulfoxides (29) on heating to about 220° (a significantly higher temperature than required for rearrangement of amine oxides) were found to yield aromatic aldehydes (30). The reaction

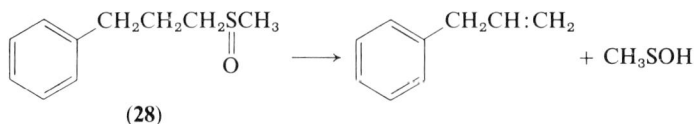

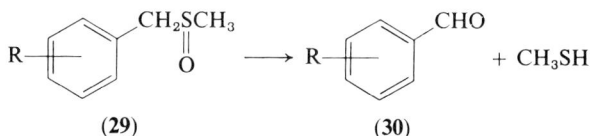

(28)

(29)   (30)

was considered to proceed through a Meisenheimer type of rearrangement to a sulfenate ester, followed by decomposition to the aldehyde and a mercaptan. Sulfenate esters (sulfur analogs of the hydroxylamines) are known to be unstable (21). In the absence of suitable mechanistic and kinetic experiments, it is not certain that this reaction should be considered as a 1,2-isomerization akin to the Meisenheimer rearrangement.

III. MECHANISTIC ASPECTS

The early work of Kleinschmidt and Cope (5) on the isomerization of N-crotyl-N-methylaniline oxide (8) had suggested an intramolecular nature for the Meisenheimer rearrangement, and by 1950 many salient features of the reaction were known. In some respects it appeared similar to the Claisen rearrangement as pointed out by Cope, but in 1958, Wragg et al. (22) suggested that the transformation was more analogous to other 1,2-electrophilic isomerizations such as the Stevens rearrangement of quaternary ammonium salts (23). Other reactions which may now be considered in this context include the 1,2-rearrangements of tertiary amines (24), sulfonium (25), stibonium and arsonium salts (26), sulfilimines (27), the Wittig rearrangement of ethers (28), and the Grovenstein-Zimmerman reaction (29). The reactions are respectively illustrated by Eqs. 1–8 and may be compared with the Meisenheimer rearrangement of N-oxides (**11**); an excellent account of some of these reactions has appeared (30). All of these reactions are characterized by a migration of a group to a negatively charged center and can be classed as 1,2-electrophilic isomerizations, but they have also been regarded as internal nucleophilic attacks ($S_N i$ or $S_N i'$) by the negatively charged center on the migrating group.

In his first reports on the rearrangement of quaternary ammonium salts, Stevens (23) suggested a cleavage–recombination mechanism in which the migrating group first became detached but not separated from the remainder of the molecule and then recombined to give the rearranged product. Reviewers (31) of his work considered an internal attack more likely, and this latter view of the rearrangement was later favored by Hauser and Kantor (32). It was perhaps not unnatural, therefore, for the Meisenheimer rearrangement to be considered also as an $S_N i$ (or $S_N i'$) reaction. An $S_N i$ mechanism was proposed for the decomposition of alkyl chlorosulphites in which an internal nucleophilic attack was thought to occur (33). However, recent work (34) indicates that this latter reaction, at least in some cases, proceeds through a cleavage–recombination mechanism, and further, Stevens' original hypothesis for such a mechanism operating in the rearrangement of quaternary ammonium salts has been revived by the work of Jenny and Druey (35). A similar history attaches to the Wittig rearrangement of ethers which was initially regarded as proceeding through an $S_N i$ mechanism (32) but was later considered to isomerize by a cleavage–recombination reaction (41,43). Based on a fabric of analogies, the Meisenheimer rearrangement was not seriously questioned as an $S_N i$ reaction until fairly recently by Schöllkopf (36). Since these 1,2-electrophilic transformations are related in many ways, the following discussion of the mechanism of the Meisenheimer rearrangement includes relevant aspects of the Stevens and Wittig rearrangements.

In methanolic solution, the rearrangement of quaternary ammonium salts has been shown to be intramolecular by Johnstone and Stevens (37),

$$PhCOCH_2\overset{+}{N}Me_2 \ \overset{-}{Br} \xrightarrow{\text{base}} PhCO\overset{-}{C}H\overset{+}{N}Me_2 \longrightarrow PhCOCHNMe_2 \quad (1)$$
$$\overset{|}{C}H_2Ph \qquad\qquad\qquad \overset{|}{C}H_2Ph \qquad\qquad \overset{|}{C}H_2Ph$$

$$PhCOCH_2NPh \xrightarrow{\text{base}} PhCO\overset{-}{C}HNPh \longrightarrow PhCOCHNPh \quad (2)$$
$$\overset{|}{C}H_2Ph \qquad\qquad\quad \overset{|}{C}H_2Ph \qquad\qquad \overset{|}{C}H_2Ph$$

$$PhCOCH_2\overset{+}{S}Me \ \overset{-}{Br} \xrightarrow{\text{base}} PhCO\overset{-}{C}H\overset{+}{S}Me \longrightarrow PhCOCHSMe \quad (3)$$
$$\overset{|}{C}H_2Ph \qquad\qquad\qquad \overset{|}{C}H_2Ph \qquad\qquad \overset{|}{C}H_2Ph$$

$$PhCH_2\overset{+}{A}sMe_2 \ \overset{-}{Br} \xrightarrow{\text{base}} Ph\overset{-}{C}H\overset{+}{A}sMe_2 \longrightarrow PhCHAsMe_2 \quad (4)$$
$$\overset{|}{C}H_2Ph \qquad\qquad\qquad \overset{|}{C}H_2Ph \qquad\qquad \overset{|}{C}H_2Ph$$

$$PhCH_2\overset{+}{S}bMe_2 \ \overset{-}{Br} \xrightarrow{\text{base}} Ph\overset{-}{C}H\overset{+}{S}bMe_2 \longrightarrow PhCHSbMe_2 \quad (5)$$
$$\overset{|}{C}H_2Ph \qquad\qquad\qquad \overset{|}{C}H_2Ph \qquad\qquad \overset{|}{C}H_2Ph$$

$$p\text{-}H_3C\cdot C_6H_4SO_2\overset{-}{\overset{+}{N}}SCH_2Ph \longrightarrow p\text{-}H_3C\cdot C_6H_4SO_2NSCH_2Ph \quad (6)$$
$$\overset{|}{C}H_2CH:CH_2 \qquad\qquad\qquad \overset{|}{C}H_2CH:CH_2$$

$$PhCH_2OMe \xrightarrow{\text{base}} Ph\overset{-}{C}HOMe \longrightarrow PhCH\overset{-}{-}\overset{-}{O} \quad (7)$$
$$\overset{|}{M}e$$

$$Ph_3C\text{---}CH_2Cl \xrightarrow{\text{Na}} Ph_3\overset{-}{C}\text{---}\overset{+}{C}H_2\overset{}{N}a \longrightarrow Ph_2\overset{-}{C}\text{---}CH_2Ph \ \overset{+}{N}a$$
$$(8)$$

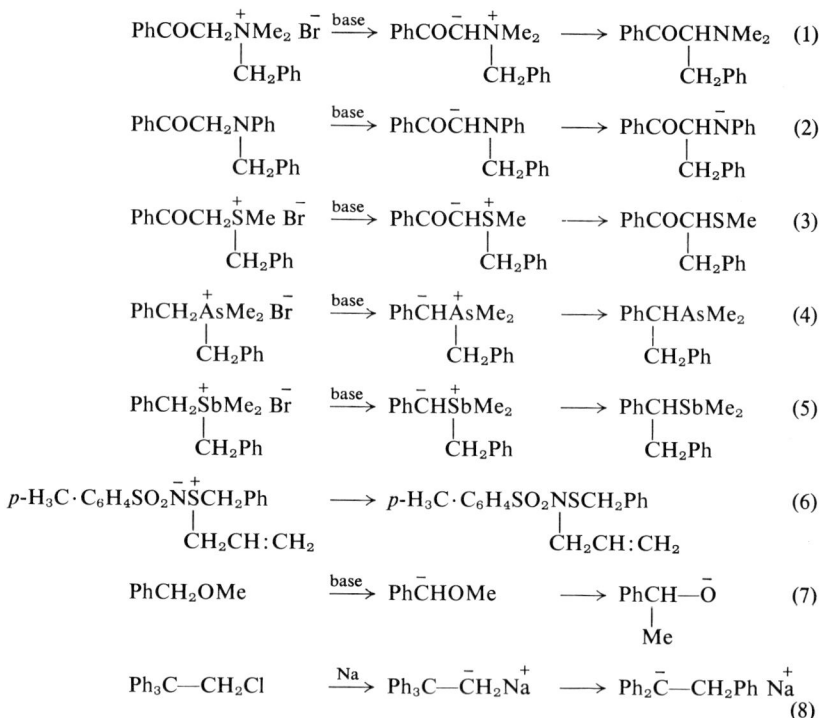

who found no interchange of migrating groups when a mixture of phenacyl[^{14}C]benzyldimethylammonium bromide and p-bromophenacylbenzyldimethylammonium bromide was rearranged. The relative rates of rearrangement of the salts were very similar, and the result confirmed earlier, less decisive, work on the rearrangement of mixed quaternary salts (38) and the demonstration by Campbell et al. (39) that during the rearrangement of a quaternary ammonium salt having an optically active migrating center little loss of activity occurred. Further, Brewster and Kline (40) proved that the optically active group had migrated with at least 97% retention of configuration. There were therefore grounds for considering an internal nucleophilic attack mechanism for the Stevens rearrangement, and at least the results showed that the migrating group was never far separated from the remainder of the molecule. More recently, this retention of the optically active center during 1,2-migration was confirmed by Jenny and Druey (35), who also reported a Stevens rearrangement involving a 1,4-shift of the migrating group. During the latter 1,4-shift, however, considerable racemization of the optically active migrating center occurred and led Jenny and Druey to the conclusion that a cleavage-recombination mechanism was far more likely than an S_Ni mechanism, which in any case would have energetically unfavorable spatial requirements. Similarly, Schöllkopf and Schäfer (41) found that the migration of optically active groups in the Wittig rearrangement of ethers was attended by considerable racemization. The use of an optically active migration center is a sensitive probe into the nature of an isomerization reaction and similar experiments have been carried out on the Meisenheimer rearrangement. Schöllkopf and Schäfer (42) isomerized optically active N-[α-^{2}H]-benzyl-N-methylaniline oxide (31) and found that in the product O-[α-^{2}H]-benzyl-N-methyl-N-phenylhydroxylamine (32) the optically active

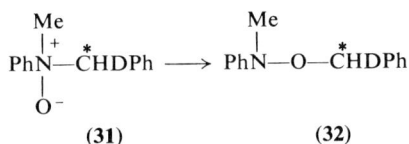

$$\begin{array}{ccc} \overset{\displaystyle Me}{\underset{\displaystyle O^-}{PhN^+{-}\overset{*}{CHDPh}}} & \longrightarrow & \overset{\displaystyle Me}{PhN{-}O{-}\overset{*}{CHDPh}} \\ (31) & & (32) \end{array}$$

center had retained its configuration but was racemized to the extent of 61–2%. Similarly, Carruthers and Johnstone (15) found that the optically active 1,2-oxazine (5) had been formed from optically active nicotine-1'-oxide (3) with retention of configuration and considerable racemization (75%). There is some uncertainty about this last figure since, in the reaction sequence leading to the determination of the optical activity of the migration center, one of the steps may have itself caused some racemization. However, the relatively close agreement of the two figures is satisfying and leaves little doubt that the Meisenheimer rearrangement is normally attended by a large amount of racemization which is not the effect expected from an $S_N i$ reaction.

Associated with the loss of optical activity is the question of the intra- or intermolecular nature of the isomerization. As has been mentioned above, the Stevens 1,2-rearrangement was shown to be intramolecular and to proceed with almost complete retention of optical activity. The Wittig rearrangement, attended by much racemization, has been regarded as strictly intramolecular, because in suitable mixing experiments no "trapped" products were isolated (32). However, Lansbury and Pattison (43) isomerized dibenzyl ether (33) with lithium methyl to the secondary

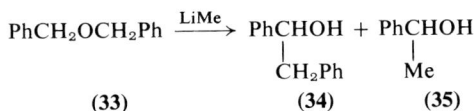

$$PhCH_2OCH_2Ph \xrightarrow{\text{LiMe}} \underset{\substack{|\\CH_2Ph\\(34)}}{PhCHOH} + \underset{\substack{|\\Me\\(35)}}{PhCHOH}$$

$$(33)$$

alcohol (34) and isolated also some of the "trapped" product, methyl phenyl carbinol (35). The amount of "trapped" product was found to increase with increasing cation solvating properties of the solvent, the highest yields being obtained in tetrahydrofuran. They also confirmed the absence of trapped products in isomerizations involving migrating normal- and isoalkyl groups and suggested that the nature of the migrating group determined the mode of rearrangement. Schöllkopf (41) has rejected this view and prefers a "solvent cage" effect and a cleavage–recombination reaction as an explanation of both the "trapping" and racemization. In a "mixed" reaction (36), the dideuteriated (36) and nondeuteriated N-oxide (37) were isomerized to the corresponding hydroxylamines (38,39). A mass

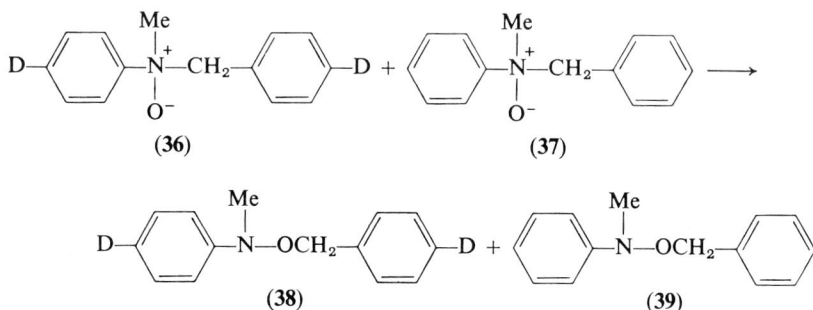

(36)   (37)

(38)   (39)

spectrum of these mixed hydroxylamines showed parent ions corresponding not only to non- and dideuteriated species, but also to monodeuteriated components in the mixtures. The presence of monodeuteriated products suggests interchange of the migrating groups during rearrangement, and it was found that the percentage of interchange increased with increasing concentration of the amine oxides. Despite the detection of an electron spin resonance spectrum characteristic of the radical (40), no signal corresponding to the other half of the molecule, a benzyl radical, was obtained (36), which indicates either its absence or its rapid removal chemically. If, as suggested by kinetic evidence, the rearrangement is first order in amine oxide, a bimolecular interchange would not be expected, but, on the other hand, if the migrating group passes intermolecularly from one molecule to another, a relatively long-lived species would be expected. The kinetic and electron spin resonance spectra conflict. In fact, contrary to Schöllkopf's results, Wragg et al. (22) had earlier been able to detect no interchange of migrating groups when a concentrated mixture (0.11 mole/liter) of the two amine oxides (41,42) was isomerized in aqueous methanol. Although the rates of rearrangement of the two amine oxides were more disparate than would be desired, the resulting hydroxylamines could be separated easily, were obtained in excellent yields, and no "mixed" products were detected. A more rigorous determination of the intra-molecularity and order of reaction of the Meisenheimer rearrangement at increasing concentration is desirable.

Millard and Stevens (44) pointed out that the inversion of the crotyl group observed by Kleinschmidt and Cope (5) in the rearrangement of N-crotyl-N-methylaniline oxide (8) was paralleled by similar inversions in the rearrangements of quaternary ammonium salts and ethers. These are the so-called $S_N i'$ reactions. As an example, the isomerization of phenacylcinnamyldimethylammonium bromide (43) gave two products, one (44) in which inversion of the migrating cinnamyl group had occurred,

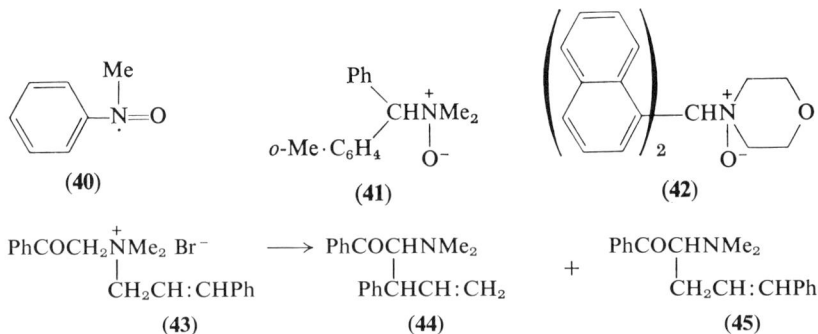

(40)

(41)

(42)

$PhCOCH_2\overset{+}{N}Me_2\ Br^-$ ⟶ $PhCOCHNMe_2$ + $PhCOCHNMe_2$

$\overset{|}{CH_2CH:CHPh}$ $\overset{|}{PhCHCH:CH_2}$ $\overset{|}{CH_2CH:CHPh}$

(43)   (44)   (45)

and the other (45) in which no inversion was apparent. Millard and Stevens found a bewildering nature to the migration of allylic systems which sometimes migrated with inversion, sometimes without, and sometimes in both modes simultaneously in a most unpredictable manner. Indeed, Cast et al. (45) had earlier found that whereas 3'-buten-1'-yl 9-fluorenyl ether (46) rearranged with inversion to give 9-crotyl-9-fluorenol (47), the isomeric crotyl 9-fluorenyl ether (48) afforded the same fluorenol (47) without inversion. However, Schöllkopf and Fellenberger (46) have shown that at -50 to $-60°$ both the fluorenyl ethers (46,48) rearranged to give the respective inverted fluorenols (47,49). At higher temperatures mixtures of inverted and noninverted products were obtained, and 9-oxy-lithium-9-3'-buten-1'-ylfluorene (50) isomerized in tetrahydrofuran at 72.5° to a cis–trans mixture of 9-oxylithium-9-crotylfluorene (51). It seems evident, therefore, that the Wittig rearrangement of ethers must be reversible to some extent and that the actual products obtained are determined by kinetic and thermodynamic control. The results favor a cleavage–recombination mechanism rather than an $S_N i$ type, but few similar experiments have been performed on the amine oxides. Kleinschmidt and Cope (5) were unable to isolate any recognizable products from the pyrolysis of N-cinnamyl-N-methylaniline oxide (52), but in view of the above work on the Stevens and Wittig rearrangements it is possible that a difficultly separable mixture had been obtained and the experiment is worth repeating.

H   O
    |
MeCHCH:CH₂

(46)

$\xrightarrow{(45,\ 46)}$

HO   CH₂CH:CHMe

(47)

(45)

(46)
$\xrightarrow{(46)}$

H   O
    |
CH₂CH:CHMe

(48)

HO   CHCH:CH₂
     |
     Me

(49)

LiO   CHCH:CH₂
      |
      Me

(50)

$\longrightarrow$

LiO   CH₂CH:CHMe

(51)

$$O^-$$
$$|$$
$$Me-N^+-CH_2CH:CHPh$$

(52)

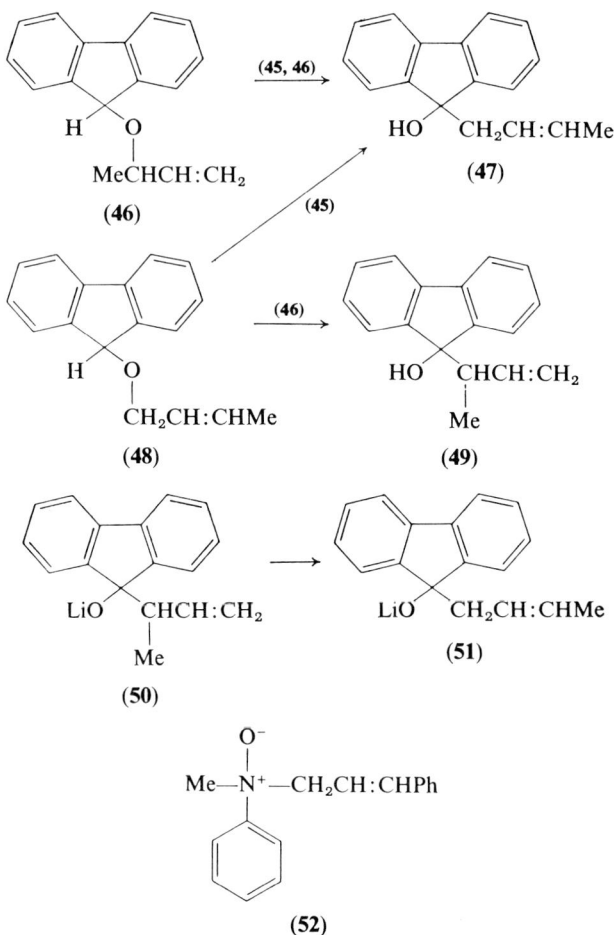

Kinetic measurements on the Meisenheimer rearrangement were first investigated by Wragg et al. (22), who found the reaction was of first order in amine oxide and independent of added base, confirming Cope's earlier observations on the latter point. In one series of experiments, the amine oxides (53–56) were rearranged in ethanolic solution at 20, 30, and 60°. Comparison of the rates of rearrangement of the oxides 53 and 54 showed

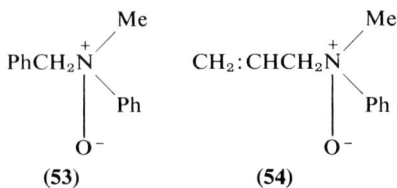

$$\overset{Me}{\underset{|}{PhCH_2\overset{+}{N}}}$$
Ph
|
O⁻

(53)

$$\overset{Me}{\underset{|}{CH_2:CHCH_2\overset{+}{N}}}$$
Ph
|
O⁻

(54)

$$\text{PhCH}_2\overset{+}{\text{N}}\overset{\displaystyle\diagup\text{Me}}{\underset{\displaystyle\underset{\text{O}^-}{|}}{\diagdown\text{C}_6\text{H}_4\text{Br}(p)}}$$

(55)

$$\text{CH}_2\text{:CHCH}_2\overset{+}{\text{N}}\overset{\displaystyle\diagup\text{Ph}}{\underset{\displaystyle\underset{\text{O}^-}{|}}{\diagdown\text{CH}_2\text{Ph}}}$$

(56)

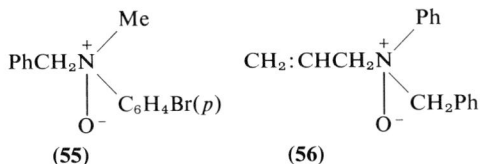

that the allyl group migrated very much faster than benzyl, and comparison of the rates for oxides **53** and **55** showed that the electron attracting *para*-bromine substituent had accelerated the rearrangement more than twofold. The rearrangement of allylbenzylaniline oxide (**56**) was rapid enough for the rate constant to be measured at 20°. A similar fast rearrangement has been reported (15) for 2,5-dihydronicotyrine oxide (**57**) which isomerized rapidly and completely to the 1,2-oxazine (**58**) at room temperature. Since Wragg et al. have reported reaction rates at only two different temperatures for only one compound, allylbenzylaniline oxide, any estimate of the activation energy for the rearrangement is liable to error. Nevertheless, from their results, the energy of activation can be calculated as 25.8 kcal, and the entropy of activation as 10.5 eu at 30°. Conversion of the dipolar *N*-oxide in a polar medium to the neutral substituted hydroxylamine should lead to a small positive change in entropy. If the allyl group migrated through a five-membered transition state (**59**), a negative entropy of activation would be expected. Hence a combination of the two effects, the removal of the dipole and a cyclic transition state, might be expected to lead to a small positive or even a negative entropy change. In fact, the change of $+10.5$ eu indicates a considerable increase in randomness in the activated complex. In more accurate determinations of the rate constants for the rearrangement of a series of substituted benzylmethylaniline oxides (**60**), Schöllkopf and co-workers (36) first brought attention in the literature to this increase in entropy associated with the Meisenheimer rearrangement. The energy of

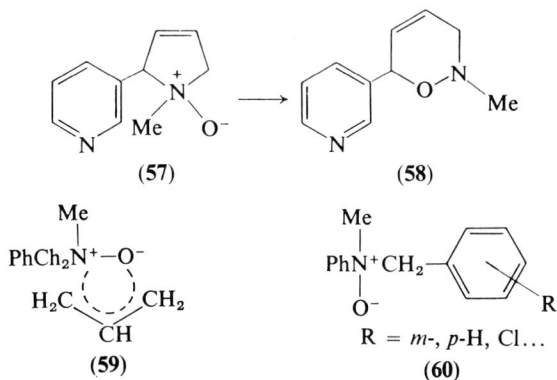

(57)   →   (58)

$$\text{PhCh}_2\overset{\displaystyle\overset{\text{Me}}{|}}{\text{N}^+}-\text{O}^-$$

$$\text{H}_2\text{C}\diagdown\underset{\displaystyle\text{CH}}{}\diagup\text{CH}_2$$

(59)

$$\text{PhN}^+\overset{\displaystyle\overset{\text{Me}}{|}}{}\text{CH}_2-\underset{\displaystyle\text{O}^-}{}$$

R = *m*-, *p*-H, Cl...

(60)

activation, approximately 35 kcal, found for the isomerization of benzyl-methylaniline oxide (60, R = H) in aqueous tetrahydrofuran is about 10 kcal greater than the energy of activation for allylbenzylaniline oxide (56) and is consistent with the greater ease of rearranging the latter compound. The entropy change associated with the isomerization of benzylmethylaniline oxide is considerably larger at +37 eu than the positive entropy change found for allylbenzylaniline oxide, and again suggests that a cyclic transition state is not involved. Further, Schöllkopf found that the entropy change for the rearrangement increased significantly as the percentage of water in the tetrahydrofuran solvent was increased. The normal effect of increasing the polarity of the solvent in a reaction involving the conversion of a charged species to a neutral one is to decrease the associated entropy change. It seems clear there is an increase in randomness during the Meisenheimer rearrangement in which an amine oxide dipole is changed to a neutral hydroxylamine. In itself, this strongly suggests that a cleavage–recombination mechanism operates and that no cyclic transition state ($S_N i$ or $S_N i'$) is involved. As the polarity of the solvent was increased by greater percentages of water in the tetrahydro-furan, the energy of activation of the Meisenheimer rearrangement increased also. The result is expected since increasing polarity of the solvent implies greater solvation of the amine oxide, with a consequent reduction in the rate of rearrangement as noted qualitatively by earlier workers (7).

The results published by Stevens in 1932 (25) allow the calculation of the energy and entropy of activation for the rearrangement of phenacyl-benzyldimethylammonium bromide (Eq. 1) in methanolic solution. The reaction was independent of added base after 1 mole had been added, so in the presence of excess base, the kinetic measurements are of the conversion of the "zwitterion" (Eq. 1), an analog of an amine oxide, to the nonionic amine (Eq. 1). The energy of activation for the Stevens rearrangement of the quaternary salt (Eq. 1) is 31.4 kcal and the entropy of activation, −2.5 eu at 37.7°. A cleavage–recombination mechanism has been pro-posed also for this rearrangement, and the entropy change shows that little net change in randomness occurs in the activated complex, unlike the Meisenheimer rearrangement. The results from optical activity experi-ments suggest that the migrating group must remain closely bound to the remainder of the molecule during the Stevens rearrangement, whereas in the Meisenheimer rearrangement a large positive entropy change is re-flected in the large amount of racemization occurring during isomerization. It is interesting to note that the 1,4-type of Stevens rearrangement (35) is accompanied by a large measure of racemization of the migrating center and some knowledge of the entropy change for this reaction would be most useful.

Wragg et al. found that diphenylmethyldialkylamine oxides were smoothly transformed at 45° in aqueous ethanolic solution to the corresponding hydroxylamines and several rates of reaction were measured together with the basic strength K_b of the amines, $R^1R^2R^3N$, from which the N-oxides had been prepared. With any particular migrating group (e.g., R^1 = diphenylmethyl), the rate of rearrangement decreased slightly as the basic strength of the amine decreased through changes in the non-migratory groups (R^2, R^3). The reaction rates ($k \times 10^3$) for the amine oxides (61–63) were 4.4, 3.5, and 1.8 sec^{-1}, respectively, while the basic strengths ($K_b \times 10^{10}$) of the corresponding amines were 350, 100, and 3.4. However, on changing the basic strength of the amine through variations in the migrating group, the rates of rearrangement were found to increase markedly as basic strength declined. The amines corresponding to the N-oxides (61,64,41,65) have relative basic strengths of 350, 210, 140, and

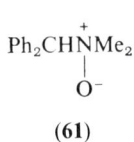

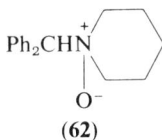

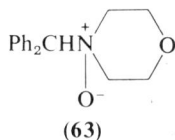

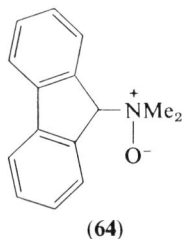

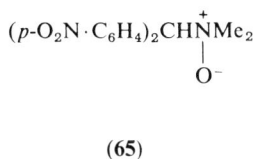

$$\text{Ph}_2\text{CH}\overset{+}{\text{N}}\text{Me}_2 \quad \quad \text{Ph}_2\text{CH}\overset{+}{\text{N}} \quad \quad \text{Ph}_2\text{CH}\overset{+}{\text{N}}$$
$$\underset{\text{O}^-}{|} \quad\quad\quad\quad \underset{\text{O}^-}{|} \quad\quad\quad\quad \underset{\text{O}^-}{|}$$

(61)   (62)   (63)

$$-\overset{+}{\text{N}}\text{Me}_2 \quad\quad\quad (p\text{-O}_2\text{N}\cdot\text{C}_6\text{H}_4)_2\text{CH}\overset{+}{\text{N}}\text{Me}_2$$
$$\underset{\text{O}^-}{|} \quad\quad\quad\quad\quad\quad\quad \underset{\text{O}^-}{|}$$

(64)   (65)

1.4 but the respective relative rates of rearrangement are 4.4, 5.3, 11.8, and 200. The decrease in reaction rate with decreasing basic strength, caused by changes in the nonmigratory groups (R^2, R^3) attached to nitrogen, is only slight and probably caused by small changes in the electron density at oxygen and nitrogen. Thus, a decrease in electron density at nitrogen (less basic) will lead to a decrease in electron density at oxygen, and therefore a reduced rate of rearrangement, but only small effects are to be anticipated. Reduction in basic strength accompanying changes in the migratory group (R^1) should, in the absence of other factors, lead to a decrease in reaction rate. In fact, in the above cases, any such small changes are more than offset by the increasing ability of the migrating group to delocalize charge density at the migrating center and decrease the bond strength to nitrogen. The overall effect is to increase the reaction rate. Stevens and co-workers realized the importance of electron density at the migrating center and showed that electron withdrawing substituents in R^1 increased the rate of the Meisenheimer rearrangement, but they did not follow up this point. Schöllkopf (36) later measured the relative rates of rearrangement of a series of substituted benzylmethylaniline oxides (60) and plotted the results against the Hammett σ function. A fairly good fit to a straight line was obtained although the range of σ values chosen was limited. However, the slope of the line gives $\rho \simeq 0.9$, so that the rate of rearrangement is not greatly affected by change in electron density at the migrating center. Again, this result may be compared with similar ones for the rearrangement of quaternary ammonium salts. Stevens (25) measured the relative rates of rearrangement of a series of phenacylbenzyldimethylammonium salts, substituted in the benzyl group. Plotting these relative rates against σ in the usual way, one obtains a fair linear relationship with a slope $\rho \simeq 3.4$. Clearly both the Stevens and Meisenheimer rearrangements are aided by electron withdrawing groups, but the effect is much more marked in the former isomerization than in the latter. Schöllkopf has argued (36) that the value of $\rho \simeq 0.9$ found for the Meisenheimer rearrangement is more consistent with an initial cleavage into a radical pair as shown (66). On this basis one can argue that the value of $\rho \simeq 3.4$ in the Stevens rearrangement suggests initial separation into an ion pair (67). These arguments lead to reasonable explanations for the findings on

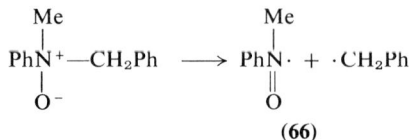

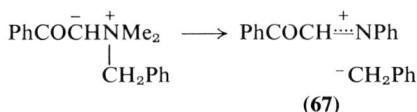

$$\text{(66)}$$

$$\text{(67)}$$

the intramolecular natures of the Stevens and Meisenheimer rearrangements, on the racemization observed at the migration center, and on the entropy changes. An ion pair held in a solvent cage with the migrating group moving as an anion would explain the retention of the optically active center, the strictly intramolecular nature of the Stevens rearrangement and the small negative entropy observed. On the other hand, a radical pair held in a solvent cage with the migrating group moving as a radical can well be expected to lead to some racemization of the migrating center along with an increase in entropy and even to some intermolecularity in the Meisenheimer rearrangement.

Schöllkopf has proposed that since a modest yield of rearrangement product was obtained on ultraviolet irradiation of the amine oxide (60,

R = H), there is additional evidence for the separation of the migrating group as a radical in the thermally induced Meisenheimer rearrangement. However, the two reactions may not follow similar mechanisms.

The evidence now available on the nature of the Meisenheimer rearrangement favors the cleavage–recombination radical mechanism taking place within a solvent cage. The evidence for an $S_N i$ mechanism is not nearly so conclusive. It is interesting to note that although the Meisenheimer rearrangement has been linked for many years with the Stevens and Wittig rearrangements and similar $S_N i$ mechanisms were at first proposed for them, all three reactions are now considered to proceed through a cleavage–recombination process as originally proposed by Stevens for the one reaction, and later invoked by Schöllkopf for the others. Even the original analogy of an $S_N i$-type reaction occurring in the decomposition of chlorosulfites can no longer be argued, since it appears that the chlorosulfites do not decompose thermally through internal nucleophilic displacement but through a cleavage–recombination reaction.

References

1. A. Pinner, *Chem. Ber.*, **28**, 456 (1895).
2. C. H. Rayburn, W. R. Harlan, and H. R. Hanmer, *J. Am. Chem. Soc.*, **72**, 1721 (1950).
3. J. Meisenheimer, *Chem. Ber.*, **52**, 1667 (1919).
4. J. Meisenheimer, H. Greeske, and A. Willmersdorf, *Chem. Ber.*, **55**, 513 (1922).
5. R. F. Kleinschmidt and A. C. Cope, *J. Am. Chem. Soc.*, **66**, 1929 (1944).
6. D. S. Tarbell, *Organic Reactions*, Vol. 2, Wiley, New York, 1944, p. 1.
7. A. C. Cope and P. H. Towle, *J. Am. Chem. Soc.*, **71**, 3423 (1949).
8. T. Kubota, *J. Am. Chem. Soc.*, **87**, 459 (1965).
9. A. C. Cope, T. T. Foster, and P. H. Towle, *J. Am. Chem. Soc.*, **71**, 3929 (1949).
10. L. Mamlock and R. Wolffenstein, *Chem. Ber.*, **33**, 159 (1900).
11. A. C. Cope and E. R. Trumbull, *Organic Reactions*, Volume 11, Wiley, New York, 1960, p. 317.
12. A. C. Cope and C. L. Bumgardner, *J. Am. Chem. Soc.*, **78**, 2812 (1956).
13. A. C. Cope, E. Ciganek, and N. A. LeBel, *J. Am. Chem. Soc.*, **81**, 2799 (1959).
14. L. D. Quin and G. L. Roof, *J. Org. Chem.*, **27**, 4451 (1962).
15. W. Carruthers and R. A. W. Johnstone, *J. Chem. Soc.*, **1965**, 1653.
16. L. D. Quin and F. A. Shelburne, *J. Org. Chem.*, **30**, 3135 (1965).
17. D. W. Henry and E. Leete, *J. Am. Chem. Soc.*, **79**, 5254 (1957).
18. C. A. Kingsbury and D. J. Cram, *J. Am. Chem. Soc.*, **82**, 1810 (1960); C. Walling and L. Bollyky, *J. Org. Chem.*, **29**, 2699 (1964); I. D. Entwistle and R. A. W. Johnstone, *Chem. Commun.*, **1965**, 29; J. L. Kice and J. D. Campbell, *J. Org. Chem.*, **31**, 1631 (1967).
19. A. C. Cope, D. E. Morrison, and L. Field, *J. Am. Chem. Soc.*, **72**, 59 (1950).
20. W. Carruthers, I. D. Entwistle, R. A. W. Johnstone, and B. J. Millard, *Chem. Ind. (London)*, **1966**, 324; I. D. Entwistle, R. A. W. Johnstone, and B. J. Millard, *J. Chem. Soc.*, **1967**, 302.

21. N. Kharasch, *Organic Sulphur Compounds*, Vol. 1, Pergamon Press, London, 1961.
22. A. H. Wragg, T. S. Stevens, and D. M. Ostle, *J. Chem. Soc.*, **1958**, 4057.
23. T. S. Stevens, *J. Chem. Soc.*, **1928**, 3193.
24. W. F. Cockburn, R. A. W. Johnstone, and T. S. Stevens, *J. Chem. Soc.*, **1960**, 3340; R. A. W. Johnstone and T. S. Stevens, *J. Chem. Soc.*, **1960**, 3346.
25. T. Thomson and T. S. Stevens, *J. Chem. Soc.*, **1932**, 69.
26. G. Wittig and H. Laib, *Ann. Chem.*, **580**, 57 (1953).
27. A. S. F. Ash, F. Challenger, T. S. Stevens, and J. L. Dunn, *J. Chem. Soc.*, **1952**, 2792.
28. G. Wittig and L. Lohmann, *Ann. Chem.*, **550**, 260 (1942).
29. E. Grovenstein, *J. Am. Chem. Soc.*, **79**, 4985 (1957); H.E. Zimmerman and F. J. Smentowski, *J. Am. Chem. Soc.*, **79**, 5455 (1957).
30. H. E. Zimmerman in *Molecular Rearrangements*, Vol. 1, P. de Mayo, Ed., Interscience, New York, 1963, p. 345.
31. G. M. Bennett and A. W. Chapman, *Ann. Rept.*, **1930**, 122.
32. C. R. Hauser and S. W. Kantor, *J. Am. Chem. Soc.*, **73**, 1437 (1951).
33. W. A. Cowdrey, E. D. Hughes, C. K. Ingold, S. Masterman, and A. D. Scott, *J. Chem. Soc.*, **1937**, 1252.
34. C. E. Boozer and E. S. Lewis, *J. Am. Chem. Soc.*, **76**, 794 (1954); D. J. Cram, *ibid.*, **75**, 332 (1953); A. Streitwieser and W. D. Schaeffer, *ibid.*, **79**, 379 (1957).
35. E. F. Jenny and J. Druey, *Angew. Chem.*, **74**, 152 (1962).
36. U. Schöllkopf, U. Ludwig, M. Patsch, and W. Franken, *Ann. Chem.*, **703**, 77 (1967).
37. R. A. W. Johnstone and T. S. Stevens, *J. Chem. Soc.*, **1955**, 4487.
38. T. S. Stevens, *J. Chem. Soc.*, **1930**, 2107.
39. A. Campbell, A. H. J. Houston, and J. Kenyon, *J. Chem. Soc.*, **1947**, 93.
40. J. H. Brewster and M. W. Kline, *J. Am. Chem. Soc.*, **74**, 5179 (1952).
41. U. Schöllkopf and H. Schäfer, *Ann. Chem.*, **663**, 22 (1963).
42. U. Schöllkopf and H. Schäfer, *Ann. Chem.*, **683**, 42 (1965); U. Schöllkopf, M. Patsch, and H. Schäfer, *Tetrahedron Letters*, **1964**, 2515.
43. P. T. Lansbury and V. A. Pattison, *J. Am. Chem. Soc.*, **84**, 4295 (1962); *J. Org. Chem.*, **27**, 1933 (1962).
44. B. J. Millard and T. S. Stevens, *J. Chem. Soc.*, **1963**, 3397.
45. J. Cast, T. S. Stevens, and J. Holmes, *J. Chem. Soc.*, **1960**, 3521.
46. U. Schöllkopf and K. Fellenberger, *Ann. Chem.*, **698**, 80 (1966).

Rearrangements Involving Nitrene Intermediates

J. H. BOYER

Chemistry Department, University of Illinois
Chicago Circle Campus, Chicago, Illinois

I. INTRODUCTION AND SCOPE OF CHAPTER

As recent treatises include molecular rearrangements of nitrenes (1–5), an exhaustive review of the literature is not needed here. The material for this chapter has been selected primarily from recent publications on the basis of interest and need for discussion. Hypotheses and generalizations now developing from the explosive appearance of new observations have not yet stood the test of time. At the risk of selecting and presenting what will prove to be misleading or incorrect, the chapter contains a liberal amount of speculation.

Considerable progress in strengthening the hypothesis of nitrene intermediacy has been made; nevertheless, proposed nitrenes may often be but a part of a broader spectrum of mechanisms extending, for example, to a concerted process of bond formation and bond breaking at nitrogen.

Examples covering a wide range of persuasive reasons for their intermediacy are included here. With few exceptions rearrangements of
nitrenium ($R_2\overset{\oplus}{N}$) and diazenium ($R_2\overset{\oplus}{N}=NH$) ions are not included.

Throughout the following discussions, a differentiation between
singlet or triplet excited states as the reacting nitrene species is not attempted except in certain examples where assignments have been made.
Intermolecular reactions have shown that a singlet nitrene may react
stereospecifically, whereas a triplet nitrene may react nonstereospecifically.
For example, carbethoxynitrene combines as a singlet with *cis*-4-methyl-
pentene-2 to produce exclusively the corresponding *cis*-aziridine, but both
cis- and *trans*-aziridines are obtained from the same reaction with the
triplet nitrene (6) (Eq. 1). It has also been demonstrated with cyanonitrene

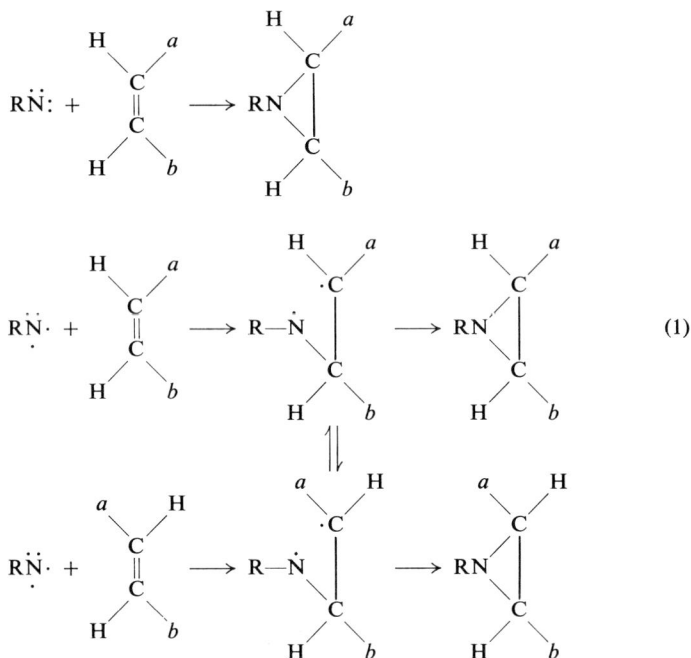

(1)

which gives stereospecific insertion of the singlet with a tertiary CH bond
of *cis*-1,2-dimethylcyclohexane producing *cis*-1,2-dimethylcyclohexyl-
cyanamide. Both *cis*- and *trans*-1,2-dimethylcyclohexylcyanamide are obtained from the triplet nitrene by nonstereospecific insertion (7) (Eq. 2).

A delocalized nitrene not only has excited states in which a reactive
site may be located at another atom, but also it may participate in valence
isomerization. For example, a vinyl nitrene apparently may also react as a

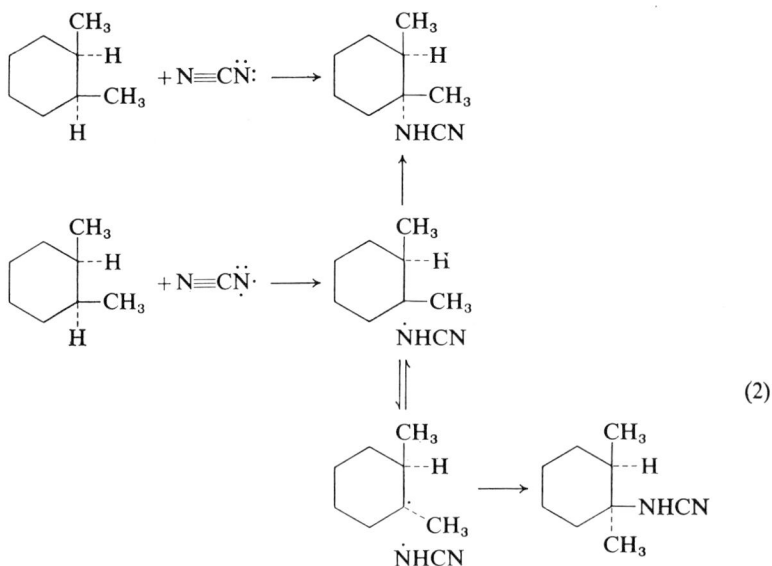

$$(2)$$

1,3-diradical or as a 1,3-zwitterion (Eq. 3), and through reversible iso-merizations it may be transformed into an azirine and perhaps into an electron-deficient intermediate with carbenoid properties (Eq. 3). The

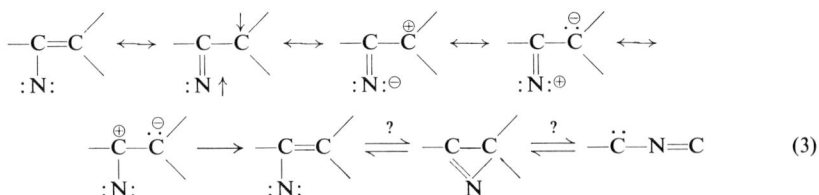

$$(3)$$

reaction of an azirine as its carbenoid counterpart may have been demon-strated in the formation of an aminoazepine from phenyl nitrene and a secondary amine, in a reaction which apparently involves an intermediate bicyclic azirine (see Eqs. 98 and 99).

Similar considerations must be given to other delocalized nitrenes, e.g., acyl, thioacyl, azomethine, sulfonyl, and aromatic nitrenes. It is conceivable that valence isomerization interchanges an azomethine nitrene, a diazirine, and an azocarbene (otherwise recognized as a nitrile imine), but a known example is lacking (Eq. 4).

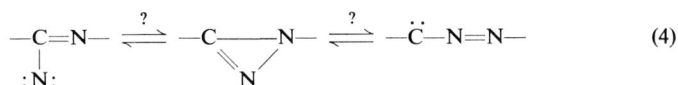

$$(4)$$

A nitrile imine is considered to be the intermediate during both pyrolysis and photolysis of 2-benzoyl-5-substituted tetrazole into a corresponding 1,3,4-oxadiazole (8,9) (Eq. 5). Unfortunately, a similar study of

$$
\begin{array}{c}
\text{C}_6\text{H}_5\text{C}=\!\!=\!\!\text{N} \\
\mid \quad\quad \mid \\
\text{N}_{\diagdown\text{N}}\diagup\text{NCOC}_6\text{H}_5
\end{array}
\xrightarrow[-\text{N}_2]{\substack{h\nu \text{ or} \\ \text{heat}}}
\text{C}_6\text{H}_3\text{C}\!\!\equiv\!\!\overset{+}{\text{N}}\overset{-}{\text{N}}\text{COC}_6\text{H}_5
\longrightarrow
\begin{array}{c}
\text{N}\!\!-\!\!\text{N} \\
\parallel \quad\quad \parallel \\
\text{C}_6\text{H}_5\text{C}_{\diagdown\text{O}}\diagup\text{CC}_6\text{H}_5
\end{array}
\quad (5)
$$

1-acyltetrazoles has not been reported. By a modification, a convenient preparation of 1,3,4-oxadizoles consists of the interaction between a 5-alkyl- or 5-aryltetrazole with an acylating agent without isolating the intermediate N-acyltetrazole. Loss of nitrogen may occur at a temperature as low as 60° (8). Support for the mechanism (8,9) requiring elimination of nitrogen from a 5-substituted-2-acyltetrazole in this latter process was offered in an experiment with 5-phenyltetrazole containing ^{15}N labeling in the 1 (equivalent with 4) position. Treatment with benzoyl chloride gave 2,5-diphenyl-1,3,4-oxadiazole containing half of the ^{15}N. The conclusion that nitrogen atoms at positions 3 and 4 (equivalent with 1 and 2) were eliminated from 2-benzoyl-5-phenyltetrazole is not entirely justified. The possibility of a fragmentation from 1-benzoyl-5-phenyltetrazole leading to diphenyl-1,3,4-oxadiazole demonstrates the need for an investigation of the pyrolysis and photolysis of known 1-acyl derivatives of tetrazoles. An alternate mechanism for the formation of 2,5-diphenyl-1,3,4-oxadiazole requires the intermediacy of a diazirine or related species (see Eq. 4) generated from 1-benzoyl-5-phenyltetrazole with nitrogen elimination from positions 3 and 4 (Eq. 6). Other 1,5-disubstituted derivatives of

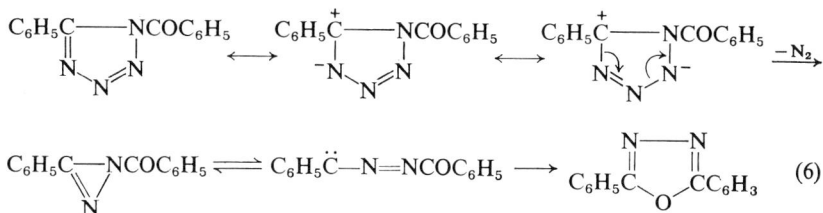

$$
\begin{array}{c}
\text{C}_6\text{H}_5\text{C}\!\!-\!\!\text{NCOC}_6\text{H}_5 \\
\parallel \quad\quad \mid \\
\text{N}_{\diagdown\text{N}}\diagup^{\diagdown}\text{N}
\end{array}
\longleftrightarrow
\begin{array}{c}
\overset{+}{\text{C}_6\text{H}_5\text{C}}\!\!-\!\!\text{NCOC}_6\text{H}_5 \\
\mid \quad\quad \mid \\
^{-}\text{N}_{\diagdown\text{N}}\diagup^{\diagdown}\text{N}
\end{array}
\longleftrightarrow
\begin{array}{c}
\overset{+}{\text{C}_6\text{H}_5\text{C}}\!\!-\!\!\text{NCOC}_6\text{H}_5 \\
\mid \quad\quad \mid \\
\text{N}\!\!\stackrel{\frown}{\diagup}\!\!\text{N}^{-} \\
\text{N}
\end{array}
\xrightarrow{-\text{N}_2}
$$

$$
\begin{array}{c}
\text{C}_6\text{H}_5\text{C}\!\!-\!\!\text{NCOC}_6\text{H}_5 \\
\diagdown\!\!\diagup \\
\text{N}
\end{array}
\rightleftharpoons
\text{C}_6\text{H}_5\ddot{\text{C}}\!\!-\!\!\text{N}\!\!=\!\!\text{NCOC}_6\text{H}_5
\longrightarrow
\begin{array}{c}
\text{N}\!\!-\!\!\text{N} \\
\parallel \quad\quad \parallel \\
\text{C}_6\text{H}_5\text{C}_{\diagdown\text{O}}\diagup\text{CC}_6\text{H}_3
\end{array}
\quad (6)
$$

tetrazole apparently lose nitrogen atoms from the tetrazole positions 2 and 3 and azomethine nitrenes or related species (Eq. 4) have been assumed intermediates. Such an intermediate generated from 1-benzoyl-5-phenyltetrazole would be expected to produce 3,5-diphenyl-1,2,4-oxadiazole or a diazirine by cyclization, as well as a carbodiimide by rearrangement (see Section VI).

In the photolysis of dimethyl diazidomalonate it is believed that 1,5-dicarbomethoxytetrazole is initially produced. With subsequent fragmentation a compound is formed which agrees with the assignment of either

3-carbomethoxy-5-methoxy-1,2,4-oxadiazole or the isomeric 2-carbo-methoxy-5-methoxy-1,3,4-oxadiazole (10).

Other nitrenes may be subject to electron delocalization and valence isomerization. Electron delocalization makes cyanonitrene a symmetrical reagent (7) and permits the ground state of a cyanocarbene to be identical with the ground state of a corresponding ethynyl nitrene (see Eq. 63). An extension of the valence isomerism which relates certain triazole nitrenes and corresponding linear nitriles (see Eq. 30) to other doubly unsaturated five-membered rings can be expected (see Eqs. 33 and 101).

Throughout this chapter it is intended to include appropriate mechanistic explanations based on their biradical, zwitterionic, and valence isomeric counterparts as well as nitrenes themselves.

II. SURVEY OF C-NITRENE GENERATION

The strongest defense for the hypothesis of C-nitrene intermediacy has been developed from observations on certain reactions which require α-elimination at nitrogen (Table 1), in particular, examples of Eqs. 7 and 8. Equation 7 also includes the generation of a nitrene from a tetrazole insofar as the latter may isomerize to an azidoazomethine derivative prior to the elimination of nitrogen (1,2) (see Section VI); on the other hand, concerted elimination of nitrogen from the tetrazole ring could lead directly to a mixture of the corresponding diazirine and nitrene (see Eq. 81). In most examples, the energy of activation for the elimination of nitrogen from an azide is supplied by either heat or light and less frequently by shock, sonic vibration, electron impact (11), or electric discharge.

Reversible valence isomerization between a nitrene and an azirine (Eq. 29) was first considered for a bicyclic azirine and the corresponding aryl nitrene (3,27) (Eq. 31) (see Section VII). For a monocyclic azirine it

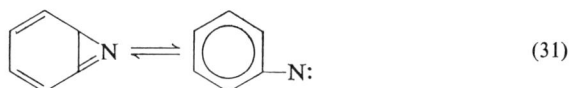

$$\text{(31)}$$

offers a basis for an explanation of catalytic reduction to a primary enamine (29) (Eq. 32) under conditions in which the corresponding aziridine is stable to reduction. A similar equilibrium between an aromatic azirinyl cation and the corresponding vinyl nitrenium cation (30) may account for the ability of the CN single bond of the azirinyl cation to react with unsaturated bonds as a 1,3-dipole (29,31).

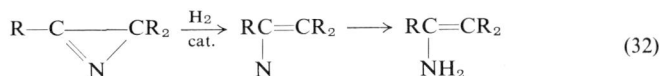

$$\text{(32)}$$

TABLE 1

Generation of C-Nitrenes

Reaction	Equation number	Ref.
R = alkyl, aryl, acyl, sulfonyl, etc. as appropriate		
X = halogen, Z = SO_2Ar and other groups		
$RN_3 \xrightarrow[\text{or } h\nu]{\text{heat}} RN + N_2$	7	1–5
$R\overset{\ominus}{N}OZ \longrightarrow RN + OZ^{\ominus}$	8	1–5
$R\overset{\ominus}{N}X \longrightarrow RN + X^{\ominus}$	9	1–5
$RNHX(RNHOZ) \longrightarrow RN + HX(HOZ)$	10	1–5
$RNX_2 \longrightarrow RN + X_2$	11	1–5
$R\overset{\ominus}{N}O\overset{\oplus}{P}R_3 \longrightarrow RN + R_3PO$	12	1–12
$RNCO \xrightarrow{h\nu} RN + CO$	13	13
$RN{=}PR_3 \xrightarrow{h\nu} RN + R_3P$	14	14
$RCH_2C\underset{\substack{\parallel \\ NOZ}}{C}H_2R + B^{\ominus} \xrightarrow[-BH]{-OZ^{\ominus}} RCH{=}C\underset{\substack{\parallel \\ N}}{C}H_2R$	15	1–5

$$\begin{array}{c} \text{S}\!-\!-\!-\!-\!\text{CR} \\ | \qquad \parallel \\ \text{O}\!-\!\text{C} \qquad \text{N} \\ \;\;\backslash \quad / \\ \quad \text{O} \end{array} \longrightarrow \begin{array}{c} RCN + CO_2 \\ \parallel \\ S \end{array}$$

	16	15

$$\begin{array}{c} \text{RN}\!-\!-\!-\!-\!\text{CR} \\ | \qquad \parallel \\ \text{O}{=}\text{C} \qquad \text{N} \\ \;\;\backslash \quad / \\ \quad \text{O} \end{array} \xrightarrow[\text{or } h\nu]{\text{heat}} RN{=}C(R)N + CO_2$$

	17	16

$$\begin{array}{c} \text{RN}\!-\!-\!-\!-\!\text{CR} \\ | \qquad \parallel \\ \text{O}{=}\text{S} \qquad \text{N} \\ \;\;\backslash \quad / \\ \quad \text{O} \end{array} \xrightarrow{\text{heat}} RN{=}C(R)N + SO_2$$

	18	17

$$\begin{array}{c} \text{RCH}\!-\!-\!-\!\text{C}\!-\!\text{R} \\ | \qquad \parallel \\ R_3'P \qquad N \\ \;\;\backslash \quad / \\ \quad \text{O} \end{array} \longrightarrow \begin{array}{c} RCH{=}CR + R_3'PO \\ | \\ N \end{array}$$

	19	18

$$\begin{array}{c} \text{RN}\!-\!-\!-\!-\!\text{CR} \\ | \qquad \parallel \\ R_3'P \qquad N \\ \;\;\backslash \quad / \\ \quad \text{O} \end{array} \longrightarrow RN{=}C(R)N + R_3'PO$$

	20	18

(continued)

TABLE 1 (*continued*)

Reaction	Equation number	Ref.
$RN\overset{\diagdown\diagup}{\underset{O}{\quad}}CHR \xrightarrow{h\nu} RN + RCHO$	21	12,19,20
$RN{=}N(O)R \xrightarrow{heat} RN + RNO$	22	12,21
$R_FN{=}NR_F \xrightarrow{heat} R_FN$	23	3
$R_FNCO \xrightarrow{AgF_2} R_FN + COF_2$	24	3,22
$R_FCN \xrightarrow{AgF_2} R_FCF_2N$	25	2,23
$N + C_2H_2 \longrightarrow NCH{=}\overset{.}{C}H$	26	3,24
$R_2C{=}CR_2 \xrightarrow{HN} R_2C\underset{\cdot NH}{-}\overset{.}{C}R_2 \longrightarrow R_2CCHR_2\underset{N}{\mid}$	27	25
$RCNO \xrightarrow{NCO_2R} RC{=}\overset{\oplus}{N}CO_2R\underset{NO^-}{\overset{\parallel}{\mid}} \longrightarrow RC{-}N\underset{NOCO_2R}{\overset{\parallel}{\mid}}$	28	36
$R_2C\overset{\diagdown\diagup}{\underset{\underset{CN}{N}}{\quad}}CR \rightleftharpoons R_2C{=}CR\underset{N}{\mid}$	29	3,27
$R{-}\overset{\mid}{\underset{}{C}}{=}N{-}N{=}N{-}R \rightleftharpoons R{-}N\overset{\diagdown}{\underset{N}{\underset{\diagdown}{N}}}\overset{C{-}N}{\underset{C{-}R}{\parallel}}$	30	28a
$RCNO \xrightarrow{h\nu} RNCO + RCON$	30a	28b

With the assumption that an azirine and a corresponding vinyl nitrene may participate in an equilibrium, Table 1 contains other reactions, for example Eq. 19, in which an azirine, but not a nitrene, has heretofore been considered as an intermediate or isolated as a product.

By a straightforward extension the reversible valence isomerization between a vicinal triazole nitrene and a linear nitrile (Eq. 30) has offered the basis for an explanation of the transformation of certain N-amino-s-triazole nitrenes into aminotetrazines (32) (Eq. 33).

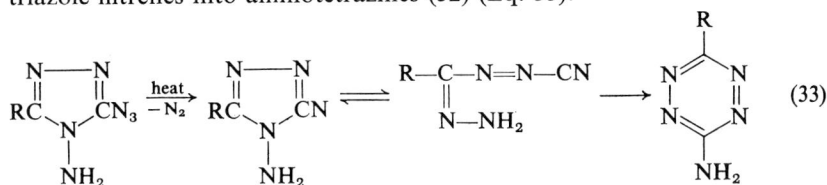

$$\underset{NH_2}{RC\overset{N{-}N}{\underset{N}{\diagup\diagdown}}CN_3} \xrightarrow[-N_2]{heat} \underset{NH_2}{RC\overset{N{-}N}{\underset{N}{\diagup\diagdown}}CN} \rightleftharpoons \underset{N{-}NH_2}{R{-}C{-}N{=}N{-}CN} \longrightarrow \underset{NH_2}{\overset{R}{\underset{N}{\underset{\diagdown}{N}}}\overset{N}{\underset{\diagup}{N}}} \qquad (33)$$

Fragmentation of an oxazirane ring (Eq. 21) may produce both a nitrene and a carbene in analogy with the photolysis of an epoxide to a carbene and a carbonyl compound (33). Benzaldehyde, benzaldehyde anil, nitrosobenzene, and a trace of benzanilide obtained from the irradiation of 2,3-diphenyloxazirane (19) suggest that both phenylcarbene and phenylnitrene were generated (12) (Eq. 33a). More recently phenylnitrene, generated by irradiation of 2-phenyl-3,3-pentamethyleneoxazirane, has been captured by diethylamine in a reaction producing diethylamino-azepine (20) (Eq. 33a).

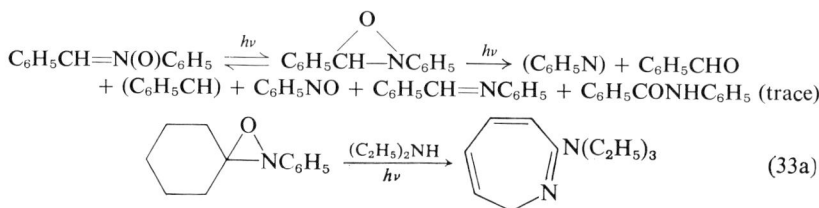

$$C_6H_5CH{=}N(O)C_6H_5 \overset{h\nu}{\rightleftharpoons} C_6H_5\overset{\overset{\displaystyle O}{\diagup\diagdown}}{CH{-}N}C_6H_5 \overset{h\nu}{\longrightarrow} (C_6H_5N) + C_6H_5CHO$$

$$+ (C_6H_5CH) + C_6H_5NO + C_6H_5CH{=}NC_6H_5 + C_6H_5CONHC_6H_5 \text{ (trace)}$$

$$\underset{}{\overset{\displaystyle O}{\diagup\diagdown}}{-NC_6H_5} \xrightarrow[h\nu]{(C_2H_5)_2NH} \quad \underset{N}{\bigcirc}N(C_2H_5)_3 \tag{33a}$$

Support for Eq. 22 is found in the dry distillation of azoxybenzene producing nitrosobenzene, aniline, and azobenzene (21). The formation of aniline would be expected from the proposed intermediate, phenyl nitrene, by abstraction of hydrogen.

Equations 27, 28, and 30a are of special interest insofar as nitrene generation by molecular rearrangement has been proposed. Certain other reactions in Table 1 will be discussed later.

III. REARRANGEMENTS IN ALKYL NITRENES

Electron spin resonance at $4°K$ has provided physical evidence for primary, secondary, and tertiary alkyl nitrenes (33). Each was prepared photolytically from an azide probably in a bimolecular reaction in accordance with a kinetic analysis of the photolysis of hydrogen, methyl, and ethyl azides at $-80°$ (34). The facility for alkyl nitrenes to enter into both intramolecular and intermolecular reactions is revealed in the failure to detect their ESR at $77°K$, at which temperature delocalized nitrenes, such as certain aryl and sulfonyl nitrenes, are found to be appreciably stable (35).

Both intra- and intermolecular abstraction and insertion reactions are available for alkyl nitrenes. Mechanistically, the rearrangement proceeding by a 1,2-hydride shift has not been differentiated from rearrangement by alkyl nitrene insertion with other CH bonds. Apparently, neither intramolecular abstraction of hydrogen with the formation of an unsaturated

primary amine, nor rearrangement with cyclization offers serious competition for either the 1,2-hydride shift or 1,2-migration of another group
from tertiary carbon to nitrogen in an alkyl nitrene (36–38). The 1,2-
migration appears to be predominant for alkyl nitrenes generated both
photolytically and pyrolytically, but with the possibility of different
migratory aptitudes. A preference for phenyl migration was found in the
pyrolysis of α-phenylisopropyl azide (Eq. 34), but not in its photolysis. The
statistically corrected migratory aptitude factors for phenyl and methyl
are 4.05 and 0.96, respectively. Phenyl migration occurs preferentially in
both the pyrolysis and photolysis of α,α-diphenylethyl azide. Here statistically corrected pyrolysis migration aptitude factors for phenyl and methyl
are 2.36 and 2.18, respectively (38) (Eq. 35). Qualitatively, the same results

$$C_6H_5C(CH_3)C{=}NCH_3 \xleftarrow[-N_2]{h\nu} (CH_3)_2C(C_6H_5)N_3 \xrightarrow[-N_2]{\Delta} (CH_3)_2C{=}NC_6H_5 \quad (34)$$

$$(C_6H_5)_2C(CH_3)N_3 \xrightarrow[-N_2]{\Delta \text{ or } h\nu} C_6H_5C(CH_3){=}NC_6H_5 \quad (35)$$

were obtained from pyrolysis and photolysis of triarylmethyl azides, but
significant differences in migratory aptitudes of phenyl versus substituted
phenyl were noted. Substitution was found to have little, if any, effect in
photochemical rearrangement, while electron-donating substituents were
found to aid and electron-withdrawing substituents were found to hinder
migration during pyrolysis (sec Section VIII-D for further discussion and
comparison with similar reactions of diaryl boron azides).

The formation of carbenes during a sensitized photolysis of geminal
diazides at 77°K in rigid matrices (39) (Eq. 36) was recently observed. In

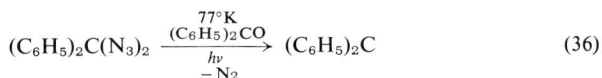

Investigations revealed that triplet azides and probably discrete
triplet nitrenes are involved in both direct and sensitized photolyses of
triarylmethyl azides (38). It was concluded that direct photolysis produced
first a singlet excited azide, and subsequently, by intersystem crossing, a
triplet azide through which nitrogen elimination and rearrangement
occurs. An absence of appreciable substituent effects on migratory aptitudes presents a favorable argument that migration is not concerted with
nitrogen elimination. A further observation was made that rearrangement
of a triarylmethyl nitrene should have a very low energy of activation in
comparison with a rearrangement concerted with nitrogen loss, so that
minimal discrimination amongst the migrating groups would be expected
even if the energy content at this state is barely in excess of that needed
for the reaction (38).

The formation of carbenes during a sensitized photolysis of geminal
diazides at 77°K in rigid matrices (39) (Eq. 36) was recently observed. In

$$(C_6H_5)_2C(N_3)_2 \xrightarrow[-N_2]{\substack{77°K \\ (C_6H_5)_2CO \\ h\nu}} (C_6H_5)_2C \quad (36)$$

contrast, a nonsensitized photolysis of diphenyldiazidomethane in solution phase at usual reaction temperatures occurs with migration of phenyl from carbon to nitrogen and the formation of 1,5-diphenyltetrazole, 2-phenyl-benzimidazole, and diphenylcarbodiimide (10) (Eq. 37, and see Eq. 81). It has long been known that pyrolysis of diphenyldiazidomethane produces 1,5-diphenyltetrazole (40). This photolysis reaction has special significance insofar as diphenylcarbodiimide is produced. By separate experiment it was confirmed that photolysis of 1,5-diphenyltetrazole does not give this product (see Section VI) and produces 2-phenylbenzimidazole in lower yield (10).

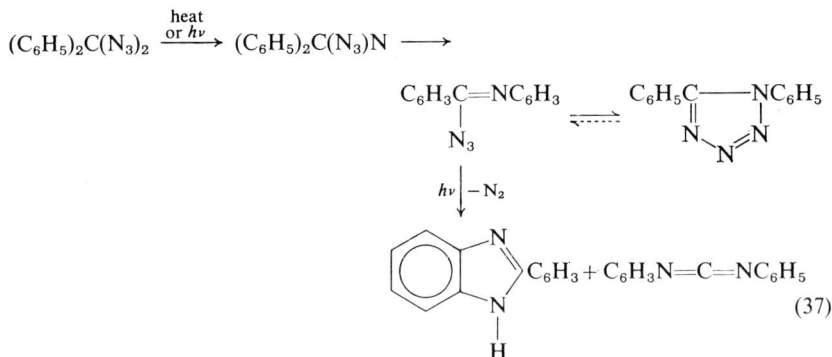

$$(C_6H_5)_2C(N_3)_2 \xrightarrow{\text{heat} \atop \text{or } h\nu} (C_6H_5)_2C(N_3)N \longrightarrow$$

(37)

In the formation of 2-aminobiphenyl by hydrolysis following pyrolysis of 2-azidomethylbiphenyl, the migration of an aromatic group has apparently successfully competed with hydrogen in migration from carbon to nitrogen (41) (Eq. 38). Probably a nitrene is involved in the interesting

$$o\text{-}C_6H_5C_6H_4CH_2N_3 \xrightarrow{-N_2} CH_2{=}NC_6H_4C_6H_5\text{-}o + HN{=}CHC_6H_4C_6H_5\text{-}o \qquad (38)$$

pyrolytic transformation of 2,2'-diazidomethylbiphenyl into phenanthridine and a dibenzoazepine (41) (Eq. 39).

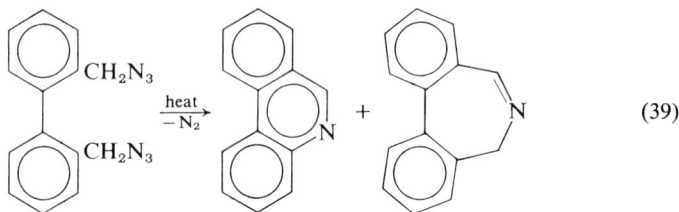

(39)

Very little is known about the rearrangement of alkyl nitrenes containing an atom in the β position other than carbon or hydrogen. Azidomethyldimethylborane loses nitrogen slowly at room temperature and much more rapidly at 125°. Comparison of NMR and VPC data of the product with that of an authentic specimen permits the tentative assignment of the product as B,B,B-trimethyl-N,N,N-triethylborazine (42) (Eq. 40). Its formation by a mechanism calling for initial migration of a dimethylboron group from carbon to a nitrene nitrogen, followed by a migration of methyl from boron to carbon was proposed (42). Both pyrolysis and photolysis of compounds belonging to the family, $RXCH_2N_3$,

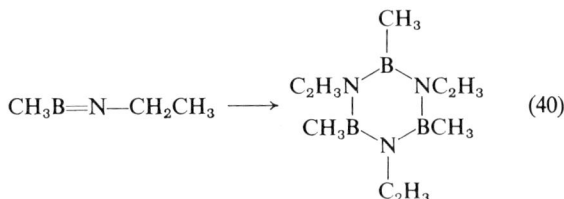

$$(CH_3)_2BCH_2N_3 \xrightarrow{-N_2} (CH_3)_2BCH_2N \longrightarrow (CH_3)_2BN{=}CH_2 \longrightarrow$$

$$CH_3B{=}N{-}CH_2CH_3 \longrightarrow \quad \text{(40)}$$

should be investigated. In addition to compounds where RX is $(CH_3)_2B$, compounds are also known where RX is CH_3O, C_2H_5O, CH_3S, C_2H_5S, C_3H_7S, N_3CH_2S, C_6H_5S, $C_6H_5CH_2S$, $(CH_3)_2N$, $C_5H_{10}N$, and $C_6H_4O_2N$ (43). An interesting formation of N-silyl amides consists in the Lewis acid catalyzed reaction between an aldehyde and trimethylsilyl azide (44a) (Eq. 41).

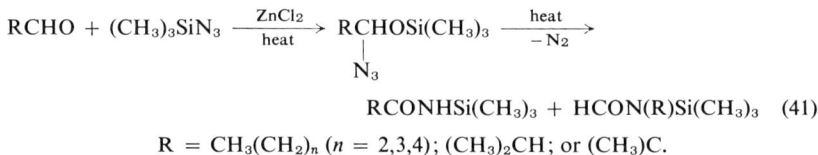

$$RCHO + (CH_3)_3SiN_3 \xrightarrow[\text{heat}]{ZnCl_2} \underset{\underset{N_3}{|}}{RCHOSi(CH_3)_3} \xrightarrow[-N_2]{heat}$$

$$RCONHSi(CH_3)_3 + HCON(R)Si(CH_3)_3 \quad \text{(41)}$$

$$R = CH_3(CH_2)_n \ (n = 2,3,4); (CH_3)_2CH; \text{ or } (CH_3)C.$$

A possible demonstration of the difficulty for alkylnitrene rearrangement by cyclization is found in the absence of formation of dihydroindole during either pyrolysis or photolysis of β-phenylethyl azide (44b). In confirmation, the photolysis of n-octyl azide apparently brings about the formation of only trace amounts of 2-n-butylpyrrolidine (36,45–47) (Eq. 42), and the factors governing reproducibility have not been elucidated.

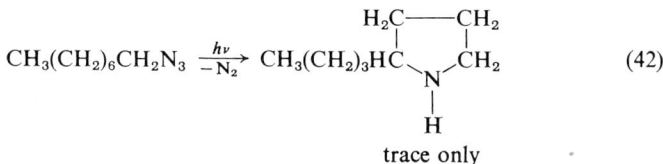

$$CH_3(CH_2)_6CH_2N_3 \xrightarrow[-N_2]{h\nu} CH_3(CH_2)_3HC \quad \text{(42)}$$

trace only

Pyrolysis of certain γ- and δ-azidoolefins produced pyrrolines and 1-azabicyclo[3.1.0]hexanes (48) (Eq. 43) through the intermediate formation and breakdown of triazolines which could be isolated. Pyrolysis of 4-azido-1-pentene gave unidentified resinous products and similar treatment of allyl azide gave unidentified fragmentation products (48).

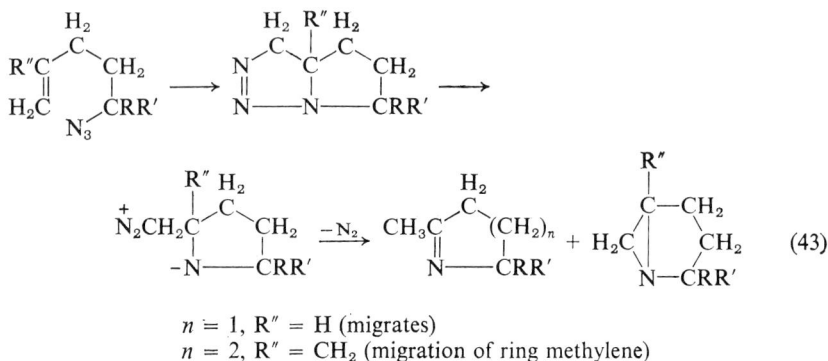

$$
\underset{\substack{\text{H}_2\text{C} \quad \text{CRR}' \\ \text{N}_3}}{\overset{\substack{\text{H}_2 \\ \text{C}}}{\text{R}''\text{C}\diagdown\text{CH}_2}} \longrightarrow
\underset{\text{N}\!-\!\!-\!\text{N}\!-\!\!-\!\text{CRR}'}{\overset{\substack{\text{H}_2 \ \text{R}''\ \text{H}_2 \\ \text{C}\diagup\text{C}\diagdown\text{C}}}{\text{N}\diagup\quad\text{CH}_2}} \longrightarrow
$$

$$
\underset{-\text{N}\!-\!\!-\!\text{CRR}'}{\overset{\substack{\text{R}'' \ \text{H}_2 \\ \text{C}}}{\overset{+}{\text{N}_2}\text{CH}_2\text{C}\diagdown\text{CH}_2}}
\xrightarrow{-\text{N}_2}
\underset{\text{N}\!-\!\!-\!\text{CRR}'}{\overset{\substack{\text{H}_2 \\ \text{C}}}{\text{CH}_3\text{C}\diagdown(\text{CH}_2)_n}} + \text{H}_2\text{C}\underset{\text{N}\!-\!\text{CRR}'}{\overset{\substack{\text{R}'' \\ \text{C}\!-\!\text{CH}_2}}{\diagup\quad\diagdown\text{CH}_2}}
\qquad (43)
$$

$n = 1$, $\text{R}'' = \text{H}$ (migrates)
$n = 2$, $\text{R}'' = \text{CH}_2$ (migration of ring methylene)

Aziridine was produced during solution photolysis (25,49) and pyrolysis (37) of ethyl azide (Eq. 44), and the corresponding 2,2-dimethyl-

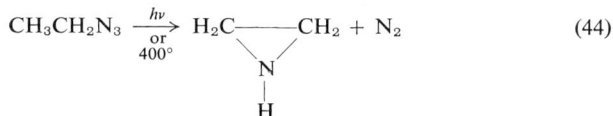

$$
\text{CH}_3\text{CH}_2\text{N}_3 \xrightarrow[\substack{\text{or} \\ 400^\circ}]{h\nu} \underset{\substack{\text{N} \\ | \\ \text{H}}}{\text{H}_2\text{C}\!-\!\!-\!\!-\!\text{CH}_2} + \text{N}_2
\qquad (44)
$$

aziridine has been a reported product from the photolysis of *tert*-butyl azide (46), but the latter undergoes pyrolysis with the migration of a methyl group and the formation of the *N*-methylimine of acetone (37). Neither the *N*-methylimine of acetone nor 2,2-dimethylaziridine was found in the products (*tert*-butyl amine, di-*tert*-butyl amine, and 2-cyclohexen-1-yl-*tert*-butyl amine) generated from *tert*-butyl nitrene, an assumed intermediate, in the photolysis of triphenylphosphine-*tert*-butyl imine in cyclohexene (14).

Rearrangement of an alkyl nitrene by insertion to form a ring with other than three or five members has not been observed (see Eq. 67).

Pyrazolidine formation by nitrene insertion with an NH bond in δ-aminopropyl nitrene apparently could not compete with 1,2-migration of hydrogen with the formation of the imine of β-aminopropionaldehyde (50). There is a need for additional information on the relative ease of nitrene insertion or abstraction by inter- or intramolecular reaction with CH, NH, OH, and other bonds to hydrogen.

Nitrene insertion with a CF bond has been proposed (3) to explain the formation of perfluoropyrrolidine from perfluorosuccinonitrile and fluorine (51) (Eq. 45). This explanation is at variance with other observa-

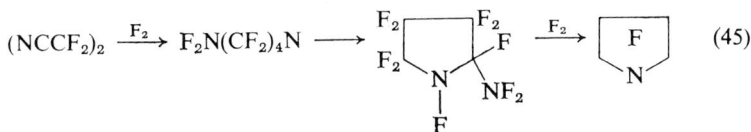

$$(NCCF_2)_2 \xrightarrow{F_2} F_2N(CF_2)_4N \longrightarrow \underset{F_2}{\overset{F_2}{\bigvee}} \overset{F_2}{\underset{N}{\bigwedge}} \underset{NF_2}{\overset{F}{\bigvee}} \xrightarrow{F_2} \boxed{F} \tag{45}$$

tions in which 1,2-alkyl migration to nitrogen has been found to occur in preference to nitrene insertion with a CF bond (52) (Eq. 46).

$$CF_3CF_2CHFCF_2N_3 \xrightarrow{-N_2} CF_3CF_2CFH-N=CF_2 \tag{46}$$

IV. REARRANGEMENTS IN VINYL AND ETHYNYL NITRENES

Vinyl azide apparently undergoes elimination of hydrogen azide (isolated as ammonium azide) with the formation of acetylene (assumed but not detected) (53) rather than elimination of nitrogen with the formation of vinylnitrene upon pyrolysis at 70°. It is probably more typical for terminal vinyl nitrenes to be generated from terminal vinyl azides undergoing pyrolysis. β-Styryl nitrene is an assumed intermediate in the nearly quantitative pyrolytic conversion and in the photolytic conversion of β-styryl azide into phenylacetonitrile (13) (Eq. 47). The same intermediate has been proposed for the photochemical transformation of β-styryl isocyanate into phenylacetonitrile and for the transformation of β-nitrostyrene by deoxygenation with triethyl phosphite into the same product (3,13) (Eq. 47).

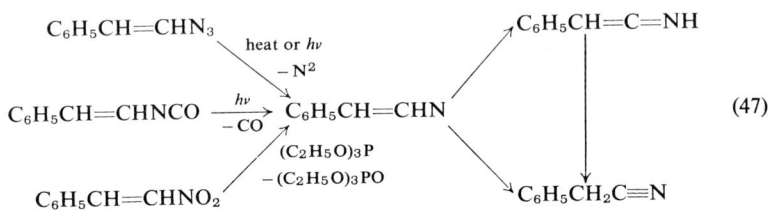

$$
\begin{array}{c}
C_6H_5CH=CHN_3 \\
\searrow{\scriptstyle heat\ or\ h\nu} \\
{\scriptstyle -N^2}
\end{array}
\qquad
\begin{array}{c}
\nearrow C_6H_5CH=C=NH \\
\\
\end{array}
$$

$$
C_6H_5CH=CHNCO \xrightarrow[-CO]{h\nu} C_6H_5CH=CHN \tag{47}
$$

$$
\begin{array}{c}
\nearrow {\scriptstyle (C_2H_5O)_3P} \\
{\scriptstyle -(C_2H_5O)_3PO}
\end{array}
$$

$$
C_6H_5CH=CHNO_2
\qquad\qquad
\searrow C_6H_5CH_2C\equiv N
$$

In a similar reaction β-azidovinyl phenyl ketone has been transformed into 5 phenylisoxazole and ω-cyanoacetophenone during either pyrolysis or photolysis (53a) (Eq. 47a).

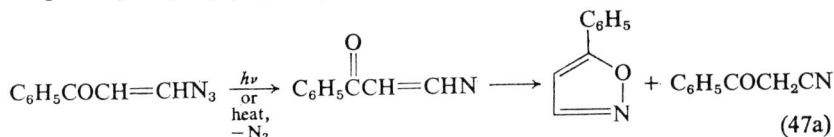

$$C_6H_5COCH=CHN_3 \xrightarrow[\substack{or \\ heat, \\ -N_2}]{h\nu} C_6H_5\overset{\overset{\displaystyle O}{\|}}{C}CH=CHN \longrightarrow \underset{\underset{N}{\diagdown}}{\overset{C_6H_5}{\diagup}}\!\!\!\diagup\!O + C_6H_5COCH_2CN \tag{47a}$$

Following the assumption that β-styryl nitrene and the valence tautomeric azirine participate in an equilibrium, the absence of the formation of indole demonstrates an apparent inability of β-styryl nitrene to undergo pyrrole ring closure by insertion and of 3-phenylazirine to enter into the required valence isomerization followed by tautomerization (Eq. 48).

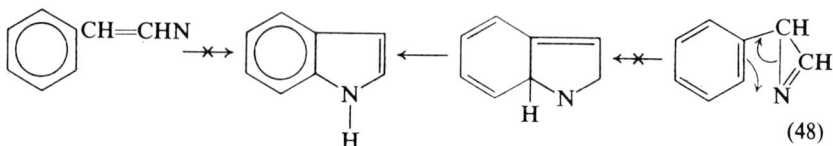

(48)

An explanation (54) for the pyrolytic transformation of 3,5-dibromo-2-hydroxybenzal diazide into 2,4-dibromo-6-cyanophenol (55) is based on terminal azide and nitrene intermediates (Eq. 49). It is now proposed that

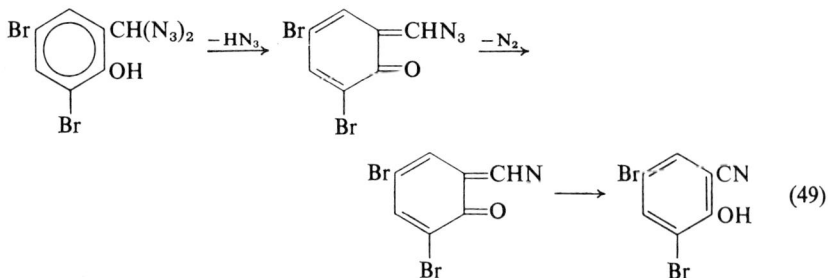

(49)

a related vinyl nitrene is an intermediate in the photolysis of benzisoxazoles, from which the corresponding cyanophenols and benzoxazoles are obtained (56) (Eq. 50). An attractive explanation based on valence isomerization of an intermediate azirine and nitrene may account for both products.

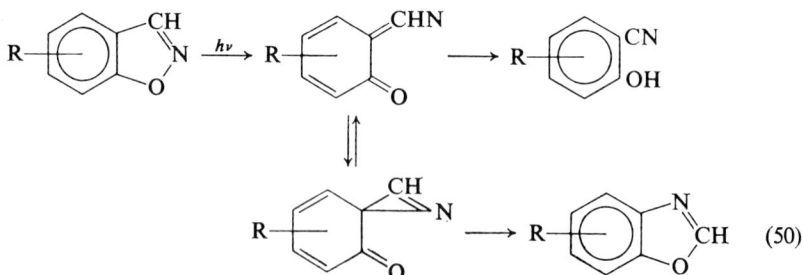

(50)

Terminal vinyl nitrenes may also be produced in the reaction between acetylene and active nitrogen (57) (Eq. 51); however, rearranged products were not reported. In a similar reaction between butadiene and active nitrogen, the formation of pyrrole may require rearrangement of a nitrene (58).

$$N + HC \equiv CH \longrightarrow NCH = CH \cdot \longrightarrow NCH = CHCH = CH \cdot \longrightarrow \text{polymer} \quad (51)$$

Unstable perfluoropropenyl azide undergoes loss of nitrogen at 20°. Perhaps valence isomerization of perfluoropropenyl nitrene accounts for the formation of perfluoro (2-methyl-2-H-azirine) (59) (Eq. 52). An earlier report (60) that the nitrene undergoes rearrangement by insertion with a CF bond and the formation of a four-membered ring is incorrect.

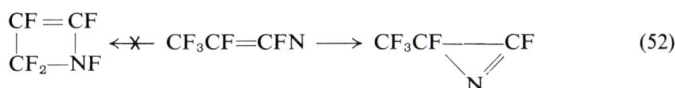

$$
\begin{array}{c}
CF = CF \\
| \quad\quad | \\
CF_2 - NF
\end{array}
\longleftarrow\!\!\!\times\!\!\!- \; CF_3CF = CFN \longrightarrow CF_3CF\!\!-\!\!\!-\!\!\!-\!\!CF \atop \diagdown \; \diagup \atop N \quad\quad\quad (52)
$$

Nonterminal vinyl nitrenes show a preference for valence isomerization into azirines over rearrangement into ketenimines (61a). On pyrolysis, both α-styryl azide and 2-azidohexene-2 are transformed into corresponding azirines (Eq. 53), and the former reaction has also been realized photochemically (50). A rationalization for the absence of ESR at 77°K for α-styryl nitrene was offered by noting that this and certain other nitrenes can undergo further reaction by processes less likely to occur with aryl and sulfonyl nitrenes which do exhibit resonance at this temperature (35). An inspection for resonance at 4°K has apparently not been reported but would seem to be warranted since at 4°K, but not at 77°K, carbethoxy

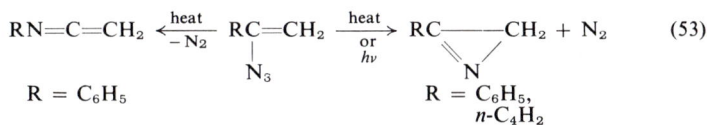

$$
RN = C = CH_2 \xleftarrow[-N_2]{\text{heat}} RC = CH_2 \xrightarrow[\substack{\text{or} \\ h\nu}]{\text{heat}} RC\!\!-\!\!\!-\!\!\!-\!\!CH_2 + N_2 \quad (53)
\atop
\begin{array}{lll}
R = C_6H_5 & \quad N_3 & \quad\quad R = C_6H_5, \\
& & \quad\quad n\text{-}C_4H_2
\end{array}
$$

nitrene resonance was measured (6,35). It is of especial interest to note that rearrangement of neither 2-hexenylnitrene nor o-methyl-α-styrylnitrene by CH insertion with cyclization to a pyrroline ring was competitive with azirine formation (61a). Based at least in part on this observation, the suggestion was made that nitrogen elimination might be concerted with azirine formation from either the azide or its cyclic isomer, a triazole (Eq. 54). The limited evidence (Section II) on the preferred opening of the

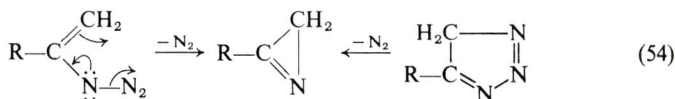

$$
R\!\!-\!\!C\!\!\begin{array}{c} CH_2 \\ \diagup \\ \diagdown \\ N\!\!-\!\!N_2 \end{array} \xrightarrow{-N_2} R\!\!-\!\!C\!\!\begin{array}{c} CH_2 \\ \diagup \\ \diagdown \\ N \end{array} \xleftarrow{-N_2} \begin{array}{c} H_2C\!\!-\!\!\!-\!\!N \\ | \quad\quad \| \\ R\!\!-\!\!C\!\!\diagdown_{N}\!\!\diagup\!\!N \end{array} \quad (54)
$$

azirine ring through cleavage of the CN single bond is further supported by the slow generation at room temperature of 3,6-diphenylpyridazine (62) (Eq. 55) from α-styryl azide. The intermediate formation of an azo dimer of α-styryl azide with subsequent spontaneous cyclization by valence isomerization and dehydrogenation was assumed. Photolysis of 2-phenylazirine apparently opens the azirine ring prior to, or with, an alternate dimerization to 3,6-dihydro-2,5-diphenylpyrazine (50) (Eq. 55). Tetraphenylpyrazine is produced from α-azidostilbene probably by a similar photochemical mechanism (63).

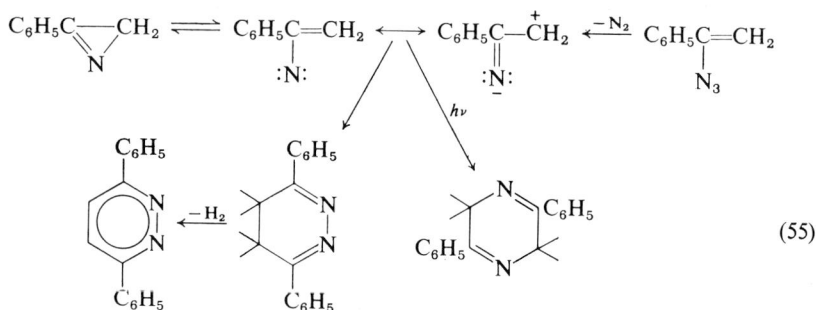

(55)

Assuming an equilibrium between a vinyl nitrene and an azirine, it would seem that pyrrole and pyrroline ring closures are at least as difficult for suitably constructed vinyl nitrenes or the corresponding azirines as it is for the similar pyrrolidine ring closure from alkyl nitrenes. In agreement with the failure of either β-styryl nitrene or its valence tautomer 3-phenylazirine to isomerize into indole, 2-phenylazirine apparently does not undergo valence isomerization and tautomerization into isoindole.

Vinyl nitrene intermediates have been considered for other reactions. To explain the pyrolytic conversion of α-phenylcyclohexanone oxime into tetrahydrocarbazole, intermediate 2-phenylcyclohexenylnitrene was pro-

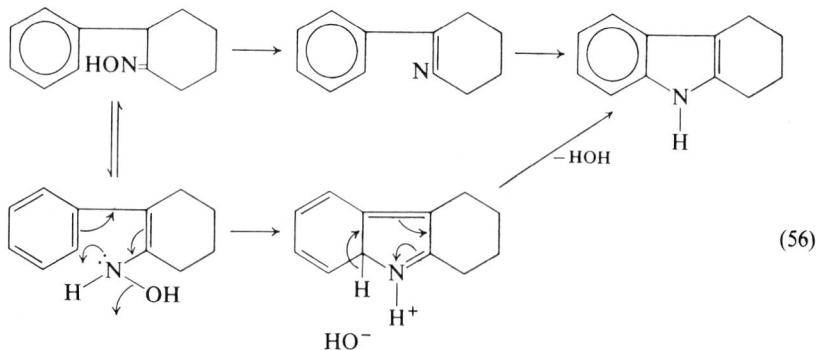

(56)

posed (64) (Eq. 56); however ring closure from a vinyl hydroxylamine, tautomeric with α-phenylcyclohexanone oxime, also provides a satisfactory explanation for the formation of tetrahydrocarbazole (Eq. 56). An alternate generation of the nitrene from the corresponding azide was abandoned because of difficulties encountered in the preparation of the azide (61a).

A structurally related nitrene may have been produced during the pyrolysis of α-methyl-β-styryl azide. The reaction in mesitylene led to the formation of β-methylindole in 80% yield together with α-phenylpropionitrile in 9% yield, but in ethanol the major product is 2,5-dimethyl-2,5-diphenyldihydropyrazine in 48% yield with a trace of β-methylindole and nitrile (61b) (Eq. 56a). In contrast, only N-methylphenylketenimine, but neither an indole nor an azirine, has been detected in the reaction products

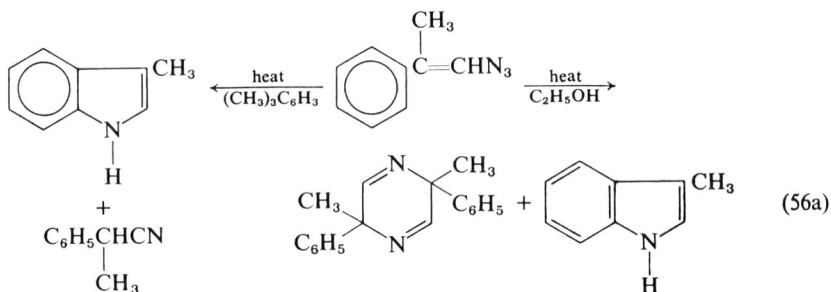

$$\text{(56a)}$$

obtained from the photolysis of β-methyl-β-styryl isocyanate (64b) (Eq. 56b). Pyrolysis of α-phenyl-β-styryl azide produced β-phenylindole. A

$$C_6H_5CH{=}\overset{\overset{\displaystyle CH_3}{|}}{C}NCO \xrightarrow{\ h\nu\ } C_6H_5CH{=}C{=}NCH_3 \qquad \text{(56b)}$$

solvent effect similar to that described above permitted an 82% yield for the reaction in toluene and 53% in ethanol. In the latter reaction 2,2,5,5-tetraphenyldihydropyrazine was also formed in 20% yield (61b). At room temperature gem-diazidodibenzofulvene loses 1 mole of nitrogen to give 9-azido-9-cyanofluorene in 34% yield (61b). The migration of an azido group may require the intermediate formation of a triazole (Eq. 56c, compare Eq. 30).

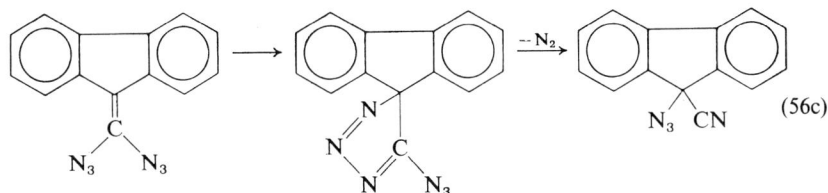

$$\text{(56c)}$$

An intermediate vinyl nitrene and corresponding azirine, possibly forming an equilibrium mixture, in the related Neber reaction (Eq. 57) satisfies the observation that *syn*- and *anti*-oxime tosylates produce the same product (oxime interconversion prior to the Neber reaction was eliminated). Correlation of product with relative acidities of α-protons (65) apparently failed to account for an example of the reaction in the steroid series (66). Catalytic reduction of an isolated intermediate to an eneamine (67) rather than to an aziridine suggests that the reactive species undergoing hydrogenation is a nitrene (see Section II).

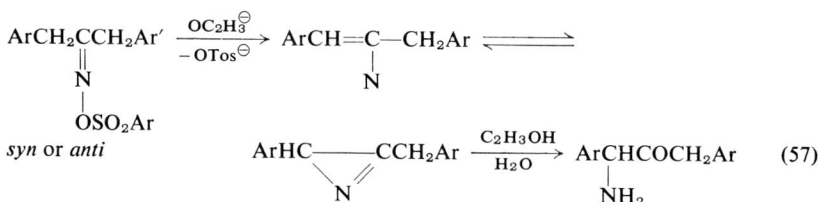

$$ArCH_2CCH_2Ar' \xrightarrow[-OTos^{\ominus}]{OC_2H_3^{\ominus}} ArCH{=}C{-}CH_2Ar \rightleftharpoons$$

with the first structure showing ‖N and OSO₂Ar below, and the product showing N below.

syn or *anti*

$$ArHC\underset{N}{\overset{\diagup\diagdown}{\rule{1.5cm}{0pt}}}CCH_2Ar \xrightarrow[H_2O]{C_2H_3OH} ArCHCOCH_2Ar \quad (57)$$

with NH₂ below.

An additional preparative method for α-aminoketones consists in the treatment of *sec*-alkyl primary amines with *tert*-butyl hypochlorite followed by sodium methoxide and by dilute hydrochloric acid. The possibility that vinyl nitrenes are intermediates has been recognized (68,69) (Eq. 58).

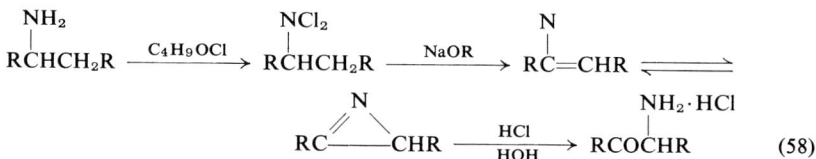

$$\underset{RCHCH_2R}{\overset{NH_2}{\rule{0pt}{0pt}}} \xrightarrow{C_4H_9OCl} \underset{RCHCH_2R}{\overset{NCl_2}{\rule{0pt}{0pt}}} \xrightarrow{NaOR} \underset{RC{=}CHR}{\overset{N}{\rule{0pt}{0pt}}} \rightleftharpoons$$

$$RC\underset{N}{\overset{\diagup\diagdown}{\rule{1.5cm}{0pt}}}CHR \xrightarrow[HOH]{HCl} \underset{RCOCHR}{\overset{NH_2\cdot HCl}{\rule{0pt}{0pt}}} \quad (58)$$

A third reaction leading to the formation of an α-aminoketone may also proceed by the formation of an intermediate vinyl nitrene and azirine on treatment of quaternary hydrazones with sodium ethoxide (3,70,71) (Eq. 59).

$$\underset{\overset{\parallel\oplus}{NN(CH_3)_3I^{\ominus}}}{RCCH_2R} \xrightarrow{OR^{\ominus}} \underset{N}{\overset{}{RC{=}CHR}} \rightleftharpoons RC\underset{N}{\overset{\diagdown\diagup}{\rule{1.2cm}{0pt}}}CHR \longrightarrow \underset{NH_2}{RCOCHR} \quad (59)$$

In each of two reports that azirines are produced in reactions between nitrile oxides and Wittig reagents (72,73), certain rearranged products may be explained in terms of vinyl nitrene and/or azirine intermediates (Eq. 60).

Photolytic cleavage of the NO bond in triphenylisoxazole occurs

$$R'CNO \xrightarrow{R_3P=CR_2} \underset{\underset{PR_3}{R_2C}}{\overset{\displaystyle R'C=N}{\diagdown O}} \xrightarrow{-R_3PO} \underset{R_2C}{\overset{\displaystyle R'CN}{\parallel}} \rightleftharpoons \underset{CR_2}{\overset{\displaystyle R'C=N}{\diagdown}}$$

$$\underset{R_2C}{\overset{\displaystyle R'CN}{\parallel}} \longrightarrow R_2C=C=NR' \xrightarrow{ArNH_2} R_2CHC(=NR')NHAr$$

$$\underset{CR_2}{\overset{\displaystyle R'C=N}{\diagdown}} \xrightarrow{HCl} R'COCR_2NH_2 \cdot HCl \tag{60}$$

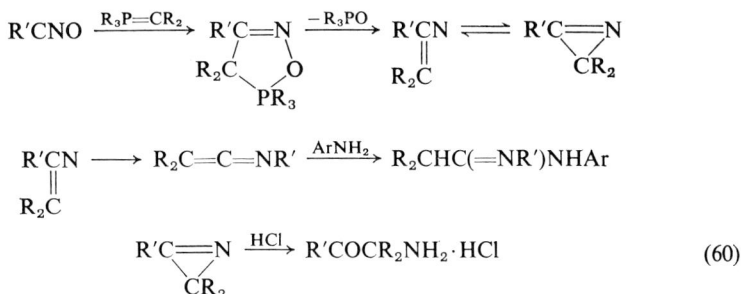

with the formation of *N*-phenylbenzoylphenylketenimine, 3-benzoyl-2,3-diphenylazirine, and triphenyloxazole (74) (Eq. 61) and differs from the photolysis of 3,5-diphenylisoxazole insofar as the latter reaction apparently does not produce a detectable amount of a ketenimine (75) (Eq. 62). The data are consistent with an interpretation which requires initial formation of both a vinyl nitrene and the corresponding azirine. Migration of phenyl is apparently slower than valence isomerization into an oxazole or an isoxazole, but becomes competitive after the introduction of a β-phenyl substituent in the nitrene (2-phenyl substituent in the isomeric azirine) apparently retards the latter isomerization.

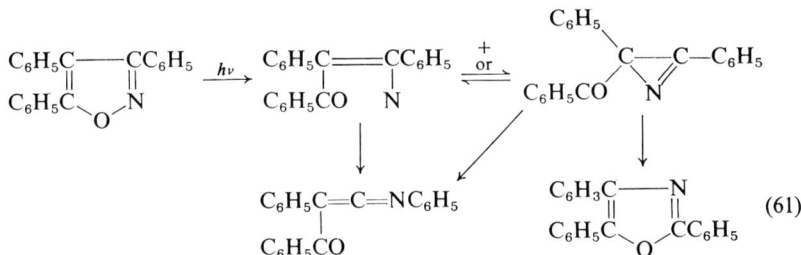

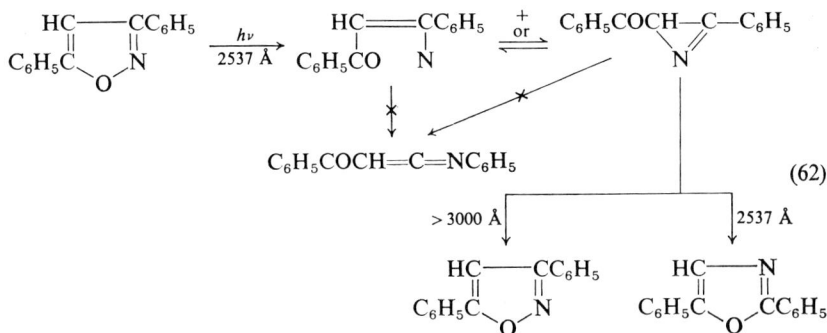

$$\tag{61}$$

$$\tag{62}$$

Electron delocalization through an adjacent triple bond provides a common feature for a triad of electron-deficient carbenes and nitrenes which includes cyanonitrene (76), ethynylcarbene ("propargylene") (77) and ethynylnitrene cyanomethylene (Eq. 63).

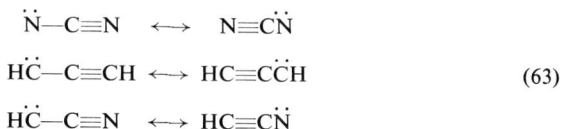

$$\ddot{N}-C\equiv N \quad \longleftrightarrow \quad N\equiv C\ddot{N}$$

$$H\ddot{C}-C\equiv CH \quad \longleftrightarrow \quad HC\equiv C\ddot{C}H \qquad (63)$$

$$H\ddot{C}-C\equiv N \quad \longleftrightarrow \quad HC\equiv C\ddot{N}$$

Attempts to obtain phenylethynyl azide (78) have been apparently unsuccessful; however, phenylethynylnitrene may be an intermediate in the transformation of an iodine azide adduct of phenylethynyl bromide into *trans*-dicyanostilbene (78) (Eq. 64).

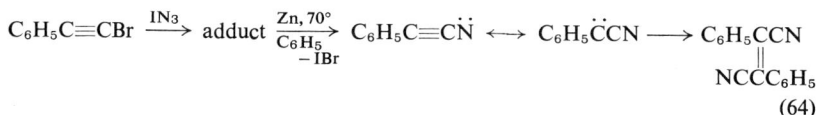

$$C_6H_5C\equiv CBr \xrightarrow{IN_3} adduct \xrightarrow[-IBr]{\frac{Zn,70°}{C_6H_5}} C_6H_5C\equiv C\ddot{N} \longleftrightarrow C_6H_5\ddot{C}CN \longrightarrow C_6H_5CCN$$
$$\underset{NCCC_6H_5}{\overset{\|}{}}$$
$$(64)$$

Both cyanomethylene (79) and phenylcyanocarbene (80) have been obtained by the elimination of diazo nitrogen from carbon, and the latter has also resulted from the photolysis of di- and triphenylcyanooxirane (81). Apparently neither displayed evidence of a nitrene excited state.

V. REARRANGEMENTS IN ACYL NITRENES

In the Curtius rearrangement (82) which accompanies the elimination of nitrogen from an acyl azide, both heat and light have provided the necessary activation energy (83). Apparently both the pyrolytic and the photolytic rearrangements may proceed with a concerted elimination of nitrogen (84); however, in addition to the rearrangement to an isocyanate, photolysis of an acyl azide may generate an acyl nitrene. It does not re-arrange to an isocyanate at a detectable rate, but instead inserts with and abstracts hydrogen from solvent CH bonds (84). Neither intramolecular nor intermolecular abstraction nor insertion with CH bonds has been observed during pyrolysis of an acyl azide.

To illustrate, pivaloyl azide may undergo rapid pyrolysis above room temperature in either cyclohexene or 2-methylbutane with nearly quanti-tative transformation into *tert*-butyl isocyanate (Eq. 65); however, photo-lysis in cyclohexene or cyclohexane produces, in addition to *tert*-butyl isocyanate, compounds best explained by pivaloyl nitrene participation in either insertion with a CH bond or addition to a double bond (84) (Eq. 66).

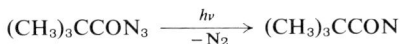

$$(CH_3)_3CCON_3 \xrightarrow[-N_2]{\substack{h\nu \text{ or} \\ \text{heat}}} (CH_3)_3CNCO \qquad (65)$$

$$(CH_3)_3CCON_3 \xrightarrow[-N_2]{h\nu} (CH_3)_3CCON$$

$$\overset{\text{NCOR}}{\bigcirc} \xleftarrow{C_6H_{10}} (CH_3)_3CCON \xrightarrow{C_6H_{12}} (CH_3)_3CCONH- \overset{}{\bigcirc} \qquad (66)$$

Other observations support the presence of a nitrene during a photolytic Curtius reaction but its absence during the thermal reaction. When sterically disposed to cyclization certain acyl nitrenes undergo intramolecular insertion with CH bonds during photolysis but not during pyrolysis (85). During the photolysis of 1,1-dimethyl-*cis*- or *trans*-decalin-10-carbonyl azide, predominant rearrangement to an isocyanate was accompanied by rearrangement through insertion to form γ- and δ-lactams and by hydrogen abstraction to form an amide (86) (Eq. 67). As expected, hexanoyl nitrene being less disposed to cyclization underwent photolysis with rearrangement to form an isocyanate and hydrogen abstraction to form an amide, but without intramolecular insertion with a CH bond (86).

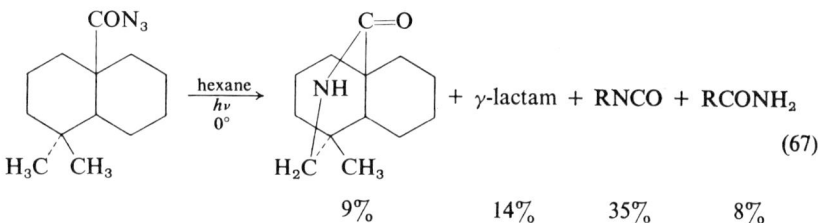

At least one other example of the formation of a δ-lactam during photolysis of an acyl azide has been reported (87), and a remarkably efficient rearrangement by insertion produced an oxazolone during both photolysis (88) and pyrolysis (89) of *tert*-butyl azidoformate (Eq. 68).

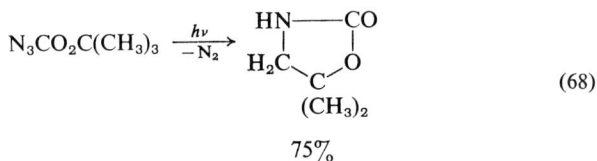

$$N_3CO_2C(CH_3)_3 \xrightarrow[-N_2]{h\nu} \begin{array}{c} HN\!-\!\!-\!CO \\ | \qquad | \\ H_2C \diagdown \underset{C}{} \diagup O \\ (CH_3)_2 \end{array} \qquad (68)$$

$$75\%$$

From intermolecular reactions it is learned that carbethoxy nitrene inserts with primary, secondary, and tertiary CH bonds in the ratio of $1:10:30$ (90), making it more selective than carbethoxycarbene by about a factor of 10 (91). It has been estimated that the double bond in cyclohexene reacts with carbethoxy nitrene 360 times as fast as the nitrene inserts with a CH bond in a methyl group in 2-methylbutane, corresponding to a difference in free energies of activation of about 3.5 kcal/mole (91). Toward a sulfonyl nitrene a benzene "double bond" appears to be eight times as reactive as the secondary CH bonds in cyclohexane. It was assumed that the reaction with benzene proceeds by addition with subsequent rearrangement (90).

Both photolysis and pyrolysis of succinamoyl azide produced β-isocyanatopropionamide with no trace of cyclic succinic hydrazide (92) (Eq. 69). Pyrolysis of vicinal di- and tricarboxylic acid azides produced the

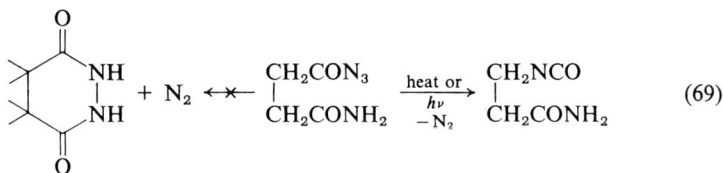

$$
\begin{array}{c}
\text{(cyclic imide structure)} \\
+ N_2 \xleftarrow{\quad\times\quad}
\begin{array}{l} CH_2CON_3 \\ | \\ CH_2CONH_2 \end{array}
\xrightarrow[\substack{h\nu \\ -N_2}]{\text{heat or}}
\begin{array}{l} CH_2NCO \\ | \\ CH_2CONH_2 \end{array}
\end{array}
\tag{69}
$$

cyrresponding di- and triisocyanates (93) (Eq. 70); however, pyrolysis of o-phthalyl azide gives an unidentified isomer of o-phenylenediisocyanate (94) rather than a dimer (95).

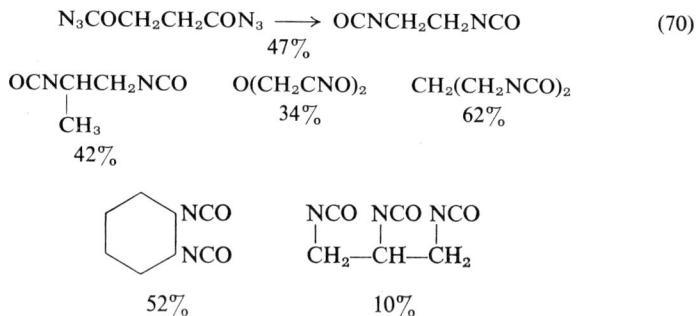

$$
N_3COCH_2CH_2CON_3 \longrightarrow OCNCH_2CH_2NCO \tag{70}
$$
$$
47\%
$$

$$
\begin{array}{l} OCNCHCH_2NCO \\ \qquad | \\ \qquad CH_3 \\ \quad 42\% \end{array}
\qquad
\begin{array}{c} O(CH_2CNO)_2 \\ 34\% \end{array}
\qquad
\begin{array}{c} CH_2(CH_2NCO)_2 \\ 62\% \end{array}
$$

$$
\underset{52\%}{\text{(benzene-NCO/NCO)}}
\qquad
\underset{10\%}{\begin{array}{c} NCO\ NCO\ NCO \\ |\quad\ |\quad\ | \\ CH_2-CH-CH_2 \end{array}}
$$

During photolysis, but not pyrolysis, acetyl azide in benzonitrile or phenylacetylene was transformed into an oxadiazole and an oxazole, respectively (96) (Eq. 71). Benzoyl nitrene has been captured before re-

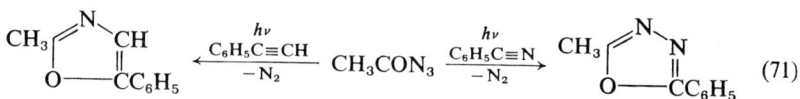

$$
\begin{array}{c}
\text{(oxazole)} \xleftarrow[-N_2]{\substack{h\nu \\ C_6H_5C\equiv CH}} CH_3CON_3 \xrightarrow[-N_2]{\substack{h\nu \\ C_6H_5C\equiv N}} \text{(oxadiazole)}
\end{array}
\tag{71}
$$

arrangement by dimethyl sulfoxide (97) (Eq. 72). More recently, products

$$C_6H_5CON_3 + (CH_3)_2SO \xrightarrow{h\nu} C_6H_5CON=S(O)(CH_3)_2 \qquad (72)$$

generated from the transformation of benzoyl nitrene into its dimer, azobenzoyl, have been claimed (98) (Eq. 73).

$$C_6H_5CON_3 \xrightarrow[-N_2]{h\nu} C_6H_5CON \longrightarrow C_6H_5CON=NCOC_6H_5 \xrightarrow[C_6H_5CON]{C_6H_5CON_3}$$

$$\underset{\overset{|}{\underset{COC_6H_5}{}}}{C_6H_5CON=\overset{\oplus}{N}-\overset{\ominus}{N}COC_6H_5} \longrightarrow C_6H_5CON=N-N(COC_6H_5)_2 \qquad (73)$$

$$\swarrow H_2O \qquad\qquad \searrow C_6H_5NH_2$$

$$(C_6H_5CO)_2NH \qquad\qquad\qquad C_6H_5CONHC_6H_5$$

This increasing amount of evidence discounting nitrene intermediacy in the thermal Curtius reaction supports an older claim for a concerted mechanism based on the failure of both the Hofmann rearrangement of N-bromobenzamide and the Curtius rearrangement of benzoyl azide in the presence of water to produce detectable amounts of benzoylhydroxamic acid (99). This expected adduct from benzoyl nitrene and water has been produced during the photolysis of benzoyl azide in the presence of water (100). It suggests that the claim for benzoyl nitrene intermediacy based on the measurement of volume change of activation for the thermal Curtius reaction of benzoyl azide (101) should be reexamined, and that in the absence of other evidence for an acyl nitrene intermediate, the oxidative transformation of primary amides by lead tetraacetate into isocyanates by rearrangement (102) (Eq. 74) may proceed by a concerted or other mechanism which does not require a discrete nitrene.

$$RCONH_2 \xrightarrow{Pb(OAc)_4} RNCO \xrightarrow{t-C_4H_9OH} t-C_4H_9OCONHR \qquad (74)$$

Azides traditionally inert to rearrangement on pyrolysis include the azidoformates, certain azidocarbamates (103), and sulfonyl azides. When it was discovered that each of these undergoes photolytic rearrangement in methanol but not in hydrocarbon solvents, the definition of "rigid" azides was accordingly revised (104) (Eq. 75). Rearrangement by insertion with an aromatic CH bond accounts for the formation of benzoxazolone-2 from phenyl azidoformate during pyrolysis (105).

$$C_2H_3OCON_3 \xrightarrow{h\nu}{}_{CH_3OH} C_2H_5ONHCO_2CH_3 \ (13\%)$$
$$+ C_2H_5OCONHOCH_3 \ (44\%) + C_2H_5OCONH_2 \ (30\%)$$

$$C_2H_5NHCON_3 \xrightarrow{h\nu}{}_{CH_3OH} C_2H_5NHNHCO_2CH_3 \ (57\%) \qquad (75)$$

$$(C_2H_5)_2NCON_3 \xrightarrow{h\nu}{}_{CH_3OH} (C_2H_5)_2NNHCO_2CH_3 \ (63\%)$$

$$C_6H_5SO_2N_3 \xrightarrow{h\nu}{}_{CH_3OH} C_6H_5NH_2 \ (28\%)$$

An interesting preparation of hydrazine consists in the hypochlorite oxidation of urea. Carbamyl nitrene may be an intermediate (106) (Eq. 76).

$$H_2NCONH_2 \xrightarrow{\overline{OCl}} H_2NCONHCl \longrightarrow H_2NCON \longrightarrow$$
$$H_2NNCO \xrightarrow[-CO_2]{HOH} N_2H_4 \quad (76)$$

An explanation for the formation of 1,3,4-oxadiazoles from the reaction between carbethoxynitrene and nitriles during either pyrolysis or photolysis of ethyl azidoformate assumed electrophilic attack on nitrile nitrogen (88) (Eq. 77).

$$RCN + N_3CO_2C_2H_5 \xrightarrow[-N_2]{\substack{heat\ or \\ h\nu}} RC{\equiv}\overset{+}{N}-\overset{-}{N}CO_2C_2H_5$$

$$
\begin{array}{c}
RC{=\!=\!=}N \\
\mid \quad\quad \mid \\
O_{\diagdown}\ {\diagup}^{N} \\
\quad C \\
\mid \\
OC_2H_5
\end{array}
\quad \longleftarrow \quad
R\overset{+}{C}{=}N{-}N{=}\overset{\displaystyle O^-}{\underset{\displaystyle \mid}{C}}OC_2H_5
\quad (77)
$$

Photolysis of gaseous ethyl and methyl azidoformates, using light with energy above 95 but below 130 kcal/mole, produces a carbalkoxynitrene whose lifetime is between 3×10^{-7} and 10^{-5} sec. The evidence was interpreted to give weak support to the assignment of the nitrene as a singlet for which a cyclic oxazirine structure was also considered. A higher energy decomposition apparently proceeds through the formation of a transient CO_2N_3 intermediate (107) (Eq. 78). In this reaction there is a curious

$$ROCON_3 \xrightarrow[-N_2]{h\nu} ROC(=O)N \rightleftharpoons ROC\underset{N}{\overset{\diagdown\quad\diagup}{\text{———}O}} \longrightarrow RO\cdot + \cdot NCO$$

$$ROCON_3 \xrightarrow[\lambda < 2200\ \text{Å}]{h\nu} R\cdot + \cdot O{-}CON_3(\rightarrow CO_2 + \cdot N_3)$$

and $\quad\quad\quad\quad\quad\quad\quad RO\cdot + CO + N_2 \quad (78)$

formation of nitrous oxide which was accounted for by an alternative fragmentation of CO_2N_3 (107) (Eq. 79). From this observation there

$$N_3C(=O)O\cdot \longrightarrow \overset{O{-}C{=}O}{\underset{N}{N\diagdown\quad\diagup N}} \longrightarrow N_2O + \cdot NCO \quad (79)$$

develops the intriguing question concerning the fate of certain other acyl azides on photolysis by the shorter wavelengths ($\lambda < 2200$ Å). An elimination of nitrous oxide from otherwise unknown oxatriazoles, which might be intermediates, would produce nitriles (see Eq. 96 for the formation of nitriles from corresponding thiatriazoles). Another transformation of an acyl azide into a nitrile has been observed in the pyrolysis of an *N*-acyl-phosphinimine, which in turn was prepared from the azide and a phosphine (108) (Eq. 80).

$$RCON_3 + (C_6H_5)_3P \xrightarrow{-N_2} RCON{=}P(C_6H_5)_3 \xrightarrow{heat} RCN + (C_6H_5)_3PO \qquad (80)$$

VI. REARRANGEMENTS IN AZOMETHINE NITRENES

Assuming that even the more stable tetrazoles under certain conditions may participate in an equilibrium with corresponding azomethine azides (109), both pyrolysis and photolysis of diaryltetrazoles may proceed with loss of nitrogen from either the azido group or the tetrazole ring. Conceivably either event may enable the reaction to produce both a carbodiimide and a 2-arylbenzimidazole (110,111a) (Eq. 81). From diphenyl-

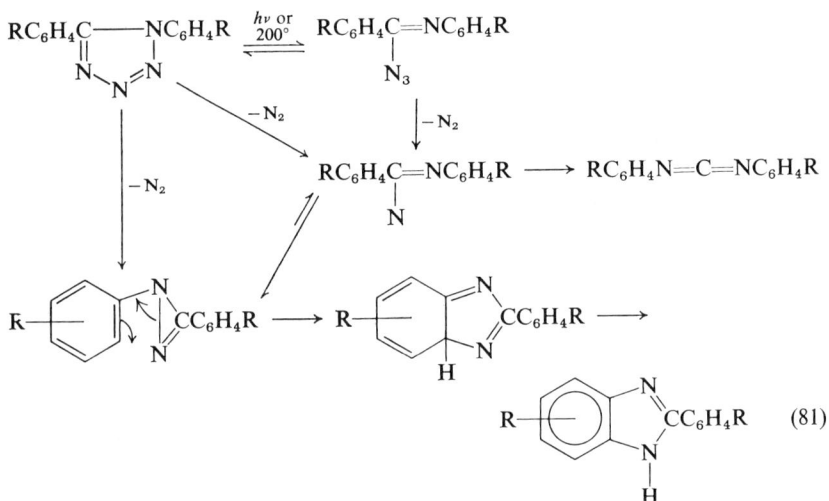

tetrazole, 2-phenylbenzimidazole and diphenylcarbodimide are produced in yields of 14 and 65%, respectively, during pyrolysis and 64 and 0%, respectively, during photolysis (10,112). In agreement with the corresponding Beckmann rearrangements and the rearrangement during pyrolysis of triarylmethyl azides (Section III), a *para*-chlorosubstituent may retard and a *para*-methyl substituent may accelerate migration of an aryl group during pyrolysis from carbon to nitrogen for the formation of appropriate carbodiimides (111a). This conclusion, based on yields of 14, 19, and 8% for 2-arylbenzimidazole (where aryl is phenyl, *para*-chloro-phenyl, and *para*-tolyl, respectively) (111a), needs further investigation since yields of 23 and 8.5% for 2-arylbenzimidazole (where aryl is phenyl and *ortho*-chlorophenyl, respectively) (111b) have more recently been reported for the pyrolysis of corresponding tetrazoles. Support for the assumption that carbodiimides result from nitrene rearrangement is found in the recent work of the pyrolysis of hydrazidic azides (113), a class of azomethine azides which do not give a detectable equilibrium with corresponding tetrazoles and which undergo elimination of nitrogen with the formation of carbodiimides but without the formation of cyclic compounds (Eq. 82).

$$ \underset{\underset{N_3}{|}}{RC}\text{=}NNHAr \xrightarrow{-N_2} RN\text{=}C\text{=}NNHAr \xrightarrow{H_2O} RNHCONHNHAr \qquad (82) $$

Comparison of the available information reveals both differences and similarities between the electron-deficient intermediate generated either by the photolytic release of nitrogen from α-azido stilbene or by the deoxygenation of α-nitro stilbene (see Eq. 116) and the corresponding intermediate in Eq. 81. The formation of 2-phenylindole in one and 2-phenylbenzimidazole (Eq. 81, R = H) in the other may require a similar mechanism perhaps involving either azirine and diazirine intermediates, respectively, or the corresponding nitrenes. Diarylazirines (Eq. 116), but not diaryldiazirines (Eq. 81), have been isolated. Dimerization of an azirine (Eqs. 55 and 116) is now established, however, dimerization of either a diazirine or its isomeric azomethine nitrene is apparently unknown. Rearrangement to a carbodiimide (Eq. 81) and to a ketenimine (Eq. 53) may proceed from either a diazirine and an azirine, respectively, or the corresponding nitrene; however, a carbodiimide and a ketenimine may also be produced from an azomethine azide and a vinyl azide, respectively, by a rearrangement concerted with loss of nitrogen.

Just as cleavage of its CN single bond accounts for certain reactions of an azirine, cleavage of a CN single bond in a diazirine should permit isomerization into a nitrile imine (Eq. 83), a type of intermediate which has been discussed with the reaction between nitriles and carbethoxy nitrene (114) (Eq. 84).

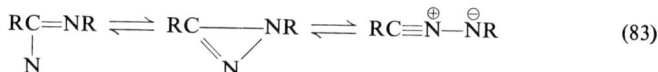

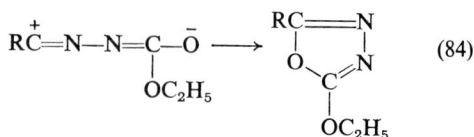

$$ \underset{\underset{N}{|}}{RC}\text{=}NR \rightleftharpoons RC{\diagdown}\underset{N}{\diagup}NR \rightleftharpoons RC\text{≡}\overset{\oplus}{N}\text{-}\overset{\ominus}{N}R \qquad (83) $$

$$ RC\text{≡}N \xrightarrow{NCO_2C_2H_5} RC\text{≡}\overset{+}{N}\overset{-}{N}CO_2C_2H_5 \longleftrightarrow $$

$$ \underset{\underset{OC_2H_5}{|}}{R\overset{+}{C}}\text{=}N\text{-}N\text{=}C\text{-}\overset{-}{O} \longrightarrow \underset{\underset{OC_2H_5}{|}}{\overset{RC\text{=}N}{\underset{C}{O}{\diagdown}{\diagup}N}} \qquad (84) $$

A mechanistic relationship between the Tiemann rearrangement of amidoximes to cyanamides (115) (Eq. 85) and the transformation of azidoazomethine derivatives to carbodiimides (110) does not depend on nitrene intermediacy but the analogy is strengthened by nitrene generation from *O-p*-nitrobenzenesulfonylhydroxylamine (Eq. 8). From suitably substituted amidoximes, the Tiemann reaction gives predominantly

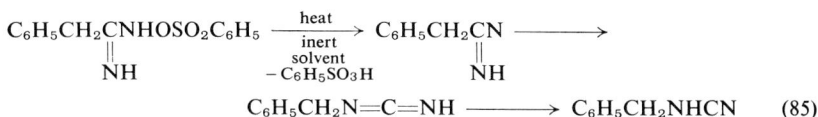

$$C_6H_5CH_2\underset{\underset{NH}{\|}}{C}NHOSO_2C_6H_5 \xrightarrow[\substack{inert \\ solvent \\ -C_6H_5SO_3H}]{heat} C_6H_5CH_2\underset{\underset{NH}{\|}}{C}N \longrightarrow$$

$$C_6H_5CH_2N{=}C{=}NH \longrightarrow C_6H_5CH_2NHCN \qquad (85)$$

benzimidazoles (116) (Eq. 86) in anhydrous pyridine and initially carbodiimides in aqueous bases. An inefficient pyrolysis of benzanilidoxime into

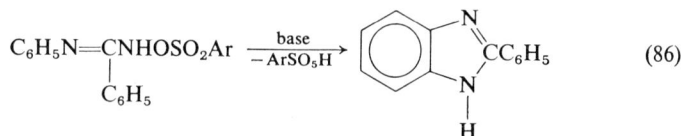

$$C_6H_5N{=}\underset{\underset{C_6H_5}{|}}{C}NHOSO_2Ar \xrightarrow[-ArSO_5H]{base} \quad \text{} \qquad (86)$$

2-phenylbenzimidazole (117) (Eq. 87) is reminiscent of the Lossen rearrangement of benzohydroxamic acid (118) (Eq. 88). An absence of the migration of phenyl from carbon to nitrogen in the former may be reconciled by postulating cyclization to an imidazole from an azomethine hydroxylamine (Eq. 87) rather than from either a nitrene or a diazirine (see Eqs. 56 and 81).

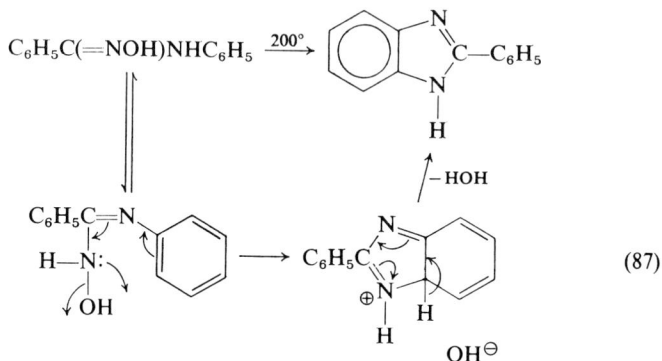

$$C_6H_5C({=}NOH)NHC_6H_5 \xrightarrow{200°} \quad \text{}$$

 (87)

$$C_6H_5CONHOH \xrightarrow{heat} C_6H_5NCO + HOH \qquad (88)$$

Carbodiimides are also produced by α-elimination of hydrogen chloride from certain *N*-chloroamidines which is either concerted with rearrangement or followed by rearrangement of an intermediate nitrene (119) (Eq. 89). Apparently imidazoles are not formed.

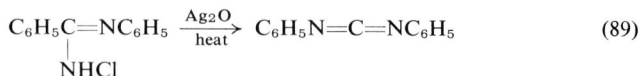

$$C_6H_5C{=}NC_6H_5 \xrightarrow[\text{heat}]{Ag_2O} C_6H_5N{=}C{=}NC_6H_5 \qquad (89)$$
$$\underset{\text{NHCl}}{|}$$

Both alkyl- and arylamidines are transformed into corresponding 3-halodiazirines on halogenation (120) (Eq. 90). This important reaction

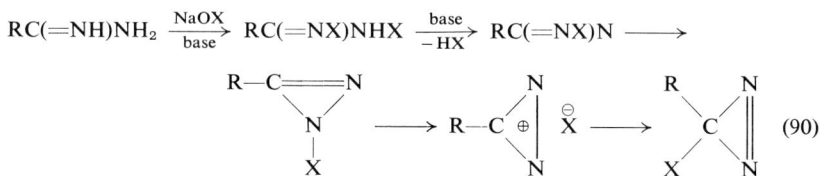

$$RC({=}NH)NH_2 \xrightarrow[\text{base}]{NaOX} RC({=}NX)NHX \xrightarrow[-HX]{\text{base}} RC({=}NX)N \longrightarrow$$

$$(90)$$

is analogous to the ring closure of vinyl nitrenes to azirines (see Section IV) and to the suggested ring closure of acyl nitrenes to oxazirines (see Eq. 78). Of greater significance is the possibility that this reaction could provide the aromatic diazirinyl cations for investigation and comparison with the isoelectronic cyclopropenyl cations.

Fragmentation of certain other five-membered heterocycles may also produce intermediate nitrenes and/or diazirines. With the elimination of carbon dioxide during either pyrolysis or photolysis of 3,4-diphenyl-1,2,4-oxadiazol-5-one, 2-phenylbenzimidazole is produced in high yield but diphenylcarbodiimide has not been detected (117) (Eq. 17 in Table 1 and Eq. 91).

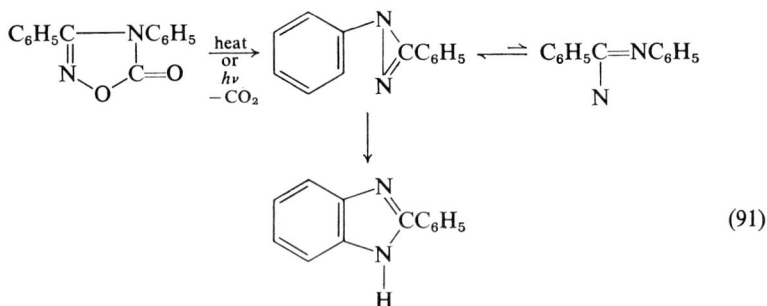

$$(91)$$

On the other hand, carbodiimides, but not imidazoles, are formed from certain 1,5-dihydro 4,5-disubstituted-1-oxo-1,2,3,5-thiaoxadiazoles (17) (Eq. 92) and from certain combinations of nitrile oxides and phosphinimines (18) (Eq. 93). In the latter example the formation of an initial

$$p\text{-}ClC_6H_4C\!\!-\!\!NC_6H_4CH_3\text{-}p \xrightarrow[-SO_2]{\text{heat}} p\text{-}ClC_6H_4N\!=\!C\!=\!NC_6H_4CH_3\text{-}p \qquad (92)$$

with bridge: N—O—S=O

$$\begin{array}{c} C_6H_5CNO \\ + \\ C_6H_5N\!=\!P(C_6H_5)_3 \end{array} \longrightarrow \begin{array}{c} C_6H_5C\!=\!\!N \\ | \quad\quad | \\ C_6H_5N\diagdown_{P}\diagup^{O} \\ (C_6H_5)_3 \end{array} \longrightarrow (C_6H_5)_3PO \;+\; C_6H_5N\!=\!C\!=\!NC_6H_5$$

$$+ \begin{array}{c} C_6H_5C\!=\!\!N \\ | \quad\quad | \\ C_6H_5N\diagdown_{C}\diagup^{O} \\ \| \\ N \\ | \\ C_6H_5 \end{array} \qquad (93)$$

1,3-dipolar adduct may be required. The possibility that these dihydro-aromatic heterocycles may fragment with the initial formation of nitrenes and/or diazirines is recognized by including Eqs. 18 and 20 in Table 1.

An alternative pyrolytic transformation for 1,5-dihydro 4-ethyl-5-aryl-1,1-dioxo-1,2,3,5-thiaoxadiazoles has been reported (121) (Eq. 94).

$$\begin{array}{c} C_2H_5C\!\!-\!\!NC_6H_4X\text{-}p \\ \| \qquad | \\ N\diagdown_{O}\diagup^{SO_2} \end{array} \xrightarrow{\text{heat}} \text{(bicyclic benzothiadiazine product)} \qquad (94)$$

A nitrile oxide may combine with a methylenephosphorane to produce the expected 1,3-dipolar adduct. Subsequent pyrolysis brings about the elimination of triphenylphosphine oxide and possibly the generation of a nitrene. The corresponding azirine and rearranged ketenimine are isolated (18) (Eqs. 19 and 95).

$$\begin{array}{c} C_6H_5CNO \\ + \\ CH_2\!=\!P(C_6H_5)_3 \end{array} \longrightarrow \begin{array}{c} C_6H_5C\!=\!\!N \\ | \quad\quad | \\ H_2C\diagdown_{P}\diagup^{O} \\ (C_6H_5)_3 \end{array} \xrightarrow{-(C_6H_5)_3PO} \begin{array}{c} C_6H_5C\!=\!\!N \\ \diagdown\diagup \\ CH_2 \end{array} + H_2C\!=\!C\!=\!NC_6H_5$$

$$(95)$$

Both thiatriazole (122) and thiaoxazolone (123) rings fragment with the probable initial formation of a corresponding thioacyl nitrene and/or a thiazirine (Eq. 96). Attempts to trap an intermediate nitrene during pyrolysis of a thiatriazole by carrying out the reaction in nitrile solvents were unsuccessful (122). This observation, together with the pyrolytic formation of a nitrile (without molecular rearrangement) from a thia-triazole and an isothiocyanate (with rearrangement) from a thiaoxazolone, permits the tentative conclusion that concerted elimination of nitrous sulfide, which simultaneously or subsequently dissociates into nitrogen and sulfur, from a thiatriazole is occurring in a manner reminiscent of the elimination of nitrous oxide from a proposed oxatriazole radical (see Eq. 79) and that elimination of carbon dioxide from a thiaoxazolone generates a thioacyl nitrene which rearranges. It would be of interest to attempt to trap the proposed nitrene in either the latter reaction or in the photolysis of a thiatriazole which produces both an isothiocyanate in about 10% yield and a nitrile (15,124) (Eq. 96). Alkoxythiatriazoles undergo a similar

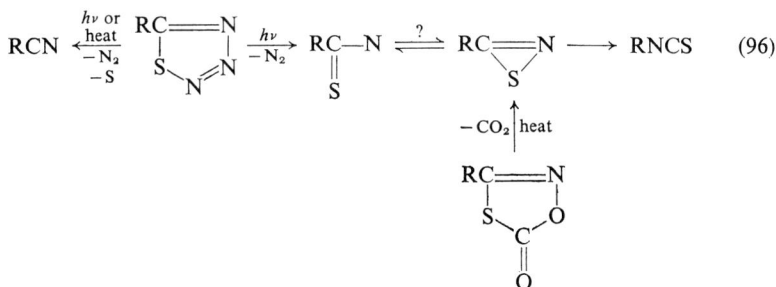

$$RCN \xleftarrow[\substack{-N_2 \\ -S}]{\substack{h\nu \text{ or} \\ \text{heat}}} \begin{array}{c} RC{=\!=\!=}N \\ | \quad\quad | \\ S{\diagdown}{\diagup}N \\ \quad N \end{array} \xrightarrow[-N_2]{h\nu} \begin{array}{c} RC{-}N \\ \| \\ S \end{array} \xrightleftharpoons{?} \begin{array}{c} RC{=\!=\!=}N \\ {\diagdown}S{\diagup} \end{array} \longrightarrow RNCS \quad\quad (96)$$

$$\big\downarrow {\scriptstyle -CO_2}\ \text{heat}$$

$$\begin{array}{c} RC{=\!=\!=}N \\ | \quad\quad | \\ S{\diagdown}{\diagup}O \\ \quad C \\ \quad \| \\ \quad O \end{array}$$

pyrolysis to give cyanate esters (125) (Eq. 97).

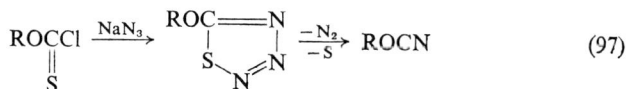

$$ROCCl \xrightarrow{NaN_3} \begin{array}{c} ROC{=\!=\!=}N \\ | \quad\quad | \\ S{\diagdown}{\diagup}N \\ \quad N \end{array} \xrightarrow[-S]{-N_2} ROCN \quad\quad (97)$$

VII. REARRANGEMENTS IN AROMATIC NITRENES

Rearrangements of aromatic nitrenes include ring expansion, ring contraction, ring interchange, hydrogen abstraction from CH bonds in adjacent substituents, and insertion with CH and CC bonds in adjacent substituents. Alterations in size and interchange of the ring attached to the nitrene function may proceed from an azirine intermediate, while the abstraction and insertion reactions sometimes appear to be required to satisfy electron deficiency at nitrogen, and at other times hydrogen or other group migration to nitrogen may follow valence isomerization of a suitably substituted azirine.

The hypothesis (3) that an aryl nitrene may be in equilibrium with a corresponding bicyclic azirine developed from the observations that pyrolysis of phenyl azide in the presence of a secondary amine produced an azepine (126) and that *ortho*-nitrobiphenyl may undergo the formation of both an azepine and a carbazole (27) (Eq. 98). It is unreasonable that both types of product in the latter reaction should be formed from a nitrene or some other electron-deficient species without the intervention of a bicyclic azirine. Both types of product could be formed from isomeric bicyclic azirines; nevertheless, the attractive possibility that an equilibrium exists between the azirine and the nitrene, thereby permitting carbazole formation from the nitrene and azepine from a bicyclic azirine, must be considered. In a brief report the basis for structure assignment of the product as 2-diethylamino-3-phenylazepine rather than 2-diethyl-amino-7-phenyl-

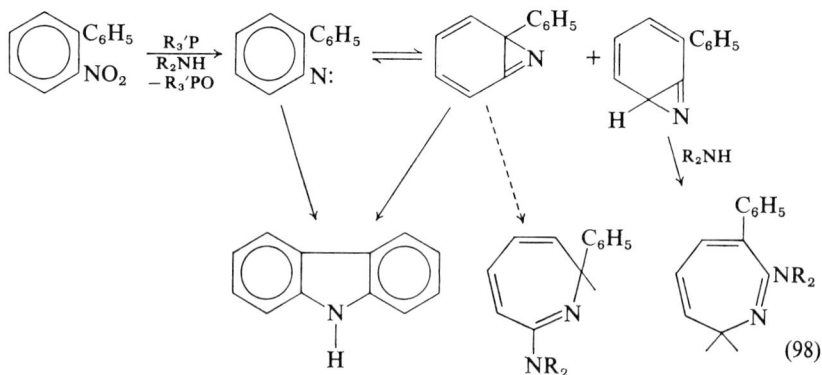

azepine, the product to be expected from the isomerically possible bicyclic azirine from *ortho*-nitrobiphenyl, was not given. That an azepine is formed when phenyl azide is pyrolyzed in the presence of a primary or secondary amine but apparently not in the presence of certain other nucleophiles such as thiophenol led to an earlier recognition of a possible equilibrium between phenyl nitrene and a bicyclic azirine, the latter being detected only in the presence of a strong nucleophile (3).

This hypothesis that phenyl nitrene is in equilibrium with a bicyclic azirine may be deficient by not accounting for the absence of formation of either hydrazobenzene or diaryl amines by insertion reactions between phenyl nitrene and CH or NH bonds unless it can be assumed that these are sufficiently kinetically less probable. Phenyl nitrene has also been suggested as an intermediate in the formation of azepines from the reaction between nitrosobenzene, triphenyl phosphine, and a dialkyl amine (127).

A straightforward extension of this hypothesis provides an explanation for the transformation of *ortho*-nitrosotoluene by deoxygenation into the *ortho*-methylanil of α-acetylpyridine (128) through a sequence of valence isomerizations which may interchange *ortho*-tolyl nitrene with methyl α-pyridyl carbene. In a formal sense the anil represents direct combination of the nitrene and the carbene; however, it is more reasonable that the nitrene was formed first by a similar combination of either the carbene or its bicyclic precursor with nitrosotoluene and that triethyl phosphite deoxygenated the nitrone to the anil (Eq. 99). The last step was verified in a separate experiment (128).

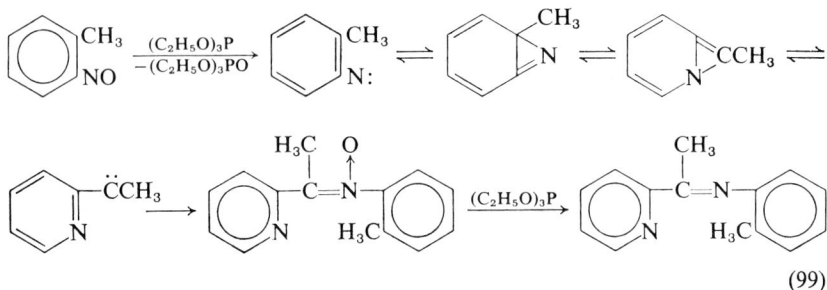

$$\tag{99}$$

An ESR of ground-state triplet aromatic nitrenes (35), including *para*-phenylene dinitrene (129) has been measured at 77°K, and UV absorption measured under similar conditions has been assigned to aromatic nitrenes (130). A nitrene's shorter lifetime at higher temperatures decreases the probability that a mononitrene may be transformed into a dinitrene before other changes take over in either a solution- or gas-phase reaction under usual reaction temperatures. In the pyrolytic conversion of 1,2-diazido-benzene into mucononitrile, the intermediacy of both a dinitrene and CC bond cleavage before expulsion of the second molecule of nitrogen has been recognized (131) (Eq. 100).

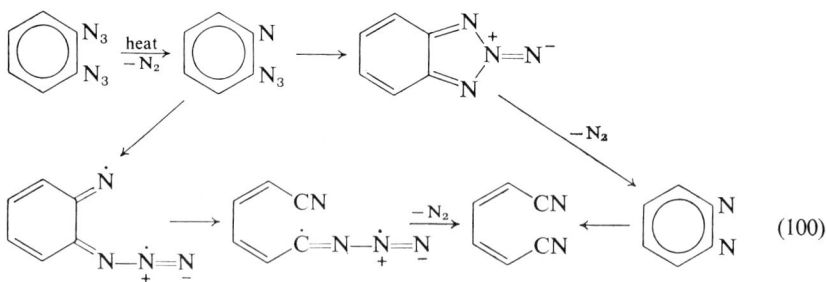

$$\tag{100}$$

An alternate explanation (Eq. 101) for the formation of mucononitrile during the pyrolysis of *ortho*-phenylene diazide is based on the probable equilibrium between *ortho*-azidophenyl nitrene and the corresponding bicyclic azirine. Each of the two explanations accounts for the formation of the correct methyl derivative of mucononitrile from the appropriately substituted 2- and 3-methyl-6-azidophenyl nitrene. Support for ring contraction of a bicyclic azirine may be found in the pyrolytic or photolytic

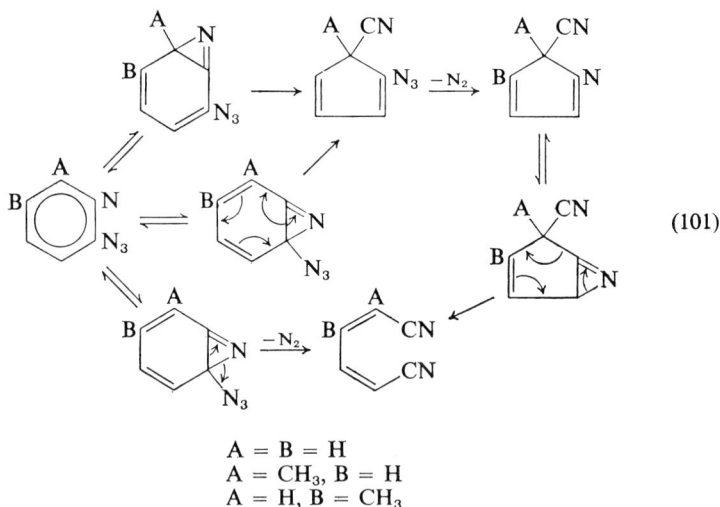

$$A = B = H$$
$$A = CH_3, B = H$$
$$A = H, B = CH_3$$

(101)

isomerization of α-nitrenotropone into *ortho*-cyanophenol (132) (Eq. 102). In addition to *ortho*-cyanophenol both pyrolysis and photolysis to α-azidotropone lead to the formation of a ketene, either simultaneously with or following the evolution of nitrogen. It may be trapped as a methyl ester when the reaction is carried out in methanol. The ketene was assumed to be the precursor for *ortho*-cyanophenol; however, an alternate explanation may be offered based on ring contraction from an azirine (Eq. 102).

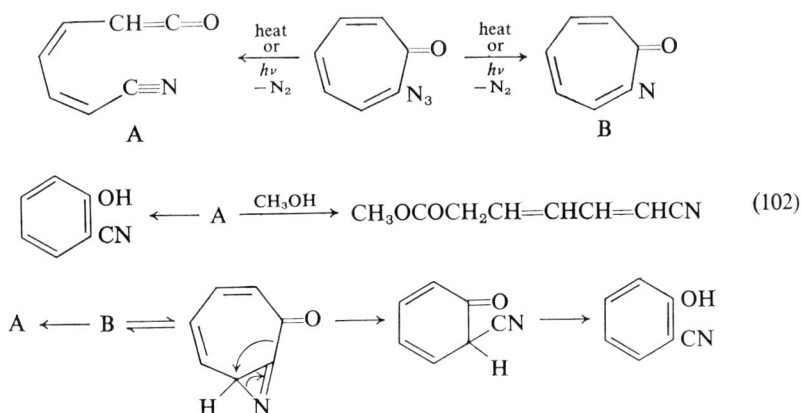

(102)

Isomerization of a cyanocyclopentadienyl nitrene or the corresponding bicyclic azirine into a muconitrile, the last step in Eq. 101, is analogous to the isomerization of diphenyltriazole nitrene into a noncyclic nitrile (28) (Eq. 30, R = C_6H_5). The mechanism given in Eq. 101 suggests that pyrolysis and photolysis of other aromatic azides may also produce cyclopentadiene derivatives. Polymerization of these intermediates would be an attractive way to account for certain polymers obtained from many aromatic azides as nitrogen is liberated.

Diazido-N-phenylmaleimide undergoes a strikingly similar pyrolytic transformation into the N-phenylimide of cyanoformic acid (61a). The intermediate formation of a mononitrene and a bicyclic azirine may be involved (Eq. 103).

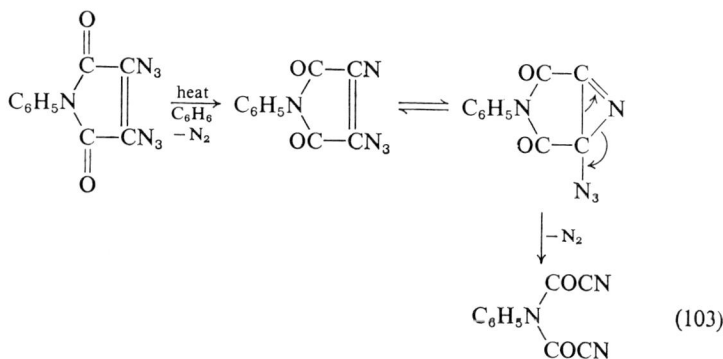

(103)

The well-known molecular rearrangements of an aromatic nitrene by insertion with CH or CC bonds have developed from the observation that carbazole is formed as nitrogen is eliminated by either pyrolysis or photolysis of ortho-azidobiphenyl (133) (Eq. 104), a reaction in which product

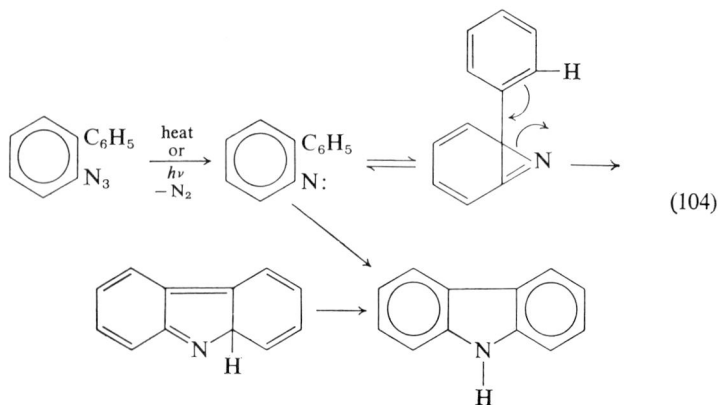

(104)

formation may proceed from either a nitrene or bicyclic azirine intermediate. Shortly thereafter rearrangement by insertion with a CH bond at
sp^3 carbon was observed (134) (Eq. 105). More recently it has been observed that both pyrolysis and photolysis of 2,2′-diazidobiphenyl produced

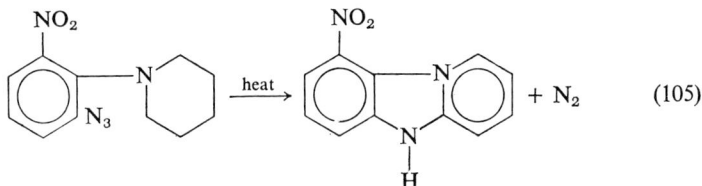

$$+ \ N_2 \qquad (105)$$

4-azidocarbazole (135) (Eq. 106). There was no evidence that either a
dinitrene had been generated or that a benzocinnoline had been formed.
Similar treatment of 2,2′-diazido-6,6′-dimethylbiphenyl gave a tar from
which no product was identified; however, deoxygenation of 2,2′-dinitro-
6,6′-dimethylbiphenyl produced the expected 1,10-dimethylbenzo[c]-
cinnoline (41) (Eq. 107). Further pyrolytic or photolytic treatment of
4-azidocarbazole produced the corresponding aminocarbazole by hydrogen abstraction. Carbazole is also produced during the photolysis of
ortho-isocyanatobiphenyl (136).

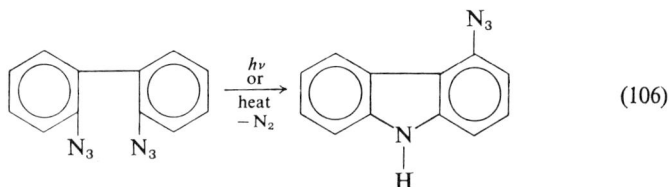

$$(106)$$

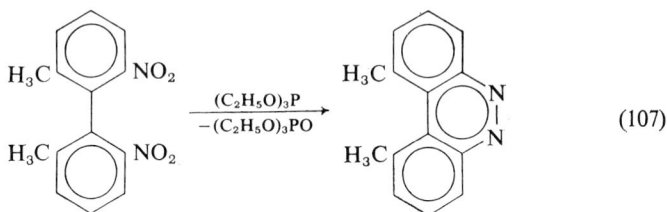

$$(107)$$

Numerous cyclizations by intramolecular insertion have been reported from deoxygenation of ortho-alkyl- or aryl nitro- or nitrosobenzene.
From ortho-nitropropylbenzene and triethyl phosphite, 2-methyl-2,3-
dihydroindole (7%) and ortho-allylaniline (6%) are obtained along with
ortho-propylaniline (3%) and ethyl N-ortho-tolylphosphorimidate (40%)
(128) (Eq. 108). From ortho-ethylnitrosobenzene there is apparently no
cyclization to dihydroindole, instead an azoxy compound (137) and N-

(*ortho*-ethylphenyl)phosphorimidate (128) are formed. That no rearranged products are found when this reaction with triethyl phosphite is carried out

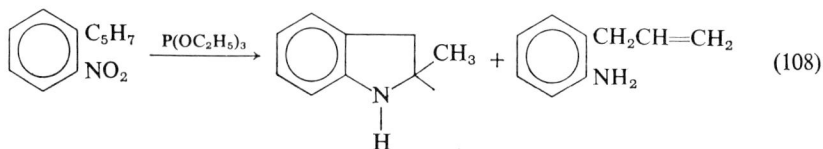

(108)

in benzene has brought forth the suggestion (128) that the rearrangement will not occur in hydrocarbon solvents, in concurrence with the known sensitivity of phenyl nitrene to solvent during rearrangement (138,139).

Cyclization of *ortho-n*-butylphenyl nitrene produces 2-ethyl-2,3-dihydroindole, 2-methyl-1,2,3,4-tetrahydroquinoline, and *ortho-n*-butyl-aniline in almost the same ratio for the nitrene generated from an azide (solution-phase pyrolysis) or from the corresponding nitro-compound (128,140). Similarly, triethyl phosphite transformed (+)-(*S*)-2-nitro-1-(2-methylbutyl)benzene into partially active (about 50%) 2-methyl-2-ethyl-2,3-dihydroindole (140), the same product (65% optical purity) obtained from the corresponding azide (Eq. 109).

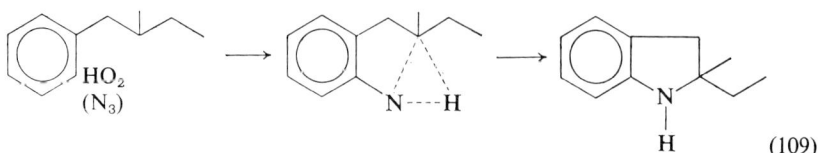

(109)

A selectivity in abstracting hydrogen from an *ortho*-alkyl sidechain is demonstrated by a nitrene obtained both from an azide and a nitro- or nitroso- compound. The formation of only the unconjugated olefin from both *ortho-n*-propyl- and *n*-butylphenyl nitrene can be accounted for by a concerted mechanism for the abstraction process (128) (Eq. 110).

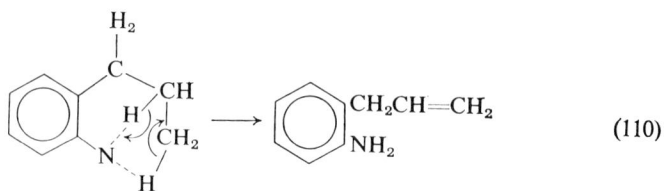

(110)

Convincing evidence for nitrene intermediacy from 2'-nitro-2,4,6-trimethylbiphenyl in a reaction with triethyl phosphite partially consists in isolating the products of hydrogen abstraction, CH bond insertion, and

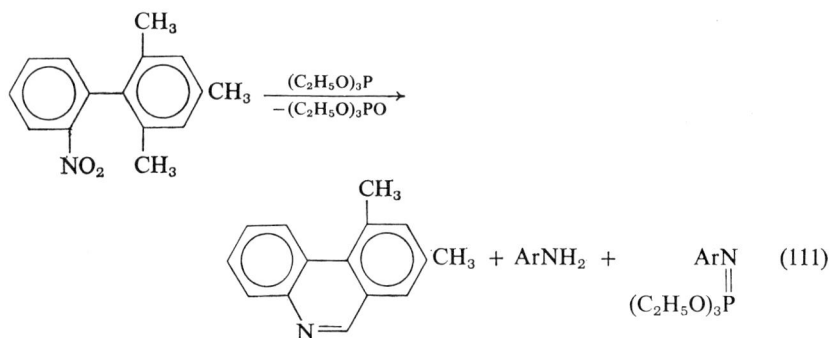

$$\text{(111)}$$

coupling with the tervalent phosphorus reagent (27) (Eq. 111). Similar results were obtained from the pyrolysis of 2,4,6-trimethyl-2'-azido-biphenyl at 230° which produced 2,4,6-trimethyl-2'-aminobiphenyl-2,4,9-trimethyl carbazole by CC insertion and 8,10-dimethylphenanthridine by CH insertion (141) (Eq. 112).

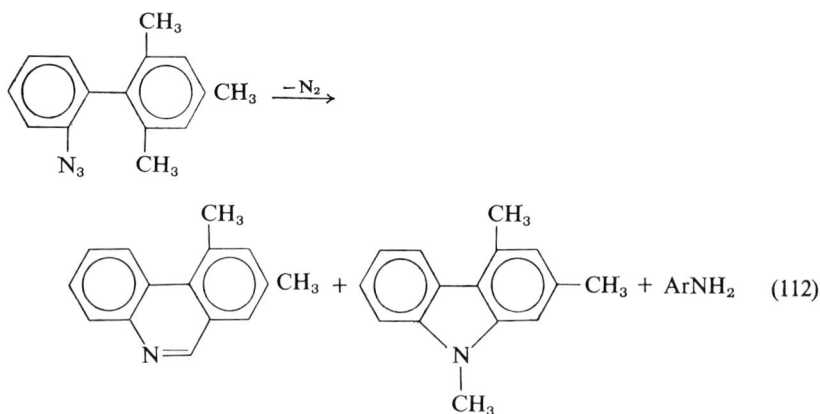

$$\text{(112)}$$

A strong tendency toward cyclization accompanies deoxygenation in triethyl phosphite of aromatic nitro and nitroso compounds in which an α,β-unsaturated group occupies the *ortho* position. Cyclization from a nitrene may account for the formation of a rearranged indole from a β,β-disubstituted *ortho*-nitrostyrene, but it apparently cannot be a precursor for a 1-hydroxyindole, a 3-indolinone, or a biindoline. Initial deoxygenation to the corresponding *ortho*-nitrosostyrene was considered to be an important step (142,143) (Eq. 113); however, at the present time the extent of further deoxygenation to a nitrene cannot be evaluated. An investigation of the pyrolysis and/or photolysis of an *ortho*-styryl azide, apparently unknown, as an alternate route to an *ortho*-styryl nitrene would be helpful. Structurally related *ortho*-azidoanils have been observed to undergo pyrolysis with the elimination of nitrogen and the formation of

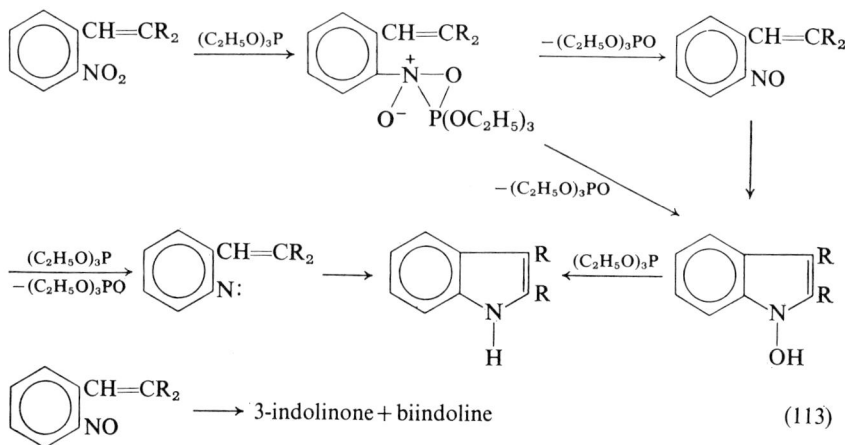

$$\xrightarrow{} \text{3-indolinone} + \text{biindoline} \qquad (113)$$

expected benzimidazoles (144) (Eq. 114). To account for an apparent assistance in the elimination of nitrogen by the unsaturated *ortho* substituent, it has been proposed that rearrangement by migration of hydrogen from carbon to nitrogen occurs after ring closure (145). On the other hand, ring

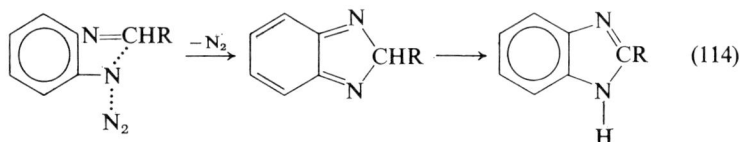

$$(114)$$

closure apparently occurs with migration of hydrogen from carbon to nitrogen during the pyrolysis of similar Schiff bases derived from certain azidotriazole amines (146,147) (Eq. 115).

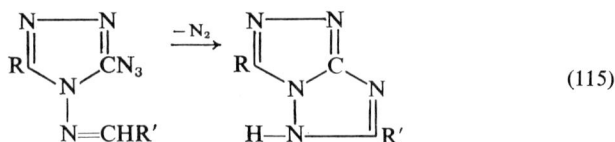

$$(115)$$

Deoxygenation of both *cis*- and *trans-ortho*-nitrostilbene produced 2-phenylindole (148), also obtained from α-nitrostilbene (149). Cyclization from a nitrene in the latter example is unlikely since it would be in contrast with the isomerization to an azirine or dimerization to a pyrazine of pre-

sumably the same intermediate generated by the photolysis of α-azidostilbene (150) (Eq. 116).

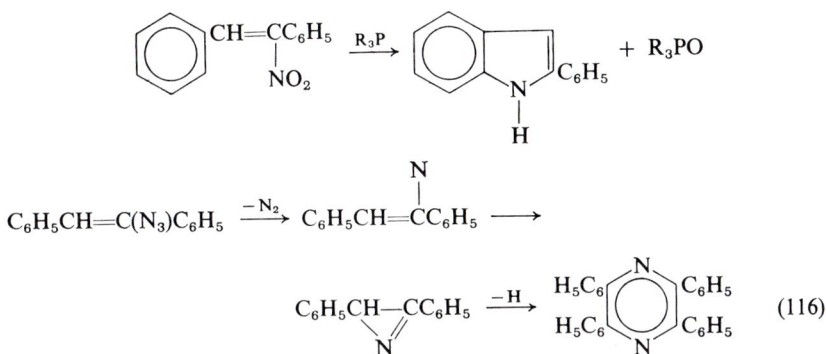

$$C_6H_5CH=C(N_3)C_6H_5 \xrightarrow{-N_2} C_6H_5CH=CC_6H_5 \longrightarrow$$

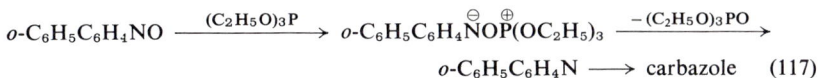

(116)

A related transformation is found in the reaction between *ortho*-
nitrosobiphenyl and triethyl phosphite which produces carbazole. Ring
closure from both a nitrene and a zwitterion (which otherwise might be the
nitrene precursor) has been proposed (149) (Eqs. 117 and 118).

$$o\text{-}C_6H_5C_6H_4NO \xrightarrow{(C_2H_5O)_3P} o\text{-}C_6H_5C_6H_4\overset{\ominus}{N}\overset{\oplus}{O}P(OC_2H_5)_3 \xrightarrow{-(C_2H_5O)_3PO}$$

$$o\text{-}C_6H_5C_6H_4N \longrightarrow \text{carbazole} \quad (117)$$

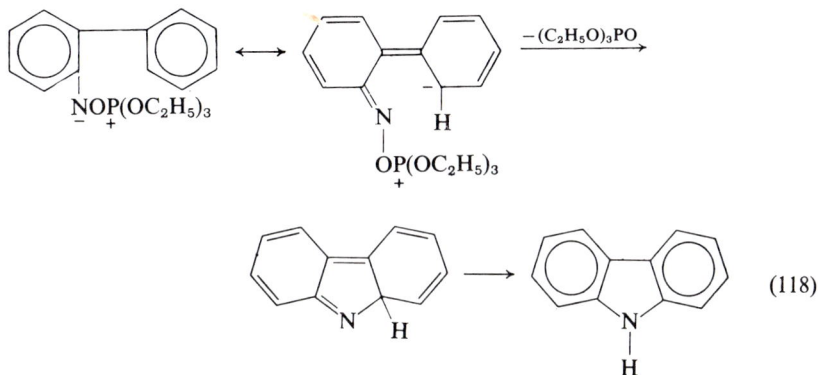

(118)

VIII. REARRANGEMENTS IN NITRENES CONTAINING
α-ATOMS OTHER THAN CARBON

A. Aminonitrenes

The generation of intermediate aminonitrenes (151), also referred to
as diazenes or azamines, from appropriately 1,1-disubstituted hydrazines
has been proposed in oxidations, in pyrolyses of their 2-sulfonyl hydrazine

salts, and in base-catalyzed reactions of their 2-chloro derivatives. Amino-nitrenes may also be generated during certain reductions of nitrosamines and in reactions between secondary amines and difluoroamine or Angeli's salt (Na_2ONNO_2) (152).

In the solvent-dependent pyrolysis of 1,1-dialkyl-2-benzenesulfonyl-hydrazine sodium salts, tetrazenes are formed predominantly in tetra-glyme, but rearrangement to hydrazones may be predominant in diethylene glycol (151) (Eq. 119). In contrast, the 1,1-diphenyl analog gives diphenyl-amine in both solvents with no rearrangement to azobenzene. Hydrazone formation has been explained by an initial tautomerization of an amino-

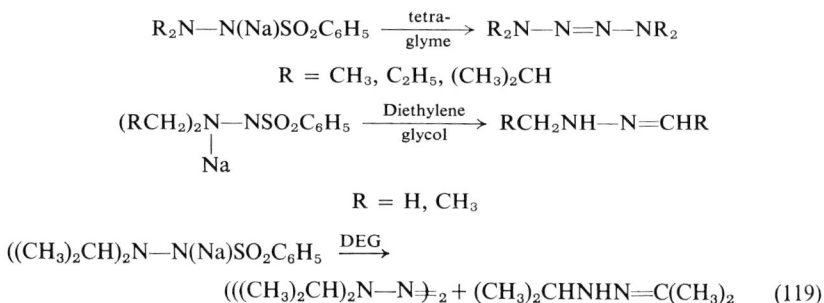

$$R_2N-N(Na)SO_2C_6H_5 \xrightarrow[\text{glyme}]{\text{tetra-}} R_2N-N{=}N-NR_2$$

$$R = CH_3, C_2H_5, (CH_3)_2CH$$

$$(RCH_2)_2N-NSO_2C_6H_5 \xrightarrow[\text{glycol}]{\text{Diethylene}} RCH_2NH-N{=}CHR$$
$$\underset{Na}{|}$$

$$R = H, CH_3$$

$$((CH_3)_2CH)_2N-N(Na)SO_2C_6H_5 \xrightarrow{\text{DEG}}$$

$$(((CH_3)_2CH)_2N-N{\rightarrow}_2 + (CH_3)_2CHNHN{=}C(CH_3)_2 \qquad (119)$$

nitrene intermediate followed by migration of an alkyl group (151) (Eq. 120). It was independently established that neither a linear azo compound

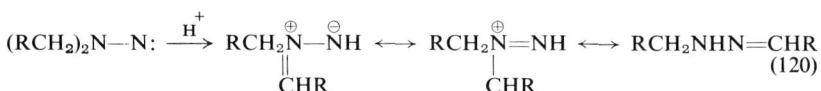

$$(RCH_2)_2N-N: \xrightarrow{\overset{+}{H}} RCH_2\overset{\oplus}{N}-\overset{\ominus}{NH} \longleftrightarrow RCH_2\overset{\oplus}{N}{=}NH \longleftrightarrow RCH_2NHN{=}CHR \atop \underset{CHR}{\|} \qquad \underset{CHR}{|} \qquad (120)$$

nor a cyclic diaziridine were involved. This requires the migration of an alkyl group in Eq. 119 to occur faster or more irreversibly than cyclization to a diaziridine.

A stereoselective oxidation of cis-1-amino-2,6-diphenylpiperidine with yellow mercuric oxide gives cis-1,2-diphenylcyclopentane (65%), and similar oxidation of the trans-amine gives trans- (59%) and cis- (12%) 1,2-diphenylcyclopentane. The formation of 1,5-diphenylpentene-1 accom-panies each oxidation which may proceed with the initial formation of an aminonitrene followed by loss of molecular nitrogen with rearrangement. A transition state with partial ionic character, but indistinguishable from a radical process, has been considered in an explanation for olefin formation (153) (Eq. 121). The same products in similar ratios were obtained from the reduction with hydrosulfite of the corresponding geometric isomers of N-nitroso-2,6-diphenylpiperidine (154). Elimination of nitrogen was found not completely concerted with the formation of hydrocarbon in both the oxidation of optically active N-amino-α,α'-dimethyldibenzylamine and the

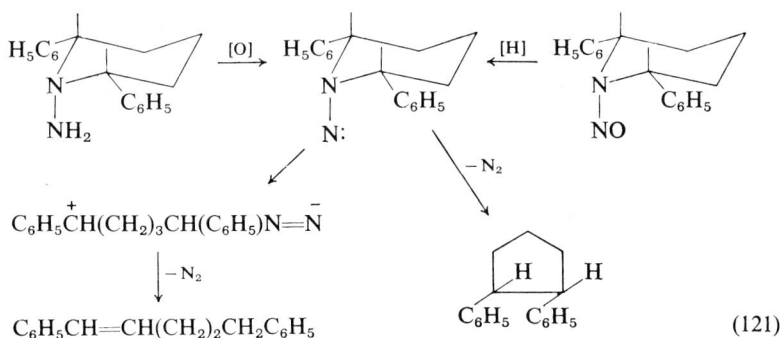

$$C_6H_5\overset{+}{C}H(CH_2)_3CH(C_6H_5)N{=}\overset{-}{N}$$

$$\downarrow -N_2$$

$$C_6H_5CH{=}CH(CH_2)_2CH_2C_6H_5 \qquad\qquad (121)$$

reduction of the corresponding optically active nitrosamine since a product, 2,3-diphenylbutane, consisted of a mixture of the *meso* and partially optically active isomers (154) (Eq. 122).

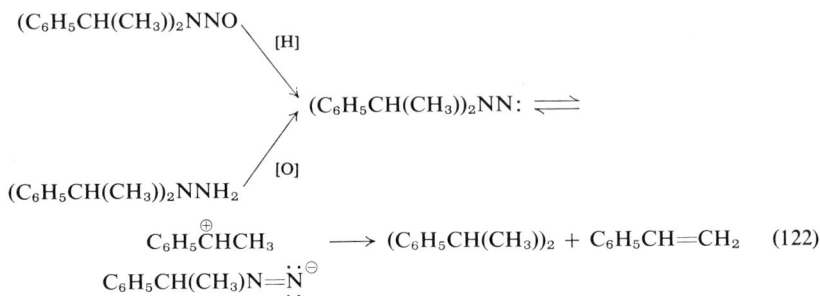

$$(C_6H_5CH(CH_3))_2 + C_6H_5CH{=}CH_2 \qquad (122)$$

Apparently this rearrangement of an aminonitrene to hydrocarbons as nitrogen is released occurs when a substituent, e.g., aryl or cyano, capable of stabilizing charge or radical character in the transition state is attached to one or both α-carbon atoms (155). In addition to the oxidation of a suitable hydrazine or the reduction of a suitable nitrosamine, the base-catalyzed reaction of 1,1-dibenzyl-2 benzenesulfonylhydrazine produced nitrogen and bibenzyl in high yield (156). By an extension of the latter reaction the sodium salt of N-benzenesulfonamidopyrrolidine was found to undergo pyrolysis with the formation of ethylene and nitrogen (155) (Eq. 123); however, the corresponding pyrrole and carbazole derivatives produced pyrrole and a tetrazene, respectively (155). An important difference between the pyrolysis of 1,1-disubstituted 2-arenesulfonylhydrazine salts and oxidation of corresponding hydrazines is revealed in the oxidation

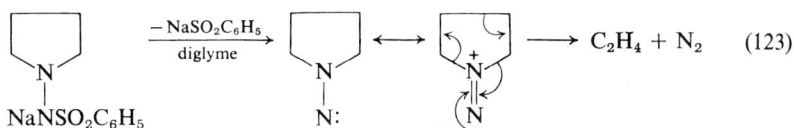

$$\longrightarrow C_2H_4 + N_2 \qquad (123)$$

of *N*-aminopyrrolidine by mercuric oxide or of *N*-amino-2,5-dimethyl-pyrrolidine with potassium permanganate to corresponding tetrazenes (155). On the other hand, both oxidation of 1,3-diphenyl-2-aminodihydro-isoindole and alkaline treatment of its *para*-toluenesulfonhydrazide produced the expected 1,2-diphenylbenzocyclobutene (157,158). In the oxidation reactions it was established that *cis* and *trans* starting materials produced *cis* and *trans* product, respectively (157) (Eq. 124).

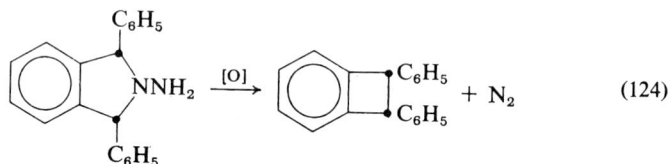

$$ \tag{124} $$

Substitution of water for diglyme as solvent in reaction 123 brings about a dramatic suppression of gas evolution as a rearrangement of an aminonitrene into a hydrazone takes over and 2,3,4,5-tetrahydropyridizane is the dominant product (152) (Eq. 125) (compare with the effect of aqueous solvents during the Tiemann reaction, Eqs. 85 and 86).

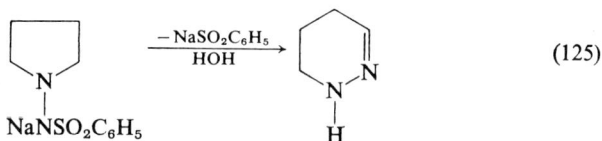

$$ \tag{125} $$

A dihydropyridazine is not formed on treating 3-pyrroline with Angeli's salt ($Na_2N_2O_3$) in dilute hydrochloric acid (159). Instead, the elimination of nitrogen, presumably from an aminonitrene intermediate, occurs with a completely stereospecific formation of butadiene as revealed in the transformation of *cis*- and *trans*-2,5-dimethylpyrroline-3 into *trans*, *trans*- and *cis,trans*-2,4-hexadiene, respectively, by a disrotatory sigma-symmetric mechanism (Eq. 126). *cis,cis*-2,4-Hexadiene was not produced from *cis*-2,5-dimethylpyrroline-3 probably because of methyl–methyl repulsion.

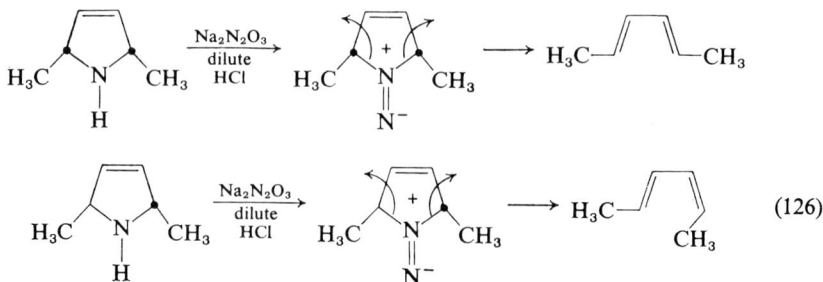

$$ \tag{126} $$

Aminonitrene intermediacy offers a basis for a reasonable explanation of reactions between difluoroamine and aziridine, azetidine, dibenzylamine, or 3,5,5-trimethylpyrazoline (160) (Eqs. 127–130).

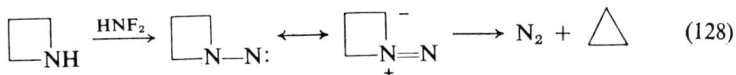

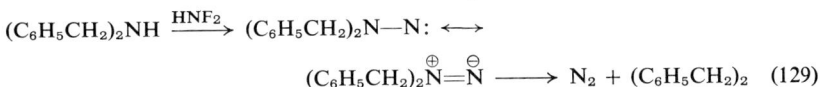

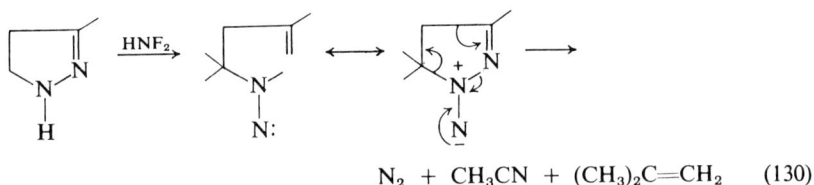

$$\text{(127)}$$

$$\text{(128)}$$

$$(C_6H_5CH_2)_2NH \xrightarrow{HNF_2} (C_6H_5CH_2)_2N\!-\!N: \longleftrightarrow$$

$$(C_6H_5CH_2)_2\overset{\oplus}{N}\!=\!\overset{\ominus}{N} \longrightarrow N_2 + (C_6H_5CH_2)_2 \quad \text{(129)}$$

$$N_2 + CH_3CN + (CH_3)_2C\!=\!CH_2 \quad \text{(130)}$$

There is a strong similarity between the oxidation of 1-aminobenzotriazole (161) (Eq. 131) and Eqs. 122 and 129. Benzyne, an assumed intermediate in the former example, was detected by its addition to tetracyclone (Eq. 131), anthracene or furan. On the other hand, if 1-nitreno-

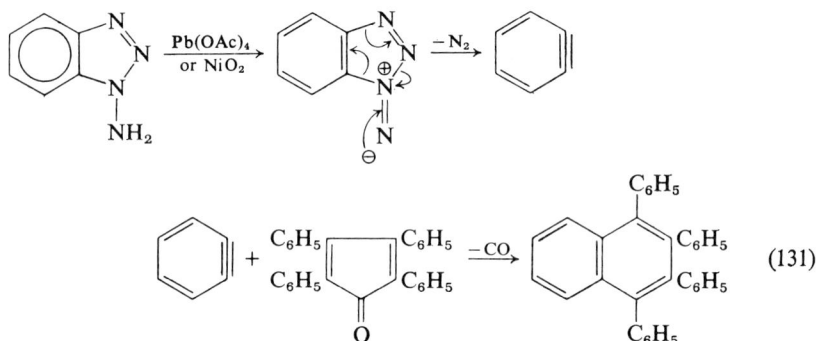

$$\text{(131)}$$

oxindole is an intermediate in the similar oxidation of 1-aminooxindole it undergoes rearrangement with ring-enlargement (162) (Eq. 132) rather than elimination of nitrogen.

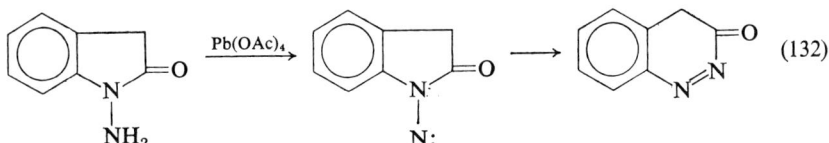

$$\text{(132)}$$

Two N-azido secondary amines, $(CH_3)_2NN_3$ and $((CH_3)_3Si)_2NN_3$, have recently been reported. Each is thermally unstable but pyrolysis products have not been described (163,164).

B. Imino- and Azonitrenes

During the irradiation of cyanogen azide at wavelengths below 3000 Å diazocarbon is formed (165) (Eq. 133) apparently by a molecular rearrangement. It is not known whether or not it is a precursor to carbon, also a product of the reaction.

$$N{\equiv}CN_3 \xrightarrow[< 3000 \text{ Å}]{hv} \quad :C{=}N{=}\overset{\oplus}{\underset{\ominus}{N}} \longleftrightarrow \quad :C{=}\overset{..}{N}{-}\overset{..}{N} \qquad (133)$$

In general, an imino- and azonitrene are included in representations of resonance hybrids of diazoalkanes and azides, respectively. Perhaps phenyl azide reacts as an azonitrene during its photolytic transformation into benzotriazole (50) (Eq. 134). The cyclization of a guanyl azide into a tetrazole (166) provides another likely example of an azonitrene intermediate.

$$C_6H_5N_3 \xrightarrow{hv} \qquad \qquad \longrightarrow \qquad \qquad (134)$$

C. Alkoxynitrenes

It has been suggested that alkoxynitrenes may be intermediates in the bromine oxidation of O-alkylhydroxylamines into hyponitrite esters (167) (Eq. 135). Deoxygenation of nitrite esters by tervalent phosphorous re-

$$RONH_2 \xrightarrow{Br_2} RON \xrightarrow{RONHBr} RON{=}NOR \qquad (135)$$

agents apparently produces hyponitrite esters, which are subsequently transformed into alcohols (168) (Eq. 136). Intermediate alkoxynitrenes were considered to be unlikely.

$$R'ONO + R_3P \longrightarrow R'O\overset{\ominus}{N}O\overset{\oplus}{P}R_3 \xrightarrow{R'ONO} R'ONO\overset{\oplus}{P}R_3 \xrightarrow{-R_3PO}$$
$$R'O\overset{}{N}{-}O^{\ominus}$$

$$R'ON \xrightarrow[-R_3PO]{R_3P} R'ON \xrightarrow{-N_2} R'O\cdot \xrightarrow{CH} R'OH \qquad (136)$$
$$\overset{\parallel}{R'ON{\rightarrow}O} \qquad \overset{\parallel}{R'ON}$$

D. Organometallic and Nonmetallic Nitrenes

The first rearrangement of a sulfonyl nitrene was claimed for the gas-phase pyrolysis of benzene sulfonyl azide from which azobenzene was obtained (169). The same product has more recently been obtained during pyrolysis in cyclohexanone (170). Sulfonyl nitrenes derived from sulfonyl azides during photolysis are now known to rearrange in methanol and presumably other protic solvents (104) (Eq. 137).

$$C_6H_5SO_2N_3 \xrightarrow[CH_3OH]{hv} C_6H_5SO_2N \longrightarrow C_6H_5NSO_2 \longrightarrow$$
$$C_6H_5NHSO_2OCH_3 \quad (137)$$

Other types of nitrenes containing α-sulfur are apparently unknown, with the possible exception of sulfenyl nitrenes. In a reaction between 2,4-dinitrobenzenesulfenyl chloride and sodium azide leading to unidentified products (171) the corresponding sulfenyl azide and sulfenyl nitrene might be intermediates.

From recent investigations on organometallic azides the first observation on molecular rearrangements during photolysis has been made. The remarkably stable triphenylsilyl azide undergoes pyrolysis at 725° with the release of nitrogen and the formation of the silicon analog of benzophenone anil isolated as a dimer. At the same time a linear polymer is produced (169) (Eq. 138). Pyrolyses of triphenylgermanium azide $[(C_6H_5)_3GeN_3]$ and diphenylphosphinic azide $[(C_6H_3)_2P(O)N_3]$ follow

$$(C_6H_5)_3SiN_3 \xrightarrow[-N_2]{725°} (C_6H_3)_2Si=NC_6H_5 \longrightarrow (C_6H_5)_2Si-NC_6H_5$$
$$\begin{array}{c} | \qquad\qquad | \\ C_6H_5-N--Si(C_6H_5)_2 \quad (138) \end{array}$$
$$+ \text{ polymer}$$

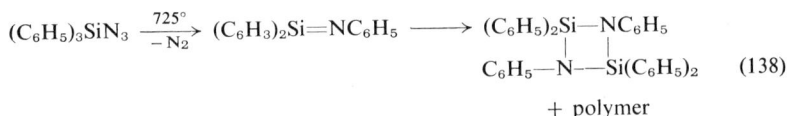

similar reactions with the formation of polymeric products which contain the phenyl group attached to nitrogen (169). In contrast triphenyltin azide and triphenyllead azide each undergo pyrolysis with the release of all azide nitrogen and the formation of tetraphenyltin and tetraphenyllead (169). Triphenyltin nitrene has been produced photolytically from the azide and its ESR has been measured (35). Di(2,4,6-trimethylphenyl)boron azide also undergoes pyrolysis with the release of nitrogen and the migration of an aryl group from boron to nitrogen (172) (Eq. 139).

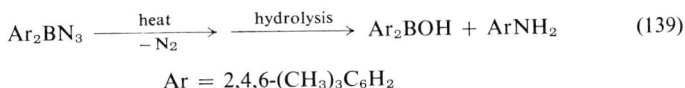

$$Ar_2BN_3 \xrightarrow[-N_2]{heat} \xrightarrow{hydrolysis} Ar_2BOH + ArNH_2 \quad (139)$$
$$Ar = 2,4,6\text{-}(CH_3)_3C_6H_2$$

More recently, oligomeric products of rearrangement have been obtained from organoboron azides undergoing either pyrolysis or photolysis

(173) (Eq. 140). Kinetic measurements revealed that electron-donating

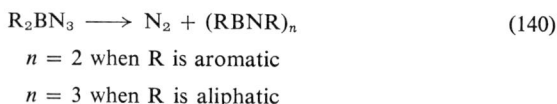

$$R_2BN_3 \longrightarrow N_2 + (RBNR)_n \qquad (140)$$

$n = 2$ when R is aromatic

$n = 3$ when R is aliphatic

ortho or *para* substituents in aryl groups increase azide stability and that substituted phenyl migrates more readily than phenyl when it more powerfully attracts electrons and is bulkier according to the sequence: *meta*-trifluoromethylphenyl > *ortho*-tolyl > α-naphthyl > phenyl > *para*-chlorophenyl > *para*-tolyl. It was concluded that both kinetic measurements and migratory tendencies supported a synchronous rearrangement.

These results are in contrast with an earlier observation that electron-donating *para* substituents decrease stability in triarylmethyl azides (174) where, for example, *para*-dimethylaminophenyldiphenylmethyl azide decomposes 2.5 times as rapidly as triphenylmethyl azide at 180° in dibutylcarbitol. It is recognized that the pyrolytic elimination of nitrogen from triarylmethyl azides, simple phenyl azides, and 2-azidobiphenyls proceeds by kinetics of the same order of magnitude (with triarylmethyl azides being slower); and also that the enthalpies of activation for all three types of azides are comparable (in the range 24–36 kcal/mole) and that substituent effects in equivalent positions are similar. The probability that these three types of azides are each transformed into a nitrene during pyrolysis was considered, but with the reservation that a concerted process for nitrogen evolution and rearrangement from a triarylmethylazide may offer a better rationalization for the observed substituent effects (175).

The more stable bis(dialkylamino)boron azides undergo pyrolysis at 270° to give unidentified resins. Good yields of tetrakis(dialkylamino)-1,3,2,4-diazadiboretidines are obtained by rearrangement during photolysis (173) (Eq. 141).

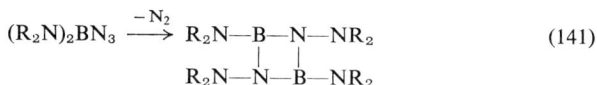

$$(R_2N)_2BN_3 \xrightarrow{-N_2} \begin{array}{c} R_2N-B-N-NR_2 \\ | \quad | \\ R_2N-N-B-NR_2 \end{array} \qquad (141)$$

IX. CONCLUDING REMARKS

It is anticipated that future work will continue to strengthen the hypothesis of nitrene intermediacy. This will develop from greater understanding of reaction mechanisms; however, as a consequence, certain critical reactions now thought to proceed through nitrene intermediates may become established examples of alternate mechanisms, as has been recently established for the pyrolytic and photolytic Curtius reaction (Section V). Particular interest will surely develop from research on intramolecular changes of nitrenes, including additional investigation on the structural relationship between α,β-unsaturated nitrenes and the corresponding isomeric unsaturated three-membered ring. A similar problem of valence isomerism is unfolding in the interrelationship between the nitrene function attached to an aromatic five-membered ring and the corresponding linear nitrile. New fields may rapidly develop from nitrene generation by molecular rearrangement, e.g. Eqs. 27, 28, and 30a, and those molecular species in which the nitrene function is attached to or located near an atom other than carbon.

The rapid development of nitrene chemistry in the past decade has served well the diverse interests of organic and physical organic chemists in problems of reaction mechanisms, molecular structure, and preparative procedures. It is a topic which will soon need to be treated in a comprehensive monograph rather than to be updated again by another chapter or review.

Acknowledgment

The financial assistance for this work from a NASA grant, NGR 14-012-004, is gratefully acknowledged.

References

1. P. A. S. Smith, "Rearrangements Involving Migration to an Electron Deficient Nitrogen or Oxygen," in *Molecular Rearrangements*, Part 1, P. de Mayo, Ed., Interscience, New York, 1963, pp. 457–591.
2. P. A. S. Smith, *Open-chain Nitrogen Compounds*, Vols. 1 and 2, Benjamin, New York, 1965.
3. R. A. Abramovitch and B. A. Davis, *Chem. Rev.*, **64**, 149 (1964).
4. L. Horner and A. Christmann, *Angew. Chem. Intern. Ed. Engl.*, **2**, 599 (1963); *Angew. Chem.*, **75**, 707 (1963).
5. W. Lwowski, Ed., *Nitrenes*, Wiley, New York, 1968.
6. J. S. McConaghy and W. Lwowski, *J. Am. Chem. Soc.*, **89**, 2357, 4450 (1967); see also K. Hafner, W. Kaiser, and R. Puttner, *Tetrahedron Letters*, **1964**, 3953.
7. A. G. Anastassiou, *J. Am. Chem. Soc.*, **89**, 3184 (1967).
8. R. Huisgen, H. J. Sturm, and M. Seidel, *Chem. Ber.*, **94**, 1555 (1961).
9. R. M. Herbst, *J. Org. Chem.*, **26**, 2372 (1961).
10. R. M. Moriarty, private communication.
11. R. M. Moriarty and A. M. Kirkien-Konasiervicz, *Tetrahedron Letters*, **1966**, 4123.

12. J. H. Boyer, "Deoxygenation of Nitro and Nitroso Groups," in *Nitrenes*, W. Lwowski, Ed., Wiley, New York (1968).

13. J. H. Boyer, W. E. Krueger, and G. J. Mikol, *J. Am. Chem. Soc.*, **89**, 5504 (1967).

14. H. Zimmer and M. Jayawant, *Tetrahedron Letters*, **1966**, 5061.

15. F. Eloy, *Helv. Chim. Acta*, **48**, 380 (1965).

16. T. Bacchetti and A. Alemagna, *Gazz. Chim. Ital.*, **91**, 1475 (1961) and earlier publications.

17. R. Rajagopalan and B. G. Advani, *J. Org. Chem.*, **30**, 3369 (1965).

18. R. Huisgen and J. Wulff, *Tetrahedron Letters*, **1967**, 917, 921.

19. H. Shindo and B. Umezawa, *Chem. Pharm. Bull. (Tokyo)*, **10**, 492 (1962); *Chem. Abstr.*, **57**, 14598 (1962).

20. E. Meyer and G. W. Griffin, *Angew. Chem. Intern. Ed. Engl.*, **6**, 634 (1967).

21. E. Bamberger, *Chem. Ber.*, **27**, 1182 (1894).

22. J. A. Young, W. S. Durrell, and R. D. Dresdner, *J. Am. Chem. Soc.*, **82**, 4553 (1960).

23. J. B. Hynes, B. C. Bishop, and L. A. Bigelow, *J. Org. Chem.*, **28**, 2811 (1963).

24. G. McTurk and J. G. Waller, *J. Chem. Soc.*, **1963**, 262.

25. D. W. Cornell, R. S. Berry, and W. Lwowski, *J. Am. Chem. Soc.*, **88**, 544 (1966).

26. P. Rajagopalan and C. N. Talaty, *Tetrahedron Letters*, **1966**, 4877.

27. J. I. G. Cadogan and M. J. Todd, *Chem. Commun.*, **1967**, 178.

28. (a) P. A. S. Smith, L. O. Krebchek, and W. Resemann, *J. Am. Chem. Soc.*, **86**, 2025 (1964); (b) G. Just and W. Zehetner, *Tetrahedron Letters*, **1967**, 3389.

29. G. R. Harvey and K. W. Ratts, *J. Org. Chem.*, **31**, 3907 (1966).

30. J. H. Boyer and L. R. Morgan, Jr., *J. Am. Chem. Soc.*, **81**, 3369 (1959).

31. N. J. Leonard and B. Zwanenberg, *J. Am. Chem. Soc.*, **89**, 4456 (1967).

32. H. Takimoto and G. C. Denault, *Tetrahedron Letters*, **1966**, 5369.

33. E. Wasserman, G. Smolinsky, and W. A. Yager, *J. Am. Chem. Soc.*, **86**, 3166 (1964).

34. E. Koch, *Tetrahedron*, **23**, 1747 (1967).

35. G. Smolinsky, E. Wasserman, and W. A. Yager, *J. Am. Chem. Soc.*, **84**, 3220 (1962); R. M. Moriarty, M. Rahman, and G. J. King, *J. Am. Chem. Soc.*, **88**, 842 (1966).

36. R. M. Moriarty and M. Rahman, *Tetrahedron*, **21**, 2877 (1965).

37. W. Pritzkow and D. Timm, *J. Prakt. Chem.*, **32**, 178 (1966).

38. W. H. Saunders, Jr., and E. A. Caress, *J. Am. Chem. Soc.*, **86**, 861 (1964); F. D. Lewis and W. H. Saunders, Jr., *J. Am. Chem. Soc.*, **89**, 645 (1967).

39. L. Barash, E. Wasserman, and W. A. Yager, *J. Am. Chem. Soc.*, **89**, 3931 (1967).

40. F. R. Benson, "The Tetrazoles," in *Heterocyclic Compounds*, R. C. Elderfield, Ed., Wiley, New York, 1967, pp. 1–104.

41. B. Coffin and R. F. Robbins, *J. Chem. Soc.*, **1965**, 1252.

42. R. Schaeffer and L. J. Todd, *J. Am. Chem. Soc.*, **87**, 488 (1965).

43. E. Lieber and A. E. Thomas III, *Appl. Spectry.*, **15**, 144 (1961).

44. (a) L. Birkofer, F. Muller, and W. Kaiser, *Tetrahedron Letters*, **1967**, 2781; (b) P. A. S. Smith and B. B. Brown, *J. Am. Chem. Soc.*, **73**, 2435 (1951).

45. G. Smolinsky and B. Feuer, *J. Am. Chem. Soc.*, **86**, 3085 (1964).

46. D. H. R. Barton and L. R. Morgan, Jr., *J. Chem. Soc.*, **1962**, 622; *Proc. Chem. Soc.*, **1961**, 206.

47. D. H. R. Barton and A. N. Staratt, *J. Chem. Soc.*, **1965**, 2444.

48. A. L. Logothetis, *J. Am. Chem. Soc.*, **87**, 749 (1965).

49. J. A. Leermakers, *J. Am. Chem. Soc.*, **55**, 2098, 2719 (1933).

50. L. Horner, A. Christmann, and A. Gross, *Chem. Ber.*, **96**, 399 (1963); J. Jander and R. Schneider, *Chem. Ber.*, **92**, 1756 (1959).
51. B. C. Bishop, J. B. Hynes, and L. A. Bigelow, *J. Am. Chem. Soc.*, **85**, 1606 (1963).
52. I. L. Knunyants, E. G. Bykhovskaya, and V. N. Frosin, *Dokl. Akad. Nauk SSSR*, **132**, 357 (1960).
53. R. H. Wiley and J. Moffat, *J. Org. Chem.*, **22**, 995 (1957).
53a. S. Maiorana, *Ann. Chim. (Rome)*, **56**, 1531 (1966); *Chem. Abstr.*, **67**, 32420m (1967).
54. J. H. Boyer and F. C. Canter, *Chem. Rev.*, **54**, 34 (1954).
55. H. Lindemann and H. Thiele, *Ber.*, **61**, 1529 (1928).
56. H. Goeth and H. Schmid, *Chimia*, **20**, 148 (1966).
57. G. McTurk and J. G. Waller, *J. Chem. Soc.*, **1963**, 262.
58. A. Tsukamoto and N. N. Lichtin, *J. Am. Chem. Soc.*, **84**, 1601 (1962).
59. R. E. Banks and G. J. Moore, *J. Chem. Soc.*, **1966**, 2304.
60. I. L. Knunyants and E. G. Bykhovskaya, *Dokl. Akad. Nauk SSSR*, **131**, 1338 (1960).
61. (a) G. Smolinsky, *J. Org. Chem.*, **27**, 3557 (1962); (b) G. Smolinsky, private communication.
62. J. H. Boyer and R. Modler, unpublished results.
63. F. W. Fowler, A. Hassner, and L. A. Levy, *J. Am. Chem. Soc.*, **89**, 2077 (1967).
64. (a) E. Wenkert and B. F. Barnett, *J. Am. Chem. Soc.*, **82**, 4671 (1960); (b) J. H. Boyer and G. J. Mikol, unpublished results.
65. H. O. House and W. F. Berkowitz, *J. Org. Chem.*, **28**, 307, 2271 (1963).
66. D. F. Morrow, M. E. Butler, and E. C. Y. Huang, *J. Org. Chem.*, **30**, 579 (1965).
67. D. J. Cram and M. J. Hatch, *J. Am. Chem. Soc.*, **75**, 33 (1953).
68. H. E. Baumgarten and J. M. Petersen, *J. Am. Chem. Soc.*, **82**, 495 (1960).
69. E. Schmitz, *Angew. Chem.*, **73**, 23 (1961).
70. P. A. S. Smith and E. E. Most, Jr., *J. Org. Chem.*, **22**, 358 (1957).
71. R. F. Parcell, *Chem. Ind. (London)*, **1963**, 1396.
72. H. J. Bestmann and R. Kunstmann, *Angew. Chem. Intern. Ed. Engl.*, **5**, 1039 (1966).
73. R. Huisgen and J. Wulff, *Tetrahedron Letters*, **1967**, 917.
74. D. W. Kurtz and H. Shechter, *Chem. Commun.*, **1966**, 689.
75. E. F. Ullman and B. Singh, *J. Am. Chem. Soc.*, **88**, 1844 (1966).
76. F. D. Marsh and H. E. Simmons, *J. Am. Chem. Soc.*, **87**, 3529 (1965).
77. P. S. Skell and J. Klebe, *J. Am. Chem. Soc.*, **82**, 247 (1960); P. S. Skell, paper presented at 137th Meeting, American Chemical Society, Cleveland, 1960.
78. J. H. Boyer and R. Selvarajan, unpublished results.
79. R. A. Bernheim, R. J. Kempf, P. W. Humer, and P. S. Skell, *J. Chem. Phys.*, **41**, 1156 (1964).
80. R. Breslow and C. Juan, *J. Am. Chem. Soc.*, **80**, 5991 (1958).
81. P. C. Petrellis, H. Dietrich, E. Meyer, and G. W. Griffin, *J. Am. Chem. Soc.*, **89**, 1967 (1967).
82. A detailed discussion of the Curtius rearrangement and the related Hofmann hypohalite reaction on amides, the Beckmann rearrangement of oximes, the Schmidt reaction and the Lossen rearrangement of hydroxamic acids is given in reference 1.
83. L. Horner, E. Spietschka, and A. Gross, *Ann. Chem.*, **573**, 17 (1951).
84. W. Lwowski and G. T. Tisue, *J. Am. Chem. Soc.*, **87**, 4022 (1965); G. T. Tisue, S. Linke, and W. Lwowski, *J. Am. Chem. Soc.*, **89**, 6303 (1967); S. Linke, G. T. Tisue, and W. Lwowski, *J. Am. Chem. Soc.*, **89**, 6308 (1967).

85. J. W. ApSimon and O. E. Edwards, *Proc. Chem. Soc.*, **1961**, 461; *Can. J. Chem.*, **40**, 896 (1962); W. Antkowiak, J. W. ApSimon, and O. E. Edwards, *J. Org. Chem.*, **27**, 1930 (1962).

86. W. L. Meyer and A. S. Levinson, *J. Org. Chem.*, **28**, 2859 (1963); R. F. C. Brown, *Australian J. Chem.*, **17**, 47 (1964).

87. S. Masamune, *J. Am. Chem. Soc.*, **86**, 290 (1964).

88. R. Puttner and K. Hafner, *Tetrahedron Letters*, **1964**, 3119.

89. R. Kreher and D. Kuehling, *Angew. Chem.*, **77**, 42 (1965).

90. M. F. Sloan, T. J. Prosser, N. R. Newburg, and D. S. Breslow, *Tetrahedron Letters*, **1964**, 2945.

91. W. Lwowski and T. J. Maricich, *J. Am. Chem. Soc.*, **86**, 3164 (1964).

92. R. A. Clement, *J. Org. Chem.*, **27**, 1904 (1962).

93. C. King, *J. Am. Chem. Soc.*, **86**, 437 (1964).

94. J. H. Boyer and G. Mikol, unpublished results.

95. H. Lindemann and W. Schultheis, *Ann. Chem.*, **464**, 237 (1928).

96. R. Huisgen and J. P. Anselme, *Chem. Ber.*, **98**, 2998 (1965).

97. L. Horner and A. Christmann, *Chem. Ber.*, **96**, 388 (1963); *Angew. Chem. Intern. Ed. Engl.*, **2**, 331 (1963).

98. J. P. Anselme, *Chem. Ind. (London)*, **1966**, 1794.

99. C. R. Hauser and S. W. Kantor, *J. Am. Chem. Soc.*, **72**, 4284 (1950).

100. L. Horner, G. Bauer, and J. Dorges, *Chem. Ber.*, **98**, 2631 (1965).

101. K. R. Brower, *J. Am. Chem. Soc.*, **83**, 4370 (1961).

102. H. E. Baumgarten and A. Staklis, *J. Am. Chem. Soc.*, **87**, 1141 (1965).

103. E. Lieber, R. L. Minnis, Jr., and C. N. Rao, *Chem. Rev.*, **65**, 377 (1965).

104. W. Lwowski, R. De Mauriac, T. W. Mattingly, Jr., and E. Scheiffele, *Tetrahedron Letters*, **1964**, 3285; W. Lwowski and E. Scheiffele, *J. Am. Chem. Soc.*, **87**, 4354 (1965).

105. R. J. Cotter and W. F. Beach, *J. Org. Chem.*, **29**, 751 (1964).

106. F. Fehler and K. H. Linde, *J. Prakt. Chem.*, **32**, 190 (1966).

107. D. W. Cornell, R. S. Berry, and W. Lwowski, *J. Am. Chem. Soc.*, **87**, 3626 (1965).

108. H. Staudinger and E. Hauser, *Helv. Chem. Acta.*, **4**, 861 (1921).

109. C. Temple, Jr., C. L. Kussner, and J. A. Montgomery, *J. Org. Chem.*, **31**, 2210 (1966) and earlier papers in a series discuss this equilibrium.

110. P. A. S. Smith and E. Leon, *J. Am. Chem. Soc.*, **80**, 4647 (1958).

111. (a) J. Vaughan and P. A. S. Smith, *J. Org. Chem.*, **23**, 1909 (1958); (b) T. Bacchetti and A. Alemagna, *Rend. Ist. Lombardo Sci., Pt. I., Classe Sci. Mat. Nat.*, **94A**, 351 (1960); *Chem. Abstr.*, **55**, 16527 (1961).

112. W. Kirmse, *Angew. Chem.*, **71**, 537 (1959).

113. A. F. Hegarty, J. B. Aylward, and F. L. Scott, *Tetrahedron Letters*, **1967**, 1259.

114. W. Lwowski, A. Hartenstein, C. de Vita, and R. L. Smick, *Tetrahedron Letters*, **1964**, 2497.

115. M. W. Partridge and H. A. Turner, *J. Pharm. Pharmacol.*, **5**, 103 (1953).

116. M. W. Partridge and H. A. Turner, *J. Chem. Soc.*, **1958**, 2086.

117. T. Bacchetti and A. Alemagna, *Atti Accad. Nazl. Lincei, Rend. Classe Sci. Fis., Mat. Nat.*, **28**, 824 (1960); *Chem. Abstr.*, **56**, 7304 (1962).

118. Reference 1, p. 565.

119. E. Haruki, T. Inaike, and E. Imoto, *Bull. Chem. Soc., Japan*, **38**, 1806 (1965); *Chem. Abstr.*, **63**, 17960 (1965).

120. W. H. Graham, *J. Am. Chem. Soc.*, **87**, 4396 (1965).

121. F. Eloy, *Helv. Chim. Acta.*, **48**, 380 (1965).

122. P. A. Smith and D. H. Kenny, *J. Org. Chem.*, **26**, 5221 (1961).

123. R. Fusco and C. Musante, *Gazz. Chim. Ital.*, **68**, 665 (1938).

124. W. Kirmse, *Chem. Ber.*, **93**, 2353 (1960).

125. K. A. Jensen, M. Due, and A. Holm, *Acta Chem. Scand.*, **19**, 438 (1965); D. Martin and W. Mucke, *Chem. Ber.*, **98**, 2059 (1965).

126. R. Huisgen and M. Appl, *Chem. Rev.*, **91**, 12 (1958).

127. R. A. Odum and M. Brenner, *J. Am. Chem. Soc.*, **88**, 2074 (1966).

128. R. J. Sundberg, *J. Am. Chem. Soc.*, **88**, 3781 (1966).

129. A. M. Trozzolo, R. W. Murray, G. Smolinsky, W. A. Yager, and E. Wasserman, *J. Am. Chem. Soc.*, **85**, 2526 (1963).

130. A. Reiser and V. Frazer, *Nature*, **208**, 682 (1965); A. Reiser, G. Bowes and R. J. Horne, *Trans. Faraday Soc.*, **62**, 3162 (1966); A. Reiser, G. C. Terry, and F. W. Willets, *Nature*, **211**, 410 (1966); A. Reiser, H. Wagner, and G. Bowes, *Tetrahedron Letters*, **1966**, 2635.

131. J. H. Hall, *J. Am. Chem. Soc.*, **87**, 1147 (1965); J. H. Hall and E. Patterson, *J. Am. Chem. Soc.*, **89**, 5856 (1967).

132. J. D. Hobson and J. R. Malpass, *Chem. Commun.*, **1966**, 141; *J. Am. Chem. Soc.*, **89**, 1645 (1967).

133. P. A. S. Smith and B. B. Brown, *J. Am. Chem. Soc.*, **73**, 2435 (1951),

134. K. H. Saunders, *J. Chem. Soc.*, **1955**, 3275.

135. J. H. Boyer and G. J. Mikol, unpublished results.

136. J. S. Swenton, *Tetrahedron Letters*, **1967**, 2855.

137. P. J. Bunyan and J. I. G. Cadogan, *J. Chem. Soc.*, **1963**, 42.

138. G. Smolinsky, *J. Org. Chem.*, **26**, 4108 (1961); W. Lwowski, T. W. Mattingly, Jr., and T. J. Maricich, *Tetrahedron Letters*, **1964**, 1591.

139. W. von E. Doering and R. A. Odum, *Tetrahedron*, **22**, 81 (1961).

140. G. Smolinsky and B. Feuer, *J. Org. Chem.*, **31**, 3882 (1966).

141. G. Smolinsky, *J. Am. Chem.*, **82**, 4717 (1960).

142. R. J. Saundberg, *J. Org. Chem.*, **30**, 3604 (1965).

143. R. J. Sundberg and T. Yamazaki, *J. Org. Chem.*, **32**, 290 (1967).

144. L. Krbechek and H. Takimoto, *J. Org. Chem.*, **29**, 3630 (1964).

145. J. H. Hall and D. R. Kamm, *J. Org. Chem.*, **30**, 2092 (1965).

146. H. H. Takimoto, G. C. Denault, and S. Hotta, *J. Org. Chem.*, **30**, 711 (1965).

147. H. H. Takimoto, G. C. Denault, and S. Hotta, *J. Heterocyclic Chem.*, **3**, 119 (1966).

148. J. I. G. Cadogan and M. Cameron-Wood, *Proc. Chem. Soc. (London)*, **1962**, 361.

149. J. I. G. Cadogan, M. Cameron-Wood, R. K. Mackie, and J. G. Searle, *J. Chem. Soc.*, **1965**, 4831.

150. A. Hassner and L. A. Levy, *J. Am. Chem. Soc.*, **87**, 4203 (1965).

151. D. M. Lemal, F. Menger, and E. Coats, *J. Am. Chem. Soc.*, **86**, 2395 (1964). This article contains a brief review of the reactions for which aminonitrene intermediates have been proposed.

152. D. M. Lemal and T. W. Rave, *J. Am. Chem. Soc.*, **87**, 393 (1965).

153. C. G. Overberger and L. P. Herin, *J. Org. Chem.*, **27**, 2423 (1962).

154. C. G. Overberger, N. P. Marullo, and R. G. Hiskey, *J. Am. Chem. Soc.*, **83**, 1374 (1961).

155. D. M. Lemal, T. W. Rave, and S. D. McGregor, *J. Am. Chem. Soc.*, **85**, 1944 (1963).

156. L. A. Carpino, *J. Am. Chem. Soc.*, **79**, 4427 (1957).

157. L. A. Carpino, *J. Am. Chem. Soc.*, **84**, 2196 (1962).

158. W. Baker, J. F. McOmie, and D. R. Preston, *J. Chem. Soc.*, **1961**, 2971.
159. D. M. Lemal and S. D. McGregor, *J. Am. Chem. Soc.*, **88**, 1335 (1966).
160. C. L. Bumgardner, K. J. Martin, and J. P. Freeman, *J. Am. Chem. Soc.*, **85**, 97 (1963).
161. C. D. Campbell and C. W. Rees, *Proc. Chem. Soc.*, **1964**, 296.
162. H. E. Baumgarten, P. L. Creger, and R. L. Zey, *J. Am. Chem. Soc.*, **82**, 2977 (1960).
163. H. Back and K. L. Kompa, *Angew. Chem.*, **74**, 327 (1962).
164. N. Wiberg and A. Girien, *Angew. Chem.*, **74**, 942 (1962).
165. E. Wasserman, L. Barish, and W. A. Yager, *J. Am. Chem. Soc.*, **87**, 2075 (1965).
166. Reference 40, p. 64.
167. Reference 2, Vol. 2, p. 13.
168. J. H. Boyer and J. D. Woodyard, unpublished results.
169. W. T. Reichle, *Inorg. Chem.*, **3**, 402 (1964).
170. G. P. Balabanov, Yu. I. Dergunov, and V. A. Gal'perin, *Zh. Org. Khim.*, **2**, 1828 (1966); *Chem. Abstr.*, **66**, 54848p (1967).
171. N. Kharasch, *J. Chem. Educ.*, **33**, 585 (1956).
172. J. E. Leffler and L. J. Todd, *Chem. Ind. (London)*, **1961**, 512.
173. P. Paetzold, *Angew. Chem. Intern. Ed. Engl.*, **6**, 572 (1967).
174. W. H. Saunders and J. C. Ware, *J. Am. Chem. Soc.*, **80**, 3328 (1958).
175. P. A. S. Smith and J. H. Hall, *J. Am. Chem. Soc.*, **84**, 480 (1962).

The Uncatalyzed Rearrangement of Tervalent Phosphorus Esters

VICTOR MARK

Hooker Chemical Corporation
Niagara Falls, New York

I. INTRODUCTION

Beginning essentially with the publications of C. A. A. Michaelis almost 100 years ago, there was a gradual but brisk activity in phosphorus chemistry in both fundamental approach and sophistication, by an ever increasing number of investigators from practically every country where chemistry is studied. As a result of this activity it became increasingly evident that phosphorus displays a chemical behavior significantly different from those of its group neighbors in the periodic table, nitrogen and arsenic, a behavior which confers unique synthetic capabilities to many phosphorus compounds. One of the most apparent characteristics of trivalent phosphorus compounds is their propensity to acquire one to three additional substituents in a variety of reactions by many characteristic mechanisms. Especially well investigated were those reactions in which a salt or an alkyl ester of a trivalent phosphorus acid irreversibly acquires, in the presence of another reactant, a fourth substituent (the Michaelis-Becker and the Michaelis-Arbuzov reactions, respectively). In a variant of the latter, the second reactant or its equivalent is generated in the reaction which thus becomes a catalytic process, and it is this reaction which was often used to effect the transformation of numerous tervalent phosphorus esters into tetrasubstituted derivatives.

It was recognized only recently that certain unsaturated phosphorus esters can readily undergo a rearrangement even in the absence of catalysts and can acquire a fourth substituent intramolecularly, concomitant with the development of a phosphoryl moiety and with changes in one of the hydrocarbon portions of the molecule. In certain cases the rearrangement was so spontaneous that for years the allenylphosphorus compounds remained undetected and the reaction products of acetylenic alcohols and phosphorous halides were thought to be acetylenic phosphites and phosphonites.

The present chapter describes only the uncatalyzed rearrangement of tervalent phosphorus esters.

II. THE REARRANGEMENT OF 2-ALKYNYL ESTERS

A. Nature and Mechanism of the Rearrangement

The rapid progress in characterizing organophosphorus compounds by spectroscopic methods led to the realization of the elusive nature of the propargylic esters of tervalent phosphorus compounds and of their probable absence, even in trace quantities, in preparations described in the

scientific and patent literature. Within two years four independent research groups reported on the spontaneous rearrangement of various
2-alkynyl esters of phosphorous, phosphonous, and phosphinous acids to
tetrasubstituted, allenic phosphorus compounds (1–4). Only when the
preparations were carried out below or close to room temperature were
the propargyl esters isolable and characterizable by infrared and NMR
spectroscopy (2). In most cases the acetylenic esters underwent a fast
rearrangement to allenic derivatives which were readily diagnosed by
several instrumental methods.

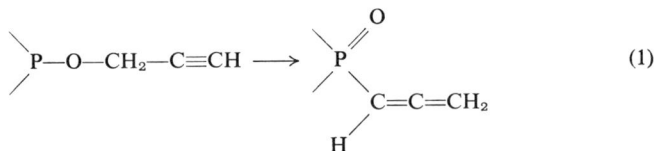

$$\begin{array}{c}\diagdown \\ \diagup \end{array} P-O-CH_2-C\equiv CH \longrightarrow \begin{array}{c}\diagdown\ \ \ \ \overset{O}{\diagup\!\!/}\\ \diagup P \diagdown \\ \ \ \ \ \ \ \ \underset{\underset{H}{\diagup}}{C}=C=CH_2\end{array} \tag{1}$$

It soon became apparent that all of the earlier literature examples (5–8)
claiming trivalent phosphorus esters of propargyl alcohol and its homologs
were in error (2,3).

Detailed investigations indicated that the rearrangement of various
phosphorous esters of propargyl alcohol represents a general reaction of
considerable scope and that extensive variations in both the phosphorus
and the acetylenic moieties are feasible (2,3). The essential feature of the
ester undergoing the rearrangement is a trivalent phosphorus connected
through oxygen to a 2-alkynyl radical (2).

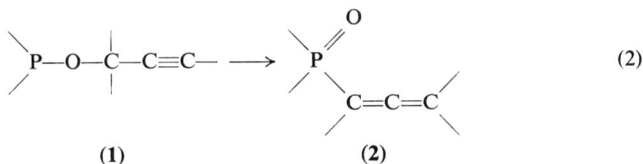

$$\begin{array}{c}\diagdown \\ \diagup \end{array} P-O-\overset{|}{\underset{|}{C}}-C\equiv C- \longrightarrow \begin{array}{c}\diagdown\ \ \ \ \overset{O}{\diagup\!\!/}\\ \diagup P \diagdown \\ \ \ \ \ \ \ \ \underset{\diagup}{C}=C=\overset{\diagup}{\underset{\diagdown}{C}}\end{array} \tag{2}$$

$$\qquad\qquad\quad \textbf{(1)} \qquad\qquad\quad\quad \textbf{(2)}$$

The structure of the two remaining substituents on phosphorus in **1**
is rather inconsequential and literature examples of the atoms nearest to
phosphorus comprise oxygen (2–4a,9–13), nitrogen (2), carbon (1–3,12,13),
and sulfur (2). Similarly, the 2-propynyl moiety in the generalized structure
1 can carry variations of hydrogen and all kinds of unsubstituted or substituted (by heteroatom) hydrocarbon radicals, saturated and unsaturated,
open chain and cyclic, which, although significantly influencing the rate,
do not alter the nature of the rearrangement.

The combination of various substituents on phosphorus and on the
2-propynyl moiety in **1** thus renders reaction 2 of a wide scope. This is
documented in Table 1, where structure, physical constants, and means of
characterization of the various rearrangement products are summarized.

TABLE 1

Allenylphosphorus Compounds Obtained by the Rearrangement of Tervalent Phosphorus Esters

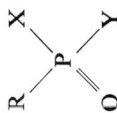

$$\begin{array}{c} R \\ \backslash \\ P{-}X \\ / \backslash \\ O \quad Y \end{array}$$

Substituent			Characterized by			
R	X	Y	mp or bp/mm	$n_D/t°$	Other[a]	Ref.
$H_2C=C=CH-$	C_2H_5O-	C_2H_5O-	89/0.4	1.4544/25	A,H,I,P	2a,2b
$H_2C=C=CH-$	C_2H_5O-	C_2H_5O-			H,I	10
$H_2C=C=CH-$	C_2H_5O-	C_2H_5O-	60–62/0.025	1.4615/20	A,MR	12
$H_2C=C=CH-$	C_2H_5O-	C_2H_5O-	62.5–64.5/0.25	1.4640/20	A,H,I,M	120b
$H_2C=C=CH-$	C_3H_7O-	C_3H_7O-	86–87/0.06	1.4590/20	A,MR	12
$H_2C=C=CH-$	C_3H_7O-	C_3H_7O-	126–127/9	1.4580/20	I	4a
$H_2C=C=CH-$	$(CH_3)_2CHO-$	$(CH_3)_2CHO-$ (ortho)	83–84/2	1.4550/20	A,MR	12
$H_2C=C=CH-$	$-OC_6H_4O-$		52–53		A,I	148
$H_2C=C=CH-$	$HC{\equiv}CCH_2O-$	$HC{\equiv}CCH_2O-$	117/0.3	1.4842/25	A,H,I	2a,2b
$H_2C=C=CH-$	$HC{\equiv}CCH_2O-$	$HC{\equiv}CCH_2O-$	115–116/0.25		A,I	13
$H_2C=C=CH-$	$HC{\equiv}CCH_2O-$	$(Ba/2)^{\oplus}O^{\ominus}$			A,I	13
$H_2C=C=CH-$	$HC{\equiv}CCH_2O-$	C_2H_5-	108/0.3	1.5071/25	I,P	2a,2b
$H_2C=C=CH-$	$HC{\equiv}CCH_2O-$	C_2H_5-	113–115/2.5	1.5056/20	A,I	12
$H_2C=C=CH-$	$HC{\equiv}CCH_2O-$	C_6H_5-	128–132/0.3		A,I	13
$H_2C=C=CH-$	$HO-$	C_6H_5-	94–96		A,I	13
$H_2C=C=CH-$	$HO-$	C_6H_5-			D,M	14
$H_2C=C=CH-$	CH_3-	CH_3-	58–60		A,I,P	2a,2b
$H_2C=C=CH-$	C_6H_5-	C_6H_5-	96–99		A,I	3

H₂C=C=CH—	C₆H₅—			H	119
H₂C=C=CH—	(CH₃)₂N—	85/0.17	1.5046/25	A,I,H,P	2a,2b
H₂C=C=CH—	(CH₃)₂N—	80-83/0.25	1.5021/20	A,H,I,M	120b
H₂C=C=CH—	CH₃S—	103/0.3	1.5840/25	A,I,H,P	2a,2b
H₂C=C=CH—	F—	36-36.5/14	1.4053/20	A,H,I,M	122, 120b
H₂C=C=CH—	Cl—	63.5-64/2.5	1.5226/20	A,H,I,M	120a, 120b
H₂C=C=C(CH₃)—	C₂H₅O—	73/0.1	1.4587/25	A,I,H,P	2a,2b
H₂C=C=C(CH₃)—	C₂H₅O—	112-118/8	1.4561/20	A,MR	12
H₂C=C=C(CH₃)—	C₆H₅—			H	119
H₂C=C=C(CH₂Cl)—	C₂H₅O—		1.4660/25	A,I	31
H₂C=C=C(C₆H₅)—	C₂H₅O—	157-159/0.6	1.5290/20	A,MR	12
H₂C=C=C(C₆H₅)—	C₆H₅—	125-126		H,I	147
(CH₃)HC=C=CH—	C₂H₅O—	105/1.0	1.4497/25	A,H,I,P	2a,2b
(CH₃)HC=C=CH—	C₂H₅O—			H,I	10
(CH₃)HC=C=CH—	C₂H₅O—	123-125/12	1.4637/20	A,I,MR	12
(C₃H₇)HC=C=CH—	C₂H₅O—			A,I	13
(C₃H₇)HC=C=CH—	C₂H₅O—			A,I	13
(C₃H₇)HC=C=CH—	(Ba/2)⊕O⊖			A,I	13
(C₃H₇)HC=C=CH—	—OCH₂CH(CH₃)O—		1.4910/20	A,I	3
HC≡C(C₃H₇)HC=C=CH—	C₆H₅—		1.5325/20	A,I	3
HC≡C(C₃H₇)HC=C=CH—	C₆H₅—	43-46		A,I	14
(C₃H₇)HC=C=CH—	C₆H₅—			A,I	3
(C₆H₅)HC=C=CH—	C₂H₅O—			A,I	13
(C₆H₅)HC=C=CH—	(Ba/2)⊕O⊖			A,I	13
(C₆H₅)HC=C=CH—	C₆H₅—			H	119

(continued)

Table 1 (continued)

R	X	Y	mp or bp/mm	$n_D/t°$	Other[a]	Ref.
	Substituent			Characterized by		
[(CH₃O)₂P(O)]-HC=C=CH—	C₂H₅O—	C₂H₅O—	147-148/0.025	1.4710/20	A	123
[(C₂H₅O)₂P(O)]-HC=C=CH—	C₂H₅O—	C₂H₅O—	146-146.5/0.025	1.4670/20	A,I	123
(CH₃)₂C=C=CH—	CH₃O—	CH₃O—	94-95/2	1.4733/20	A,I,M	120b
(CH₃)₂C=C=CH—	C₂H₅O—	C₂H₅O—	95/0.8	1.4588/25	A,H,I,P	2a,2b
(CH₃)₂C=C=CH—	C₂H₅O—	C₂H₅O—			H,I	10
(CH₃)₂C=C=CH—	C₂H₅O—	C₂H₅O—	122-123/10	1.4642/20	A,MR	12
(CH₃)₂C=C=CH—	C₂H₅O—	C₂H₅O—	100-101/2	1.4650/20	A,I,M	120b
(CH₃)₂C=C=CH—	C₃H₇O—	C₃H₇O—	136/10	1.4615/20	A,MR	12
(CH₃)₂C=C=CH—	C₄H₉O—	C₄H₉O—	123-124/1	1.4490/20	A,MR	12
(CH₃)₂C=C=CH—	HC≡C(CH₃)₂CO—	HC≡C(CH₃)₂CO—		1.4859/20	A,I	3
(CH₃)₂C=C=CH—	HC≡C(CH₃)₂CO—	HC≡C(CH₃)₂CO—		1.4859/20	A,I	13
(CH₃)₂C=C=CH—	HC≡C(CH₃)₂CO—	(Ba/2)⊕O⊖—			A,I	13
(CH₃)₂C=C=CH—	HO—	HO—	93-94		A,I	13
(CH₃)₂C=C=CH—	HO—	HO—			M	14
(CH₃)₂C=C=CH—	—OCH₂CH(CH₃)O—			1.4917/20	A,I	3
(CH₃)₂C=C=CH—	HC≡C(CH₃)₂CO—	C₆H₅—		1.5344/20	A,I	3
(CH₃)₂C=C=CH—	HC≡C(CH₃)₂CO—	C₆H₅—			A,I	13
(CH₃)₂C=C=CH—	HO—	C₆H₅—	79-80		A,I	13
(CH₃)₂C=C=CH—	HO—	C₆H₅—			D	14
(CH₃)₂C=C=CH—	C₆H₅—	C₆H₅—	70-73		A,I	3
(CH₃)₂C=C=CH—	C₆H₅—	C₆H₅—			H	119

Compound	Substituent	Substituent	bp (°C/mm)	n/t	Methods	Refs.
$(CH_3)_2C=C=CH—$	F—	F—	26/1.5	1.4215/20	A,I,M	120a, 120b
$(CH_3)_2C=C=CH—$	Cl—	Cl—	79/1.5	1.5240/20	A,H,I,M	120a, 120b
$C_2H_5(CH_3)C=C=CH—$	—OCH_2CH_2CH(CH_3)O—			1.4950/20	A,I	3
$C_2H_5(CH_3)C=C=CH—$	C_6H_5—	C_2H_5O—	69–71		A,I	3
$C_6H_5(CH_3)C=C=CH—$	C_2H_5O—	C_6H_5—			A,I,P	2a,2b
$(C_6H_5)_2C=C=CH$	C_6H_5—	C_6H_5—			H	119
$[(CH_3O)_2P(O)](CH_3)-C=C=CH—$	C_2H_5O—	C_2H_5O—	141–142/0.025	1.4755/20	A,I	123
$(CH_2)_4C=C=CH—$	C_2H_5O—	C_2H_5O—	123/0.2	1.4738/25	A,I,H,P	2a,2b
$(CH_2)_5C=C=CH—$	C_2H_5O—	C_2H_5O—	110/0.05	1.4850/25	A,I,H,P	2a,2b
$(CH_2)_5C=C=CH—$	HC≡C(CH_2)_5CO—	HC≡C(CH_2)_5CO—	78–79		A,I	3
$(CH_2)_5C=C=CH—$	HC≡C(CH_2)_5CO—	HC≡C(CH_2)_5CO—	78–79		A,I	13
$(CH_2)_5C=C=CH—$	HC≡C(CH_2)_5CO—	Na⊕O⊖—			A,I	13
$(CH_2)_5C=C=CH—$	HO—	HO—	142–142.5		A,I	13
$(CH_2)_5C=C=CH—$	HO—	HO—			M	14
$(CH_2)_5C=C=CH—$	HO—	C_6H_5—	109–110		A,I	13
$(CH_2)_5C=C=CH—$	HO—	C_6H_5—			D,M	14
$(CH_2)_5C=C=CH—$	—OCH_2CH_2CH(CH_3)O—		89–91		A,I	3
$(CH_2)_5C=C=CH—$	C_6H_5—	C_6H_5—	107–109		A,I	3
$(CH_3)_2C=C=C(CH_3)—$	C_2H_5O—	C_2H_5O—	75/0.1	1.4588/28	A,I,H,P,U	2b
$(CH_3)_2C=C=C·[C(CH_3)_2OH]—$	C_2H_5O—	C_2H_5O—	109/2	1.4700/20	A,MR	11
$(CH_3)_2C=C=C·[C(CH_3)_2OH]—$	C_3H_7O—	C_3H_7O—	141/3	1.4675/20	A,MR	11

(continued)

TABLE 1 (*continued*)

	Substituent			Characterized by		
R	X	Y	mp or bp/mm	$n_D/t°$	Other[a]	Ref.
(CH₃)₂C=C=C· [C(CH₃)₂OH]—	C₄H₉O—	C₄H₉O—	127–129/1	1.4662/20	A,MR	11
(CH₃)₂C=C=C· [C(CH₃)(C₂H₅)OH]—	C₆H₅—	C₆H₅—		1.5711/20	A,I	3
(CH₃)₂C=C=C· [C(CH₃)(C₂H₅)OH]—	"ClC₆H₄"—	"ClC₆H₄"—		1.5840/20	A,I	3
CH₃(CF₃)C=C=C· (C₆H₅)—	C₂H₅O—	C₂H₅O—	99–100/0.01	1.4850/25	A,I,F, H,U,P	31
(C₆H₅)₂C=C=C· (C₆H₅)—	C₂H₅O—	C₂H₅O—	51–53	1.5962/25	A,I,U,P	31
	C₆H₅—	C₆H₅—			H	121

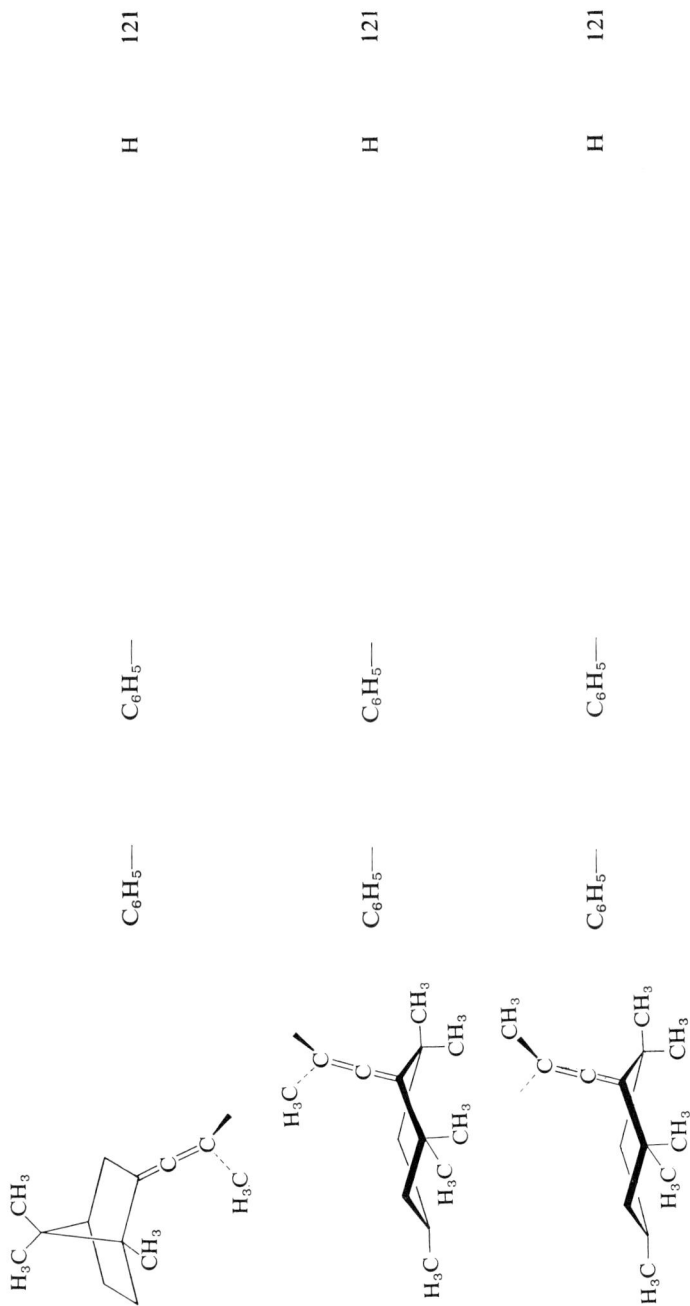

	C_6H_5-	C_6H_5-	H	121
	C_6H_5-	C_6H_5-	H	121
	C_6H_5-	C_6H_5-	H	121

[a] Abbreviations: A, elemental analysis; D, dipole moment; F, fluorine NMR; H, proton NMR; I, infrared spectroscopy; M, mass spectrometry; MR, molecular refraction; P, phosphorus NMR; U, ultraviolet spectroscopy.

Since NMR (both ^{1}H and ^{31}P) and infrared were particularly useful to characterize the new compounds and were literally instrumental in uncovering them, separate sections are devoted to spectroscopic methods.

Although reactive in isomerization and addition reactions, due to the presence of the allene group, compounds of structure **2** are readily isolable by conventional methods, such as distillation and recrystallization. Examples in Table 1 include compounds which were distilled at temperatures as high as between 130 and 160° without apparent loss in assay. Claims to "*polymérisation*, qui peut-être explosive" have not been documented (13). Attention was called, however, to the uncontrollably violent isomerization of **1** to **2** in the absence of internal or external cooling (2). It is very likely that a reported detonation (3) was caused by the sudden rise in temperature due to the highly exothermic rearrangement, rather than to contact with air.

The basis for the highly exothermal rearrangement of tervalent phosphorus esters of acetylenic alcohols into tetrasubstituted phosphorus derivatives is the formation of much better bonds in the rearrangement products. Phosphorus compounds with a phosphoryl group are best considered having a tetrahedral sp^3 structure, $X_3P^{\oplus}$—$O^{\ominus}$ in which back-coordination from the nonbonding $2p$ electrons of oxygen to the vacant $3d$ orbitals of phosphorus can provide various degrees of double and triple bond character to the phosphoryl moiety (15–17). Further modification in the stability of the molecule can also arise from a possible back-coordination from the donor electrons of the X substituents. An illustration of the orbitals involved is shown schematically in Fig. 1.

An indication of the magnitude of the energy change which accompanies the transformation of a triply into a quadruply substituted phosphorus (phosphoryl, thiophosphoryl, and imino) compound is available from bond dissociation energies, several of which are listed in Table 2.

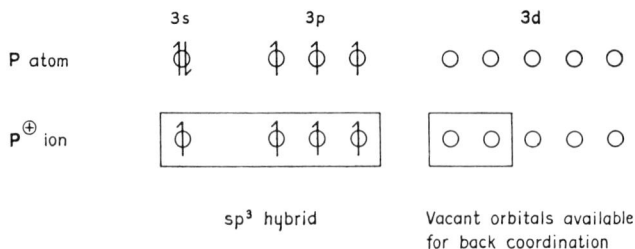

Fig. 1. Valence electronic diagram of X_3P^+—O^-.

TABLE 2
Gas Phase Dissociation Energies of Phosphorus
Compounds (kcal/mole) (16,17)

		$R_3PO \longrightarrow R_3P + O$	
R	D(P=O)	R	D(P=O)
F	130	C_6H_5	128
Cl	128	C_2H_5O	151
Br	125	C_3H_7O	146
CH_3	139	$(CH_3)_2N$	139
C_3H_7	138	$(C_2H_5)_2N$	156–160
C_4H_9	137		

		$R_3PX \longrightarrow R_3P + X$	
R	D(P=S)	R	D(P=NC$_2$H$_5$)
C_3H_7	92	CH_3	99
C_2H_5O	91	C_6H_5	125

The dependence of D(PO) on the nature of R reflects primarily the importance of the relative electron-donating ability of the substituents, which can effect changes as much as 35 kcal/mole in the strength of the phosphoryl bond, thus indicating the wide latitudes in the single-double-triple bond character of the phosphoryl group. The most often encountered single bond energies in phosphorus compounds are listed in Table 3.

Changes in bonds and bond energies which accompany the rearrangement in reaction (2) are shown in Table 4, where, for simplicity, the case of a propargyl ester is analyzed. Since there are discrepancies in the energy values of the carbon–carbon and carbon–hydrogen bonds connecting

TABLE 3
Empirical Bond Energy Values of Phosphorus
Compounds (16–19)[a]

Bond	Energy, kcal/mole	Bond	Energy, kcal/mole
P—H	77	P—Cl	76–79
P—F	117	P—S	(55)[b]
P—O	82–92	P—P	51
P—N	67–77	P—Br	62–65
P—C	65–71	P—I	44–51

[a] All values from P^{III} compounds.
[b] Calculated value (20).

TABLE 4

Changes in Bonds and Bond Energies in the Rearrangement

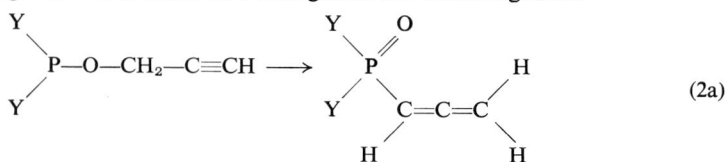

$$\begin{array}{c} Y \\ \diagdown \\ P\!-\!O\!-\!CH_2\!-\!C\!\equiv\!CH \\ \diagup \\ Y \end{array} \longrightarrow \begin{array}{c} Y \quad O \\ \diagdown \diagup \\ P \\ \diagup \diagdown \quad \diagup H \\ Y \quad C\!=\!C\!=\!C \\ \diagup \quad \diagdown \\ H \quad H \end{array} \qquad (2a)$$

	Bond disappearing in reactant			Bonds formed in product	
Bond	Bond energy, kcal/mole[a]	Bond energy, kcal/mole[b]	Bond	Bond energy, kcal/mole[a]	Bond energy, kcal/mole[b]
$sp^3C\!-\!p^3O$	84	84	$sp^2C\!-\!sp^3P$	$(>)\,71$	$(>)\,71$
$spC\!\equiv\!spC$	194	171	$sp^2C\!=\!spC$	$(>)\,147$	138
$sp^3C\!-\!spC$	$(>)\,83$	101	$sp^2C\!=\!spC$	$(>)\,147$	138
$2(H\!-\!sp^3C)$	198	192	$2(H\!-\!sp^2C)$	$(>)\,198$	201
$H\!-\!spC$	$(>)\,99$	109	$H\!-\!sp^2C$	$(>)\,\,99$	101
$p^3P\!-\!sp^3O$	82–92	82–92	$sp^3P\!=\!sp^2O$	137–151	137–151
$2(Y\!-\!p^3P)$	X	X	$2(Y\!-\!sp^3P)$	$(>)\,X$	$(>)\,X$
Total	740–750 + X	739–749 + X	Total	799–813 + X	786–800 + X

[a] Refs. 16 19.

[b] Carbon–carbon and carbon–hydrogen values from ref. 22.

atoms of various hybridization states, two sets of values are utilized. The $(>)$ sign in front of some of the data indicates that the bond connects two atoms, one or both of which have higher s character than the atoms in the model compound and that, very likely, the actual bond energy is higher than shown (cf. refs. 21 and 22).*

It is apparent from the summation of bond energies that the rearranged product in reaction 2a has better bonds than the propargyl ester by at least 37 kcal/mole, and possibly by as high as 73 kcal/mole or even higher. Thus given an accessible and convenient mechanistic pathway, the rearrangement reaction in 2a will occur. If the reaction path is facile and the intermediate steps do not require much expenditure of energy (as, e.g., in the case of allyl phosphites, see Section IV), the rearrangement reaction could be highly exothermic.

Important aspects of the mechanism became apparent when esters of substituted propargyl alcohols were studied in the rearrangement. It was recognized already in the earliest examples of structure determinations that

---

* Additional support for this premise is provided by earlier bond energy values, which were calculated to be higher by 3.3 to 15.7 kcal/bond in phosphoryl compounds than in their tervalent analogs (19b). Because of the approximation used in assigning the same (and crude) $D(P\!=\!O)$ for all phosphoryl compounds, the data can only be used to indicate a trend, rather than to provide accurate values.

the terminal *sp* carbon of ester **3** became attached directly to phosphorus in product **4** in the isomerization process (2–4).

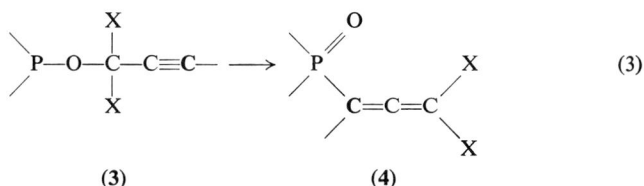

(3)

        (3)   (4)

Evidence for the inversion of the 2-propynyl substituent with respect to phosphorus was obtained by structure proof using synthetic (2,3) and spectral methods [proton NMR (2), phosphorus NMR (2), and infrared (2–4)], and was supported by the force of logic in the interpretive rationale.

The transformation represented in reaction 3 can be visualized to take place via an intramolecular rearrangement (a priori concerted or stepwise) initiated by phosphorus in a nucleophilic attack on the terminal acetylenic carbon and concluded by the rupture of the carbon–oxygen bond.

A possible concerted pathway is outlined in Fig. 2.

Support for the postulation of an intramolecular nucleophilic substitution mechanism, accompanied by rearrangement (represented conventionally by the symbol $S_N i'$), is provided by the following observations:

1. Alkyl substitution on the acetylenic carbon in **1** (or **3**) decreases the rate of the reaction, as evidenced by the esters of 2-butyn-1-ol which undergo the rearrangement less readily than those of 2-propyn-1-ol (2).

$$HC \equiv CCH_2OH > CH_3C \equiv CCH_2OH$$

The replacement of hydrogen by methyl increases by induction the electron density on the terminal *sp* carbon and renders it less susceptible to a nucleophilic attack. Substitution at this position thus affects the sigma bond forming or initiation phase of the cyclic process. In support of this postulate, the presence of an electronegative substituent on the methyl group was found to enhance the rate of rearrangement over that of the unsubstituted compound: 4-chloro-2-butynyl diethyl phosphite underwent the rearrangement spontaneously at room temperature within hours after its preparation, while the 2-butynyl ester did so only in about two days (24).

2. Alkyl substitution on the saturated carbon in **1** (or **3**) increases markedly the rate of rearrangement (2):

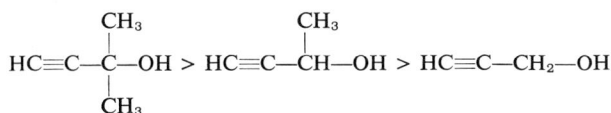

$$HC \equiv C - \underset{\underset{CH_3}{|}}{\overset{\overset{CH_3}{|}}{C}} - OH > HC \equiv C - \underset{}{\overset{\overset{CH_3}{|}}{C}H} - OH > HC \equiv C - CH_2 - OH$$

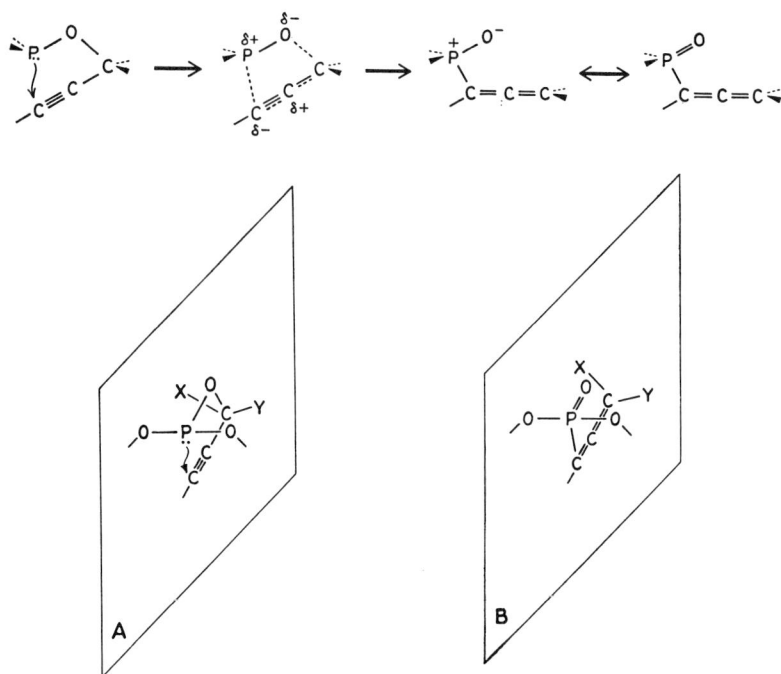

Fig. 2. The possible concerted mechanism of the propargyl ester rearrangement. *A* and *B* give the planar alignments of the atoms participating in the five-membered cyclic transition state **5**: (*A*) starting material, (*B*) product.

This sequence parallels the ease of carbonium ion formation (2), which is: tertiary > secondary > primary. Substituents which stabilize carbonium ions promote the heterolytic cleavage of the carbon–oxygen bond in **5** and thus facilitate the reaction by assistance rendered in the sigma bond breaking or concluding phase of the rearrangement.

Since substitution by methyl on the terminal (*sp*) carbon has an effect opposite to that on the proximal (*sp*^{3}) carbon, the relative rates of re-arrangement of **1** may vary over a wide range. Thus while the phosphite of 2-butyn-1-ol rearranges only slowly (in about 2 days) at room temperature, all attempts to detect, even spectroscopically, the presence of esters of tertiary alcohols (e.g., 1,1-dimethyl-2-propyn-1-ol), at +3° and only minutes after the mixing of the reactants were unsuccessful (2b).

3. The finding that dilution did not retard the rearrangement of the 2-butynyl ester, the most stable of the series investigated, supports the intramolecular pathway and argues against an intermolecular mechanism, stepwise or concerted (2).

4. Similarly, the negative outcome of attempted substituent transfer in simultaneous rearrangement experiments, using two distinct and readily analyzable phosphites, also lends support to the intramolecular pathway (12).

5. Strong support for the cyclic, intramolecular mechanism was provided by the finding that the phosphorous ester of an optically active acetylenic alcohol yielded an optically active allene (145) and that epimeric pairs of acetylenic phosphites yield the stereoisomeric allenylphosphonates required by the cyclic mechanism (121). The following examples are illustrative:

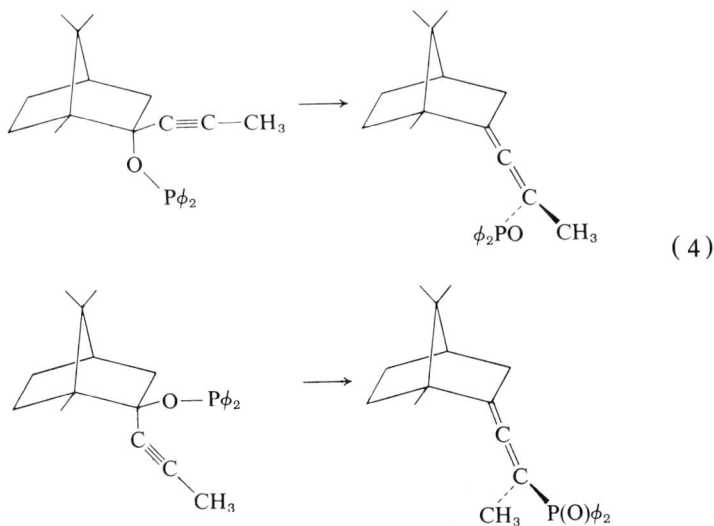

$$(4)$$

6. Phosphorous esters of 3-alkyn-1-ols, for which no transition state corresponding to 5 can be constructed, are stable under conditions at which the 2-alkynyl esters undergo the rearrangement. Thus 3-butynyl diethyl phosphite, $HC\equiv CCH_2CH_2OP(OC_2H_5)_2$ (6), showed no change in its NMR and infrared spectra after storage for weeks at room temperature, while the 2-butynyl ester underwent rearrangement in about 2 days and the 2-propynyl ester in a few hours at the same temperature (2b).

7. An increase in the electron density of the acetylenic carbon in 2-butynyl phosphites was suggested to account for their decreased rate of rearrangement relative to the 2-propynyl esters (vide supra). A similar rationale can be used to account for the failure of cyanohydrin esters of tervalent phosphorus acids to undergo the rearrangement characteristic of their acetylenic analogs. Thus a phosphorus ester of the cyanohydrin of acetaldehyde, $[N\equiv C(CH_3)CHO]P(OC_2H_5)_2$ (7), and of the cyanohydrin

of acetone, [N≡C(CH₃)₂CO]P(OC₂H₅)₂ (**8**) (Table 5), are readily isolable and distillable compounds, which underwent no change in their infrared and NMR spectra when subjected to heat treatment in the temperature range studied with the acetylenic esters (2b). The failure for the rearrangement to take place might be attributed to the presence of the nonbonding electrons on the *sp* nitrogen, itself nucleophilic, which renders the approach of atoms with unshared electrons difficult.

Related compounds which failed also to undergo the uncatalyzed rearrangement are the arsenic analogs of the phosphorous esters, (HC≡CCH₂O)As(CH₃)₂ (2b) and (HC≡CCH₂O)₃As (13) (Table 5). The negative outcome of these experiments was actually anticipated based on the failure of trialkyl arsenites to react with organohalogen compounds with which analogous trialkyl phosphite react readily. Thus hexachlorocyclopentadiene remained unaffected by trimethyl and triethyl arsenites, but it reacted with the corresponding phosphites exothermally to yield alkyl polychlorocyclopentadienes and dialkylphosphorochloridates (23). Bis(2-propynyl) sulfite and tris(2-propynyl) borate were also found to be stable compounds (13).

Another class of 2-propynyl derivatives of tervalent phosphorus compounds which withstood all attempts toward thermal rearrangement is the phosphorous amides. No change in the infrared and ³¹P NMR scans (*vide infra*) was observed when [(HC≡CCH₂)₂N]P(OC₂H₅)₂ (**9**) and [(HC≡CCH₂)(C₆H₅CH₂)N]P(OC₂H₅)₂ (**10**) (Table 5) were heated on the steam bath for several hours (24). Since the bond dissociation energy of trialkylphosphinimines [e.g., (CH₃)₃P=NC₂H₅] is significantly less than that of phosphine oxides [e.g., (CH₃)₃P=O] [99 versus 139 kcal/mole,

TABLE 5

Compounds Related to Acetylenic Phosphorus Esters Which did not
Undergo Rearrangement

Compound	bp, deg/mm	$n_D/t°$	Characterization by[a]	Ref.
[N≡C(CH₃)CHO]P(OC₂H₅)₂	42–43/0.25	1.4198/25	A,I,P	2b
[N≡C(CH₃)₂CO]₃P	125–127/0.4	1.4418/25	A,I,H,P	2b
[(HC≡CCH₂)₂N]P(OC₂H₅)₂		1.4612/22	A,I,P	2b
[(HC≡CCH₂)(C₆H₅CH₂)N]P(OC₂H₅)₂		1.4930/24	A,I,P,H	2b
HC≡CCH₂OAs(CH₃)₂		1.4839/25	I,H	2b
(HC≡CCH₂O)₃As	94–95/0.7		A,I	13
(HC≡CCH₂O)₂SO	55–56/0.3		A,I	13
(HC≡CCH₂O)₃B	72–73/1.0		A,I	13

[a] A, elemental analysis; H, proton NMR; I, infrared; P, phosphorus NMR.

Table 2] the molecule would gain much less in the rearrangement than its oxygen analog.*

The spontaneous and highly exothermal nature of the rearrangement suggests that a very simple and accessible reaction path must be available for the 2-alkynyl esters of tervalent phosphorus acids. A possible mechanistic pathway, where bond forming and bond breaking take place essentially in concert, was outlined in Fig. 2. One of the characteristic features of this pathway arises from the geometry of the atoms directly involved in the rearrangement: they all are in the same plane (2). When the phosphorus and the sp^3 carbon in 3 (and 4) each carry identical substituents, the plane placed through the five atoms forming the cycle becomes a plane of symmetry, as illustrated in Fig. 2A.

Another characteristic feature of the cyclic mechanism in Fig. 2 is that only small changes in bond angles occur in the transition of 3 to 4. Due to these aspects, reaction 4 can evolve along the concerted mechanistic pathway with a minimum expenditure of energy for altering bond angles and moving around atoms (2). It was pointed out that olefinic analogs of 3, for which no planar transition state corresponding to 5 can be constructed, are stable under conditions at which the acetylenic esters rearrange (2). The rearrangement of allylic esters requires higher temperatures and is discussed in Section IV.

The higher reactivity of the acetylenic compared with that of the olefinic esters is expected on the basis of the principle of least motion, which states that those elementary reactions which involve the least change in atomic position and electronic configuration will be favored (25.) Although additional features, e.g., the higher electronegativity of the sp carbon which invites a nucleophilic attack by phosphorus, also favor the rearrangement of the acetylenic esters, comparison of the geometry of the transition states alone suffices to predict unambiguously the much smoother rearrangement of the propargylic phosphites.

The principle of least motion renders unlikely the occurrence of intermediate 5a in the hypothetical stepwise, ionic mechanism outlined in Fig. 3, since its formation involves bending of the linear propargyl moiety by

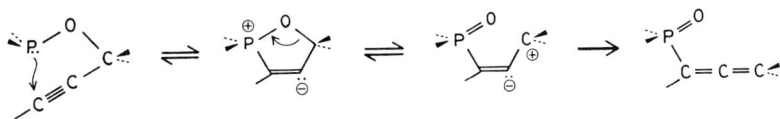

Fig. 3. A possible, not likely, stepwise ionic mechanism of the propargyl ester rearrangement.

* The thermal behavior of acetylenic anilines is being currently investigated by Dr. B. S. Thyagarajan.

about 60°, followed by an unbending of the same magnitude to return to another linear structure. In mechanism **4a** there is thus a waste in energy in comparison with the concerted mechanism of **4** where the three-carbon unit remains linear along the reaction path.

The rearrangement of tervalent phosphorus esters of 2-alkyn-1-ols can be compared, and has been compared, with the *ortho*-Claisen rearrangement of phenol esters (12,13), in which the pi electrons of the enolic double bond play the same role as the unshared electron pair of the tervalent phosphorus (Eq. 5).

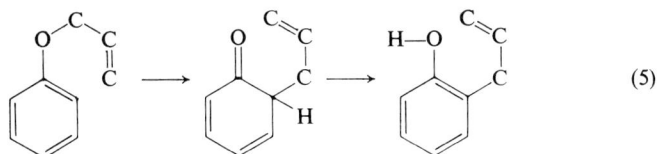

$$\tag{5}$$

Although it has been stated that no rearrangement takes place if the double bond in the olefinic phenyl ethers is replaced by a triple bond (13,27,28),* two independent studies of the thermal behavior of aryl propargylic ethers in *N,N*-diethylaniline at 210–220° revealed the occurrence of a facile and clean cyclization reaction, resulting in the formation of 2-chromenes (29a,29b):

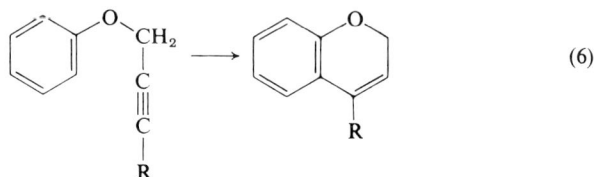

$$\tag{6}$$

When the propargylic ether used was difunctional, a second cyclization took place to yield fused bis(heterocyclic) derivatives of the aromatic ethers (29b) Scheme 1.†

---

* The conclusion in ref. 13, that "pour les dérivés des phénols et énols, la similitude s'arrête aux éthers allyliques, car l'éther propargylique du phénol est stable à basse température et peut être distillé sous vide (Eb. 52.5–53°/2 Torr.); si on le chauffe plus haut, il se décompose sans que l'on ait jamais pu constater la formation de produits de réarrangement [7]," is based on a mistaken structure, since in the reference quoted [L. F. Hatch and H. D. Weiss, *J. Am. Chem. Soc.*, **77**, 1798 (1955)] the preparation and characterization of the nonpertinent phenyl 1-propynyl ether $C_6H_5OC\equiv CCH_3$ and not of the quoted phenyl 2-propynyl ether (phenyl propargyl ether) $C_6H_5OCH_2C\equiv CH$, are described.

† The relationship outlined in the reaction diagram was formulated and suggested by Dr. B. S. Thyagarajan in a personal communication.

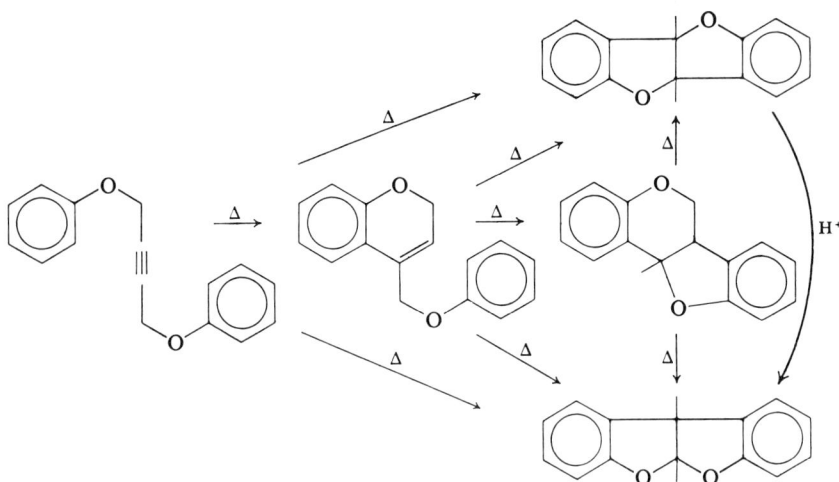

Scheme 1

Studying the effect of electron-releasing and electron-withdrawing substituents on yield, the authors concluded that the reaction takes place via an electrophilic attack by the triple bond (29a) (which is equivalent to a nucleophilic attack by the aromatic pi electrons on the acetylenic carbon).*

A reaction mechanism for the cyclization reaction could feasibly consist of two steps:

a. Initiation step, which is the analog of the nucleophilic attack by phosphorus on the acetylenic carbon in mechanism 4a:

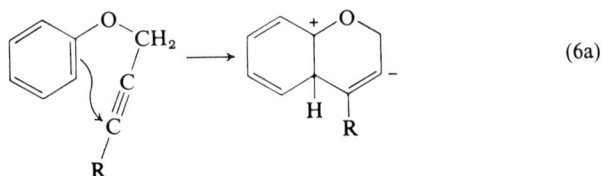

(6a)

b. Proton transfer step(s) in the dipolar intermediate:

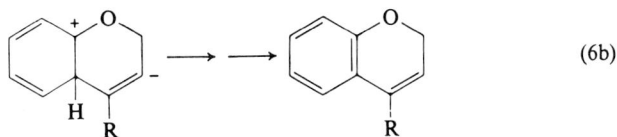

(6b)

* See chapter by I. Iwai on the base-catalyzed rearrangements of acetylenic ethers in this volume.

The tertiary amine, used as the reaction medium, might participate in the second step of the mechanism by assistance in the removal and relay of the proton from the tertiary carbon to the carbanion site.

In the rearrangement of the propargyl esters of tervalent phosphorus acids, there is no proton source equivalent to that of the ionic intermediate in 6a; the positively charged species (the phosphonium ion) effects therefore the rupture of another beta bond (the C—O bond in 5) in a presumably concerted process, thus bypassing the carbanion stage (*vide supra*).

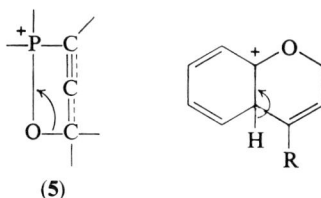

(5)

Recently a clean and illustrative example of the propargylic Claisen rearrangement became available in the thermal isomerization of a poly-halocyclobutenyl propargyl ether (131).

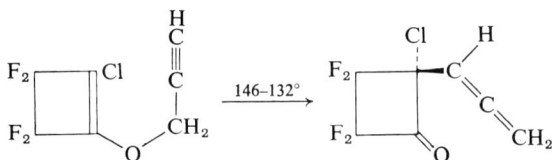

The fact that the allenic ketone was isolable in 55% yield as a stable and readily characterizable reaction product underlines the mechanistic similarities in the rearrangements of propargylic esters of phosphorous acids and of propargylic ethers of olefins. Allenic ketones were also the products of the isomerization of propargyl enol ethers of ketosteroids (140), while allenic aldehydes were formed in the thermal rearrangement of propargyl vinyl ethers (141,142).

While characterized with distinctive features, there are significant similarities between the *ortho*-Claisen rearrangement of the alkenyl and the alkynyl phenyl ethers and between these and the uncatalyzed isomerization of the 2-propynyl phosphites. One of the most apparent similarities is the failure of both cyanohydrin ethers and phosphites (7,8) and of phenyl-allylamines and N-propargylphosphorous amides (9,10) to undergo re-arrangement.

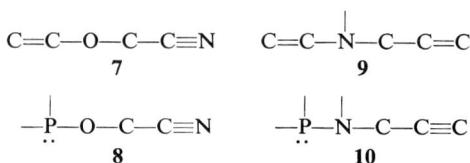

That resistance to the rearrangement of phenyl allyl amines is due probably to an energy barrier rather than to a mechanistic feature is indicated by two recent papers, in which two general cases of the "amino-Claisen" rearrangement have been described (132,133). In both cases inversion of the allyl groups was observed.

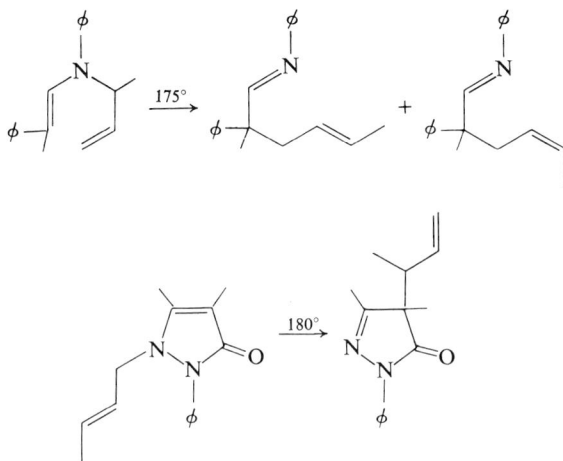

The "thio-Claisen" rearrangement was also shown to take place by inversion of the allyl group (134).

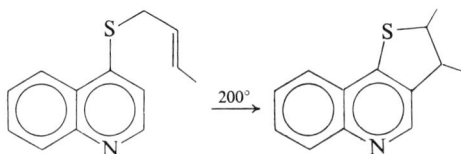

Although phosphorous esters of even the primary (i.e., the least reactive) acetylenic alcohols (e.g., propargyl alcohol) underwent isomerization near room temperature, it was possible to characterize some of them by spectroscopic means or to intercept them by various reagents (Table 6).

The most stable member of the phosphorous ester series was the 2-butynl derivative, e.g., $CH_3C\equiv CCH_2OP(OC_2H_5)_2$. This compound was readily isolable and stable at or below room temperature, but underwent smooth isomerization to the allenic phosphonate at steam bath temperature (2,24). Diethyl propargyl phosphite was isolable by distillation at low temperature and pressure (9,12) and propargyl ortho-phenylenephosphite,

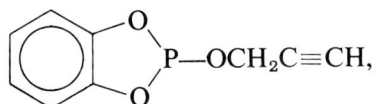

TABLE 6

Tervalent Phosphorus Esters of Acetylenic Alcohols

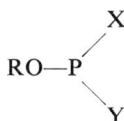

$$RO-P\overset{X}{\underset{Y}{\diagup}}$$

Substituent			Characterization by			
R	X	Y	bp°/mm	$n_D/t°$	Other[a]	Ref.
HC≡CCH$_2$—	C$_2$H$_5$O—	C$_2$H$_5$O—		1.4334/25	I,P	2a,2b
HC≡CCH$_2$—	C$_2$H$_5$O—	C$_2$H$_5$O—	34–35/0.03	1.4360/20	A,I[b]	9,12
HC≡CCH$_2$—	HC≡CCH$_2$O—	HC≡CCH$_2$O—		1.4825/25	I,P	2a,2b
HC≡CCH$_2$—	C$_6$H$_5$O—	C$_6$H$_5$O—			I	12
HC≡CCH$_2$—	Cl—	Cl—	43/20	1.5010/20	A,I,M	120b
HC≡CCH$_2$—	—O$_6$C$_4$HO—	ortho	44–45		A,I	148
CH$_3$C≡CCH$_2$—	C$_2$H$_5$O—	C$_2$H$_5$O—		1.4417/25	I,P	2a,2b
HC≡C(CH$_3$)CH—	C$_2$H$_5$O—	C$_2$H$_5$O—		1.4315/25	I	2b
HC≡CCH$_2$CH$_2$—	C$_2$H$_5$O—	C$_2$H$_5$O—		1.4322/25	I	2b
C$_6$H$_5$C≡CCH$_2$—	C$_2$H$_5$O—	C$_2$H$_5$O—			I	12

[a] A, elemental analysis; I, infrared; P, phosphorus NMR.

[b] One of the diagnostic infrared bands quoted in the paper is in conflict with the claimed structure (see Table 10).

was also found to be stable at room temperature, but underwent isomerization in refluxing benzene solution (148).

To be able to intercept the acetylenic phosphorous esters, the reagent has to react at a rate comparable to or faster than the rate of rearrangement. Thus while diethyl propargyl phosphite failed to react with ethyl iodide between room temperature and 50° to give a Michaelis-Arbuzov reaction product (9,12) (only the rearrangement product was formed), it was intercepted smoothly below room temperature by hexachlorocyclopentadiene to yield 5-(2-propynyl)pentachlorocyclopentadiene (11) (23a). Similarly, and expectedly, the 2-butynyl and the 3-butynyl esters also yielded the corresponding alkylated pentachlorocyclopentadienes (12,13) and even the diethyl phosphorous ester of a secondary alcohol, 1-methyl-2-propyn-1-ol, was intercepted to yield 14 (23a). The analogous ester of a tertiary alcohol, 1,1-dimethyl-2-propyn-1-ol, however, underwent iso-

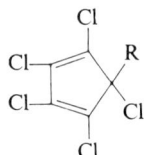

R = —CH$_2$C≡CH   (11)
R = —CH$_2$C≡CCH$_3$ (12)
R = —CH$_2$CH$_2$C≡CH (13)
R = —CH(CH$_3$)C≡CH   (14)

merization too rapidly to be intercepted by the same reagent or to be detected by spectroscopic analyses (2a,2b). Sulfur (9,12) and chloral (12) were two other reagents successful in trapping the diethyl propargyl ester:

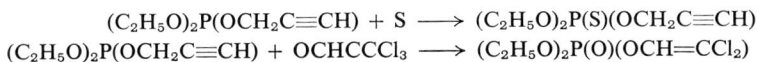

$$(C_2H_5O)_2P(OCH_2C\equiv CH) + S \longrightarrow (C_2H_5O)_2P(S)(OCH_2C\equiv CH)$$
$$(C_2H_5O)_2P(OCH_2C\equiv CH) + OCHCCl_3 \longrightarrow (C_2H_5O)_2P(O)(OCH=CCl_2)$$

B. Spectroscopic Analyses

The analytical method which was literally instrumental in uncovering and diagnosing the acetylenic phosphite-allenylphosphonate rearrangement was spectroscopy. Both infrared and NMR indicated unambiguously that spectra of reaction products obtained by reported procedures were irreconcilable with the claimed acetylenic phosphite structures (2,3). They also indicated that the propargylic group, present in the alcohol starting material, disappeared in the reaction to give rise to an allenic moiety and that phosphorus turned into a tetrasubstituted species. Thus while demonstrating once again the inadequacies of the "classical" methods of structure identification—elemental analyses, molecular weight, boiling point, melting point, density, refractive index, molecular refraction, all of which let the new structures slip by unrecognized—the success of the infrared and NMR spectroscopic analyses in dealing with the novel and unexpected established them as the most reliable and unavoidable simple means of positive structure determination.

1. Infrared

Due to a strong and sharp absorbtion maximum associated with the allene, $C=C=C$, system of carbon atoms in the relatively void 1950 cm^{-1}

TABLE 7

Characteristic Infrared Frequencies of Acetylenes, Allenes,
and Pertinent Phosphorus Moieties (30)

Group	Range, cm^{-1}	Range, μ	Assignment, intensity
H—C≡	3315–3270	3.02–3.08	Stretch; strong
XC≡CY	2260–2190[a]	4.43–4.57[a]	Stretch; variable
HC≡CY	2140–2100[b]	4.68–4.76[b]	Stretch; variable
C=C=C	2000–1900	5.00–5.26	Stretch; strong
P=O	1350–1140	7.41–8.77	Stretch; strong
P—O—C(sp^3)	1055–950	9.52–10.52	Stretch; strong
C=C=CH$_2$	~850	11.8	Wag; strong

[a] Extension of the range from 2260 to 2060 cm^{-1}, or 4.42 to 4.85μ, is suggested (Section II-C-1).

[b] Extension of the range from 2140 to 2030 cm^{-1}, or 4.67 to 4.92μ is suggested (Section II-C-1).

TABLE 8. Characteristic Infrared Parameters of

Compound		
R	X	Y
$H_2C=C=CH-$	C_2H_5O-	C_2H_5O-
$H_2C=C=CH-$	C_2H_5O-	C_2H_5O-
$H_2C=C=CH-$	C_2H_5O-	C_2H_5O-
$H_2C=C=CH-$	C_2H_5O-	C_2H_5O-
$H_2C=C=CH-$	C_3H_7O-	C_3H_7O-
$H_2C=C=CH-$	$HC\equiv CCH_2O-$	$HC\equiv CCH_2O-$
$H_2C=C=CH-$	$HC\equiv CCH_2O-$	$HC\equiv CCH_2O-$
$H_2C=C=CH-$	$HC\equiv CCH_2O-$	$(Ba/2)^{\oplus}O^{\ominus}-$
$H_2C=C=CH-$	$-OC_6H_4O-$	(ortho)
$H_2C=C=CH-$	$HC\equiv CCH_2O-$	C_2H_5-
$H_2C=C=CH-$	$HC\equiv CCH_2O-$	C_2H_5-
$H_2C=C=CH-$	$HC=CCH_2O-$	C_6H_5-
$H_2C=C=CH-$	$HO-$	C_6H_5-
$H_2C=C=CH-$	CH_3-	CH_3-
$H_2C=C=CH-$	C_6H_5-	C_6H_5-
$H_2C=C=CH-$	CH_0S-	CH_3S-
$H_2C=C=CH-$	CH_3S-	$HC\equiv CCH_2O-$
$H_2C=C=CH-$	$(CH_3)_2N-$	$(CH_3)_2N-$
$H_2C=C=CH-$	$(CH_3)_2N-$	$(CH_3)_2N-$
$H_2C=C=CH-$	$F-$	$F-$
$H_2C=C=CH-$	$Cl-$	$Cl-$
$H_2C=C=C(CH_3)-$	C_2H_5O-	C_2H_5O-
$H_2C=C=C(CH_3)-$	C_2H_5O-	C_6H_5-
$H_2C=C=C(CH_2Cl)-$	C_2H_5O-	C_2H_5O-
$H_2C=C=C(C_6H_5)-$	C_6H_5-	C_6H_5-
$CH_3CH=C=CH-$	C_2H_6O-	C_2H_5O-
$CH_3CH=C=CH-$	C_2H_5O-	C_2H_5O-
$C_3H_7CH=C=CH-$	C_2H_5O-	C_2H_5O-
$C_3H_7CH=C=CH-$	C_2H_5O-	$(Ba/2)^{\oplus}O^{\ominus}-$
$C_3H_7CH=C=CH-$	C_6H_5-	$HC\equiv C(C_3H_7)CHO-$
$C_3H_7CH=C=CH-$	C_6H_5-	$HC\equiv C(C_3H_7)CHO-$
$C_3H_7CH=C=CH-$	$-OCH_2CH(CH_3)O-$	
$C_3H_7CH=C=CH-$	C_6H_5-	C_6H_5-
$C_6H_5CH=C=CH-$	C_2H_5O-	C_2H_5O-
$C_6H_5CH=C=CH-$	C_2H_5O-	$(Ba/2)^{\oplus}O^{\ominus}-$
$[(C_2H_5O)_2P(O)]HC=C=CH-$	C_2H_5O-	C_2H_5O-
$(CH_3)_2C=C=CH-$	CH_3O-	CH_3O-
$(CH_3)_2C=C=CH-$	C_2H_5O-	C_2H_5O-

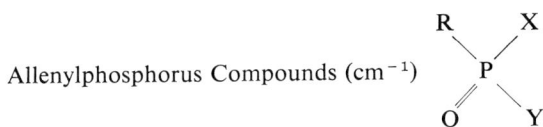

Allenylphosphorus Compounds (cm⁻¹)

$$\begin{array}{ccc} R & & X \\ & \diagdown\ \diagup & \\ & P & \\ & \parallel\ \diagdown & \\ O & & Y \end{array}$$

C—H stretch			C—C stretch		Stretch		Wag	
H—C≡	P‑C=C=C‑H (H)		C≡C	C=C=C	P=O	P—O—C	=CH₂	Ref.
	3203	3060		1961, 1942	1250	1030	835	2a,2b
				1938	1267			10
				1970, 1939	1275	1047	841	120b
				1960				124
				1950				4a
3308	3225	3070	2122	1961, 1939	1250	1030	855	2a,2b
3290			2130	1975, 1945				13
3320			2130	1980				13
		3080		1980, 1950			880	148
3280	3182	3050	2111	1951, 1923	1264	1030	850	2a,2b
3290			2114	1960				12
3290			2130	1975, 1945				13
				1980, 1960				13
	3225	3070		1942	1292		870	2b
				1950, 1925				3
	3203	3050		1961, 1939	1202		840	2b
3308	3225	3050		1961, 1940	1206	1030		2b
	3175	3041		1942	1190		850	2b
				1970, 1941	1188		850	120b
	3085	3009		1972, 1935	1350		848	120b
	3077	3001		1962, 1926	1285		850	120b
		3050		1942	1260	1030	840	2b
				1960, 1945	1267			12
		3052		1955, 1930	1260	1023	848	31
				1940, 1920	1180			147
	3202			1951	1243	1030		2a,2b
				1940	1253			10
				1960				13
				1985				13
a			2100	1940	1237			3
3290			2105	1965	1230			14
				1950	1265			3
				1930	1190			3
				1950				13
				1975				14
				1960				123
				1962	1266	1039		120b
	3203			1958	1243	1030		2b

(continued)

TABLE 8

	Compound	
R	X	Y
$(CH_3)_2C=C=CH-$	C_2H_5O-	C_2H_5O-
$(CH_3)_2C=C=CH-$	C_2H_5O-	C_2H_5O-
$(CH_3)_2C=C=CH-$	$HC\equiv C(CH_3)_2CO-$	$HC\equiv C(CH_3)_2CO-$
$(CH_3)_2C=C=CH-$	$HC\equiv C(CH_3)_2CO-$	$HC\equiv C(CH_3)_2CO-$
$(CH_3)_2C=C=CH-$	$HC\equiv C(CH_3)_2CO-$	$(Ba/2)^{\oplus}O^{\ominus}-$
$(CH_3)_2C=C=CH-$	$HO-$	$HO-$
$(CH_3)_2C=C=CH-$	$-OCH_2CH(CH_3)O-$	
$(CH_3)_2C=C=CH-$	$HC\equiv C(CH_3)_2CO-$	C_6H_5-
$(CH_3)_2C=C=CH-$	$HC\equiv C(CH_3)_2CO-$	C_6H_5-
$(CH_3)_2C=C=CH-$	$HO-$	C_6H_5-
$(CH_3)_2C=C=CH-$	C_6H_5-	C_6H_5-
$(CH_3)_2C=C=CH-$	$F-$	$F-$
$(CH_3)_2C=C=CH-$	$Cl-$	$Cl-$
$CH_3(C_2H_5)C=C=CH-$	C_6H_5-	C_6H_5-
$CH_3(C_2H_5)C=C=CH-$	$-OCH_2CH_2CH(CH_3)O-$	
$CH_3(C_6H_5)C=C=CH-$	C_2H_5O-	C_2H_5O-
$[(CH_3O)_2P(O)](CH_3)C=C=CH-$	C_2H_5O-	C_2H_5O-
$(CH_2)_4C=C=CH-$	C_2H_5O-	C_2H_5O-
$(CH_2)_5C=C=CH-$	C_2H_5O-	C_2H_5O-
$(CH_2)_5C=C=CH-$	$HC\equiv C(CH_2)_5CO-$	$HC\equiv C(CH_2)_5CO-$
$(CH_2)_5C=C=CH-$	$HC\equiv C(CH_2)_5CO-$	$HC\equiv C(CH_2)_5CO-$
$(CH_2)_5C=C=CH-$	$HC\equiv C(CH_2)_5CO-$	$Na^{\oplus}O^{\ominus}-$
$(CH_2)_5C=C=CH-$	$HC\equiv C(CH_2)_5CO-$	C_6H_5-
$(CH_2)_5C=C=CH-$	$-OCH_2CH(CH_3)O-$	
$(CH_2)_5C=C=CH-$	$HO-$	$HO-$
$(CH_2)_5C=C=CH-$	$HO-$	C_6H_5-
$(CH_2)_5C=C=CH-$	C_6H_5-	C_6H_5-
$(CH_3)_2C=C=C(CH_3)-$	C_2H_5O-	C_2H_5O-
$(CH_3)_2C=C=C\cdot[C(OH)(CH_3)_2]-$	C_2H_5O-	C_2H_5O-
$(CH_3)_2C=C=C\cdot[C(OH)(CH_3)_2]-$	C_3H_7O-	C_3H_7O-
$(CH_3)_2C=C=C\cdot[C(OH)(CH_3)_2]-$	C_4H_9O-	C_4H_9O-
$CH_3(C_2H_5)C=C=C\cdot[C(OH)CH_3(C_2H_5)]-$	C_6H_5-	C_6H_5-
$CH_3(C_2H_5)C=C=C\cdot[C(OH)CH_3(C_2H_5)]-$	C_6H_4Cl-	C_6H_4Cl-
$CH_3(CF_3)C=C=C(C_6H_5)-$	C_2H_5O-	C_2H_5O-
$(C_6H_5)_2C=C=C(C_6H_5)-$	C_2H_5O-	C_2H_5O-

[a] Two values are given: 3250 and 3150.
[b] Two values are given: 3300 and 3200.
[c] Two values are given: 3285 and 3200.

(*continued*)

C—H stretch		C—C stretch		Stretch		Wag	
H—C≡	$\overset{P}{\underset{H}{C}}=C=C\overset{}{\underset{H}{}}$	C≡C	C=C=C	P=O	P—O—C	=CH$_2$	Ref.
			1954	1252			10
			1965	1262	1054		120b
b		2110	1950	1248			3
3280			1970				13
3280		2140	1970				13
			1960				13
			1950	1265			3
c		2110	1950	1230			3
3280			1960				13
			1965				13
			1950	1170			3
			1965	1331			120b
			1955	1274			120a, 120b
			1950	1190			3
			1950	1265			3
	3225		1939	1250	1030		2b
			1960				123
	3203		1958	1255	1030		2b
	3209		1961	1259	1030		2b
3200		2110	1950	1244			3
3240		2120	1975				13
3280		2120	1970				13
3280			1975				13
			1960	1270			3
			1960				13
			1970				13
			1950	1185			3
			1965	1260	1028		2b
			1945	1250			11
			1945	1250			11
			1945	1250			11
			1950	1175			3
			1950	1170			3
			1970	1295	1030		31
			1930	1255	1025		31

(5.1 μ) region (asymmetric stretching), a simple infrared scan of the reaction products of acetylenic alcohols and phosphorous halides was sufficient to diagnose promptly the presence of the allene moiety. When the phosphorous halide contained one halogen only [e.g., $(C_2H_4O)_2PCl$, $(C_6H_5)_2PCl$], it became apparent that the development of the allene band paralleled the decrease of the acetylenic absorbtion.

The most useful and characteristic bands of the acetylene, allene, and phosphoryl groups are listed in Table 7. Infrared spectral data of allenylphosphorus compounds are abstracted in Table 8.

Comparison of the two tables indicates a good match of the data, as evidenced by the following ranges obtained from Table 8: HC≡C, 2140–2100; C=C=C, 1985–1920; P=O, 1350–1160; P—O—C, 1053–1010; and C=C=CH$_2$, 835–880 cm^{-1}. The only exception noted was in the H—C≡C group where the lower frequency limit of the 3320–3150 cm^{-1} range is significantly outside of the literature value (3270 cm^{-1}). Perusal of the original reference indicated that in four compounds two frequencies, one in the expected range and one at a much lower cm^{-1}, were assigned to the H—C≡ stretch and that the low energy band was attributed to hydrogen bonded species (3). The validity of this assignment, however, can be questioned for the following reason: a common feature of the four compounds with the second, low range (3200–3150 cm^{-1}) frequencies assigned to the hydrogen bonded, sp C—H $\cdots$ O=P stretch (3), is that they contain a hydrogen on the allenic carbon which is substituted by phosphorus. It is apparent from the values given in Table 8 that compounds with the C=C=CH(PO) group show characteristic absorbtion in the 3225–3175 cm^{-1} range, irrespective of the presence or absence of propargyl moieties, and that this range can be assigned to the C=C=C(P)—H stretching mode (2a,2b). Since no assignment of this mode was given in the spectra of the four compounds in question (all of which contain the C=C=CH(PO) moiety), it becomes somewhat dubious whether the 3200–3175 cm^{-1} frequencies are "undoubtedly" assignable exclusively, if at all, to hydrogen bonded acetylenic species (3).

The finding of consistent absorbtion between 3070 and 3040 cm^{-1} in compounds with the PC=C=C—H moiety suggests this range for the assignment of the corresponding carbon-hydrogen stretch (2b). The ranges given to these two kinds of allenic carbon–hydrogen stretching frequencies seem noteworthy since there was "insufficient information available on the =C—H stretching modes of these compounds (allenes) to permit the use of the 3000 cm^{-1} region for structural analysis" (30a).

These new ranges of sp^2 C—H stretch fit well between the olefinic carbon–hydrogen and acetylenic carbon–hydrogen values and allow the construction of Table 9 where various sp, sp^2, and sp^3 carbon–hydrogen

TABLE 9

Carbon–Hydrogen Stretching Vibrations

Moiety	Range, cm^{-1}	Range, μ
H—C≡C	3315–3270	3.02–3.08
H—C(PO)=C=C	3225–3175	3.10–3.15
H—CH=C	3097–3075	3.23–3.26
H—C=C=C(PO)	3070–3041	3.27–3.29
H—C(C)=C	3040–3010	3.29–3.32
H—CH$_2$—C	2972–2952[a]	3.36–3.39[a]
H—CH—	2936–2916[a]	3.41–3.43[a]
H—C—	2900–2880	3.45–3.47
H—CH$_2$—C	2882–2862[b]	3.47–3.49[b]
H—CH—	2863–2843[b]	3.49–3.52[b]

[a] Asymmetric.
[b] Symmetric.

stretching frequency ranges are listed. There seems to be a general correlation between the extent of *s* character of the carbon–hydrogen bond and the frequency of the stretching vibration, the higher *s* character requiring, as expected, higher frequency radiation.

Allenes absorb strongly between 2000 and 1900 cm^{-1} due to the asymmetric C=C=C stretch. All of the allenylphosphorus compounds have characteristic, usually sharp and strong, frequencies in this range, the limits of which appear to be 1985 and 1920 cm^{-1}. In several compounds the bands appear as doublets, specifically in those in which the phosphorylated allene moiety is substituted by hydrogen only. A similar splitting of the asymmetric frequency had been observed in allenes which were substituted by a carbonyl, nitrile, and trifluoromethyl group (30e). No explanation for this effect has been advanced.

Another characteristic frequency of mono- or 1,1-disubstituted allenes is attributed to the wagging vibration of the =CH$_2$ group (out of plane bending of hydrogen) and shows up as a strong absorbtion peak around 850 cm^{-1}. The presence of this bond was observed in several compounds (Table 8).

The bands associated with the P=O and the P—O—C groups were found to fit well into the framework established by previous references.

In several instances it was possible to record the infrared scans of the trivalent phosphorus esters of acetylenic alcohols (Table 10). All of the values, except for one, match the ranges quoted above. The vibration at

TABLE 10
Infrared Parameters of Acetylenic Phosphites (cm^{-1})

Compound	H—C≡C	HC≡C—	RC≡C	P—O—R	Ref.
$(HC≡CCH_2O)P(OC_2H_5)_2$	3308	2122		1030	2b
$(HC≡CCH_2O)P(OC_2H_5)_2$	3290	2215[a]			9
$(HC≡CCH_2O)_3P$	3308	2122		1020	2a,2b
$(HC≡CCH_2O)P(OC_6H_5)_2$	3293	2100			12
$HC≡CCH_2OPCl_2$	3303	2136			120b
$HC≡CCH_2OP\overset{O}{\underset{O}{\diagdown\diagup}}$ (benzodioxaphosphole)	3280	2120			148
$[HC≡C(CH_3)CHO]P(OC_2H_5)_2$	3308	2120		1030	2a,2b
$(CH_3C≡CCH_2O)P(OC_2H_5)_2$			2222	1024	2b
$(HC≡CCH_2CH_2O)P(OC_2H_5)_2$	3308	2129		1033	2b
$(C_6H_5C≡CCH_2O)P(OC_2H_5)_2$			2237		12

[a] This value is in conflict with the claimed structure.

2215 cm^{-1}, assigned to a terminal acetylene moiety (9), is obviously too high and is probably the result of an error.

Infrared data on compounds related to acetylenic phosphites are abstracted in Table 11. All values are consistent with the structures indicated. The literature range of the aliphatic nitrile stretching modes is between 2240 and 2260 cm^{-1}. The As—O—C stretching band in $(CH_3)_2AsOCH_2C≡CH$ is at 1040 cm^{-1} (9.60 μ), and the CH_3—As vibrations show up at 1420 cm^{-1} (7.04 μ) and at 1270 cm^{-1} (7.96 μ). The N—P stretch in the first two compounds of Table 11 is at 970 cm^{-1} (10.30 μ).

TABLE 11
Infrared Parameters of Compounds Related to Acetylenic
Phosphorus Esters (cm^{-1})

Compound	H—C≡C	HC≡C	N≡C	P—O—C	Ref.
$[(HC≡CCH_2)_2N]P(OC_2H_5)_2$	3308	2120		1026	2b
$[(HC≡CCH_2)(C_6H_5CH_2)N]P(OC_2H_5)_2$	3308	2120		1026	2b
$[N≡C(CH_3)CHO]P(OC_2H_5)_2$			2242	1037	2b
$[N≡C(CH_3)_2CO]_3P$			2231	967	2b
$(HC≡CCH_2O)As(CH_3)_2$	3308	2120		1042–1030	2b
$(HC≡CCH_2O)_3As$	3290	2120			13
$(HC≡CCH_2O)_2SO$	3290	2140			13
$(HC≡CCH_2O)_3B$	3290	2130			13

2. Proton NMR

While infrared spectroscopy called attention to the spontaneous re-arrangement of propargylic phosphites, and led thus to the discovery of a new reaction, proton NMR drew a sharp and unambiguous picture of the novel products, revealing, with the help of substituted acetylenic esters, the inversion of the unsaturated organic moiety in the course of the reaction.

To illustrate, the proton NMR spectrum of the allenylphosphorus product obtained from 2-butynyl diethyl phosphite, $CH_3C\equiv CCH_2OP\cdot(OCH_2CH_3)_2$, is reproduced in Fig. 4. Using the well-established methyl triplet in the ethoxy substituent, which accounts for six hydrogens in the molecule, as an internal standard, there are, proceeding downfield, two symmetrical triplets, which integrate to three hydrogens, then a group of peaks centered at 4.03 ppm, characteristic of the methylenes coupled to phosphorus in ethoxy substituents, and finally two symmetrical quartets in the region of vinyl protons, which account for two hydrogens. The symmetry of the latter indicates that they experience the same magnetic environment, and their splitting pattern reveals that they are coupled with one nucleus by $J = 13.2$ Hz and with three identical nuclei by $J = 3.18$ Hz. The latter value is identical with the smaller spacings in the two triplets of the region where the methyl group attached to a double bonded system resonates (at 1.80 ppm); this part of the spectrum indicates that the methyl group is coupled to one nucleus by $J = 13.7$ Hz and to two identical nuclei by $J = 3.18$ Hz. Combining these data with the supporting information provided by elemental analyses and that the compound is a single chemical entity (constant boiling point, identical infrared spectra and refractive

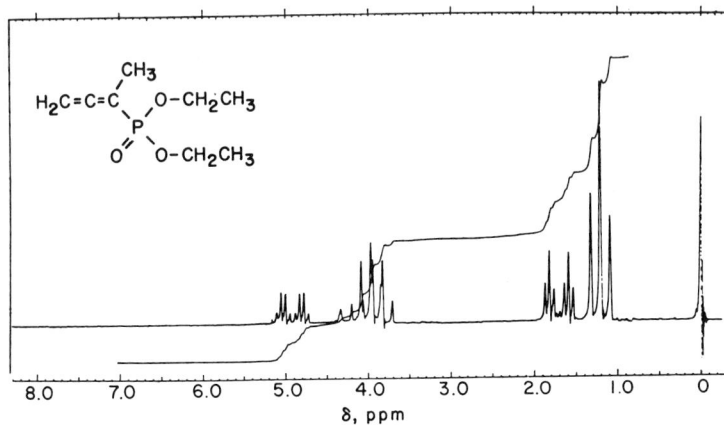

Fig. 4. The proton NMR spectrum of diethyl 1-methyl-1,2-propadienylphosphonate, $H_2C=C=C(CH_3)P(O)(OCH_2CH_3)_2$ (neat, internal TMS, 60 Mc).

TABLE 12

Proton NMR Analyses of Allenylphosphorus Compounds

Compound	H	δ, ppm	No. of peaks	J_{HP}, Hz	J_{HH}, Hz	Solvent[a]	Ref.[b]
$H^BC{=}C{=}CH^AP(O)(OCH_3^C)_2$	A	5.43		± 2.5	B7.0	Ca	138
	B	5.10		∓ 13.6	A7.0	Ca	138
	C	3.50		11.18		Ca	138
$H_2^BC{=}C{=}CH^AP(O)(OCH_2^CCH_3^D)_2$	A	5.29	8	$+0.2$	B-6.76	Be	2b,31
	B	4.79	8	-13.5	A-6.76	Be	2b,31
	C	4.00	2×4	8.2	D7.0	Be	2b,31
	D	1.18	3		C7.0	Be	2b,31
	A,B	5.2–5.7	M				10
	C	4.20	M				10
	D	1.50	3				10
	A	5.53		± 2.2	B7.0	Ca	138
	B	5.20		± 12.9	A7.0	Ca	138
	C	4.43		8.7	D7.3	Ca	138
	D	1.29			C7.3	Ca	138
$H_2^BC{=}C{=}CH^AP(O)(CH_2^ECH_3^F)(OCH_2^CC{\equiv}CH^D)$	A	5.49	8	$+3.0$	B-6.75	Ne	2b,31
	B	5.11	8	-11.3	A-6.75	Ne	2b,31
	C	4.50	2×2	9.6	D2.4	Ne	2b,31
	D	3.27	3		C2.4	Ne	2b,31
	E	1.85	2×4	14.5	F7.5	Ne	2b,31
	F	1.09	2×3	19.5	E7.5	Ne	2b,31
$H_2^CC{=}C{=}CH^BP(O)(C_6H_5^A)(OH)$	A	7.4–7.7					13
	B	5.5					13
	C	4.7–5.0					13

Compound							
$H_2^BC=CH^AP(O)(CH_2CH_3)_2$	A	5.80		±4.3	B6.5	Ca	138
	B	5.20		∓10.4	A6.5	Ca	138
$H_2^BC=CH^AP(O)(C_6H_5)_2$	A	5.86		3.8	B6.8	De	119
	B	4.89		11.2	A6.8	De	119
$H_2^BC=CH^AP(O)[N(CH_3^C)_2]_2$	A	5.53	8	+1.45	B-6.7	Ne	2b,31
	B	5.03	8	-11.6	A-6.7	Ne	2b,31
	C	2.61	2	10.1		Ne	2b,31
	A	5.42		±1.4	B6.5	Ca	138
	B	5.00		∓10.8	A6.5	Ca	138
	C	2.55		10.0		Ca	138
$H_2^BC=CH^AP(O)Cl_2$	A	6.21		±15.3	B5.8		120a
	B	5.62		±14.5[b]	A5.8		120a
	A	6.21	8	±15.2	B6.0	Ca	138
	B	5.62	8	∓14.6	A6.0	Ca	138
$H_2^BC=CH^AP(O)F_2$	A	5.67	8	±4.2	B6.6	Ca	138
	B	5.36	8	∓14.9	A6.6[e]	Ca	138
$CH_3^DH^BC=C=CH^AP(O)(OCH_2^CCH_3^E)_2$	A,B	5.2–5.7	M				10
	C	4.2	M				10
	D	2.0					10
	E	1.5					10
$H_2^AC=C(CH_3^C)P(O)(OCH_2^BCH_3^D)_2$	A	4.72	2 × 4	13.2	C3.18	Be[d]	2b,31
	B	4.00	2 × 4	8.2	D7.0	Be[d]	2b,31
	C	1.80	2 × 3	13.7	A3.18	Be[d]	2b,31
	D	1.16	3		B7.0	Be[d]	2b,31
$H_2^AC=C(CH_3^B)P(C_6H_5)_2$	A	4.325		1.6	B3.07	Ca	119
	B	1.78		8.95	A3.07	Ca	119

(continued)

TABLE 12 (*continued*)

Compound	H	δ, ppm	No. of peaks	J_{HP}, Hz	J_{HH}, Hz	Solvent[a]	Ref.[b]
$H_2^A C=C(CH_3^B)P(O)(C_6H_5)_2$	A	4.57		∓11.15	B3.1	Ca	119
	B	1.91		±11.7	A3.1	Ca	119
$H_2^A C=C(C_6H_5)P(O)(C_6H_5)_2$	A	4.88	2	11			147
$(CH_3)_2C=C=CH^A P(O)(OCH_2^B CH_3^D)_2$	A	5.17	9	6.10	C3.3	Be	2b,31
	B	4.00	2 × 4	8.10	D7.0	Be	2b,31
	C	1.58	2 × 2	7.18	A3.3	Be	2b,31
	D	1.17	3		B7.0	Be	2b,31
	A	5.2–5.7	M				10
	B	4.2	M				10
	C	2.0					10
	D	1.5					10
$(CH_3^B)_2C=C=CH^A P(O)(C_6H_5)_2$	A	5.70		7.4	B3.25	De	119
	B	1.48		6.3	A3.25	De	119
$(CH_3^B)_2C=C=CH^A P(O)Cl_2$	A	5.90		26.7	B3.5		120a
	B	1.86	4	12.5	A3.5		120a
$(CH_3)_2C=C=CHP(O)F_2$					—f		120a
$(C_6H_5)_2C=C=CH^A P(O)(C_6H_5)_2$	A	6.39		1.7		De	119
$(C_6H_5)H^B C=C=CH^A P(O)(C_6H_5)_2$	A	6.29		±2.7	B6.5	De	119
	B	6.23		∓10.99	A6.5	De	119
(cyclopentylidene)=CH^A P(O)(OCH_2^B CH_3^E)_2, ring H_2^C, H_2^D	A	5.06	M			Ca	2b,31
	B	3.97	2 × 4		E7.0	Ca	2b,31
	C	2.24–2.66	M			Ca	2b,31
	D	1.52–1.87	M			Ca	2b,31
	E	1.26	3		B7.0	Ca	2b,31

Structure		δ	Mult.	J	Code	Method	Ref.
$\mathrm{H_2^D}\ \mathrm{H_2^C}$ ring $=\mathrm{CH^A P(O)(OCH_2^B CH_3^E)_2}$; $\mathrm{H_2^D}\ \mathrm{H_2^C}$	A	5.18	2×5	5.7	C2.05	Ne	2b,31
	B	4.00	2×4	8.5	E7.0	Ne	2b,31
	C	2.16	M			Ne	2b,31
	D	1.58	M			Ne	2b,31
	E	1.26	3		B7.0	Ne	2b,31
cyclohexane $=\mathrm{CH^B P(O)(C_6H_5^A)(OH)}$; $\mathrm{H_{10}^C}$	A	5.3					13
	C,D	1.5–2.2					13
	A	7.3–7.7					13
	B	5.3–5.5					13
	C	1.4–1.95					13
$\mathrm{(CH_3)_2 C{=}C{=}C(CH_3)P(O)(OCH_2^C CH_3^D)_2}$	A	3.97	2×4	8.4	D7.0	Ne	2b,31
	B	1.73	2	13.22		Ne	2b,21
	C	1.72	2	6.60		Ne	2b,31
	D	1.27	3		A7.0	Ne	2b,31
	A	4.00	2×4	8.4	D7.0	Ch	2b,31
	B	1.76	2	13.40		Ch	2b,31
	C	1.72	2	6.72		Ch	2b,31
	D	1.30	3		A7.0	Ch	2b,31
$\mathrm{H_3C^C}\ \mathrm{CH_3^D}$ bicyclic, $\mathrm{CH_3^B}$, $=\mathrm{C{=}C{=}C^{\cdots}CH_3^A}$; $\mathrm{(C_6H_5)_2PO}$	A	1.93				De	121
	B	0.85				De	121
	C	0.816				De	121
	D	0.783				De	121

(continued)

TABLE 12 (*continued*)

Compound	H	δ, ppm	No. of peaks	J_{HP}, Hz	J_{HHs}, Hz	Solvent[a]	Ref.[b]
	A	1.93[g]				De	121
	B,C	0.75[g]				De	121
	D	0.0[g]				De	121
	A	1.03					121
	B	0.68					121
	A	1.15					121
	B	0.90					121

$(CF_3)(CH_3)C=C(C_6H_5^{A})P(O)(OCH_2^{B}CH_3^{D})_2$

A	7.22–7.68	M	c		De	31
B	4.13	M		D7.0	De	31
C	1.98	2	6.04		De	31
D	1.30	3 × 2 × 2	0.6	B7.0	De	31
D′	1.26	c	0.6	B7.0	De	31

a Be, benzene; Ca, carbon tetrachloride; Ch, chloroform; Ne, neat; De, deuteriochloroform.

b The scans in refs. 2b and 31 were run with tetramethylsilane (TMS) as internal reference.

c Nonequivalent methyl and methylene groups and nonequivalent protons in each of the nonequivalent methylene groups.

d In the neat sample, with internal tetramethylsilane, the chemical shifts of A, B, C, and D are at 4.96, 4.03, 1.77, and 1.28 ppm respectively.

e $J_H B_F$ = 1.7 Hz.

f $^1J_{PF}$ is 772 Hz.

g External TMS.

h Subsequently the relative sign was reversed (138).

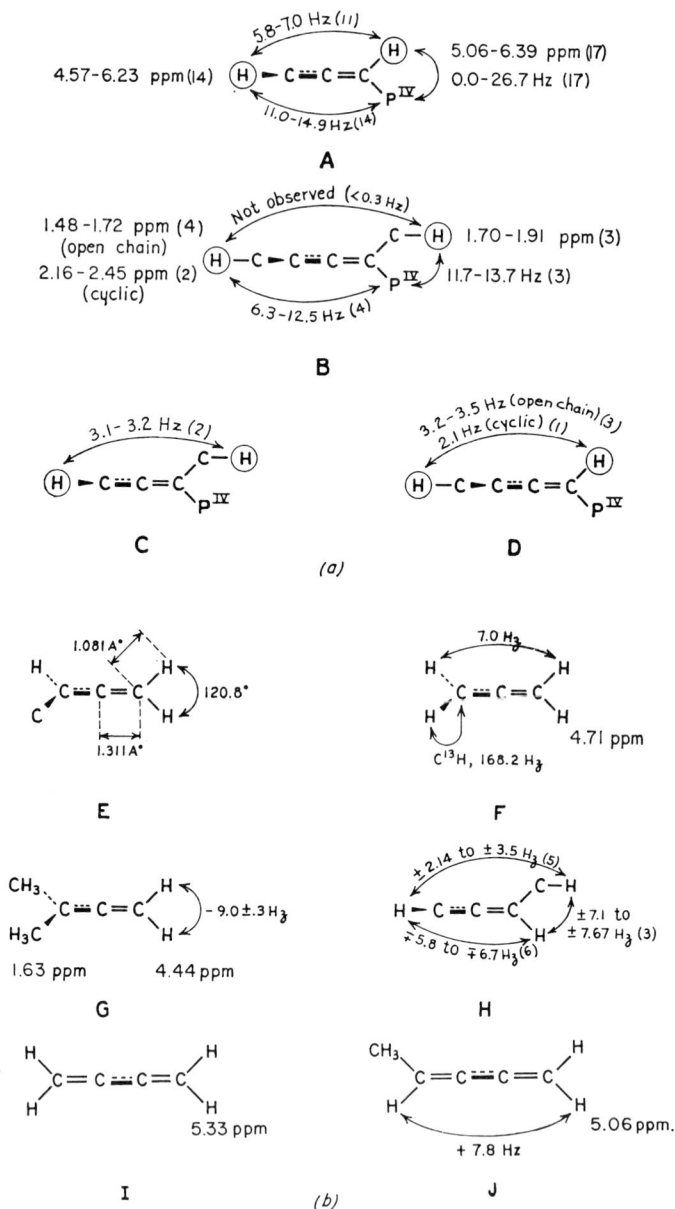

Fig. 5. Parameters of allene [F(32)], 1,1-dimethylallene [G(33)], substituted allenes [H, composite (34–36)], butatriene [I(137)] and 1,2,3-pentatriene [J(137)]. The numbers in parentheses of the illustrations indicate the number of examples available for the construction of the composite diagrams.

indices in arbitrarily taken distillation cuts), one can draw the correct, and only, structure of the molecule, which is

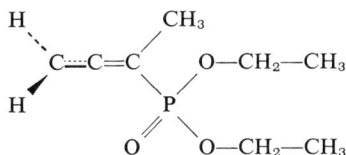

Confirmation of the structure is provided by infrared (allene, phosphoryl) and phosphorus NMR spectroscopy (*vide infra*).

Abstracted in Table 12 are the chemical shifts and coupling constants of the structures analyzed by proton NMR. The presence of substituents on the allene backbone provides examples of various coupled systems comprising the AM_6X, $[(CH_3)_2C=C=CHP(O)]$; A_2M_3X, $[H_2C=C=C(CH_3)P(O)]$; A_6B_3X, $[(CH_3)_2C=C=C(CH_3)P(O)]$; AX, $[(C_6H_5)_2C=C=CHP(O)]$; ABX, $[(C_6H_5)HC=C=CHP(O)]$; and AB_2X, $[H_2C=C=CHP(O)]$ cases.

The data presented in Table 12 allow the construction of the composite diagrams of Fig. 5, where for comparison NMR data on allene hydrocarbons and the molecular dimension of allene proper are also included. A similar treatment of the olefinic phosphorus compounds, which are the subject of Section IV, are shown adjacently in Fig. 6 for easier comparison.

It is apparent that the protons in both the parent hydrocarbon and in the phosphonic acids are more shielded in the allenic than in the olefinic systems. Thus the protons in allene are upfield from those of ethylene by about 0.6 ppm, and the alpha protons in the allenylphosphonic acid derivatives are upfield by about 0.7–1.8 ppm from those in vinylphosphonic acids. Similar relationship holds for protons on the sp^2 carbons of the methylene portion of the allenic and olefinic phosphonic acids, and even protons on sp^3 carbons alpha to the unsaturated systems are shielded more in the allenic than in the olefinic esters. Further examples of the more shielded allenic protons become available from the comparison of the haloallenes (34) with haloethylenes (47), where the differences in chemical shifts in the chloro-, bromo-, and iodohydrocarbon sequence between the alpha hydrogens are 0.42, 0.68, and 0.86 ppm, and between the beta hydrogens (*trans* to the halogen in the olefins) are 0.21, 1.01, and 1.98 ppm, respectively. It is thus not unexpected to find that not only the hydrogens but phosphorus itself in allenylphosphonic acid esters occupy more shielded positions than in the olefinic systems. Phosphorus in allenylphosphonic acids shows signals at about 4–8 ppm upfield from its position in vinylphosphonic acid esters (*vide infra*).

±30.2 Hz
5.64 ppm (H) (H) 6.16 ppm
±11.74 H₃
C=C
5.51 ppm (H) P^III
±13.62 H₃

A

±11.76 H₃
(H) (H)
±2.02 H₃
C=C
(H) P^III
18.37 H₃

A'

±43.80–±50.52 Hz (4)
(H) (H)
C=C ±20.59–±23.98 Hz (4)
(H) P^IV
±21.71–±25.29 Hz (4)

B

±12.64–±12.84 Hz (4)
(H) (H)
±0.05–±2.39 Hz (4) C=C
(H) P^IV
±18.68–±19.00 Hz (4)

B'

1.086 A°
H H
C=C 117.5°
H H
1.34 A°

C

+19.1 H₃
+11.5 H₃
H H
C=C +2.3 H₃
H H
5.34 ppm
+156.2 H₃ –2.4 H₃
C^13H

D

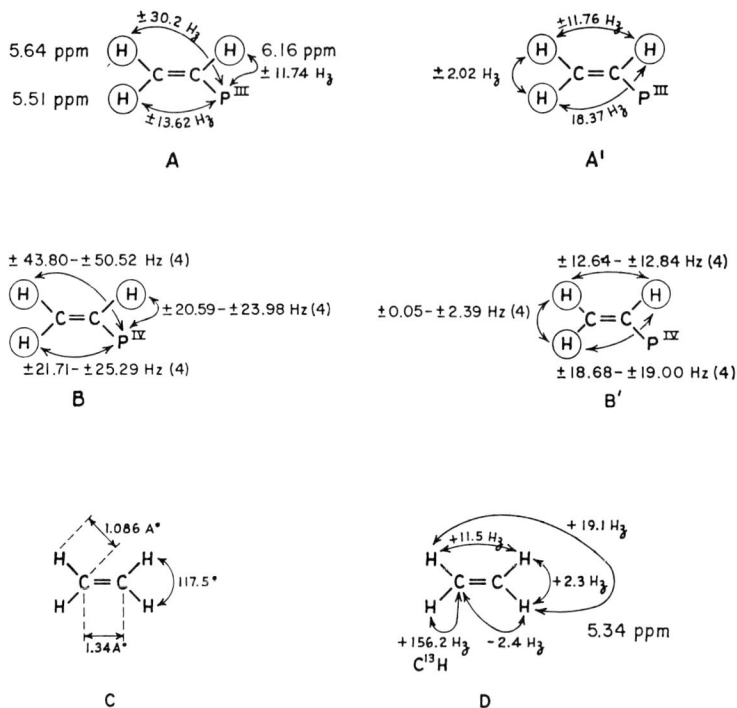

Fig. 6a. Chemical shifts and coupling constants of vinylphosphorus compounds [composite (38, 39, 45, 111)] and ethylene [D(42–44)] and structure of ethylene [C(40, 41)].

The higher shielding of nuclei in the allenic systems is attributable to a long-range anisotropic shielding associated with the pi electrons on the *sp* carbon. This arises largely from diamagnetic circulation in the cylindrically symmetrical pi electron distribution in the vicinity of the diagonally hybridized central atoms. In compounds with two diagonal, *sp* carbon atoms [acetylene, δ_H 1.85 ppm, (32i) and acetylenic phosphorus derivatives (Section II-C)] the anisotropic shielding is, expectedly, much more pronounced.

Another effect associated with the presence of *sp* carbons is the high coupling observed between nuclei separated by four or five bonds in allenic systems. Cumulated double bonds and conjugated triple bonds provide the highest *s* character and shortest bond distances in carbon chains and both systems also provide the best examples of long-range coupling.

The coupling of 5.8 to 7.0 Hz between protons separated by four bonds in allenes is considerably larger than any yet reported for other

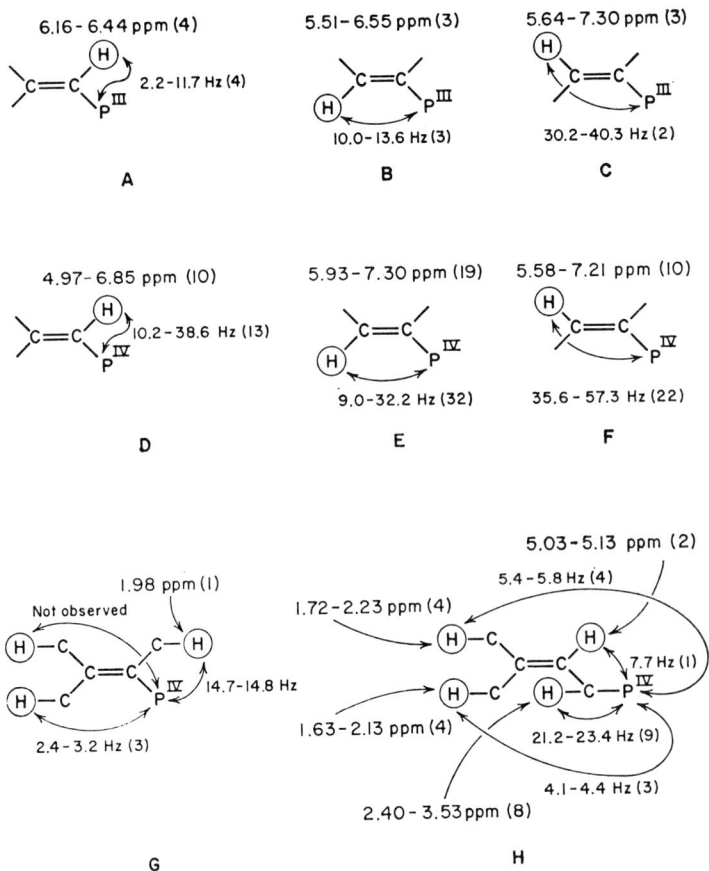

Fig. 6b. Chemical shifts and coupling constants of vinylic and allylic phosphorus compounds [composite (45)]. The numbers in parenthesis of the illustrations indicate the number of examples available for the construction of the composite diagrams.

systems and it has been compared to several couplings transmitted through one less bond (32). Recent investigators of the long-range effect in allenes concluded that despite the unfavorable geometry (the pi systems are orthogonal; cf. 48), pi electrons provide the dominant contribution to coupling (49)* and that results based on a hyperconjugative model furnish

* In this valence bond interpretation, coupling in allene between protons through four bonds is visualized to occur by two paths, each consisting of one H—C. (sp^2) radical and one H—C—C. radical hyperfine coupling. Because of the parallel spin orientation of the pi electrons on the diagonal carbon, the two paths are additive; the sign of the coupling constant is negative.

good qualitative (32) and quantitative (33) agreement with experimental data. For butatriene, which is a cumulene with a more favorable geometry (both H_2C sp^2 planes are coplanar), a single important coupling mechanism exists, resulting in antiparallel spin orientation and a predicted high and positive ($+7.8$ Hz) coupling through five bonds (49); the instability of the hydrocarbon precluded, however, the determination of the experimental value (35). Recently the predicted value was exactly confirmed by finding that the $^5J_{HH}$ coupling in 1,2,3-pentatriene was $+7.8$ Hz (137). The long-range coupling between protons separated by five bonds in the allenylphosphonic acid systems (2.1–3.5 Hz) is the same as in the parent hydrocarbons (2.1–3.5 Hz) and is comparable in magnitude to coupling through four to five bonds in acetylenes (vide infra).

The high coupling between protons is exceeded by an even higher coupling (about two- to three-fold) between phosphorus and proton through four bonds ($^4J_{HP}$ 11.0–14.9 Hz) and five bonds ($^5J_{HP}$ 6.3–12.5 Hz). The magnitude of the phosphorus–proton coupling was anticipated on the basis of a large number of examples available from isolated cases and from systematic studies (e.g., 50) of saturated hydrocarbon derivatives of tri- and tetra-substituted phosphorus compounds. It was also observed that coupling through two bonds between proton and phosphorus increases, often manyfold, on going from tri- to tetrasubstituted species in the sequence R_3P to R_3PO to $R_4P^\oplus$. The gradual increase in coupling was interpreted as the result of an increase in the s character of the phosphorus–hydrocarbon bond (50; cf. 21) and thus of an increase of the signa-electron contact contribution to the spin-spin coupling constant. Since the allenylphosphorus compounds obtained by the rearrangement of propargylic phosphites contain a phosphoryl group, coupling interactions are expected to be close to maximal. Another parallel relationship emerges from a consideration of the relative signs of coupling* in allenes and in allenic phosphorus compounds. A summary of the variations of signs and magnitudes of coupling with the number of intervening bonds in allenes and in simple unsaturated systems is outlined in Table 12a.

In the last few years the relative signs of coupled nuclei became available in an ever increasing number of phosphorus compounds, comprising allenylphosphonates, by one or more of the several methods available for this purpose. An excellent discussion of the various methods of sign determination [selective decoupling (46a,46b), tickling (155), boosting (156), general double irradiation (157), general Overhauser effects (158)] is avail-

---

* Following the suggestion of Karplus the theoretical sign of coupling is defined as positive when the interaction which minimizes the spin coupling energy is between two paired (antiparallel) nuclear spins; a negative spin coupling constant corresponds to a minimum coupling energy when the nuclear spins are parallel (49,155).

TABLE 12a
Proton Spin-Coupling Constants[a]

Separation of protons	Coupling constant (J, Hz)	
	Theoretical	Experimental
Three bonds		
H—C=C—H	+1.5	5–11 (*cis*); 10–18 (*trans*)
H—C≡C—H	+4.6	9.5–9.8 (ref. 42a,42b)
C=C=C—C—H (with H branch)		+7.2 (ref. 35)
Four bonds		
H—C=C—C—H	−1.7	−1.4--1.8
H—C≡C—C—H	−3.7	−2.1--2.9
H—C=C=C—H	−6.7	−5.8 (ref. 35)
Five bonds		
H—C—C=C—C—H	+2.0	1.2–1.5
H—C—C≡C—C—H	+2.9	+2.9
H—C=C=C—C—H	+	+2.4 (ref. 35)
H—C=C=C=C—H	+7.8	+7.8 (137)

[a] Except where noted, the data are from ref. 49b.

able (159). In some cases relative signs are accessible by direct analyses of the spectra, e.g., certain of the ABCX and A_2BX type (122,138,160). In most cases the correctness of the assignment can be checked by computer techniques (161).

The available (experimental) signs of the nuclei present in phosphorus compounds are abstracted in Table 12b. In Table 12c the signs of the most frequently encountered coupled nuclei are shown.

While the long-range proton–phosphorus interactions show only small variations in numerical values, the geminal proton–phosphorus couplings are greatly affected by substitution on the opposite end of the propadienyl system. The small geminal proton–phosphorus coupling in diethyl 1,2-propadienylphosphonate increases numerically* to 6.1 Hz by two methyl substituents and to 5.7 Hz by a pentamethylene substituent. Changes of substituents on the phosphorus atom alone also affect the geminal proton–phosphorus coupling, as evidenced by the following sequence in 1,2-propadienylphosphorus derivatives, H_2C=C=CHP(O)XY,

* Following the suggestion of the authors in ref. 44, expressions like "increase in J," "larger J," or "higher value of J" should mean that J becomes more positive. Thus −15 Hz should be referred to as a smaller coupling constant than −5 Hz.

TABLE 12b

Signs of Coupling Constants of Nuclei in Phosphorus Compounds

Type of Coupling Constant[a]	Type of Phosphorus[b]	Structural Feature	Sign	Ref.
		A. Phosphorus–Proton Coupling		
$^1J_{PH}$	P^{III}, P^{IV}	P—H	+	163,164,167,122
$^2J_{PH}$	P^{III}	P—C—H	−,+	163,164,165
	P^{IV}	P—C—H	−	164,122
	P^{IV}	P—C—H	−,+	111,119,122,138
	P^{IV}	P—P—H	+	163
$^3J_{PH}$	P^{III}	P—C—C—H	+	165,122
	P^{III}, P^{IV}	P—C—C—H	+	168
	P^{IV}	P—C—C—H	+	119
	P^{III}, P^{IV}	P—C—C—H	+	163,111,122
	P^{III}, P^{IV}	P—O—C—H	+	163,166,167,169
		P—N—C—H	+	163
	P^{IV}	P—P- C—H	+	163,122
$^4J_{PH}$	P^{III}, P^{IV}	P—C—C=C—H	−	168
	P^{IV}	P—C=C=C—H	−	122,138,119
	P^{III}	P—O—C—C—H	−	169
	P^{IV}	P—O—C—C ·II	+	166,169
		B. Other Pairs of Nuclei		
$^1J_{PF}$	P^{IV}	P—F	−	166
$^2J_{PF}$			+	166
$^3J_{PF}$			+	166
$^1J_{PC}$	P^{III}	P—C	−	164
	P^{IV}	P—C	+	164
$^2J_{PC}$	P^{IV}	P—O—C	−	167
$^1J_{PP}$	P^{III}, P^{IV}		−,+	170,163,122
$^2J_{PP}$			+	166
$^3J_{PP}$		P—C—C—P	+	163
$^2J_{HH}$		H—P—H	−	163
$^3J_{HH}$	P^{III}, P^{IV}	H—P—C—H	+	163,164
		H—P—P—H	+	163
$^5J_{HF}$	P^{IV}	H—C—C—O—P—F	+	166
$^1J_{HC}$	P^{III}, P^{IV}	H—C	+	164,167

[a] The superscript indicates the number of bonds intervening between the coupled nuclei.

[b] The roman numbers indicate the number of substituent atoms or groups on phosphorus.

TABLE 12c

Signs of Coupling Constants of Frequently Encountered Nuclei

Coupled Nuclei	^1J, Sign	^2J, Sign	^3J, Sign	^4J, Sign	^5J, Sign
HH		−	+	−,+	+
HF		+	+,−	−,+	+
HC	+	−,+			
HP	+	+,−	+	−,+	
FF		+	−,+	+	+
FC	−	+			
FP	−	+	+		
CP	+,−	−			
PP	+,−	+	+		

J_{HP} (gem): X, Y = $-OC_2H_5$, J, 0.2 Hz; X = $-OC_2H_5$, Y = $-C_2H_5$, J, 3.0 Hz; X, Y = $-N(CH_3)_2$, J, 1.4 Hz, X,Y = F, J,4.2 and X,Y = Cl, J,15.2 Hz.

The marked influence of the nature of substituents on the geminal coupling constant in unsaturated systems is evident from the comparison of ethylene (J_{gem} + 2.3 Hz) with vinylmagnesium bromide (J_{gem} + 7.4 Hz) and with vinyl fluoride (J_{gem} − 3.2 Hz) (taken from the tabulation in ref. 44). Changes in the moieties attached to the $H_2C(sp^2)$ group cause even larger changes in J_{gem} as evidenced by the two extremes $H_2C{=}O$, J, +41 Hz and ketene, $H_2C{=}C{=}O$, J − 15.8 Hz. The geminal proton–proton

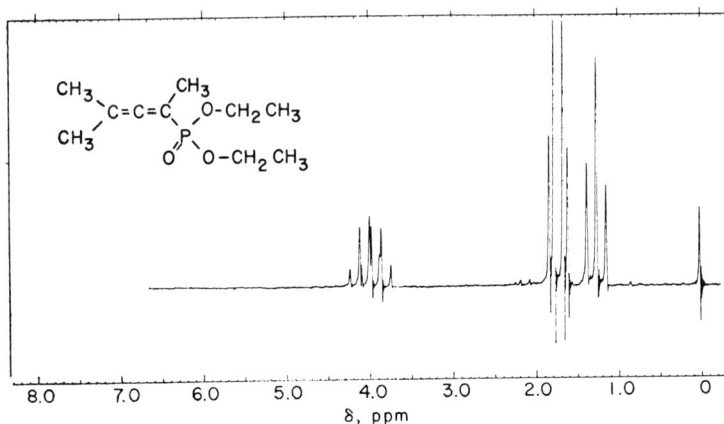

Fig. 7a. The proton NMR spectrum of diethyl 1,3-dimethyl-1,2-butadienyl phosphonate $(CH_3)_2C{=}C{=}C(CH_3)P(O)(OC_2H_5)_2$ (neat, int. TMS, 60 Mc).

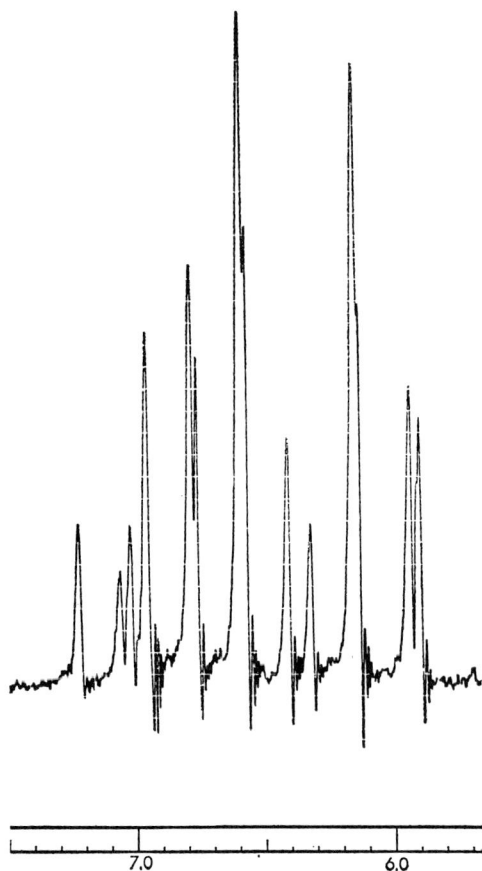

Fig. 7b. The AB$_2$ portion of a representative AB$_2$X spectrum [H$_2$C=C=CHP(O) (OCH$_2$CH$_3$)$_2$, neat, ext. TMS, 60 Mc.]

coupling in one allene, 3-methyl-1-2-butadiene, H$_2$C=C=C(CH$_3$)$_2$, is known and it is highly negative (−9.0 Hz, Fig. 5).

For the geminal proton–phosphorus coupling, like for that of the geminal proton–proton coupling, both + and − signs were reported [while the long range $^4J_{PH}$ relative sign was kept the same (−)] (Table 12). A correlation between the increase in the electronegativity of the sub-stituents on phosphorus and the increase of the $^2J_{PH}$ (it becomes more positive) was suggested (138).

The similarities in the signs of coupling constants between allenic phosphorus compounds and allenes can be shown by the following illustrations:

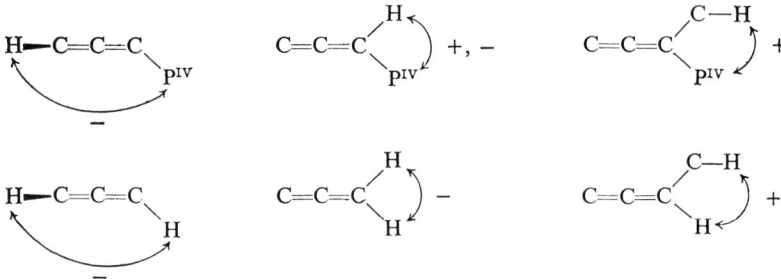

To illustrate long-range proton–phosphorus couplings in these allenic compounds, the proton NMR spectrum of diethyl 1,3-dimethyl-1,2-butadienylphosphonate, $(CH_3)_2C=C=C(CH_3)P(O)(OC_2H_5)_2$, is reproduced in Fig. 7, together with the chemical shift and coupling constant

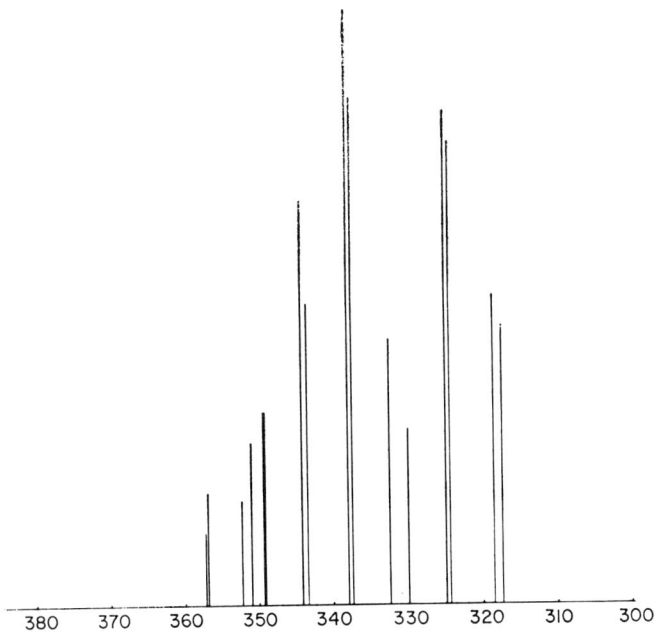

Fig. 7c. The AB_2 portion of a computed AB_2X spectrum [$H_2C=C-CHP(O)-(OCH_2CH_3)_2$, $J_{AX} + 0.2$, $J_{BX} - 13.5$, $J_{AB} - 6.8$ Hz)]. The spectrum was computed using Laocoon 3 by Dr. J. G. Colson, Research Center, Hooker Chemical Corporation.

TABLE 13
Proton NMR Analyses of Acetylenic Phosphites

Compound	H	δ, ppm	No. of peaks	J_{HP}, Hz	J_{HH}, Hz	Solvent[a]	Ref.
$(H^C C{\equiv}CCH_2^A O)P(OCH_2^B CH_3^D)_2$	A	4.66	2×2	10.3	C2.4	Ne	2b,31
	B	4.05	2×4	8.1	D7.0	Ne	2b,31
	C	3.45	3		A2.4	Ne	2b,31
	D	1.30	3		B7.0	Ne	2b,31
$(CH_3^C C{\equiv}CCH_2^A O)P(OCH_2^B CH_3^D)_2$	A	4.31	2×4	8.9	C2.4	Ne	2b,31
	B	3.82	2×4	8.0	D7.0	Ne	2b,31
	C	1.80	3		A2.4	Ne	2b,31
	D	1.21	3		B7.0	Ne	2b,31

[a] Ne = neat; scans were run with tetramethylsilane as internal reference.

assignments. The $^3J_{HP}$ of 13.2 Hz and $^5J_{HP}$ of 6.6 Hz values are directly available from the inspection of the spectrum.

A representative spectrum of the unsubstituted allenic phosphorus moiety is shown in Figure 7b, where the AB_2 portion of the AB_2X spectrum of $H_2C{=}C{=}CHP(O)(OCH_2CH_3)_2$ is reproduced. The computed spectrum is illustrated in Figure 7c.

In a few instances it was possible to record the NMR scans of acetylenic phosphites prior to their rearrangement. The data from the scans are abstracted in Table 13 and serve to confirm the structure of the acetylenic esters.

3. Phosphorus NMR

The most direct evidence for the transformation of a tervalent phosphorus ester into a tetrasubstituted species (phosphorus with four direct neighbors) is provided by ^{31}P NMR spectroscopy. Although the phosphoryl group has in the infrared a strong absorbtion in the 1200–1300 cm^{-1} region, there are other bands which fall into this region and render occasionally the diagnosis somewhat ambiguous. There can be no ambiguity, however, in deciding whether the phosphorus is present as a tri- or tetrasubstituted species in its compounds, as it becomes apparent from inspection of the data abstracted in Table 14. In the transformation of an alkyl ester of a tervalent phosphorus acid into a tetrasubstituted phosphorus derivative, there is a change in chemical shift of at least 79 ppm in the case of trialkyl phosphites, of at least 93 ppm in the case of dialkyl phosphonites, and of at least 38 ppm in the case of alkyl phosphinites. Since chemical shifts of phosphorus can be routinely determined with a

TABLE 14

^{31}P Chemical Shift Ranges of Alkyl Esters of Interrelated Tri- and Tetrasubstituted Phosphorus Compounds (52)

	δ, ppm	
$P(OR)_3$[a]	$RP(O)(OR)_2$	$P(O)(OR)_3$
$-141--120$	$-41--30$	$-17-+19$
$RP(OR)_2$	$R_2P(O)(OR)$	$RP(O)(OR)_2$
$-184--151$	$-58--32$	$-41--30$
$R_2P(OR)$	R_3PO	$R_2P(O)(OR)$
$-126--91$	$-53--23$	$-58--31$

[a] Certain strained, bicyclic analogs of trialkyl phosphites which have a characteristic resonance at around -90 ppm are not included.

precision of at least ± 1.0–0.1 ppm, it is evident that the diagnosis of the substitution state of phosphorus by ^{31}P NMR can be very definite and, in fact, the most valid, simple, and direct method available for general structure proof in phosphorus chemistry.

Chemical shift values of the various allenylphosphorus compounds are presented in Table 15. The data indicate that all dialkyl allenylphosphonates resonate between -11 and -18 ppm, which is well outside the limits of the corresponding alkylphosphonates. As it will become apparent from the chemical shift tabulations of olefinic and acetylenic phosphonates, the range of the allenylphosphonic acid esters falls between those of the alkenylphosphonates (-22–-23 ppm, Section IV) and of the more shielded alkynylphosphonates ($+5$–$+10$ ppm, Section II-C), a convenience which thus permits further structure differentiation by ^{31}P NMR in unsaturated phosphonic acid esters.

The gradual shielding of phosphorus in the alkenyl-, allenyl-, alkynyl-phosphonate sequence can be related to the presence of one and two sp carbons, which exert long-range anisotropic shielding on the phosphorus.

TABLE 15

[31]P Chemical Shift Values of Allenylphosphorus Compounds

Compound	δ, ppm (H_3PO_4)	Ref.
$H_2C{=}C{=}CHP(O)(OC_2H_5)_2$	-14.4	2a,2b
$H_2C{=}C{=}CHP(O)(OCH_2C{\equiv}CH)_2$	-17.9	2a,2b
$H_2C{=}C{=}C(CH_3)P(O)(OC_2H_5)_2$	-17.3	2a,2b
$H_2C{=}C{=}C(CH_2Cl)P(O)(OC_2H_5)_2$	-16.5	31
$CH_3CH{=}C{=}CHP(O)(OC_2H_5)_2$	-14.8	2a,2b
$CH_3CH{=}C{=}CHP(O)(OC_2H_5)_2$	-13[a]	10
$(CH_3)_2C{=}C{=}CHP(O)(OC_2H_5)_2$	-15.0	2a,2b
$={=}C{=}CHP(O)(OC_2H_5)_2$	-17.3	2a,2b
$={-}C{=}CHP(O)(OC_2H_5)_2$	-16.6	2b
$(CH_3)_2C{=}C{=}C(CH_3)P(O)(OC_2H_5)_2$	-17.6	2b
$CH_3(CF_3)C{=}C{=}C(C_6H_5)P(O)(OC_2H_5)_2$	-11.3	31
$(C_6H_5)_2C{=}C{=}C(C_6H_5)P(O)(OC_2H_5)_2$	-14.1	31
$H_2C{=}C{=}CHP(O)(C_2H_5)(OCH_2C{\equiv}CH)$	-45.3	2a,2b
$H_2C{=}C{=}CHP(O)(CH_3)_2$	-41.0	2a,2b
$H_2C{=}C{=}CHP(O)[N(CH_3)_2]_2$	-23.9	2a,2b

[a] Precision is not given; all of the other values are estimated to have a precision of ± 1.0 ppm.

TABLE 16
^{31}P NMR Characteristics of Acetylenic Phosphites

Compound	δ, ppm (H_3PO_4)	Ref.
$(HC\equiv CCH_2O)P(OC_2H_5)_2$	-137	2a,2b
$(HC\equiv CCH_2O)_3P$	-135	2a,2b
$(CH_3C\equiv CCH_2O)P(OC_2H_5)_2$	-137.2	2b
$(HC\equiv CCH_2CH_2O)P(OC_2H_5)_2$	-137.0	2b

A similar effect of the allenic moiety was noted earlier on protons and will also be apparent in acetylenic phosphonates, on both proton and phosphorus (Part C). The anisotropy in allenes is the result of the diamagnetic circulation of the pi electrons in a cylinder shape around the central carbon, with a resultant shielding effect on atoms on or near the axis connecting the allenic carbons. Due to presence of only one *sp* carbon and due also to their geometry (substituents are in a 60° angle with the three carbon axis), nuclei attached to the allene backbone are not shielded as much as those directly attached to, and thus colinear with, the acetylenic carbon (*vide infra*). Thus allenylphosphonates are shielded by 4–10 ppm, but alkynylphosphonates are shielded by 27–33 ppm relative to vinylphosphonates. A similar relationship exists also in the shielding of protons in allenes and acetylenes.

Phosphorus NMR was also used in reaction mixtures to diagnose the presence of propargylic phosphites prior to their rearrangement to allenic phosphonates (2a,2b). Their chemical shift data, which fall within the range of trialkyl phosphites, are given in Table 16. Included in the table for comparison is a nonpropargylic phosphite (diethyl 3-butynyl phosphite), which, expectedly, did not undergo the rearrangement (*vide supra*). Data on related acetylenic compounds, which also failed to give rearrangement products, are summarized in Table 17.

TABLE 17
^{31}P NMR Constants of Compounds Related to Acetylenic Phosphites Which Failed to Undergo the Rearrangement Reaction

Compound	δ, ppm (H_3PO_4)	Ref.
$[N\equiv C(CH_3)CHO]P(OC_2H_5)_2$	-138.3	2b
$[N\equiv C(CH_3)_2CO]_3P$	-143.5	2b
$[(HC\equiv CCH_2)_2N]P(OC_2H_5)_2$	-142.1	2b
$[(HC\equiv CCH_2)(C_6H_5CH_2)N]P(OC_2H_5)_2$	-141.4	2b

4. Fluorine NMR

The ^{19}F spectrum of diethyl 1-phenyl-3-methyl-4,4,4-trifluoro-1,2-butadienylphosphonate consists of a doublet, located 12.19 ppm downfield from trifluoroacetic acid (external) [or 1.22 ppm upfield from benzotrifluoride (external) (1.34 ppm from benzotrifluoride, internal)] (31). The coupling of fluorines with only the phosphorus is thus indicated. The magnitude of coupling, $J = 5.1$ Hz, which occurs through five bonds, is somewhat less than coupling through the same number of bonds between proton and phosphorus in the same molecule:

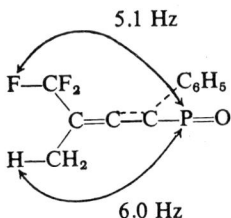

$$
\begin{array}{c}
5.1\ \text{Hz} \\[2pt]
\text{F—CF}_2 \qquad \text{C}_6\text{H}_5 \\
\qquad \text{C=C=C—P=O} \\
\text{H—CH}_2 \\[2pt]
6.0\ \text{Hz}
\end{array}
$$

The fluorine chemical shift of the acid fluoride, $(CH_3)_2C=C=CHP(O)F_2$, was found to be -9.15 ppm (CF_3COOH), $J_{PF} = 772$ Hz (120) and that of $H_2C=C=CHP(O)F_2$ at -13.5 ppm (CF_3COOH), $J_{PF} = 1080$ Hz (138). For comparison fluorine in POF_3 resonates at $+12.4$ ppm (CF_3COOH), $J = 1055$ Hz (143) and in C_6H_5COF at about -95 ppm (CF_3COOH) or -17 ppm (CCl_3F) (144).

5. Ultraviolet

The ultraviolet spectra of the allenic phosphonic acid esters analyzed (Table 18) show little if any interaction between unsaturation and the phosphoryl group (31). This was anticipated from studies of aromatic phosphoryl compounds, the ultraviolet spectra of which indicated only minor perturbation of the aromatic (phenyl, biphenyl) transitions ($^1La, ^1Lb$); similarly, the additivity relationship of the effects of several phenyl groups attached to a phosphoryl group indicated a lack of interaction between them (53).

Since substituents in allenes are fixed in two perpendicular planes, the Hückel molecular orbital theory treats allenes as two independent ethylenes. Support for this approach comes from ultraviolet spectroscopic data, which show that the first absorbtion bands of tetraphenylallene and 1,1-diphenylethylene coincide (54a–54c; cf. Table 18).

Similarly diethyl 1,3,3-triphenylallenylphosphonate can be considered constructed of one 1,1-diphenylethylene and one styrene component, having two maxima in the range characteristic of these compounds.

TABLE 18
Ultraviolet Spectra of Allenylphosphonic Acid Esters[a]
and Reference Compounds

Compound	λ_{max}, mμ	ϵ	log ϵ	Ref.
	232(s)	220	2.342	31
	249	9,200	3.964	31
	237	21,400	4.330	31
	257	21,500	4.332	31
H_2C=C=CHCH_2OH	225(s)[b]	150	2.174	31
	265	28,900	4.46	54
	248	12,600	4.1	56a
	245	15,900	4.2	56b
H_2C=C=CHCH_3	178	19,800	4.3	56c
	186	3,970	3.6	56c
H_2C=C=CHC_2H_5	177	25,000	4.4	56c
	181	25,000	4.4	56c
CH_3CH=C=CHCH_3	171	19,800	4.3	56c
	180	15,800	4.2	56c

(continued)

TABLE 18 (*continued*)

Compound	λ_{max}, mμ	ϵ	log ϵ	Ref.
$CH_3CH{=}C{=}CHCH_3$	185	12,500	4.1	56c
	194	3,970	3.6	56c
	202	3,150	3.5	56c
$H_2C{=}CHCH{=}CH_2$	217	20,800	4.32	56a,d
$(CH_3O)_3PO$	229	55	1.74	56c
	262	9.3	0.97	56c
$CH_3P(O)(OCH_3)_2$	217	13	1.12	56c

[a] In cyclohexane solution.
[b] s: shoulder.

The apparent high intensity of the shorter wavelength absorbtion might be due to contribution from the ascending slope of the longer wavelength maximum. The 1-phenyl-3(trifluoromethyl)-1,2-butadienylphosphonic acid ester similarly matches the maximum of styrene rather well. It was pointed out that vinylphosphonic acid derivatives have ultraviolet spectra similar to those of the corresponding olefins and since the molecular refractions show no exaltation, no conjugation between the vinyl and phosphoryl groups is indicated (55). This is borne out by the spectrum of diethyl 1,3-dimethyl-1,2-butadienylphosphonate, whose only absorbtion above 200 mμ corresponds to the very low intensity absorbtion of alkyl phosphates and phosphonates (c.v. Table 18).

C. Reactions of Allenylphosphonic Acid Esters

1. Rearrangement to Acetylenic Compounds

a. Nature and Mechanism of the Rearrangement. It was noted in the infrared spectral analysis of various aged samples of propadienylphosphonic acid esters that a band gradually developed at 2222–2219 cm^{-1} (4.5 μ) parallel with a diminishing of the allene vibration at 1961–1938 cm^{-1} (5.10–5.16 μ) and that the intensity of the former became constant when the allene band disappeared (2b). A parallel change was noted in the phosphorus NMR spectrum also: the characteristic resonance of the propadienylphosphonates at -14.4–-17.9 disappeared to give rise to absorbtion upfield from phosphoric acid (2b). These data indicate the rearrangement given by Eq. 7.

$$H_2C{=}C{=}CHP(O){\diagup}_{\diagdown} \longrightarrow CH_3C{\equiv}CP(O){\diagup}_{\diagdown} \qquad (7)$$

The resultant 1-propynylphosphonic acid esters, whose structures were confirmed also by proton NMR, were found to be stable and thus to represent the final stage of the rearrangement of 2-propynyl phosphites (2b). Bis(2-propynyl) 1-propynylphosphonate, $CH_3C{\equiv}CP(O)(OCH_2C{\equiv}CH)_2$, which contains two kinds of acetylenic moieties, was accordingly found to undergo no change on storage.

Further examples of the isomerization were found in experiments where little or no temperature control was exerted during the exothermal rearrangement of propargylic phosphites thus allowing the temperature to rise up to 200° (9,12). A closer study of 1,2-propadienylphosphonate-1-propynylphosphonate rearrangement indicated that it is an equilibrium reaction, catalyzed by base (sodium ethoxide) and that substituents on the propadienyl group have a profound effect on the composition of the equilibrium mixture (10):

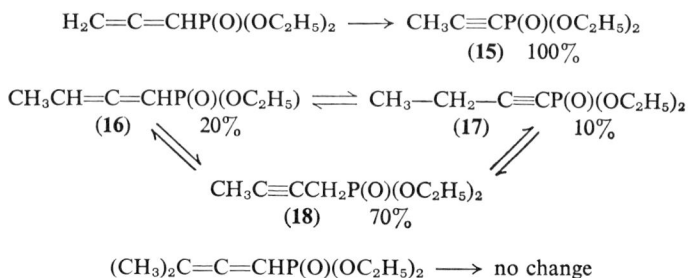

$$H_2C{=}C{=}CHP(O)(OC_2H_5)_2 \longrightarrow CH_3C{\equiv}CP(O)(OC_2H_5)_2$$
$$\textbf{(15)} \quad 100\%$$

$$CH_3CH{=}C{=}CHP(O)(OC_2H_5) \rightleftharpoons CH_3{-}CH_2{-}C{\equiv}CP(O)(OC_2H_5)_2$$
$$\textbf{(16)} \quad 20\% \qquad\qquad\qquad \textbf{(17)} \quad 10\%$$
$$CH_3C{\equiv}CCH_2P(O)(OC_2H_5)_2$$
$$\textbf{(18)} \quad 70\%$$

$$(CH_3)_2C{=}C{=}CHP(O)(OC_2H_5)_2 \longrightarrow \text{no change}$$

Although hyperconjugation was suggested to account for these data (10), a consideration of the stabilities of the carbanions, intermediate in the prototropic isomerization, leads to an alternate and more direct interpretation. The base-catalyzed isomerization* of the 1,2-propadienyl-phosphonate ester is likely to consist of the following steps:

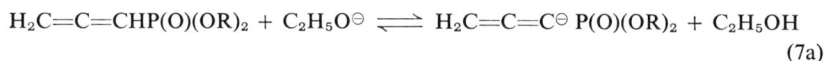

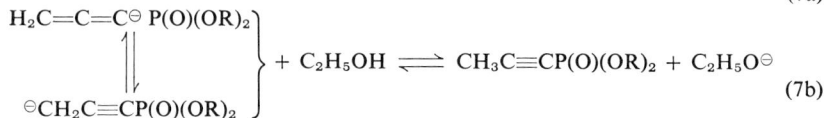

$$H_2C{=}C{=}CHP(O)(OR)_2 + C_2H_5O^{\ominus} \rightleftharpoons H_2C{=}C{=}C^{\ominus}P(O)(OR)_2 + C_2H_5OH$$
$$(7a)$$

$$\left.\begin{array}{c} H_2C{=}C{=}C^{\ominus}P(O)(OR)_2 \\ \updownarrow \\ {}^{\ominus}CH_2C{\equiv}CP(O)(OR)_2 \end{array}\right\} + C_2H_5OH \rightleftharpoons CH_3C{\equiv}CP(O)(OR)_2 + C_2H_5O^{\ominus}$$
$$(7b)$$

Since the isomerization involves change in the hydrocarbon portion of the molecule, information and interpretation used in the base-catalyzed isomerization of unsaturated hydrocarbons can be applied also to the isomerization above. The known order of stabilities of carbanions, i.e.,

---

* Base-catalyzed isomerizations of acetylenic derivatives are discussed by Iwai in this volume.

primary > secondary > tertiary, was used to interpret certain observations in the reaction of olefins with organosodium reagents (57). It was
suggested that olefins which are metalated readily by pentyl sodium are
those which form primary allylic carbanions and whose mesomeric structure involves primary anions only.

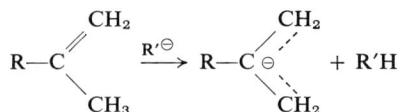

$$\underset{\overset{\displaystyle |}{CH_3}}{R-C}\overset{\displaystyle CH_2}{\diagup} \xrightarrow{R'^{\ominus}} \underset{\overset{\displaystyle |}{CH_2}}{R-C^{\ominus}}\overset{\displaystyle CH_2}{\diagup} + R'H$$

Moderately reactive olefins were those which yielded anions the mesomeric
structure of which involved a primary and a secondary carbanion.

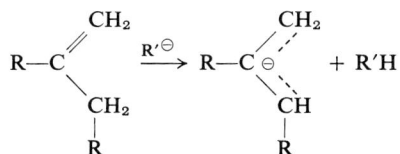

$$\underset{\overset{\displaystyle |}{\underset{\overset{\displaystyle |}{R}}{CH_2}}}{R-C}\overset{\displaystyle CH_2}{\diagup} \xrightarrow{R'^{\ominus}} \underset{\overset{\displaystyle |}{\underset{\overset{\displaystyle |}{R}}{CH}}}{R-C^{\ominus}}\overset{\displaystyle CH_2}{\diagup} + R'H$$

A similar relationship was found to exist between secondary, and secondary
and tertiary carbanions also (57).

The ready isomerization of dialkyl propadienylphosphonates is,
accordingly, explicable by the abstraction of the more acidic proton—
geminal with the phosphoryl group (see infrared and proton NMR data)
—by alkoxide to yield an sp^2 carbon anion mesomeric with a primary sp^3
anion (7a,7b). Abstraction of a proton from the terminal position of the
ester would yield an sp^2 anion mesomeric with a secondary and thus less
favored sp^3 carbanion (Scheme 2).

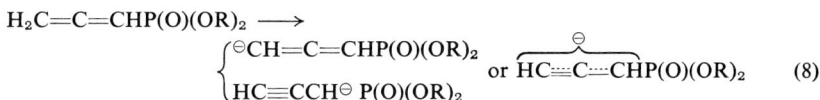

$$H_2C=C=CHP(O)(OR)_2 \longrightarrow$$

$$\begin{cases} ^{\ominus}CH=C=CHP(O)(OR)_2 \\ HC\equiv CCH^{\ominus} P(O)(OR)_2 \end{cases} \text{ or } \overset{\ominus}{\overbrace{HC\cdots C\cdots CHP(O)(OR)_2}} \qquad (8)$$

Scheme 2

The influence of the phosphoryl group is apparently not strong enough
to reverse the effect of carbanion stabilities, but its role is evidenced in the
next example, where the mesomeric anions are composed of secondary
carbanions.

In dialkyl 1,2-butadienylphosphonates abstraction of a proton from
either of the olefinic carbons yields sp^2 anions mesomeric with secondary
sp^3 anions (Scheme 3).

The multiple choices offered in the system are indicated by the actual
experiment, in which all three of the isomeric hydrocarbon phosphonates,
resulting from the protonation of all four of the contributing carbanion
structures, were found to be present (10). The formation of the 2-butynyl

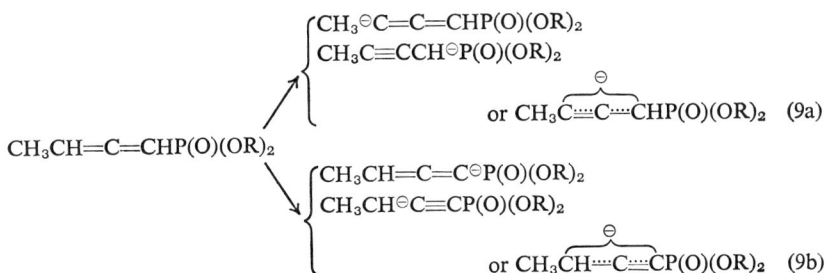

$$CH_3CH=C=CHP(O)(OR)_2$$

$$\begin{cases} CH_3{}^{\ominus}C=C=CHP(O)(OR)_2 \\ CH_3C\equiv CCH{}^{\ominus}P(O)(OR)_2 \end{cases}$$

$$\text{or } CH_3\overset{\ominus}{\overbrace{C\text{---}C\text{---}CHP(O)(OR)_2}} \quad (9a)$$

$$\begin{cases} CH_3CH=C=C{}^{\ominus}P(O)(OR)_2 \\ CH_3CH{}^{\ominus}C\equiv CP(O)(OR)_2 \end{cases}$$

$$\text{or } CH_3\overset{\ominus}{\overbrace{CH\text{---}C\text{---}CP(O)(OR)_2}} \quad (9b)$$

Scheme 3

derivative (18) as the major constituent (70%) seems reasonable due to the stabilization of the sp^3 anion in Eq. 9a by the adjacent phosphoryl group* which is thus formed preferentially prior to protonation.

The abstraction of the acidic hydrogen in diethyl 3-methyl-1,2-butadienylphosphonate would yield an anion whose mesomeric structure involves a (least stable) tertiary carbanion (Scheme 4).

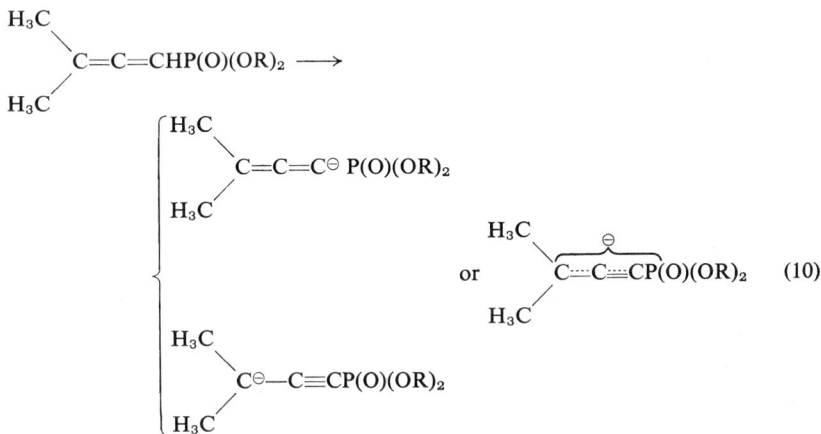

$$\underset{H_3C}{\overset{H_3C}{>}}C=C=CHP(O)(OR)_2 \longrightarrow$$

$$\begin{cases} \underset{H_3C}{\overset{H_3C}{>}}C=C=C{}^{\ominus}P(O)(OR)_2 \\[2em] \underset{H_3C}{\overset{H_3C}{>}}C{}^{\ominus}-C\equiv CP(O)(OR)_2 \end{cases} \text{ or } \underset{H_3C}{\overset{H_3C}{>}}C\overset{\ominus}{\overbrace{\text{---}C\text{---}CP(O)(OR)_2}} \quad (10)$$

Scheme 4

It was thus expected that this allenylphosphonic acid ester did not isomerize.

A related sequence of isomerization was found in the study of the Michaelis-Arbuzov reaction of triethyl phosphite with propargyl bromide: the initially formed 2-propynylphosphonate underwent isomerization to 1-propynylphosphonate via the allenic intermediate (124):

$$HC\equiv CCH_2Br + P(OC_2H_5)_3 \longrightarrow HC\equiv CCH_2P(O)(OC_2H_5)_2 \longrightarrow$$
$$H_2C=C=CHP(O)(OC_2H_5)_2 \longrightarrow H_3CC\equiv CP(O)(OC_2H_5)_2$$

---

* The ready formation of various anions alpha to the phosphoryl group is well documented by the Horner and related reactions (58,59).

TABLE 19

Acetylenic Phosphorus Compounds Prepared by the Isomerization of
Allenic Precursors

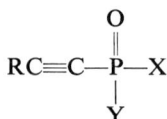

$$RC{\equiv}C{-}\underset{\underset{Y}{|}}{\overset{\overset{O}{\|}}{P}}{-}X$$

Substituent			Characterization			
R	X	Y	bp°/mm	$n_D/t°$	Other	Ref.
CH₃	C₂H₅O—	C₂H₅O—	86/0.3	1.4442/25	A,I,H	2b
CH₃	C₂H₅O—	C₂H₅O—	115–116/4	1.4460/20	A,I,MR	4a,12
CH₃	C₂H₅O—	C₂H₅O—	91–91.5/1	1.4472/20	A,H,I	10
CH₃	C₂H₅O—	C₂H₅O—	114–114.5/2.5	1.4460/20	D	60
CH₃	C₃H₇O—	C₃H₇O—	127–128/4	1.4478/20	A,I,MR	4a,12
CH₃	(CH₃)₂CHO—	(CH₃)₂CHO—	105–107/3	1.4425/20	A,MR	12
CH₃	C₄H₉O—	C₄H₉O—	152–153/6	1.4498/20	A,I	4a
CH₃	HC≡CCH₂O—	HC≡CCH₂O—	117/0.34	1.4857/20	A,H,I,P	2b
CH₃	C₆H₅O—	C₆H₅O—	171–173/0.45	1.5576/20	A,MR	12
CH₃	—OC₆H₄O	ortho	100–101		A,I	148
CH₃	HC≡CCH₂O—	C₂H₅—	121–124/3	1.4894/20	A,MR	12
CH₃	CH₃S—	CH₃S—	105–107/0.3	1.5960/24	A,I	2b
CH₃	(Ba/2)⊕O⊖—	(Ba/2)⊕O⊖—			A,I	13
C₂H₅	C₂H₅O—	C₂H₅O—			H,I,P	10

A listing of the acetylenic phosphonates obtained by the isomerization of allenylphosphonates is given in Table 19.

b. Spectroscopic Analyses. Acetylenic phosphonates are less numerous compared with aliphatic and aromatic phosphonates. Their spectroscopic analyses provide valuable information on acetylenic and phosphorus moieties and add new values and limits to spectroscopic categorizations.

(1) Infrared. The infrared spectra of the 1-alkynylphosphonates show a sharp and strong triple bond stretching band in the literature range of 2190 and 2260 cm⁻¹ (30). The characteristic infrared bands of the acetylenic phosphonates are abstracted in Table 20, where parameters of related structures are also listed. As it is apparent from the data, there are several types of compounds which have the triple bond stretching vibrations outside the low frequency limit (2190 cm⁻¹) of the literature range. These include examples where the triple bond is adjacent to a vinylic (2130–2175) or aromatic (2160–2175) or acetylenic (2060–2150) unsaturation, and where the triple bond adjacent to a phosphoryl group is substituted by chlorine (2176), bromine (2174), dimethylamino group (2154), trialkyltin group

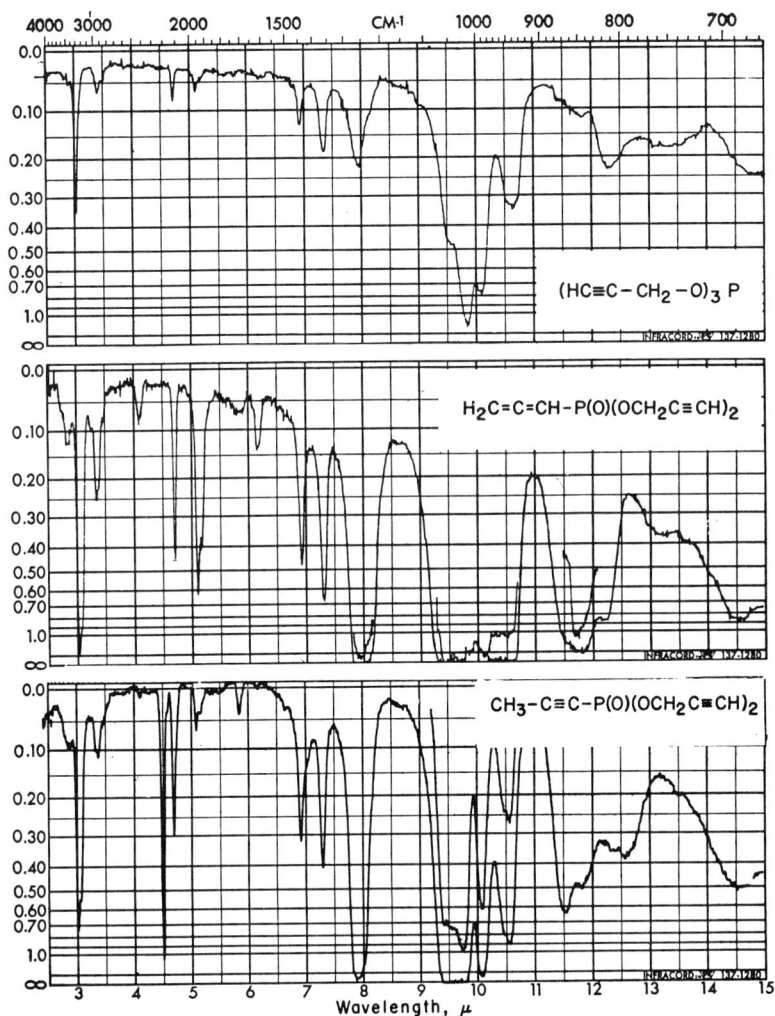

Fig. 8. Infrared spectra of interrelated acetylenic phosphorus compounds: tripropargyl phosphite and its allenic and acetylenic rearrangement products.

(2107), or another phosphoryl substituent (2137 cm^{-1}). An extension of the range of the infrared frequencies of disubstituted acetylenes to read 2060–2260 cm^{-1} is thus warranted.

It is worth noting that the C≡C stretching frequencies of the first ten compounds (monosubstituted acetylenes) of Table 20 (2030–2075 cm^{-1}) are also outside the range quoted for this mode (2100–2140 cm^{-1}) (30a–30d), which thus should be modified accordingly.

TABLE 20

Infrared Frequencies of Acetylenic Phosphonates and of Reference Compounds (cm^{-1})

(all frequencies are stretching vibrations)

Compound	H–C≡C	H–C≡C	RC≡C	HC≡C	C≡C	P=O	P–O–C	Ref.
$(HC\equiv C)_3P$	3291	2054						68
$(HC\equiv C)_3P$	3323	2061						125
$HC\equiv CP(C_2H_5)_2$	3300	2030						117
$HC\equiv CP(C_6H_5)_2$	3280	2030						117
$HC\equiv CP(O)(OC_2H_5)_2$	3240	2068				1275		61
$HC\equiv CP(O)(OC_2H_5)_2$	3293	2073				1269		115
$HC\equiv CP(O)[OCH(CH_3)_2]_2$	3165	2075				1263		62
$HC\equiv CP(O)(C_6H_5)_2$		1040				1160		117
$HC\equiv CCH_2P(O)(OC_2H_5)_2$		2110				1260		124
$HC\equiv CC\equiv CP(C_6H_5)_2$	3300	2040	2150					117
$ClC\equiv CP(O)(OC_2H_5)_2$			2176			1280		61
$BrC\equiv CP(O)(OC_2H_5)_2$			2174			1250		115
$(C_2H_5)_2NC\equiv CP(O)(OC_2H_5)_2$			2154			1255		63
$(C_2H_5)_3SnC\equiv CP(O)(OC_2H_5)_2$			2107			1272		115
$CH_3C\equiv CPCl_2$			2183					116
$CH_3C\equiv CP(C_2H_5)_2$			2180					117
$CH_3C\equiv CP(C_6H_5)_2$			2190					117
$CH_3C\equiv CP(O)(OC_2H_5)_2$			2220			1268		124
$CH_3C\equiv CP(O)(OC_2H_5)_2$			2222			1254	1030	2b
$CH_3C\equiv CP(O)(OC_2H_5)_2$			2211			1260		10
$CH_3C\equiv CP(O)(OC_3H_7)_2$			2215			1260		4a
$CH_3C\equiv CP(O)(OCH_2C\equiv CH)_2$	3292		2219	2129		1260	1030	2b
$CH_3C\equiv CP(O)(OC_6H_5)_2$			2215			1285		12

Compound				Ref.
$CH_3C{\equiv}CP(O)O_2$ Ba	2200			13
$CH_3C{\equiv}CP(O)$ (catechol cyclic phosphate)	2210			148
$CH_3C{\equiv}CP(O)(OCH_2C{\equiv}CH)C_2H_5$	2210			12
$CH_3C{\equiv}CP(O)(SCH_3)_2$	2218	1205		24
$CH_3C{\equiv}CP(O)(C_6H_5)_2$	2200	1180		117
$CH_3C{\equiv}CP^{\oplus}(CH_3)(C_6H_5)_2I^{\ominus}$	2200		1310^b	117
$CH_3CH_2C{\equiv}CP(O)(OC_2H_5)_2$	2199			10
$CH_3CH_2C{\equiv}CP(O)(OC_2H_5)_2$	2200	1258		61
$CH_3CH_2C{\equiv}CP(O)(OC_2H_5)_2$	2170			117
$(CH_3)_2C(OH)C{\equiv}CP(C_6H_5)_2$	2200			117
$(CH_3)_2C(OH)C{\equiv}CP(O)(C_6H_5)_2$	2200	1170		117
$(CH_3)_2C(OH)C{\equiv}CP(S)(C_6H_5)_2$	2200		720^c	117
$(CH_3)_2C(OH)C{\equiv}CP^{\oplus}(CH_3)(C_6H_5)_2I^{\ominus}$	2200		1310^b	117
$CH_3C{\equiv}CCH_2P(O)(OC_2H_5)_2$	2238			10
$CH_3C{\equiv}CCH_2P(O)(OC_2H_5)_2$	2240	1260		64
$C_6H_5C{\equiv}CPCl_2$	2153			116
$C_6H_5C{\equiv}CP(CH_3)Cl$	2157			116
$C_6H_5C{\equiv}CP(C_2H_5)_2$	2160			117
$C_6H_5C{\equiv}CP(C_6H_5)_2$	2170			117
$C_6H_5C{\equiv}CP(O)(OC_2H_5)_2$	2175	1260		65
$C_6H_5C{\equiv}CP(O)(OC_2H_5)_2$	2170	1180		117
$C_6H_5C{\equiv}CP(O)(C_6H_5)_2$	2180	1180		117
$C_6H_5C{\equiv}CP(S)(C_6H_5)_2$	2180		720^c	117
$C_6H_5C{\equiv}CP^{\oplus}(CH_3)(C_6H_5)_2$	2190		1310^b	117
$H_2C{=}CHC{\equiv}CPCl_2$	2148			116
	3102			

(continued)

TABLE 20 (continued)

Compound	H—C≡C	H—C—C	RC≡C	HC≡C	C=C	P=O	P—O—C	Ref.
⬠—C≡CP(C₆H₅)₂ (cyclopentenyl)			2130	1600				117
⬡—C≡CP(C₂H₅)₂ (cyclohexenyl)			2140	1620				117
⬡—C≡CP(C₆H₅)₂ (cyclohexenyl)			2130	1620				117
⬭—C≡CP(C₆H₅)₂ (cycloheptenyl)			2130	1620				117
H₂C=CHC≡CP(O)(OC₂H₅)₂		3097, 3066	2225		1595	1257		10
H₂C=CHC≡CP(O)(OC₂H₅)₂			2175			1260		65
H₂C=CHC≡CP(O)(OC₂H₅)₂			2175			1260		64
CH₃CH=CHC≡CP(O)(OC₂H₅)₂			2175		1603			10
CH₃CH=CHC≡CP(O)(OC₂H₅)₂			2180			1260		64
H₂C=C(CH₃)C≡CP(O)(OC₂H₅)₂			2175			1260		64
H₂C=CHC≡CCH₂P(O)(OC₂H₅)₂			2225					10
CH₃C≡CC≡CP(C₂H₅)₂			2100, 2200					117
CH₃C≡CC≡CP(C₆H₅)₂			2100, 2210					117
CH₃C≡CC≡CP(O)(OC₂H₅)₂			2235, 2134			1260		66
CH₃C≡CC≡CP(O)(C₆H₅)₂			2120, 2220ᵈ			1190		117
CH₃C≡CC≡CP(S)(C₆H₅)₂			2120, 2220				720ᶜ	117

Compound	Frequencies		Ref.
$CH_3CH_2CH_2C{\equiv}CC{\equiv}CP(C_6H_5)_2$	2100, 2210		117
$CH_3CH_2C{\equiv}CC{\equiv}CP(O)(OC_2H_5)_2$	2224, 2132	1270	66
$C_6H_5C{\equiv}CC{\equiv}CP(C_6H_5)_2$	2210, 2200		117
$C_6H_5C{\equiv}CC{\equiv}CP(O)(C_6H_5)_2$	2130, 2200	1190	117
$CH_3C{\equiv}CC{\equiv}CC{\equiv}CP(C_6H_5)_2$	2060, 2100, 2200		117
$(C_6H_5)_2PC{\equiv}C$—⟨ring⟩—$C{\equiv}CP(C_6H_5)_2$	2160		117
$(C_6H_5)_2PC{\equiv}C$—⟨ring⟩—$C{\equiv}CP(C_6H_5)_2$	2160		117
$(C_2H_5O)_2P(O)C{\equiv}C$—⟨ring⟩—$C{\equiv}CP(O)(OC_2H_5)_2$	2137	1272	61
$(C_6H_5)_2P(O)C{\equiv}C$—⟨ring⟩—$C{\equiv}CP(O)(C_6H_5)_2$	2180	1200	117
$(C_6H_5)_2P(O)C{\equiv}C$—⟨ring⟩—$C{\equiv}CP(O)(C_6H_5)_2$	2180	1200	117
$(C_2H_5O)_2P(O)CH_2C{\equiv}CP(O)(OC_2H_5)_2$	2215		123
$(CH_3C{\equiv}C)_3PS$	2201		67
$(H_2C{=}CHC{\equiv}C)_2(C_6H_5)PS$	2161		67
$(C_6H_5C{\equiv}C)_3PS$	2171		67
$(C_6H_5C{\equiv}C)_2(C_6H_5)PS$	2168		67
$N{\equiv}CCH_2P(O)(OC_2H_5)_2$	2252ᵃ		61

a Absorbtion of $N{\equiv}C$.
b P—C stretch.
c P—S stretch.
d The value given in the reference paper is obviously a misprint.

The formation of 1-propynylphosphonic acid esters from 1,2-prop-adienylphosphonic acid esters thus concludes the series of easy rearrangements which started with a trivalent phosphorus ester of propargyl alcohol:

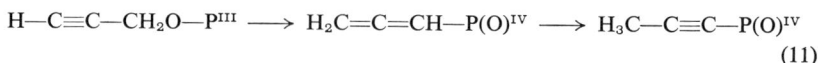

$$H-C{\equiv}C-CH_2O-P^{III} \longrightarrow H_2C{=}C{=}CH-P(O)^{IV} \longrightarrow H_3C-C{\equiv}C-P(O)^{IV}$$

(11)

To illustrate the value and efficiency of infrared in diagnosing the new structures, three scans, representing the three members of the full rearrangement sequence 11, are reproduced in Fig. 8.

(2) *Proton NMR.* The proton NMR data of acetylenic phosphonates and pertinent reference compounds are abstracted in Table 21. Like infrared, this instrumental method of structure proof is also very direct and unambiguous with acetylenic compounds. To illustrate the use of proton NMR, the scan of bis(2-propynyl) 1-propynylphosphonate is reproduced in Fig. 9.

The acetylenic phosphonates provide good examples both for the effect of the state of phosphorus on the magnitude of proton–phosphorus

TABLE 21

Proton NMR Characterization of Acetylenic Phosphorus Compounds

Compound	H	δ, ppm	No. of peaks	J_{HP}	J_{HH}	Solv.[a]	Ref.
$(HC{\equiv}C)_3P$		3.0	2	0.3			68
$H^AC{\equiv}CP(CH_2^BCH_3^C)_2$	A	2.70		<0.3		Te	113
	B	1.25				Te	113
	C	0.96				Te	113
	A	2.63				Ca	117
	A	2.63		<0.5		Ca	69
$H^AC{\equiv}CP(CH_2CH_2CH_2CH_3)_2$	A	2.67		<0.3		Te	113
	A	2.64				Ca	69
$H^AC{\equiv}CP[C(CH_3^B)_3]_2$	A	2.89		<0.3		Te	113
	B	1.20	2	12		Te	113
	A	3.07				Ca	117
$H^AC{\equiv}CP(C_6H_5)_2$	A	3.10		<0.5		Ca	69
$H^BC{\equiv}CP(O)(OCH_2^ACH_3^C)_2$	A	4.05					115
	B	3.70	2	13.9			115
	C	1.36					115
$H^AC{\equiv}CP(O)[OCH(CH_3)_2]_2$	A	3.69	2	11			62
	A	3.55	2	12			66

(continued)

TABLE 21 (*continued*)

Compound	H	δ, ppm	No. of peaks	J_{HP}	J_{HH}	Solv.[a]	Ref.
$H^AC{\equiv}CP(O)(CH_2^BCH_3^C)_2$	A	3.18	2	9		Te	113
	B	1.65				Te	113
	C	1.10				Te	113
$H^AC{\equiv}CP(O)(CH_2CH_2CH_2CH_3)_2$	A	2.97	2	9		Te	113
$H^AC{\equiv}CP(O)[C(CH_3^B)_3]_2$	A	3.08	2	8.5		Te	113
	B	1.41	2	16		Te	113
$H^AC{\equiv}CP(O)(C_6H_5)_2$	A	3.33		9.7		Ca	69
	A	3.33	2	9.7		Ca	117
$H^AC{\equiv}CC{\equiv}CP(C_6H_5)_2$	A	2.30		1.4		Ca	69
	A	2.30	2	1.45		Ca	117
$ClC{\equiv}CP(O)(OCH_2^ACH_3^B)_2$	A	4.7[b]					61
	B	1.70[b]					61
$(CH_3^DCH_2^B)_2NC{\equiv}CP(O)(OCH_2^ACH_3^C)_2$	A	4.40[b]	M				63
	B	3.45[b]	4		D7.0		63
	C,D	1.65[b]					63
$CH_3^AC{\equiv}CP(C_2H_5)_2$	A	1.93		0.9		Ca	69
	A	1.93	2	0.92		Ca	117
$CH_3^AC{\equiv}CP(C_6H_5)_2$	A	2.09		1.7		Ca	69
	A	2.09	2	1.7		Ca	117
$C_6H_5C{\equiv}CP(CH_3^A)Cl$	A			11.95			116
$CH_3^AC{\equiv}CPCl_2$	A			8.25			116
$CH_3^BC{\equiv}CP(O)(OCH_3^A)_2$	A	3.65	2	11			70
	B	2.04	2	4.6			70
$CH_3^BC{\equiv}CP(O)(OCH_2^ACH_3^C)_2$	A	4.00	2×4	8.2	C7.0	Be	2b
	B	1.65	2	4.7		Be	2b
	C	1.25	3		A7.0	Be	2b
	B			7.4			66
	A	4.35	M				10
	B	2.35	2				10
	C	1.60	3				10
	A	4.00	5				70
	B	2.02	2	4.6			70
	C	1.30	3				70
$CH_3^CC{\equiv}CP(O)(OCH_2^AC{\equiv}CH^B)_2$	A	4.66	2×2	11.0	B2.40	Ne	2b
	B	3.04	3		A2.40	Ne	2b
	C	2.07	2	4.80		Ne	2b
$H^CC{\equiv}CCH_2^BP(O)(OCH_3^A)_2$	A	3.73	2	11			70
	B	2.70	2×2	21.9	C2.8		70
	C	2.18	2×3	6.7	B2.8		70
$CH_3^CC{\equiv}CCH_2^BP(O)(OCH_2^ACH_3^D)_2$	A	4.00	2×4	8.1	D7.0	Ne	2b
	B	2.80	2×4	22.0	C2.7	Ne	2b
	C	1.79	2×3	6.2	B.27	Ne	2b
	D	1.25	3		A7.0	Ne	2b
	A	4.20	M				64

(*continued*)

TABLE 21 (continued)

Compound	H	δ, ppm	No. of peaks	J_{HP}	J_{HH}	Solv.[a]	Ref.
CH$_3^C$C≡CCH$_2^B$P(O)(OCH$_2^A$CH$_3^D$)$_2$	B	3.0	M	22			64
	C	2.05	M				64
	D	1.5–1.6	M				64
CH$_3$CH$_2^A$C≡CP(O)(OCH$_2$CH$_3$)$_2$	A	2.60[b]	M				61
N≡CCH$_2^A$P(O)(OCH$_2$CH$_3$)$_2$	A	3.45[b]	2	20.4			61
CH$_3^A$C≡CP(O)(C$_2$H$_5$)$_2$	A	2.02		3.5		De	69
	A	2.02	2	3.5		Ca	117
CH$_3^A$C≡CP(O)(C$_6$H$_5$)$_2$	A	2.11		3.8		Ca	69
	A	2.11	2	3.8		Ca	117
CH$_3^A$C≡CP(O)F$_2$	A			±[c]			118
CH$_3^A$C≡CP(S)(C$_6$H$_5$)$_2$	A	2.18		4.1		Ca	69
	A	2.15	2	4		Ca	117
CH$_3^B$C≡CP$^{\oplus}$(CH$_3^A$)(C$_6$H$_5$)$_2$I$^{\ominus}$	A	3.04		14		De	69
	B	2.43		4.6		De	69
	B	2.43	2	4.6		Ca	117
CH$_3^A$C≡CC≡CP(C$_6$H$_5$)$_2$	A	2.00		1.3		Ca	69
	A	2.00	2	1.3		Ca	117
CH$_3^A$C≡CC≡CC≡CP(C$_6$H$_5$)$_2$	A	1.99		0.7		Ca	69
	A	1.99	2	0.7		Ca	117
CH$_3^B$C≡CC≡CP(O)(OCH$_2^A$CH$_3^C$)$_2$	A	4.5					66
	B	2.4	2		2.15		66
	C	1.8	3				66
CH$_3$CH$_2^A$C≡CC≡CP(O)(OCH$_2$CH$_3$)$_2$	A	3.0	4				66
H$_2^B$C=C=CH^{A}C≡CP(O)(OCH$_2^C$CH$_3^D$)$_2$	A,B	6.2					64
	C	4.2					64
	D	1.5	3				64
CH$_3^D$CH^B=CH^{A}C≡CP(O)(OCH$_2^C$CH$_3^E$)$_2$	A,B	6.2					64
	C	4.20	M				64
	D	2.1	2				64
	E	1.5–1.6	3				64
	D	2.15	2				10
H$_2^A$C=C(CH$_3^C$)C≡CP(O)(OCH$_2^B$CH$_3^D$)$_2$	A	5.9					64
	B	4.2	M				64
	C	2.2	1				64
	D	1.5–1.6	3				64
H$_2^B$C=CH^{A}C≡CCH$_2^D$P(O)(OCH$_2^C$CH$_3^E$)$_2$	A,B	5.8					10
	C	4.2					10
	D	3.6					10
	E	1.5					10
CH$_3^A$C≡CC≡CP(O)(C$_6$H$_5$)$_2$	A	2.03		1.6		Ca	69
	A	2.03	2	1.65		Ca	117
CH$_3^A$C≡CC≡CP(S)(C$_6$H$_5$)$_2$	A	2.06		1.8		Ca	69
	A	2.03	2	1.8		Ca	117

[a] Be, benzene; Ca, carbon tetrachloride; De, deuteriochloroform; Ne, neat; Te, tetrachloroethylene.
[b] Calculated from external water reference.
[c] $^1J_{PF}$ is of the opposite sign, $\mp$.

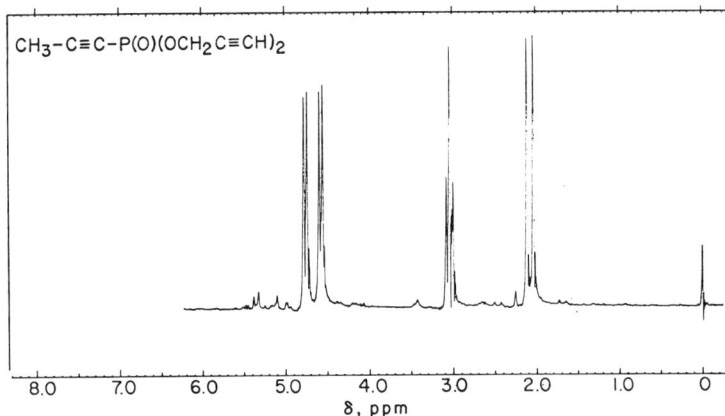

Fig. 9. The proton NMR spectrum of bis(2-propynyl) 1-propynyl phosphonate, $CH_3C{\equiv}CP(O)(OCH_2C{\equiv}CH)_2$ (neat, int. TMS, 60 Mc).

coupling and for long-range coupling between these nuclei. The inter-actions are illustrated by the examples shown in Table 22.

The first two compounds (Table 22a) underline the importance of the s character of the bond through which the coupling is taking place. Tri-alkylphosphines are considered to utilize basically the p electrons of phosphorus, leaving much of the non-bonding electrons in the s shell. Some s character in their bonds is however indicated by the greater than 90° bond angles found in these compounds. Trialkylphosphine oxides (and the alkylphosphonium compounds) are sp^3 hybrids, with much higher percentage of s character in their bonds. Since coupling in the saturated systems takes place predominantly via a sigma electron contact mecha-nism, the magnitude of coupling is proportional to the percent s character present in the hybridized orbital used in forming the bond (50). In addition to the basic hybridization state of phosphorus, the electronegative nature of the substituents also affects the s character of the bonds considerably.

TABLE 22a

The correlation of structure with J_{HP} in homologous acetylenic compounds

R	n^a	$RP(C_6H_5)_2$	$RP(O)(C_6H_5)_2$
$HC{\equiv}C-$	3	~0.3	9.7
$H_3CC{\equiv}C-$	4	1.7	3.8
$H_3CC{\equiv}CC{\equiv}C-$	6	1.3	1.6
$H_3CC{\equiv}CC{\equiv}CC{\equiv}C-$	8	0.7	—

^{a} n = number of bonds intervening between coupled nuclei.

TABLE 22b

The correlation of structure with J_{HP} and J_{HH} in various acetylenic compounds

R	n^a	R—P^{III}	R—$P(O)^{IV}$	R—H	Ref.
H—C≡C—	3	0.3	9.7–12.0	9.5–9.8	42a,42b
H₃C—C≡C—	4	0.9–1.7	4.6–4.8	2.1–3.6	32,49b, 71a,44b
H—C≡C—CH₂—	4		6.7		
H₃C—C≡C—CH₂—	5		6.2	2.7–2.9	49b,72
H—C≡C—C≡C—	5	1.4		2.2	35
H₃C—C≡C—C≡C—	6	1.3	1.6–2.15	1.27	35
H₃C—C≡C—C≡C—CH₂—	7			1.3	35
H₃C—C≡C—C≡C—C≡C—	8	0.7			
H₃C—C≡C—C≡C—C≡· C—CH(OH)—	9			0.4	35

^{a} n = number of bonds intervening between coupled nuclei.

Utilizing the concept developed by Bent (21), one can expect that the attachment of an electronegative substituent to a trivalent phosphorus will concentrate the s orbital in the hybrid orbitals directed to the less electronegative groups, while itself will make use predominantly of p orbitals. The thirtyfold increase in coupling in ethynyldiphenylphosphine on its conversion to the phosphine oxide provides good support for the concept.* The effect becomes strongly attenuated by additional intervening bonds and the ratio of $^4J_{HP}$'s is reduced to 2.2 and of $^5J_{HP}$'s to 1.2.

The second part of Table 22 compares phosphorus–proton coupling constants through increasing number of intervening bonds in tri- and tetrasubstituted phosphorus compounds and proton–proton couplings in the analogous hydrocarbon series. As it was found in allenes and allenic phosphorus compounds, the phosphorus–proton couplings are about twofold of the comparable proton–proton couplings. Based on the data provided by the hydrocarbon examples, phosphorus–proton coupling thus might be detectable through 10–12 intervening bonds.

(3) Phosphorus NMR. The unambiguity in proving the structure of products shown by ^{31}P NMR in the propargyl phosphite–allenylphos-

---

* Other cogent examples which illustrate the enhancement by an electronegative substituent of the phosphorus–proton coupling through one, two, and three bonds are dimethylphosphine, $(CH_3)_2PH$, $^1J_{HP}$ 191.6, $^2J_{HP}$ 3.6, and trimethylphosphonium chloride, $(CH_3)_3PH^{\oplus}Cl^{\ominus}$, $^1J_{HP}$ 515, $^2J_{HP}$ 16.6 Hz (73,74); trimethylphosphine, $(CH_3)_3P$, $^2J_{HP}$ 2.7, trimethylphosphine oxide, $(CH_3)PO$, $^2J_{HP}$ 13.4, and tetramethylphosphonium iodide, $(CH_3)_4P^{\oplus}I^{\ominus}$, $^2J_{HP}$ 14.4 Hz; triethylphosphine, $(CH_3CH_2)_3P$, triethylphosphine oxide, $(CH_3CH_2)_3PO$, and tetraethylphosphonium iodide, $(CH_3CH_2)_4P^{\oplus}I^{\ominus}$, in which $^2J_{HP}$ are 0.5, 11.9, and 13.0 Hz and $^3J_{HP}$ are 13.7, 16.3, and 18.0 Hz, respectively (50).

TABLE 23
^{31}P NMR Chemical Shifts of Various Diethyl
Alrylphosphonates,[a] $RP(O)(OC_2H_5)_2$ (52)

R	Carbon neighbors of P	δ, ppm
Alkyl	C—C—PO	$-30\text{-}-40$
2-Alkenyl	C=C—C—PO	$-27\text{-}-28$
1-Alkenyl	C=C—PO	$-22\text{-}-24$
2-Alkynyl	C≡C—C—PO	$-19\text{-}-20$[b]
Aryl	C_6H_5—PO	-17
Allenyl	C=C=C—PO	$-11\text{-}-18$[c]
1-Alkynyl	C≡C—PO	$+5\text{-}+10$[b]

[a] Coined name to include all kinds of hydrocarbon substituents.
[b] See Table 24.
[c] See Table 15.

phonate rearrangement manifests itself equally well in the allenylphosphonate–alkynylphosphonate isomerization also. Due to the strong
diamagnetic anisotropic shielding by the acetylenic function along the
axis of the sp carbons (75), the resonance of phosphorus is considerably
more upfield than in systems where an sp^3 or an sp^2 carbon is attached
directly to it. Outlines of the ^{31}P resonance limit of the three groups of

TABLE 24
^{31}P NMR Characterization of Dialkyl Alkynylphosphonates

Compound	δ, ppm (H_3PO_4)	Ref.
$CH_3C\equiv CP(O)(OC_2H_5)_2$	$+9$	66
$CH_3C\equiv CP(O)(OCH_2C\equiv CH)_2$	$+6.1$	2b
$CH_3CH_2C\equiv CP(O)(OC_2H_5)_2$	$+9$	10
⟨H⟩—C≡CP(O)(OC$_2$H$_5$)$_2$	$+6.2$	2b
⟨○⟩—C≡CP(O)(OC$_2$H$_5$)$_2$[a]	ca. $+5\text{-}+10$	65
$H_2C=CH—C\equiv CP(O)(OC_2H_5)_2$[a]	ca. $+5\text{-}+10$	65
$H_2C=CH—C\equiv CP(O)(OC_2H_5)_2$[a]	$+9$	64
$CH_3C\equiv CC\equiv CP(O)(OC_2H_5)_2$[a]	$+9$	66
$CH_3C\equiv CCH_2P(O)(OC_2H_5)_2$	-19	10
$CH_3C\equiv CCH_2P(O)(OC_2H_5)_2$	-20	64

[a] These compounds were not prepared via the allenic precursors.

diethyl hydrocarbonphosphonates and of several subgroups are given in Table 23. Although there is some overlap in the chemical shifts of phosphonates with sp^3 and sp^2 carbons, caused by influences of the second and third neighbors from phosphorus, the chemical shifts of sp-carbonphosphonates are far upfield and readily diagnosable.

The chemical shifts of alkynylphosphonates are abstracted in Table 24, where a few compounds, prepared by routes other than the isomerization of allenylphosphonates, are included for comparison.

(4) *Ultraviolet.* The ultraviolet spectrum of bis(2-propynyl) 1-propynylphosphonate, $CH_3CCP(O)(OCH_2CCH)_2$, has a low intensity absorbtion at λ_{max} (cyclohexane) 227 mμ, ϵ 41 (24). Since isolated acetylenes do not absorb significantly above 200 mμ, the observed maximum probably corresponds to the electronic transition observed in saturated phosphonates, e.g., $CH_3P(O)(OCH_3)_2$, λ_{max} 217 mμ, ϵ 32 (56c).

c. Reactions of the Rearrangement Products. The only type of reaction investigated, to a limited extent, was the nucleophilic addition to dialkyl 1-propynylphosphonates. This was found to proceed as with diisopropyl ethynylphosphonate (62). Thus the nucleophiles prepared from sodium ethoxide and ethyl- and propylmercaptan, diethylamine, piperidine, dimethyl, diethyl, and dipropyl phosphonates were found to yield both 1:1 and 2:1 adducts **20** and **21**, respectively, while ethanol, malonic, cyanoacetic, aceto-acetic, and phosphonoacetic esters, as well as selenophenol, yielded, under similar conditions, 1:1 adducts **20** only (76–78).

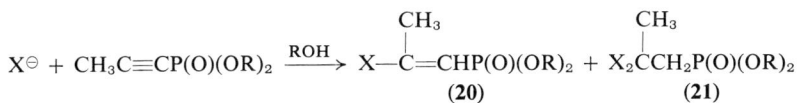

$$X^{\ominus} + CH_3C{\equiv}CP(O)(OR)_2 \xrightarrow{\text{ROH}} \underset{(20)}{X{-}\overset{CH_3}{\underset{|}{C}}{=}CHP(O)(OR)_2} + \underset{(21)}{X_2\overset{CH_3}{\underset{|}{C}}CH_2P(O)(OR)_2}$$

Only the 2:1 adduct **21** was isolated from the reaction of diethylthiophosphonate, $(C_2H_5O)_2P(S)H$, and diethyl 1-propynylphosphonate (77). No information on the stereochemistry of any of the 1-1 adducts **20** is available.

O,O-Diethyl dithiophosphoric acid was found to react with diethyl and dibutyl 1-propynylphosphonates in the absence of base, merely on heating, to yield the 1:1 addition product corresponding to **20** (127). Again, the stereochemistry of the mode of addition is not known.

The reaction of propargyl alcohol with *N,N*-dialkyl phosphoramidous esters at 80–100° was found to yield 2-(dialkylamino)propenylphosphonic esters in high yield (126). The reaction was interpreted as taking place via an alcoholysis step followed by isomerization of the incipient propargyl ester to the allenic phosphonate, followed by a second isomerization to the 1-propynylphosphonate and by addition of the dialkylamine generated in the alcoholysis step to the acetylenic compound to yield again the product represented by **20**.

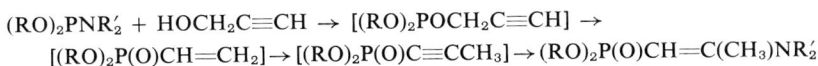

$$(RO)_2PNR_2' + HOCH_2C\equiv CH \rightarrow [(RO)_2POCH_2C\equiv CH] \rightarrow$$
$$[(RO)_2P(O)CH=CH_2] \rightarrow [(RO)_2P(O)C\equiv CCH_3] \rightarrow (RO)_2P(O)CH=C(CH_3)NR_2'$$

2. Reactions of Allenylphosphonic Acid Esters with Nucleophiles

Except for their isomerization to alkynylphosphonates (*vide supra*), the chemistry of allenylphosphonates was studied only to a very limited extent. Thus the esters of a few allenic phosphonic and phosphinic acids were transformed into the free acids and into their sodium and barium salts (13,14). Diethyl 3-methyl-1,2-butadienylphosphonate was reported to form addition products with methyl and ethyl alcohol and with diethyl phosphonate, $(C_2H_5O)_2P(O)H$, in the presence of base catalysts (27,29):

$$(CH_3)_2C=C=CHP(O)(OC_2H_5)_2 + HX \xrightarrow{base} (CH_3)_2CHCX=CHP(O)(OC_2H_5)_2$$

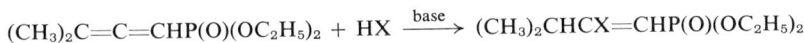

More recent work (128), however, established that the addition of nucleophiles (alcohols and dialkylphosphonates in the presence of base, and diethylamine and piperidine) takes place not as above, but according to the following equation:

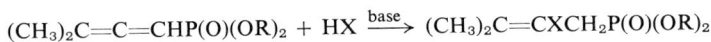

$$(CH_3)_2C=C=CHP(O)(OR)_2 + HX \xrightarrow{base} (CH_3)_2C=CXCH_2P(O)(OR)_2$$

Alkyl mercaptans, as well as malonic cyanoacetic, acetoacetic, and phosphonoacetic esters add similarly (129).

The formation of a diphosphine dioxide in the hydrogenation of l-phenylpropa-1,2-dienyldiphenylphosphine oxide is also due, very likely, to the addition of diphenlyphosphine oxide (formed by hydrogenolysis) to the allene (147):

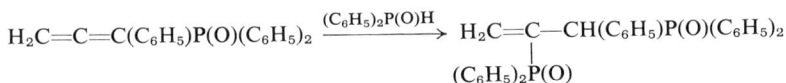

$$H_2C=C=C(C_6H_5)P(O)(C_6H_5)_2 \xrightarrow{(C_6H_5)_2P(O)H} H_2C=C-CH(C_6H_5)P(O)(C_6H_5)_2$$
$$\underset{(C_6H_5)_2P(O)}{|}$$

Dialkyl allenylphosphonate esters were found to be reduced stereospecifically by hydrogen in the presence of palladium on calcium carbonate catalyst in alcohol solution to *cis*-alkylvinylphosphonates, an underpopulated class of compounds which thus becomes readily accessible (114):

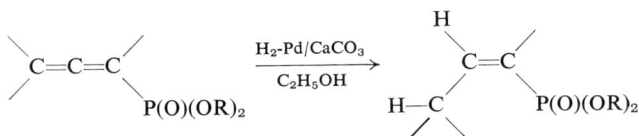

Similar was the finding of another research group: 3-methylbuta-1,2-dienyldiphenylphosphine oxide absorbed, under the same mild conditions, 1 mole of hydrogen to yield the vinylphosphine oxide as the major isomer (147).

$$(CH_3)_2C=C=CHP(O)(C_6H_5)_2 \longrightarrow$$

$$(CH_3)_2CHCH=CHP(O)(C_6H_5)_2 + (CH_3)_2C=CHCH_2P(O)(C_6H_5)_2$$
$$45\% \qquad\qquad\qquad\qquad\qquad 16\%$$

The formation of clean *cis* adducts matches the results of a study of the stereochemistry of the palladium-catalyzed hydrogenation of allenes, in which it was found that *cis* products predominated and that there was a general correlation between steric accessibility of a double bond from a particular direction and its ability to undergo hydrogenation (146).

A recent review on organophosphorus compounds containing acetylenic and dienic substituents has a small section on the chemistry and spectroscopy of the allenic and acetylenic phosphorus compounds obtained by the uncatalyzed rearrangement of tervalent phosphorus esters (149). A second review, this one on the chemistry of allenes, also contains references to the rearrangement above (150), as does a review of organometallic acetylenes of main groups III–V (151).

III. THE REARRANGEMENT OF 2,3-BUTADIENYL PHOSPHITES

A. Nature and Mechanism of the Rearrangement

The uncatalyzed rearrangement of propargylic phosphites to allenylphosphonates was shown to proceed by an intramolecular mechanism, in which the nucleophilic phosphorus approached and became attached to the distant acetylenic carbon via a five-membered cyclic transition state. Another class of compounds which has an *sp* carbon in the same relationship to phosphorus and which thus could undergo rearrangement by a similar mechanism consists of the 2,3-butadienyl esters of tervalent phosphorus acids (Eq. 12).

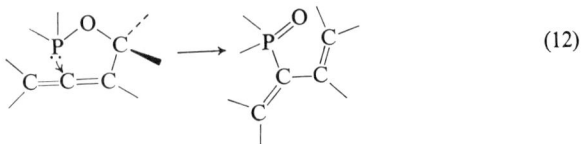

$$(12)$$

Indeed, it was found that several phosphorous esters of the allenyl alcohol, 2,3-butadien-1-ol, underwent a thermal, uncatalyzed rearrangement and yielded the butadienephosphonic acids expected from the a priori mechanism outlined above (31) (Eq. 13).

$$(H_2C{=}C{=}CHCH_2O)PX_2 \longrightarrow \underset{\underset{P(O)X_2}{|}}{H_2C{=}C{-}CH{=}CH_2} \qquad (13)$$

The rearrangement of the allenyl esters occurred only slowly at moderate (below 60–70°) temperatures, thus it was possible to use vacuum distillation in their fractionation. At higher temperatures, however, isomerization of the esters started and proceeded at 112–114° at a rate which was convenient to follow by infrared and phosphorus NMR. The rearrangement of the tervalent ester in this temperature range was essentially complete in 6–7 hr.* Under the thermolysis conditions, however, the primary product underwent excessive Diels-Alder dimerization, Phosphorus NMR indicates the formation of isomeric structures by the presence of chemical shifts at -20 and -30 ppm (H_3PO_4). Properties of the tervalent phosphorus esters and of their rearrangement products are summarized in Tables 25 and 26 (part A), respectively.

Due to their stability at room temperature, some of the tervalent phosphorus esters of the allenyl alcohol (2,3-butadien-1-ol) were readily characterized by, e.g., oxidizing them with air, sulfur, and selenium and by reacting them with hexachlorocyclopentadiene (31).

Substituted butadienylphosphonic acid derivatives (24) became available from the esterification, and subsequent rearrangement, at or below room temperature, of substituted allenyl alcohols (23), themselves products of rearrangement of acetylenic glycols (22) on esterification with one molar equivalent of phosphorous halides [(11); cf. Table 1].

$$(HO)R_2CC{\equiv}CCR_2(OH) + (R'O)_2PCl \longrightarrow$$
$$(22)$$

$$\left[\underset{\underset{OP(OR')_2}{|}}{(HO)R_2CC{\equiv}CCR_2}\right] \longrightarrow \underset{\underset{P(O)(OR')_2}{|}}{(HO)R_2C{-}C{=}C{=}CR_2} \xrightarrow{(R''O)_2PCl}$$
$$(23)$$

$$\left[\underset{\underset{P(O)(OR')_2}{|}}{(R''O)_2POCR_2{-}C{=}C{=}CR_2}\right] \longrightarrow \begin{array}{c} \underset{\underset{(R''O)_2(O)P{-}C{=}CR_2}{|}}{R_2C{=}C{-}P(O)(OR')_2} \end{array} \qquad (14)$$
$$(24)$$

* The persistence of residual characteristic allene absorbtion in the 1950–1960 and 845–850 cm^{-1} regions was traced to the presence of small amounts of the oxidation products of the tervalent esters, i.e., $(H_2C{=}C{=}CHCH_2O)P(O)(OC_2H_5)_2$ (31).

TABLE 25

Tervalent Phosphorus Esters of Allenic Alcohols

ROPX$_2$

Substituent		Characterization			
R	X	mp bp/mm	$n_D/t°$	Other	Ref.
H$_2$C=C=CHCH$_2$—	—OC$_2$H$_5$	40–41/0.03	1.4530/25	A,I,H,P	31
H$_2$C=C=CHCH$_2$—	—OCH$_2$CH=C=CH$_2$		1.4985/25	A,I,H,P	31
H$_2$C=C=CHCH$_2$—	—C$_6$H$_5$			I	31

TABLE 26

Butadienephosphonic Acid Esters

Substituent		Characterization			
X	R	bp/min	$n_D/t°$	Other[a]	Ref.

A. Monophosphonic acid

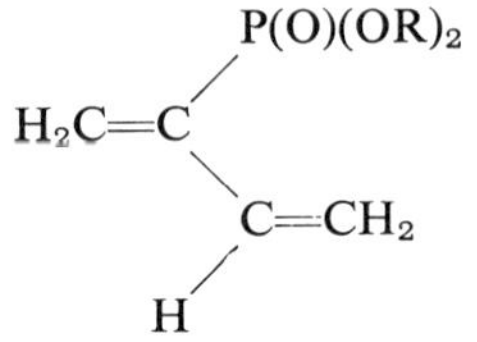

$$\underset{H}{\overset{P(O)(OR)_2}{H_2C=C}}\diagdown\underset{}{C=CH_2}$$

	C$_2$H$_5$		1.4700/25	A,I,P	31

B. Diphosphonic acids

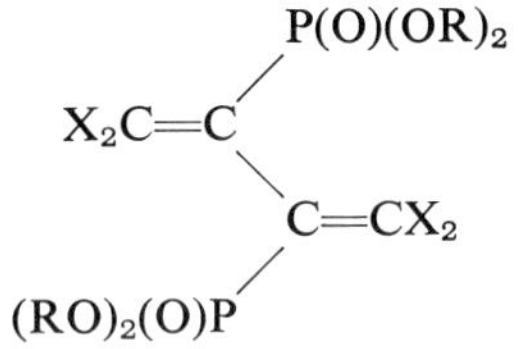

$$\underset{(RO)_2(O)P}{\overset{P(O)(OR)_2}{X_2C=C}}\diagdown C=CX_2$$

X	R	bp/min	$n_D/t°$	Other[a]	Ref.
H	C$_2$H$_5$	156–157/2	1.4638/20	A,I	4b
H	C$_3$H$_7$	183–184/4	1.4612/20	A,I	4b
H	C$_4$H$_9$	168–169/0.05	1.4605/20	A,I	4b
CH$_3$	C$_2$H$_5$	153–154/2	1.4740/20	A,I	11
CH$_3$	C$_3$H$_7$	179–181/2	1.4690/20	A,I	11
CH$_3$	C$_4$H$_9$	167–169/0.025	1.4798/20	A,I	11

[a] A, elemental analysis; I, infrared; P, phosphorus NMR.

Starting with glycol (**22**) and two moles of the phosphorous halide, butadiene-2,3-diphosphonic acid derivatives (**24**) became accessible directly without the necessity of isolation of the allenic alcohol (**23**) (4b,11).*

The physical properties of various 1,3-butadiene-2,3-diphosphonic acid esters are summarized in Table 26 (Part B).

Consideration of the stereochemistry of the rearrangement indicates that although there is a convenient all-planar alignment of the participating atoms in the initiation step, a 90° turn in each of the two incipient olefinic moieties is necessary prior to the formation of the butadiene structure (Fig. 10).

Although the available data do not allow a choice between the conceivable concerted or stepwise pathways [the ionic intermediate (**25**) shown in Fig. 10 serves only to illustrate the geometry of a hypothetical intermediate], a similarity in mechanism with the propargylic phosphite rearrangement is indicated by the rate accelerating effect of methyl substituents on the sp^3 carbons (2,11). This feature suggests the importance of the carbon–oxygen bond breaking phase of the postulated mechanism in the rate determining step (cf. Section II-A) and thus lends support to a concerted process.

Their reactivity in the rearrangement reaction of unsaturated phosphorous esters places allenyl phosphites in an intermediate position between acetylenic (propargyl) and olefinic (allyl) phosphites (*vide infra*). Directly comparable are the diethyl phosphorous esters of the parent unsaturated alcohols

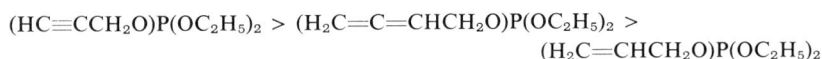

$$(HC\equiv CCH_2O)P(OC_2H_5)_2 > (H_2C=C=CHCH_2O)P(OC_2H_5)_2 >$$
$$(H_2C=CHCH_2O)P(OC_2H_5)_2$$

which undergo uncatalyzed rearrangement with rates of approximately the same order of magnitude at 30, 110, and 180–190°, respectively (31).

Although the sequence of decreasing rates follows the sequence of

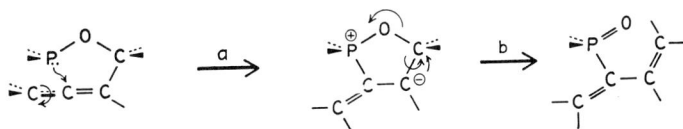

Fig. 10. A possible reaction path for the rearrangement of tervalent phosphorus esters of 2,3-butadien-1-ols.

* The reaction product of 2-butyne-1,4-diol with two moles of diphenylphosphinous chloridite (diphenylchlorophosphine) was apparently incorrectly identified as 1,3-butadiene-1,4-bis(diarylphosphine oxide), $R_2P(O)CH=CHCH=CHP(O)R_2$, (1), instead of a 2,3-disubstituted butadiene.

decreasing electronegativities of the carbon atoms in the unsaturated portions of the molecule ($sp^{1 \cdot 0}$, $sp^{1 \cdot 67}$, and $sp^{2 \cdot 0}$, respectively), a qualitative comparison is only warranted, because other features, mainly the geometry of the transition states, which would affect rates in a parallel decreasing order, are probably superposed to those originating from differences in electronegativities of the carbon atoms.

B. Spectroscopic Analyses

1. Infrared

Data of the infrared spectroscopic analyses of the tervalent phosphorus esters of 2,3-butadien-1-ol are abstracted in Table 27 and of the

TABLE 27

Characterization of Some of the Tervalent Phosphorus Esters of
2,3-Butadien-1-ol by Infrared (cm^{-1})

$(H_2C{=}C{=}CHCH_2O)PX_2$

Substituent	Stretching vibration[a]			Wag[a]	
X	H—C≡C	C=C=C	P—O—C	=CH₂	Ref.
—OC₂H₅	3070	1960	1030	846	31
—OCH₂CH=C=CH₂	3065	1955	975	848	31
—C₆H₅	3070	1952	985	848	31

[a] The corresponding vibrations in the parent alcohol, $H_2C{=}C{=}CHCH_2OH$, occur at 3060, 1955, 1012 (C—O), and 848 cm^{-1}, respectively.

TABLE 28

Characterization of Butadienephosphonic Acid Esters by Infrared (cm^{-1})

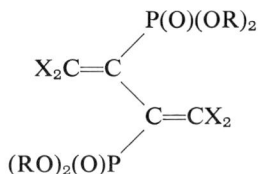

$$P(O)(OR)_2$$
$$X_2C{=}C$$
$$C{=}CX_2$$
$$(RO)_2(O)P$$

Substituent		Stretching vibration			
X	R	H—C=C	C=C	P=O	Ref.
H	C₂H₅	3104	1575	1250	4b
H	C₃H₇	3104	1575	1250	4b
H	C₄H₉	3104	1575	1250	4b
CH₃	C₂H₅		1633, 1614	1250	11
CH₃	C₃H₇		1629, 1614	1250	11
CH₃	C₄H₉		1619	1250	11

butadiene phosphonic acid derivatives are summarized in Table 28. The values fall in ranges defined earlier (Section II-B-1) and thus support the structures indicated.

2. Proton NMR

Results of the proton NMR analysis of an allenyl phosphite, diethyl 2,3-butadienyl phosphite, are summarized in Table 29. The values are in the ranges attached to the diagrams in Fig. 5 and confirm the structure indicated.

3. Phosphorus NMR

As was the case with 2-alkynyl phosphites, phosphorus NMR is again the most direct method of establishing the status of phosphorus in the esters of allenyl alcohols and in their rearrangement products. The high downfield resonance of diethyl 2,3-butadienyl phosphite at -141 ppm confirms the tervalent phosphorus ester structure for the starting material and the -20 ppm resonance is in the general area found in olefinic (vinyl) phosphonates (Tables 23 and 37). Due to the absence of additional NMR data on butadienyl mono- and diphosphonic acid derivatives, no correlations or interpretations are feasible at the present.

C. Reactions of the Rearrangement Products

While allenyl phosphites were shown to undergo various reactions characteristic for tervalent phosphorus esters (e.g., oxidation by oxygen, sulfur, selenium, reaction with hexachlorocyclopentadiene) (31), only two types of reactions were reported for the rearrangement products of substituted allenyl phosphites:

a. Nucleophiles (derived from dimethyl phosphonate, diethyl phosphonate, ethylmercaptan, and diethylamine with sodium ethoxide in ethanol) were described (80) to yield 1:1 adducts with tetraethyl 1,3-butadiene-2,3-diphosphonic and esters:

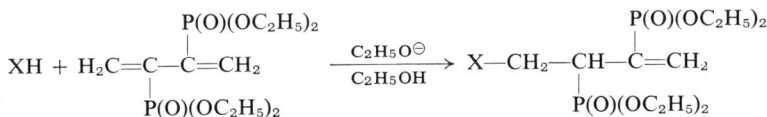

$$XH + H_2C{=}C{-}\underset{\underset{P(O)(OC_2H_5)_2}{|}}{\overset{\overset{P(O)(OC_2H_5)_2}{|}}{C}}{=}CH_2 \xrightarrow[C_2H_5OH]{C_2H_5O^{\ominus}} X{-}CH_2{-}CH{-}\underset{\underset{P(O)(OC_2H_5)_2}{|}}{\overset{\overset{P(O)(OC_2H_5)_2}{|}}{C}}{=}CH_2$$

b. The reaction of tetraethyl 1,3-butadiene-2,3-diphosphonate with acrylonitrile was reported to give the Diels-Alder adduct with the participation of the ethylene moiety as the dienophile (4b).

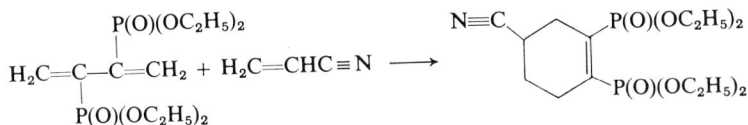

$$H_2C{=}C{-}\underset{\underset{P(O)(OC_2H_5)_2}{|}}{\overset{\overset{P(O)(OC_2H_5)_2}{|}}{C}}{=}CH_2 + H_2C{=}CHC{\equiv}N \longrightarrow$$

TABLE 29
Proton NMR Analysis of an Allenyl Phosphite

Compound	H	δ, ppm	No. of peaks	J_{HP}, Hz	J_{HH}, Hz	Solvent[a]	Ref.
$(H_2^BC{=}C{=}CH^ACH_2^CO)P(OCH_2^DCH_3^E)$	A	5.29	5		B, 6.50	De	31
	B	4.80	2×3		C, 2.50	De	31
	C	4.33	$2 \times 2 \times 3$	8.4	A, 6.80	De	31
	D	3.88	2×4	8.0	E, 7.00	De	31
	E	1.27	3		D, 7.00	De	31

[a] De, deuteriochloroform.

IV. THE REARRANGEMENT OF 2-ALKENYL ESTERS

A. Nature and Mechanism of the Rearrangement

The facile, often spontaneous, rearrangement of tervalent phosphorus esters of 2-propyn-1-ols was interpreted to take place via an $S_N i'$ mechanism (2). The ease of rearrangement was attributed to both the high electronegativity of the acetylenic carbons, which invite intramolecularly the nucleophilic attack of a conveniently located tervalent phosphorus, and to a very favorable planar transition state which requires minimum changes in the positions and in the bond angles of the participating atoms in accordance with the principle of least motion (see Section IV-A-2).

Although the double-bonded analogs of 2-propynyl esters, the 2-propenyl (allyl) phosphites, could undergo rearrangement by a similar mechanism, it was pointed out that they are stable under conditions at which the acetylenic esters isomerize readily. It was also indicated that no all-planar transition state can be constructed with the allyl esters (2).

Inspection of molecular models illustrates that in the planar alignment of the five participant atoms, the nonbonding electrons of phosphorus are orthogonal to the olefinic pi electrons and that overlap between them can occur only by considerable twisting and thus by destruction of planarity (Fig. 11).

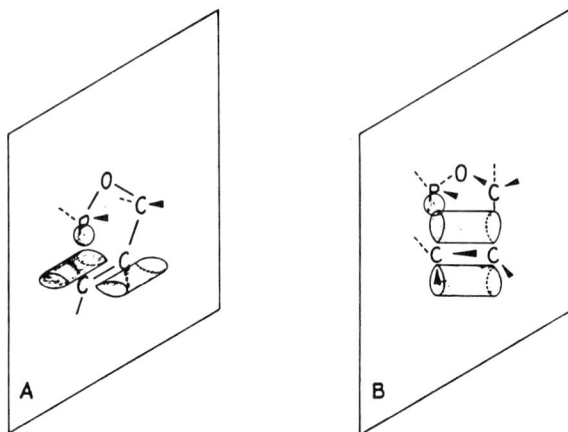

Fig. 11. Two of the possible alignments of the atoms participating in the five-membered, cyclic transition state: (A) coplanar arrangement in which there is no overlap between the unshared electron pair of phosphorus and the pi electrons of the olefinic moiety; (B) staggered arrangement in which overlap between the electrons of phosphorus and of the olefinic bond is possible.

To effect the twisting necessary for effective overlap, and thus for the reaction to take place, a thermolysis route was considered and applied (81).

Preliminary experiments at 200° with triallyl phosphite and tris-(2-methylallyl) phosphite indicated the formation of viscous or glasslike, apparently polymeric, reaction products which rendered spectral analyses difficult, although the complete disappearance of the tervalent ester and the formation of phosphonic acid esters were clearly indicated.

To eliminate or to reduce complicating side reactions which would blur the main objective, that is, to determine whether an $S_N i'$ rearrangement would occur with the double bond homologs of the 2-propynyl esters, more reactive phosphorus derivatives were sought which would allow the study of their thermolytic behavior at lower reaction temperatures. Based on data obtained with 2-propynyl phosphites, esters of α,α-dimethylallyl alcohol, (2-methyl-3-buten-2-ol) were chosen as the model compounds.

The thermolysis temperature of $144 \pm 1°$ was selected after initial experiments indicated that diethyl 2,2-dimethylallyl phosphite (26) $[H_2C{=}C(CH_3)_2CO]P(OC_2H_5)_2$, the model ester, rearranged completely at 200° within 1 hr, but only slightly at 120° during 5 hr. The progress of the rearrangement was followed by phosphorus NMR, using the small samples of the ester sealed in 5 mm o.d. precision tubes under nitrogen, which allowed analyses without opening the tubes. Graphic integration indicated the following percent of rearrangement (disappearance of 26): 1 hr, 42%; 2 hr, 54%; 3 hr, 66%; 4 hr, 69%; 5 hr, 73%; and 6 hr, 81%. On heating, the ^{31}P NMR peak of 26 at -133.9 ppm diminished parallel with the increase of a new peak at -27.5 ppm. Two additional small peaks, at -21.2 and $+7.4$ ppm (all are referenced to external phosphoric acid), appeared slowly in the scans, which were always of the same shape and of matching intensities and which were subsequently identified as belonging to diethyl phosphonate $(C_2H_5O)_2P(O)H$, (27), having the center of the doublet at -6.9 ppm and a separation of peaks, J_{HP}, of 695 Hz.

The main ^{31}P NMR peak at -27.5 ppm showed good match with that of an allylphosphonic acid ester, diethyl allylphosphonate $(-27.6$ ppm; Table 37), and consequently the reaction product was identified as diethyl 3-methyl-2-butenylphosphonate, $(CH_3)_2C{=}CHCH_2P(O)(OC_2H_5)$, (28) after the structure was confirmed by elemental analyses, proton NMR (Table 35) and infrared (Table 33). The rearrangement given by Eq. 15 is indicated.

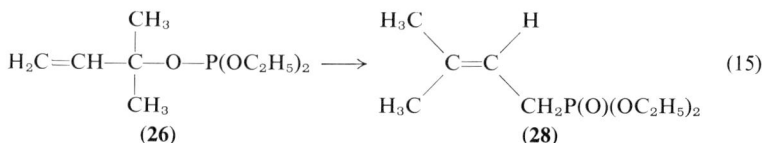

$$
\begin{array}{ccc}
& \underset{\displaystyle (26)}{\overset{\displaystyle CH_3}{\underset{\displaystyle CH_3}{H_2C{=}CH{-}\overset{|}{\underset{|}{C}}{-}O{-}P(OC_2H_5)_2}}} & \longrightarrow \qquad
\begin{array}{c}
\underset{\displaystyle (28)}{\overset{\displaystyle H_3C}{\underset{\displaystyle H_3C}{}}}\!\!\!\!\!\diagdown\!\!\!\!C{=}C\!\!\!\!\diagup\overset{\displaystyle H}{\underset{\displaystyle CH_2P(O)(OC_2H_5)_2}{}}
\end{array}
\qquad (15)
\end{array}
$$

The presence of **27** in the reaction mixture was also confirmed by proton NMR and its origin was traced to the decomposition of **26** to **27** and isoprene, which in turn was identified by infrared.

The thermolytic rearrangement of **26** to **28** is, accordingly, analogous to the spontaneous rearrangement of diethyl 1,1-dimethyl-2-propynyl phosphite, $[HC \equiv C(CH_3)_2CO]P(OC_2H_5)_2$, and follows, very likely, the S_Ni' route postulated for the latter (Section II).

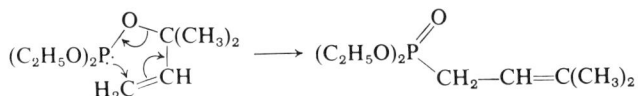

$$(C_2H_5O)_2P \underset{H_2C \overset{||}{\underset{}{\subset}} CH}{\overset{O \frown C(CH_3)_2}{\diagdown}} \longrightarrow (C_2H_5O)_2P \overset{O}{\diagdown} CH_2 - CH = C(CH_3)_2$$

Due to the reduced electronegativity of the sp^2 carbon(s) and to the nonplanar cyclic transition state postulated in the concerted mechanism (*vide supra*), considerably higher temperatures are required to effect the rearrangement of allyl phosphites than that of the corresponding propargyl phosphites. Thus while the acetylenic analog of **26** undergoes rearrangement practically instantaneously to the allenic phosphonate, the isomerization of the allyl ester requires several hours at 144°. Similar relationship emerges from the comparison of unsubstituted propargyl and allyl phosphites, e.g., $(HC \equiv CCH_2O)P(OC_2H_5)_2$ and $(H_2C = CHCH_2O)P(OC_2H_5)_2$, which have comparable rates of isomerization at about 25° and 190–200°, respectively. As it was indicated earlier (Section III) the comparable rearrangement temperature of the unsaturated phosphite with one sp and two sp^2 carbons, $(H_2C = C = CHCH_2O)P(OC_2H_5)_2$, which occupies thus an intermediate position between propargyl phosphites (two sp carbons) and allyl phosphites (two sp^2 carbons), was found to be about 110° (31).

The competing side reaction, resulting in the formation of diethyl phosphonate (**27**) and isoprene, probably also follows an intramolecular route, which is initiated by a nucleophilic attack on hydrogen and involves a five-membered cyclic transition state and a concerted process (Eq. 16).

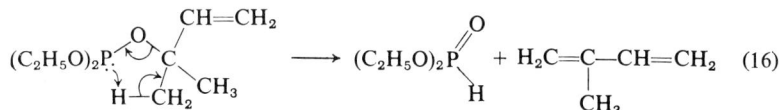

$$(C_2H_5O)_2P \underset{H - CH_2}{\overset{O \diagdown \overset{CH = CH_2}{C} }{\diagdown}} CH_3 \longrightarrow (C_2H_5O)_2P \underset{H}{\overset{O}{\diagdown}} + H_2C = \underset{CH_3}{\overset{|}{C}} - CH = CH_2 \quad (16)$$

A similar proton transfer mechanism was suggested in the thermal decomposition of tri-tert-butyl phosphite (82; cf. 83).

As turned out to be the case with propargyl phosphites, the rearrangement of allyl phosphites was also reported by various research groups within one year. Thus in addition to the investigation described above (81), which focused mainly on α,α-dimethylallyl phosphite (**26**), the rearrangements of diethyl allyl phosphite, $(H_2C = CHCH_2O)P(OC_2H_5)_2$

(29), of diethyl α-methylallyl phosphite, $[H_2C=CH(CH_3)CHO]P(OC_2H_5)_2$
(30), and of diethyl 2-butenyl (crotyl) phosphite, ($trans$-$CH_3CH=$
$CHCH_2O)P(OC_2H_5)_2$ (31) were the subject of two research papers (84,85).
The earliest observation about the instability of an allyl ester of a
tervalent phosphorus acid was made when allyl diphenylphosphinite
$(H_2C=CHCH_2O)P(C_6H_5)_2$ (32) was found to react vigorously on
attempted distillation at 160° yielding allyldiphenylphosphine oxide,
$H_2C=CHCH_2P(O)(C_6H_5)_2$ (33) (86).

The data obtained from these investigations indicate the following
order of relative reactivities of the allylic esters in the isomerization reaction:

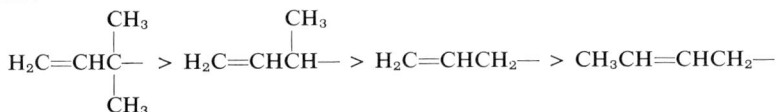

$$
\underset{\underset{CH_3}{|}}{\overset{\overset{CH_3}{|}}{H_2C=CHC-}} \;>\; \overset{\overset{CH_3}{|}}{H_2C=CHCH-} \;>\; H_2C=CHCH_2- \;>\; CH_3CH=CHCH_2-
$$

which thus parallel the relative reactivities found in the propargyl esters (2):

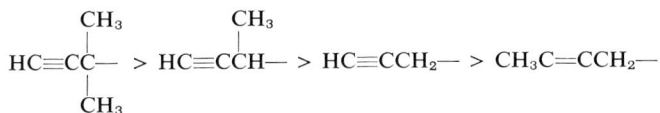

$$
\underset{\underset{CH_3}{|}}{\overset{\overset{CH_3}{|}}{HC\equiv CC-}} \;>\; \overset{\overset{CH_3}{|}}{HC\equiv CCH-} \;>\; HC\equiv CCH_2- \;>\; CH_3C\equiv CCH_2-
$$

and which, accordingly, lends support to the postulated S_Ni' mechanism
for both the propargyl and allyl esters (2,81,84,85) ($vide\ supra$). The following examples are illustrative:

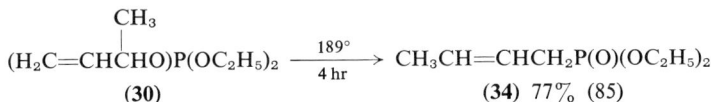

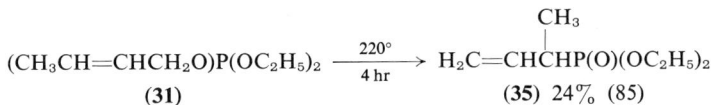

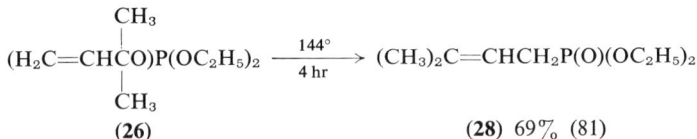

$$
\overset{\overset{CH_3}{|}}{(H_2C=CHCHO)P(OC_2H_5)_2} \xrightarrow[4\,hr]{189°} CH_3CH=CHCH_2P(O)(OC_2H_5)_2
$$
$$
\textbf{(30)} \qquad\qquad\qquad\qquad\qquad \textbf{(34)}\ 77\%\ (85)
$$

$$
(CH_3CH=CHCH_2O)P(OC_2H_5)_2 \xrightarrow[4\,hr]{220°} \overset{\overset{CH_3}{|}}{H_2C=CHCHP(O)(OC_2H_5)_2}
$$
$$
\textbf{(31)} \qquad\qquad\qquad\qquad\qquad \textbf{(35)}\ 24\%\ (85)
$$

$$
\underset{\underset{CH_3}{|}}{\overset{\overset{CH_3}{|}}{(H_2C=CHCO)P(OC_2H_5)_2}} \xrightarrow[4\,hr]{144°} (CH_3)_2C=CHCH_2P(O)(OC_2H_5)_2
$$
$$
\textbf{(26)} \qquad\qquad\qquad\qquad\qquad \textbf{(28)}\ 69\%\ (81)
$$

More insight into and support for the reaction mechanism was obtained
from a kinetic study which indicated that the rearrangement of 30 is a
first-order reaction (87). This information, plus the absence of isomeric
products (e.g., 35) in the thermolysis of 30, support the S_Ni' mechanism
and argues against a possible fragmentation-recombination mechanism
(87).

The isomerization of **31**, which required the relatively most drastic conditions (200° and above), yielded, in addition to **35**, also considerable amounts of **34** (85,87). For instance

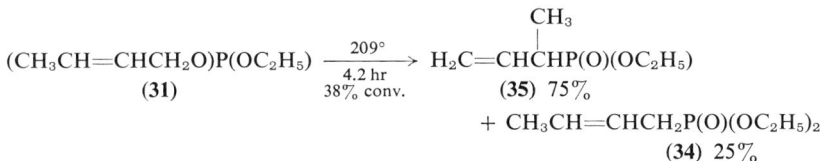

$$(CH_3CH=CHCH_2O)P(OC_2H_5) \xrightarrow[4.2\ hr]{209°} \underset{(35)\ 75\%}{H_2C=CHCHP(O)(OC_2H_5)}$$
$$\underset{(31)}{} \qquad 38\%\ conv.$$
$$\overset{CH_3}{|}$$
$$+\ CH_3CH=CHCH_2P(O)(OC_2H_5)_2$$
$$(34)\ 25\%$$

and (87)

$$(CH_3CH=CHCH_2O)P(OisoPr)_2 \xrightarrow[4.0\ hr]{209°}$$
$$\underset{(36)}{} \qquad 30\%\ conv.$$
$$\overset{CH_3}{|}$$
$$\underset{(37)\ 57\%}{H_2C=CHCHP(O)(OisoPr)_2} +\ \underset{(38)\ 43\%}{CH_3CH=CHCH_2P(O)(OisoPr)_2}$$

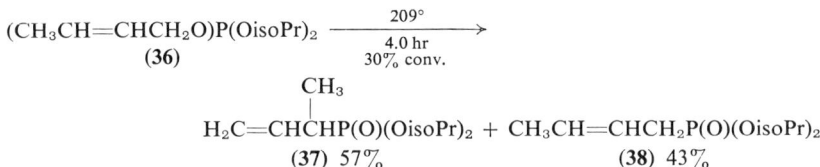

That the bulk of **34** does not originate from the isomerization of **35** was shown in separate experiments, in which **35** yielded only 7% of **34** at 220° in 2 hr (85,87).

It was found, however, that deliberate addition of **35** or diethyl phosphonate, $HP(O)(OC_2H_5)_2$ (**27**), or diethyl ethylphosphonate, $C_2H_5P(O) \cdot (OC_2H_5)_2$ (**39**) (present in small amounts in the reaction mixture), enhances the formation of **34** from **31** without influencing the slow isomerization of **35** to **34** (85,87).

A role for the phosphoryl group in facilitating the conversion of olefinic phosphites, which undergo rearrangement with difficulty and which require strenuous conditions (e.g., **31,36**), to isomeric phosphonates was suggested (87) on the basis of similar effects observed and studied in the isomerization of alkyl phosphites (81; Section V).

The rearrangement of phosphonous and phosphinous esters was studied with allyl and substituted allyl phenyl- and ethylphosphonites (135) and with diphenyl- and diethylphosphinites (88,135,139). These studies provided additional proof for the complete inversion of the allyl groups in the uncatalyzed isomerization reaction and indicated, at the same time, that the rearrangement of phosphinites takes place more readily than that of the corresponding phosphonites, which in turn require less drastic conditions than phosphites. The following examples are illustrative:

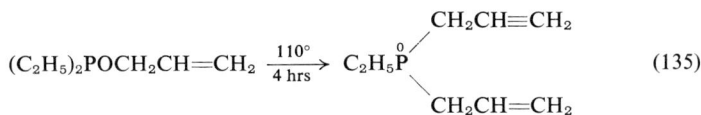

$$(C_2H_5)_2POCH_2CH=CH_2 \xrightarrow[4\ hrs]{110°} C_2H_5\overset{\displaystyle O}{\underset{\displaystyle}{P}}\!\!\begin{array}{c} CH_2CH=CH_2 \\ \\ CH_2CH=CH_2 \end{array} \qquad (135)$$

TABLE 30

Allylic Esters of Tervalent Phosphorus Acids

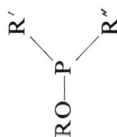

$$\text{RO}-\text{P} \begin{array}{c} \diagup \text{R}' \\ \diagdown \text{R}'' \end{array}$$

Substituents			Characterization by			
R	R'	R''	mp (°C) or bp°/mm	$n_D/t°$	Other[a]	Ref.
$H_2C=CHCH_2-$	$-OC_2H_5$	$-OC_2H_5$	38–39/0.6	1.4218/25	A,I,P	81
$H_2C=CHCH_2-$	$-OC_2H_5$	$-OC_2H_5$	98.0–0.2/60		A,H	87
$H_2C=CHCH_2-$	$-OC_2H_5$	$-OC_2H_5$	60–61/12	1.4282/20	A,M	84
$H_2C=CHCH_2-$	$-OCH(CH_3)_2$	$-OCH(CH_3)_2$	96.0/25		A,H	87
$H_2C=CHCH_2-$	$-OCH_2CH=CH_2$	$-OCH_2CH=CH_2$			A,I,P	81
$H_2C=CHCH_2-$	$-OCH_2CH=CH_2$	$-C_2H_5$	67–67.5/10	1.4450/20	A,I,M	135
$H_2C=CHCH_2-$	$-OCH_2CH=CH_2$	$-C_6H_5$	92–93/0.5	1.5300/20	A,I,M	135
$H_2C=CHCH_2-$	$-OCH_2CH=CH_2$	$-C_6H_4Cl(P)$	116–117/1	1.5410/20	A,I,M	135
$H_2C=CHCH_2-$	$-OCH_2CH=CH_2$	$-C_6H_4CH_3(P)$	97–98/0.3	1.5288/20	A,I,M	135
$H_2C=CHCH_2-$	$-OCH_2CH=CH_2$	$-C_6H_4N(CH_3)_2(P)$	114–115/0.03	1.5645	A,I,M	135
$H_2C=CHCH_2-$	$-C_2H_5$	$-C_2H_5$	46–47/17	1.4530	A,I,M	135
$H_2C=CHCH_2-$	$-C_6H_5$	$-C_6H_5$	93–94/0.2	1.590	A,I,M	135
$H_2C=CHCH_2-$	$-C_6H_5$	$-C_6H_5$			A	86
$H_2C=CH(CH_3)CH-$	$-OC_2H_5$	$-OC_2H_5$	68–69/15	1.4268/20	A,I,M	84
$H_2C=CH(CH_3)CH-$	$-OC_2H_5$	$-OC_2H_5$	87.0–87.5/27		A,H	87
$H_2C=CH(CH_3)CH-$	$-OCH(CH_3)CH=CH_2$	$-OCH(CH_3)CH=CH_2$		1.4442/24	A,I	31

			bp (°C/mm)	n_D		Ref.
H₂C=CH(CH₃)CH—	—OCH(CH₃)CH=CH₂	—C₂H₅	50–51/3	1.4470	A,I,M	135
CH₃CH=CHCH₂—	—OCH₂CH=CHCH₃	—C₂H₅	70.5–71/2	1.4628	A,I,M	135
CH₃CH=CHCH₂—	—OCH₃	—OCH₃	102/68		I,P	87
CH₃CH=CHCH₂—	—OC₂H₅	—OC₂H₅	88–89/17	1.4357/20	A,I,M	84
CH₃CH=CHCH₂—	—OC₂H₅	—OC₂H₅	81.0/8		A,H	87
CH₃CH=CHCH₂—	—OCH(CH₃)₂	—OCH(CH₃)₂	99.1–0.5/15		A	87
CH₃CH=CHCH₂—	—OCH₂CH=CHCH₃	—OCH₂CH=CHCH₃			A,I	24
H₂C=CH(CH₃)₂C—	—OC₂H₅	—OC₂H₅		1.4502/25	A,H,I,P	89,90
H₂C=CH(CH₃)₂C—	—OC₂H₅	—OC₂H₅	75.0–75.3/10	1.4298/25	A	87
H₂C=CH(CH₃)₂C—	—OC(CH₃)₂CH=CH₂	—OC(CH₃)₂CH=CH₂			A,I,P	89,90
H₂C=CH(CH₃)₂C—	—OC(CH₂)₂CH=CH₂	—OC(CH₂)₂CH=CH₂			A,I,P	89,90
CH₃CH=CH(CH₃)CH—	—OC₂H₅	—OC₂H₅	101/27		A	87

a For abbreviations see footnote of Table 1.

TABLE 31

Tetrasubstituted Phosphorus Compounds Obtained from Allylic Esters of Tervalent Phosphorus Acids

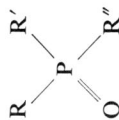

$$R \overset{R'}{\underset{O}{\overset{|}{P}}} R''$$

R	R'	R″	mp (°C) or bp°/mm	$n_D/t°$	Other[d]	Ref.
H₂C=CHCH₂—	—OC₂H₅	—OC₂H₅		1.4280/25	A,I	81
H₂C=CHCH₂—	—OC₂H₅	—OC₂H₅	97–98/16	1.4313/20	A,I,M	84
H₂C=CHCH₂—	—OC₂H₅	—OC₂H₅			A,I,H	87
H₂C=CHCH₂—	—OCH(CH₃)₂	—OCH(CH₃)₂			I	87
H₂C=CHCH₂—	—OCH₃	—OCH₂CH=CH₂			H,I	87
H₂C=CHCH₂—	—OCH₂CH=CH₂	—OCH₂CH=CH₂			A,I,P	81
H₂C=CHCH₂—	—OCH₂CH=CH₂	—C₂H₅	86.5–88/2	1.4612/25	A,M	135
H₂C=CHCH₂—	—OCH₂CH=CH₂	—C₆H₅	129–130/0.5	1.4655/20	A,M	135
H₂C=CHCH₂—	—OCH₂CH=CH₂	—C₆H₄Cl(P)	148–149/2	1.5250/20	A,M	135
H₂C=CHCH₂—	—OCH₂CH=CH₂	—C₆H₄CH₃(P)	122–123/0.3	1.5410/20	A,M	135
H₂C=CHCH₂—	—OCH₂CH=CH₂	—C₆H₄N(CH₃)₂(P)	146–147/0.03	1.5314/20	A,M	135
H₂C=CHCH₂—	—C₂H₅	—C₂H₅	78–80/2	1.5695/20	A,M	135
H₂C=CHCH₂—	—C₆H₅	—C₆H₅		1.4760/20	A,M	135
H₂C=CHCH₂—	—C₆H₅	—C₆H₅	94–94.5		A,M	86
H₂C=CH(CH₃)CH—	—OC₂H₅	—OC₂H₅	104–105/14	1.4323/20	A,I,M	84
H₂C=CH(CH₃)CH—	—OC₂H₅	—OC₂H₅			H,I	85
H₂C=CH(CH₃)CH—	—OCH(CH₃)₂	—OCH(CH₃)₂			I	87

			mp/bp	n		Ref.
$H_2C=CH(CH_3)CH-$	$-OCH_2CH=CHCH_3$	$-C_2H_5$	90–90.5/2	1.4698	A,M	135
$CH_3CH=CHCH_2$	$-OCH(CH_3)CH=CH_2$	$-C_2H_5$	97–98/2.5	1.4620	A,M	135
$H_2C=CH(CH_3)CH-$	$-C_6H_5$	$-C_6H_5$	90–91		A,H,I	88
$H_2C=CH(C_6H_5)CH-$	$-C_6H_5$	$-C_6H_5$	193–193.5		A,I	88
$CH_3CH=CHCH_2-$	$-OCH_3$	$-OCH_3$			H,I	87
$CH_3CH=CHCH_2-$	$-OC_2H_5$	$-OC_2H_5$	100.5/7	1.4379/20	A,I,M	84
$CH_3CH=CHCH_2-$	$-OC_2H_5$	$-OC_2H_5$			H,I	87
$CH_3CH=CHCH_2-$	$-OCH(CH_3)_2$	$-OCH(CH_3)_2$			H,I	87
$C_6H_5CH=CHCH_2-$	$-C_6H_5$	$-C_6H_5$	181–182		A,I	88
Z^a	$-C_6H_5$	$-C_6H_5$	113–114		A,I	88
Z^a	$-C_6H_5$	$-C_6H_5$	113–114			139
Z^b	$-C_6H_5$	$-C_6H_5$	221–222		A,H,I	88
Z^c	$-C_6H_5$	$-C_6H_5$	126–127		A,H,U	88
Z^e	$-C_6H_5$	$-C_6H_5$	68–69		A,I	139
$H_2C=CH(CH_3)_2C-$	$-C_6H_5$	$-C_6H_5$	105–106		A,H,I	139
$(CH_3)_2C=CHCH_2-$	$-OC_2H_5$	$-OC_2H_5$			A,H,I	81
$(CH_3)_2C=CHCH_2-$	$-OC_2H_5$	$-OC_2H_5$			H,I	87
$(CH_3)_2C=CHCH_2-$	$-C_6H_5$	$-C_6H_5$	124–125		A,I	88
$(CH_2)_5C=CHCH_2-$	$-C_6H_5$	$-C_6H_5$	166–167		A,I	88
$CH_3CH=CH(CH_3)CH-$	$-OC_2H_5$	$-OC_2H_5$			H,I	87

[a] Z = geranyl, $(-CH_2CH=C(CH_3)CH_2CH_2CH=C(CH_3)_2$.

[b] $Z = -CH_2CH=CHCH=CHC_6H_5$.

[c] $Z = -CH_2CH=C(CH_3)CH=CHC-\ CCH_3$.

$(CH_3)_2C-(CH_2)_3$

[d] For abbreviations see footnote of Table 1.

[e] Z = linalyl, $-C(CH_3)(CH=CH_2)CH_2CH_2CH=C(CH_3)_2$.

405

TABLE 31a
First Order Rate Constants of the Isomerization of
Diallyl Alrylphosphonites (135)

Ester	$k \times 10^5$, sec^{-1}	
	at 120°	at 130°
$C_2H_5P(OCH_2CH=CH_2)_2$	2.33 ± 0.1	6.03 ± 0.12
$C_2H_5P(OCH_2CH=CHCH_3)_2$	2.68 ± 0.16	
$C_2H_5P[OCH(CH_3)CH=CH_2]_2$	30.00 ± 1.1	
$C_6H_5P(OCH_2CH=CH_2)_2$	5.88 ± 0.25	

$$C_2H_5P(OCH_2CH=CH_2)_2 \xrightarrow[\text{8 hrs}]{135°} C_2H_5\overset{O}{P}\Big\langle\begin{matrix}OCH_2CH=CH_2\\ \\CH_2CH=CH_2\end{matrix} \qquad (135)$$

$$(C_2H_5O)_2POCH_2CH=CH_2 \xrightarrow[\text{5 hrs}]{90°} (C_2H_5O)_2\overset{O}{P}CH_2CH=CH_2 \quad (84,87)$$

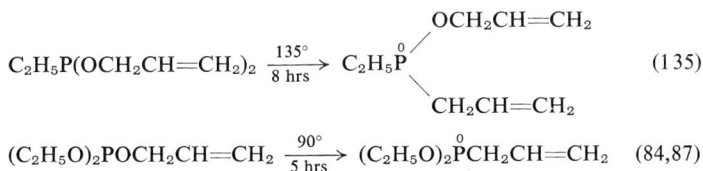

A kinetic study by dilatometric method indicated that the isomerization of allyl phosphonites, like that of allyl phosphites (87), is a first order reaction and yielded the rate constants abstracted in Table 31a.

For $C_2H_5P(OCH_2CH=CH_2)_2$ the activation energy of the rearrangement was found to be 29.9 kcal/mole and the activation entropy-4 eu (135).

The structures and methods of characterization of the allylic esters and of their rearrangement products are shown in Tables 30 and 31.

B. Spectroscopic Analyses

1. Infrared and Raman

In addition to the carbon–hydrogen stretching frequencies summarized in Table 9, characteristic vibrations, which occur in the infrared spectra of olefinic phosphorus compounds, are outlined in Table 32. The infrared characterization of allylic phosphites and of their rearrangement products, as well as related and reference compounds, is abstracted in Table 33a and 33b. Since the rearrangement of allyl esters produces allyl-phosphorus compounds, having a saturated carbon between the olefinic and phosphorus moieties, no mutual effect between these groups is feasible and therefore the infrared spectra of the primary products match closely the literature examples and data, which were obtained mainly from hydrocarbon models. Deviations from the literature ranges of isolated double bonds were, however, noted in both the infrared and Raman spectra of

TABLE 32

Infrared and Raman Vibrations of Groups Present in Olefinic Phosphorus Compounds (cm^{-1}) (30)

Assignment Group	ν_{asym} =CH₂	ν =C—H	ν_{sym} =CH₂	Overtone =CH₂	ν C=C	δ (in plane) =C—H	δ (out-of-plane) =C—H	=CH₂
R—CH=CH₂	2097–3075	3040–3010	3040–2950	1860–1800	1648–1638	1420–1400 1300–1290	995–985	910–905
R₂C=CH₂	3100–3077			1800–1750	1661–1639	1420–1400		895–885
R H \\ / C=C / \\ H R		3050–3000			1678–1668	1310–1295	980–960	
R R \\ / C=C / \\ R H		3050–3000			1662–1631	1429–1397	800–650	
R₂C=CHR R₂C=CR₂ C=C—C=C		3050–2990			1692–1665 1680–1665 1651–1600	~1380	840–790	

Stretching vibrations: P=O, 1350–1140 cm^{-1}; P—O—C(sp^3), 1055–950 cm^{-1}.

TABLE 33a

Infrared Characterization of Allyl Phosphites (cm^{-1})

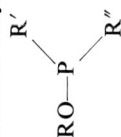

$$RO-P\begin{array}{c} R' \\ R'' \end{array}$$

Substituent			Stretch		Other	Ref.
R	R'	R''	=C–H	C=C		
H$_2$C=CHCH$_2$—	—OC$_2$H$_5$	—OC$_2$H$_5$	3096	1640		81
H$_2$C=CHCH$_2$—	—OCH$_2$CH=CH$_2$	—OCH$_2$CH=CH$_2$	3085	1645		81
H$_2$C=CH(CH$_3$)CH—	—OC$_2$H$_5$	—OC$_2$H$_5$	3080	1650		84
H$_2$C=CH(CH$_3$)CH—	—OCH(CH$_3$)CH=CH$_2$	—OCH(CH$_3$)CH=CH$_2$	3040	1640		81
CH$_3$CH=CHCH$_2$	—OCH$_3$	—OCH$_3$		1675	1186, CH$_3$OP	87
CH$_3$CH=CHCH$_2$—	—OC$_2$H$_5$	—OC$_2$H$_5$	3030	1660		84
CH$_3$CH=CHCH$_2$—	—OCH$_2$CH=CHCH$_3$	—OCH$_2$CH=CHCH$_3$	3040	1640		81
H$_2$C=CH(CH$_3$)$_2$C—	—OC$_2$H$_5$	—OC$_2$H$_5$	3086	1634		81
H$_2$C=CH(CH$_3$)$_2$C—	—OC$_2$H$_5$	—OC(CH$_3$)$_2$CH=CH$_2$	3125	1634		81

TABLE 33b

Characterization of Tetrasubstituted Allyl and Vinyl Phosphorus Compounds

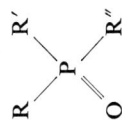

$$\begin{array}{c} R \quad R' \\ \diagdown P \diagup \\ \diagup \diagdown \\ O \quad R'' \end{array}$$

Substituent			Stretching vibrations				Ref.
R	R'	R''	=C—H	C=C	P=O	Other	
			A. By Infrared (cm^{-1})				
H_2C=$CHCH_2$—	—OC_2H_5	—OC_2H_5	3040	1640	1260		81
H_2C=$CHCH_2$—	—OC_2H_5	—OC_2H_5		1644	1260		87
H_2C=$CHCH_2$—	—OC_2H_5	—OC_2H_5	3090	1643	1262	1420	84
H_2C=$CHCH_2$—	—OC_2H_5	—OC_2H_5	3090	1625			91
H_2C=$CHCH_2$—	—OC_2H_5	—OC_2H_5	3090	1641		1422	99
H_2C=$CHCH_2$—	—$OCH(CH_3)_2$	—$OCH(CH_3)_2$		1640	1252		87
H_2C=$CHCH_2$—	—OCH_3	—OCH_2CH=CH_2		1649	1255	1188: CH_3OP	87
H_2C=$CHCH_2$—	—OCH_2CH=CH_2	—OCH_2CH=CH_2	3096	1634	1247		81
H_2C=$CH(CH_3)CH$—	—OC_2H_5	—OC_2H_5	3090	1642	1256	1420	84
H_2C=$CH(CH_3)CH$—	—OC_2H_5	—OC_2H_5		1642	1255	1208 shoulder	87
H_2C=$CH(CH_3)CH$—	—$OCH(CH_3)_2$	—$OCH(CH_3)_2$		1642	1255	1212 shoulder	87
H_2C=$CH(CH_3)CH$—	—C_6H_5	—C_6H_5			1180	990, 920, CH=CH_2	88
H_2C=$CH(C_6H_5)CH$—	—C_6H_5	—C_6H_5			1175	990, 920, CH=CH_2	88
H_2C=$CH(CH_3)_2C$—	—C_6H_5	—C_6H_5			1180	990,917, CH=CH_2	139

(continued)

TABLE 33b (*continued*)

Substituent			Stretching vibrations				
R	R'	R''	=C—H	C=C	P=O	Other	Ref.
Y^e	—C$_6$H$_5$	—C$_6$H$_5$			1170	995, 910, CH=CH$_2$	139
CH$_3$CH=CHCH$_2$—	—OCH$_3$	—OCH$_3$			1255	1188:CH$_3$OP	87
CH$_3$CH=CHCH$_2$—	—OC$_2$H$_5$	—OC$_2$H$_5$	3030	1657	1252		84
CH$_3$CH=CHCH$_2$—	—OC$_2$H$_5$	—OC$_2$H$_5$		1649	1255		87
CH$_3$CH=CHCH$_2$—	—OC$_2$H$_5$	—OC$_2$H$_5$		1630			91
CH$_3$CH=CHCH$_2$—	—OC$_2$H$_5$	—OC$_2$H$_5$	3027				99
CH$_3$CH=CHCH$_2$—	—OCH(CH$_3$)$_2$	—OCH(CH$_3$)$_2$			1252		87
C$_6$H$_5$CH=CHCH$_2$—	—OC$_2$H$_5$	—OC$_2$H$_5$		1600			91
C$_6$H$_5$CH=CHCH$_2$—	—C$_6$H$_5$	—C$_6$H$_5$			1180	970; *trans* CH=CH	88
XCH=CHCH$_2$—^{a}	—C$_6$H$_5$	—C$_6$H$_5$			1180	990; *trans* CH=CH	88
Y—^{b}	—C$_6$H$_5$	—C$_6$H$_5$			1180		88
CH$_3$CH=CH(CH$_3$)CH—	—OC$_2$H$_5$	—OC$_2$H$_5$		1686	1245	1208, shoulder	87
(CH$_3$)$_2$C=CHCH$_2$—	—OC$_2$H$_5$	—OC$_2$H$_5$					81
(CH$_3$)$_2$C=CHCH$_2$—	—OC$_2$H$_5$	—OC$_2$H$_5$			1255		87
(CH$_3$)$_2$C=CHCH$_2$—	—C$_6$H$_5$	—C$_6$H$_5$			1180		88
(CH$_2$)$_5$C=CHCH$_2$—	—C$_6$H$_5$	—C$_6$H$_5$			1180		88
H$_2$C=CH—	—OCH$_2$CH$_2$Cl	—OCH$_2$CH$_2$Cl	3085^c	1615	1242		24
CH$_3$CH=CH—	—OC$_2$H$_5$	—OC$_2$H$_5$		1625			91
CH$_3$CH=CH—	—OC$_2$H$_5$	—OC$_2$H$_5$		1634			99
CH$_3$CH$_2$CH=CH—	—OC$_2$H$_5$	—OC$_2$H$_5$		1625			91

B. By Raman (cm^{-1})^{d}

H$_2$C=CHCH$_2$—	—OC$_4$H$_9$	—OC$_4$H$_9$	1636	55
H$_2$C=CHCH$_2$—	—OC$_4$H$_9$	—H	1636	55
H$_2$C=CHCH$_2$—	—C$_4$H$_9$	—C$_4$H$_9$	1633	55
H$_2$C=CH—	—OC$_4$H$_9$	—OC$_4$H$_9$	1610	55
H$_2$C=CH—	—OC$_4$H$_9$	—H	1604	55
H$_2$C=CH—	—OC$_4$H$_9$	—CH$_3$	1605	55
H$_2$C=CH—	—OC$_2$H$_5$	—Cl	1610	55
H$_2$C=CH—	—Cl	—Cl	1598	55
H$_2$C=CH—	—N(CH$_3$)$_2$	—N(CH$_3$)$_2$	1604	55
H$_2$C=CH—	—C$_4$H$_9$	—C$_4$H$_9$	1606	55

[a] X = C$_6$H$_5$CH=CH—.

[b] Y = (CH$_3$)$_2$C=CHCH$_2$CH$_2$(CH$_3$)C=CHCH$_2$— (geranyl).

[c] And at 3035 and 3005; δ (in plane) 1402 and 1306; ν P—O—C 1020; δ (out-of-plane) 965 and 930 (?) cm^{-1}.

[d] For comparison see also [ν(C=C), cm^{-1}]: H$_2$C=CHC$_4$H$_9$, 1642; H$_2$C=CHCH$_2$P(O)(C$_4$H$_9$)$_2$, 1631; H$_2$C=CHP(OC$_4$H$_9$)$_2$, 1595; H$_2$C=CHP(C$_4$H$_9$)$_2$, 1589 (55).

[e] Y = (CH$_3$)$_2$C=CHCH$_2$(CH$_2$=CH)(CH$_3$)C— (linalyl).

TABLE 34
Proton NMR Characterization of Allyl Phosphites

Compound	H	δ, ppm	No. of peaks	J_{HP}, Hz	J_{HH}, Hz	Solvent[a]	Ref.
$(H_2^BC{=}CH^ACH_2^CO)P(OCH_2^DCH_3^E)_2$	A	5.9	M			Ca	87
	B	5.2	M			Ca	87
	C	4.25	M			Ca	87
	D	3.83	5	7.2	E7.2	Ca	87
	E	1.22	3		D7	Ca	87
$(H_2^BC{=}CH^ACH_2^CO)P[OCH_3^D(CH_3^E)_2]_2$	A	5.9	M			Ca	87
	B	5.18	M			Ca	87
	C	4.3	M			Ca	87
	D	4.3	M			Ca	87
	E	1.21	2		D6	Ca	87
$(H_2^BC{=}CH^ACH_2^CO)_3P$	A	5.9	M			Ca	87
	B	5.2	M			Ca	87
	C	4.25	M			Ca	87
$[H_2^B{=}CCH^A(CH_3^E)CH^CO]P(OCH_2^DCH_3^F)_2$	A	5.87	M			Ca	87
	B	5.11	M			Ca	87
	C	4.63	M			Ca	87
	D	3.81	5	7.2	F7.2	Ca	87
	E	1.27	2		C7	Ca	87
	F	1.22	3		D7	Ca	87
$(CH_3^ECH^B{=}CH^ACH_2^CO)P(OCH_3^D)_2$	A,B	5.7	M			Ca	87
	C	4.2	M			Ca	87
	D	3.46	2	11		Ca	87
	E	1.72	M			Ca	87

Compound		δ	Mult.	J	Coupling	Solvent	Ref.
$(CH_3^ECH^B=CH^ACH_2^CO)P(OCH_2^DCH_3^F)_2$	A,B	5.6	M			Ca	87
	C	4.18	M			Ca	87
	D	3.80	5	7.2	F7.2	Ca	87
	E	1.70	M			Ca	87
	F	1.21	3		D7	Ca	87
$(CH_3^ECH^B=CH^ACH_2^CO)P[OCH^D(CH_3^F)_2]_2$	A,B	5.6	M			Ca	87
	C	4.3	M			Ca	87
	D	4.3	M			Ca	87
	E	1.72	M			Ca	87
	F	1.20	2		D6	Ca	87
$[CH_3^ECH^B=CH^A(CH_3^C)CH^CO]P(OCH_2^DCH_3^G)_2$	A,B	5.6	M			Ca	87
	C	4.5	M			Ca	87
	D	3.82	5	7.2	G7	Ca	87
	E	1.68	M			Ca	87
	F	1.26	2			Ca	87
	G	1.20	3			Ca	87
$H^CC=CH^A$ $\quad\mid$ $H^B\ C(CH_3^E)_2OP(OCH_2^DCH_3^F)_2$	A	5.70	M	1.2	D7	Ne	81
	B	4.83	M		C10.15; A17.1; B1.65	Ne	81
	C	4.66	M		F7.0	Ne	81
	D	3.52	2 × 4	7.6	D7.0	Ne	81
	E	1.10	1			Ne	81
	F	0.88	3			Ne	81
	A	6.01	M	1.2	C10.5	Ca	87
	B,C	5.1	M			Ca	87
	D	3.79	5	7.2	F7.2	Ca	87
	E	1.41	1			Ca	87
	F	1.20	3		D7	Ca	87

---

a Ca = carbon tetrachloride; Ne = neat.

TABLE 35

Proton NMR Characterization of Allylphosphorus Compounds (Derivatives of Tetrasubstituted Phosphorus)

Compound	H	δ, ppm	No. of peaks	J_{HP}, Hz	J_{HH}, Hz	Solvent[a]	R
$H_2C=CHCH_2P(O)(OCH_3^A)_2$	A	2.64	2	10.8		Ne	92
$H_2^BC=CH^ACH_2^CP(O)(OCH_2CH_3)_2$	A,B	5.0–6.2	M			De	93
	C	2.62	2 × 2	22		De	93
$H_2^BC=CH^ACH_2^CP(O)[OCH(CH_3)_2]_2$	A,B	5.0–6.2	M			De	93
	C	2.59	2 × 2	22		De	93
$H_2^DC=CH^CCH_2^GP(O)(OCH_3)(OCH_2^ECH^A=CH_2^B)$	A–D	~5.5	M			Ca	87
	E	4.44	M			Ca	87
	F	3.65	2	11		Ca	87
	G	2.49	4	22	7	Ca	87
$H_2^DC=CH^CCH_2^FP(O)(OCH_2^ECH^A=CH_2^B)_2$	A–D	~5.5	M			Ca	87
	E	4.45	M			Ca	87
	F	2.56	4	22	6	Ca	87
$H_2^BC=CH^A(CH_3)CH^DP(O)(OCH_2^CCH_3^F)_2$	A	5.9	M			Ca	87
	B	5.0	M			Ca	87
	C	3.90	5	7.2	F7.2	Ca	87
	D	~2.5	M			Ca	87
	E	1.19	4	18	D7	Ca	87
	F	1.07	3		C7	Ca	87
	D	2.4	M			Ca	85
$H_2C=CH(CH_3^B)CH^AP(O)(O)(C_6H_5)_2$	B	1.36	4	16	A7		88
$H_2C=CH(CH_3^A)_2CP(O)(O)(C_6H_5)_2$	A	1.3	2	14			139

Compound	H	δ	Mult.	J	J	Solvent	Ref.
$CH_3CH^B=CH^ACH^D_2P(O)(OCH^C_3)_2$	A,B	5.5	M			Ca	87
	C	3.65	2	11	6	Ca	87
	D	2.47	4	22		Ca	87
	E	1.71	M			Ca	87
$CH_3CH^B=CH^ACH^D_2P(O)(OCH_2CH^F_3)_2$	A,B	5.5	M			Ca	87
	C	4.03	5	7.2	F7.2	Ca	87
	D	2.42	M	22		Ca	87
	E	1.70	M			Ca	87
	F	1.27	3			Ca	87
	D	2.42	2 × M	22	C7	Ca	85
$XCH=CHCH^AP(O)(C_6H_5)_2$[b]	A	3.18	4	15	7		88
$Y(CH_3)C=CHCH^AP(O)(C_6H_5)_2$[c]	A	3.07	4	15	7		88
$Z(CH_3)C=CHCH^AP(O)(C_6H_5)_2$[d]	A	3.22	4	15	8		88
$CH_3^E-C=CH^A$; $H_3^DC\ CH_2^CP(O)(OCH^B_3)_2$	A	5.03	4 × 4	7.7	C7.7	Ca	110
	B	3.61	2	21.6		Ca	110
	C	2.40	4 × 4	5.4	A7.7	Ca	110
	D	1.72	2 × 2	4.2		Ca	110
	E	1.63	3			Ca	110
$CH_3^E-C=CH^A$; $H_3^DC\ CH_2P(O)(OCH^B_2CH^F_3)_2$	A	5.13	4 × 4			Ne	81
	B	4.03	2 × 4			Ne	81
	C	2.50	2 × 2	21.8		Ne	81
	D					Ne	81
	E					Ne	81
	F	1.25	3			Ne	81
	A	5.2	M			Ca	87
	B	4.03	5	7.2	7.2	Ca	87

(continued)

TABLE 35 (continued)

Compound	H	δ, ppm	No. of peaks	J_{HP}, Hz	J_{HH}, Hz	Solvent[a]	Ref.
$CH_3CH^B=CH^A(CH_3^G)CH^DP(O)(OCH_2^CCH_3^F)_2$	C	2.40	4	22	6	Ca	87
	D,E	1.73	M			Ca	87
	F	1.27	3		B7	Ca	87
	A,B	5.5	M			Ca	87
	C	4.00	5	7.2	F7.2	Ca	87
	D	2.4	M			Ca	87
	E	1.68	M			Ca	87
	F	1.28	3		C7	Ca	87
	G	1.20	4	18	D7	Ca	87

[a] Ca, carbon tetrachloride; De, deuteriochloroform; Ne, neat.

[b] X = styryl, $(C_6H_5CH=CH—)$.

[c] Y = $(CH_3)_2C=CHCH_2CH_2$.

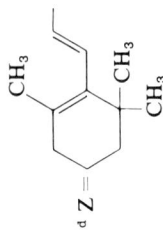

[d] Z =

vinylphosphonates, for which the C=C stretching vibrations show up between 1625 and 1598 cm^{-1}. The phosphoryl group apparently effects a low-frequency shift of the C=C absorbtion similar to conjugation with another olefinic moiety (e.g., in butadiene, which absorbs at 1597 cm^{-1}) or with a carbonyl moiety (where the shift is smaller than in dienes), and thus permits the use of this range for diagnoses. No effect on the intensities of the Raman lines was noted when the phosphoryl group moved from beta into alpha position to the carbon–carbon double bond (55), although an intensification of the double-bond stretching frequency was noted in the infrared (91,99).

2. Proton NMR

Data of the characterization of allyl phosphites and allylphosphonates by proton NMR are abstracted in Tables 34 and 35. The vinyl and crotyl portions of the spectra are complicated due to multiple proton–proton and proton–phosphorus couplings and have not been resolved in these examples. It is not very likely that the results of full analyses of these compounds would alter significantly the generalizations obtained from studies of simpler systems and of the diagrams shown in Fig. 6. Information on long-range coupling in olefinic systems was obtained from the two di-methylallylphosphonates (dimethyl and diethyl 3-methyl-2-butenyl-phosphonates), in which the methyl protons C and D were found coupled

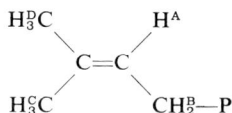

$$H_3^D C \diagdown \qquad H^A \diagup$$
$$C=C$$
$$H_3^C C \diagup \qquad \diagdown CH_2^B{-}P$$

to phosphorus by 5.4 and 4.2 Hz, respectively (in the methyl ester), which thus represent a high value for coupling through five bonds, similar to those found in acetylenic phosphonates (Table 22).

3. Phosphorus NMR

^{31}P chemical shifts of the allyl phosphites and allylphosphonates are summarized in Tables 36 and 37, in which data of vinylphosphonates are also included for comparison. The values of Table 37 were used to obtain the categorizations listed in Table 23, which underline again the diagnostic power of phosphorus NMR.

4. Ultraviolet

Data from a study (55) of vinyl and allyl phosphorus compounds by ultraviolet are given in Table 38. Neither of these classes of compounds shows significant absorbtion above 190 mμ, nor is there an effect apparent when the olefinic moiety in the allyl compounds becomes adjacent to the phosphoryl group. A similar lack of evidence for conjugation is apparent from molecular refractivity data, which showed no exaltation in the vinyl compounds (55).

TABLE 36
^{31}P NMR Chemical Shifts of Allyl Phosphites

Compound	δ, ppm (H_3PO_4)	Ref.
$(H_2C{=}CHCH_2O)P(OC_2H_5)_2$	-137.1	81
$(H_2C{=}CHCH_2O)P[OCH(CH_3)_2]_2$	-137.3	81
$(H_2C{=}CHCH_2O)_3P$	-137.1	81
$[H_2C{=}C(CH_3)CH_2O]_3P$	-138.2	24
$[H_2C{=}CH(CH_2)_2CO]P(OC_2H_5)_2$	-134.0	89,90
$[H_2C{=}CH(CH_3)_2CO]_2P(OC_2H_5)$	-132.1	89,90
$[H_2C{=}CH(CH_3)_2CO]_3P$	-140.2	89,90

TABLE 37
^{31}P NMR Chemical Shifts of Dialkyl Allyl- and Vinylphosphonates

Compound	δ, ppm (H_3PO_4)	Ref.
$H_2C{=}CHCH_2P(O)(OC_2H_5)_2$	-27.6	81
$H_2C{=}CHCH_2P(O)(OCH_2CH{=}CH_2)_2$	-27.6	81
$(CH_3)_2C{=}CHCH_2P(O)(OC_2H_5)_2$	-27.5	81
$H_2C{=}CHP(O)(OCH_2CH_2Cl)_2$	-22	94
$CH_3CH{=}CHP(O)(OC_2H_5)_2$	-23	91
$CH_3CH_2CH{=}CHP(O)(OC_2H_5)_2$	-23.4	91

TABLE 38
Ultraviolet Spectral Data of Olefinic Phosphorus Compounds

Compound	λ, mμ	ϵ	Ref.
$H_2C{=}CHCH_2P(O)(OC_4H_9)_2$	182	11,000	55
$H_2C{=}CHP(O)(OC_4H_9)_2$	177	13,400	55
$H_2C{=}CHP(O)CH_3(OC_4H_9)$	176	12,700	55
$H_2C{=}CHP(O)[N(CH_3)_2]_2$	174	16,400	55
$H_2C{=}CHP(O)(C_4H_9)_2$	179	14,600	55
$H_2C{=}CHP(O)Cl_2$	178	11,700	55
$H_2C{=}CHP(OC_4H_9)_2$	176	12,000	55
$H_2C{=}CHP(C_4H_9)_2$	182	17,000	55
$H_2C{=}CHC_4H_9$	180	11,000	55
$C_6H_5CH{=}CHCH_2P(O)(OC_2H_5)_2$	250	3580	91

C. Reactions of the Rearrangement Products

The extensive literature on the chemistry of allylic phosphorus compounds has been reviewed (95). Allyl and vinyl phosphorus compounds are part of the subject of a comprehensive treatment of organophosphorus monomers and polymers (96) and much of their chemistry is treated explicitly or is implied in the numerous preparative procedures given. More recent papers dealing with the chemistry of these and related compounds are given in refs. 97–101, 127, and 130.

As was the case with allenylphosphonates (Section II-C-1), allylphosphonic acid esters are also isomerized by base (sodium ethoxide) to substituted vinylphosphonic acid esters (91). A further similarity is apparent from the quantitative aspects of the isomerization: both propadienyl- and allylphosphonates are isomerized completely to 1-propynyl- and 1-propenylphosphonates, respectively, while their higher homologs, 1,2 butadienyl- and crotylphosphonic acid esters, yield only mixtures of isomeric compounds:

$$H_2C{=}CHCH_2P(O)(OC_2H_5)_2 \longrightarrow CH_3CH{=}CHP(O)(OC_2H_5)_2$$
$$100\%$$

$$CH_3CH{=}CHCH_2P(O)(OC_2H_5)_2 \rightleftharpoons CH_3CH_2CH{=}CHP(O)(OC_2H_5)_2$$
$$75\% \qquad\qquad\qquad\qquad 25\%$$

The mechanism suggested to explain both the qualitative and quantitative aspects of the isomerization of allenylphosphonates (*vide supra*) applies equally well to the allylic compounds also. Abstraction of the allylic proton in diethyl allylphosphonate yields a secondary carbanion which is mesomeric with a primary, and thus a more stable (57), anion:

$$H_2C{=}CHCH_2P(O)(OR)_2 \longrightarrow \begin{cases} H_2C{=}CHCH^{\ominus}\,P(O)(OR)_2 \\ {}^{\ominus}CH_2CH{=}CHP(O)(OR)_2 \end{cases}$$

It is very likely that the primary carbanion is the major or sole contributor to the structure of the mesomeric ion, which on protonation thus yields the product derived from the most stable anion.

Abstraction of a proton from the allylic position in crotylphosphonate yields a secondary anion, mesomeric with another secondary anion:

$$CH_3CH{=}CHCH_2P(O)(OR)_2 \longrightarrow \begin{cases} CH_3CH{=}CHCH^{\ominus}P(O)(OR)_2 \\ CH_3CH^{\ominus}CH{=}CHP(O)(OR)_2 \end{cases}$$

In this case both anions are approximately of the same energy and protonation thus yields a mixture of the two expected products. A preference for the allylic species is probably due to the electronegativity of the phosphoryl group, which stabilizes the carbanion nearest to it.

On the basis of the experimental data and the interpretation attached to them, it would seem safe to predict that no isomerization of the 3-methyl-2-butenylphosphonic acid ester would take place under the influence of basic reagents.

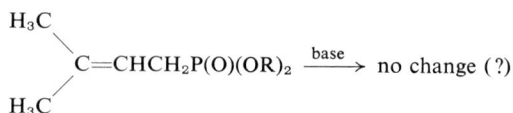

$$\begin{matrix} H_3C \\ \quad \diagdown \\ \qquad\qquad C{=}CHCH_2P(O)(OR)_2 \xrightarrow{\text{base}} \text{no change (?)} \\ \quad \diagup \\ H_3C \end{matrix}$$

V. THE REARRANGEMENT OF ALKYL ESTERS

Following on the isomerization of unsaturated esters of tervalent phosphorus acids to stable, unsaturated tetrasubstituted phosphorus derivatives, the question naturally arose whether saturated esters, for which no cyclic intramolecular pathway can be constructed, could accomplish the attainment of stable isomeric structures by other than the well-known Michaelis-Arbuzov rearrangement. Calculations similar to those in Table 4 indicate that the transformation $X_2P{-}O{-}C$ into $X_2P(O)C$ would be accompanied by a gain of at least 32 kcal/mole and possibly by as much, or more, than 56 kcal/mole* in bond energies. What is missing is an

TABLE 39
Thermal Behavior of Phosphorous Esters (81)

Heating period, hr	16 (120°)	17.5 (200°)	54.5 (200°)	28 (300°)	28 (350°)
Decrease in composition, %					
$(CH_3O)_3P$	0	100[a]			
$(CH_3CH_2O)_3P$	0	0	0	100[b]	
$[(CH_3)_2CHO]_3P$	0	~25	100[c]		
$(H_2C{=}CHCH_2O)_3P$	0	100[d]			
$[H_2C{=}C(CH_3)CH_2O]_3P$	0	100[d]			
$(C_6H_5O)_3P$	0	0	0	0	~20

[a] Pure dimethyl methylphosphonate, $CH_3P(O)(OCH_3)_2$.

[b] Diethyl ethylphosphonate, $C_2H_5P(O)(OCH_2H_5)_2$ (major), diethyl phosphonate, $HP(O)(OC_2H_5)_2$), and triethyl phosphate; pressure in the reaction tube suggests the presence of ethylene.

[c] Contains primarily diisopropyl phosphonate, $HP(O)[OCH(CH_3)_2]_2$, and presumably propylene.

[d] Polymeric material.

* Bonds disappearing: $sp^3C{-}p^3O$ (84), and $p^3P{-}p^3O$ (82–92 kcal); bonds forming: $sp^3P{=}sp^2O$ (137–151 kcal) and $sp^3P{-}sp^3C$ (71 kcal).

accessible and suitable mechanistic path which would allow the rearrangement to take place.

In a series of preliminary experiments, trimethyl phosphite (40), triethyl phosphite (41), triisopropyl phosphite (42), triallyl phosphite, tris(2-methylallyl) phosphite, and triphenyl phosphite were heated under the conditions and with the results summarized in Table 39.

Since thermolysis of 41 and 42 yielded much of the corresponding dialkyl phosphonates and olefins, a more detailed study was begun with 40.

The outcome of these experiments is shown graphically in Fig. 12.

Both phosphorus and proton NMR indicated that 40 was converted into dimethyl methylphosphonate, $CH_3P(O)(OCH_3)_2$ (43), and that no other compound was present in the samples. Quantitative analysis of the NMR scans showed that in both the neat and the diluted samples an initial slow conversion step was followed by a marked increase in the rate of disappearance of 40. Since 40 was converted exclusively to 43 and since all of the samples taken were binary mixtures, the sigma shaped curves indicated an autocatalytic process. That the rate was not unimolecular was shown by a decrease of rate on dilution with a presumably neutral component (diphenyl ether).

Support for the participation of 43 in the conversion of 40 was obtained by subjecting a 1:1 molar mixture of 40 and 43 to the original reaction conditions (200°). The data of conversion of 40 paralleled closely its original decomposition curve (Fig. 12).

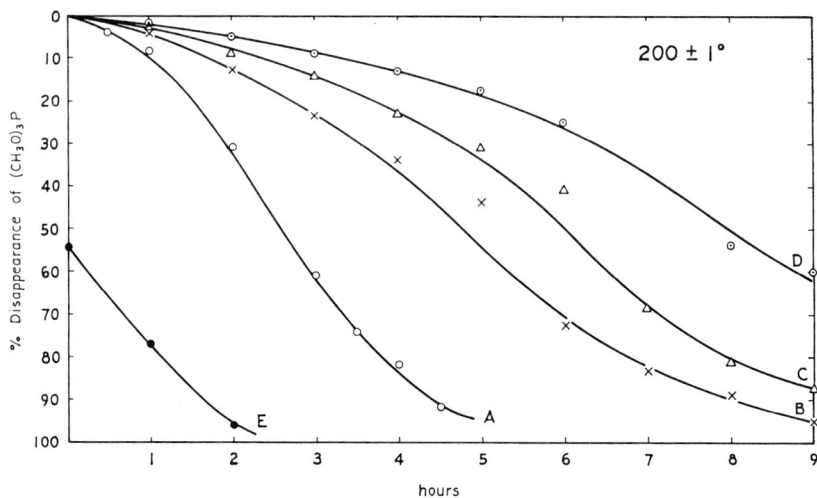

Fig. 12. Thermolysis of trimethyl phosphite at 200°: (A) neat; (B, C, and D) diluted with diphenyl ether, in 1:1, 1:2, and 1:4 proportions (wt/wt), respectively; (E) with equimolar amount of dimethyl methylphosphonate.

In the assistance provided in the isomerization of **40**, a major role is expected, based on well-documented reactions (102), from the nucleophilicity of the phosphoryl group in **43**. A priori two major pathways may be available for the bimolecular interaction:

1. A concerted, nucleophilic, double displacement process effected by the phosphoryl oxygen and the unshared electron pair of the trivalent ester, respectively (Eq. 17).

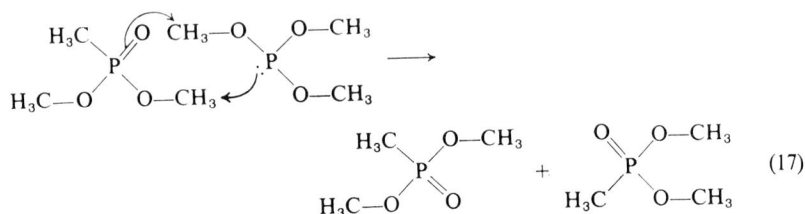

$$\text{(structure)} \qquad (17)$$

2. A process consisting of two discrete steps:

a. Nucleophilic displacement on the carbon of **40** by the phosphoryl oxygen of **43** to yield an ion pair (Eq. 18).*

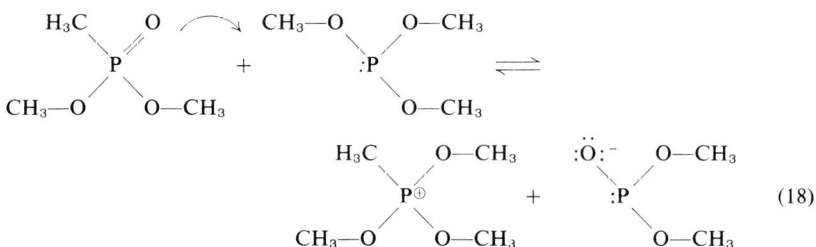

$$\text{(structure)} \qquad (18)$$

b. A second nucleophilic displacement by phosphorus on the methoxy carbon of the phosphonium ion (Eq. 19).

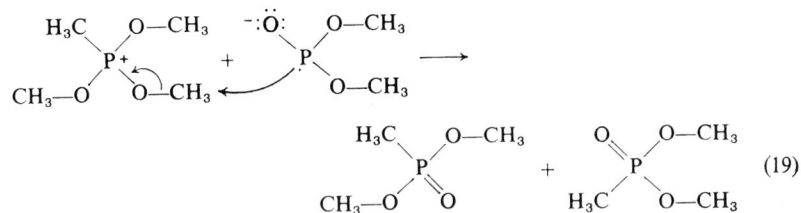

$$\text{(structure)} \qquad (19)$$

* It is known from phosphorus NMR data that in the alkali metal salts of dialkyl phosphonates phosphorus is present as a tervalent species (103) of the structure indicated in the anion of reaction 18, even though in its reaction products (e.g., from the Michaelis-Becker reaction) as well as in the parent ester, $HP(O)(OR)_2$, phosphorus is exclusively in the form of a tetrasubstituted moiety. Repulsion between nonbonding electrons might be responsible for the tervalent structure of the anion, and the high nucleophilicity of phosphorus, compared to that of the oxygen, can account for the structure of its reaction products.

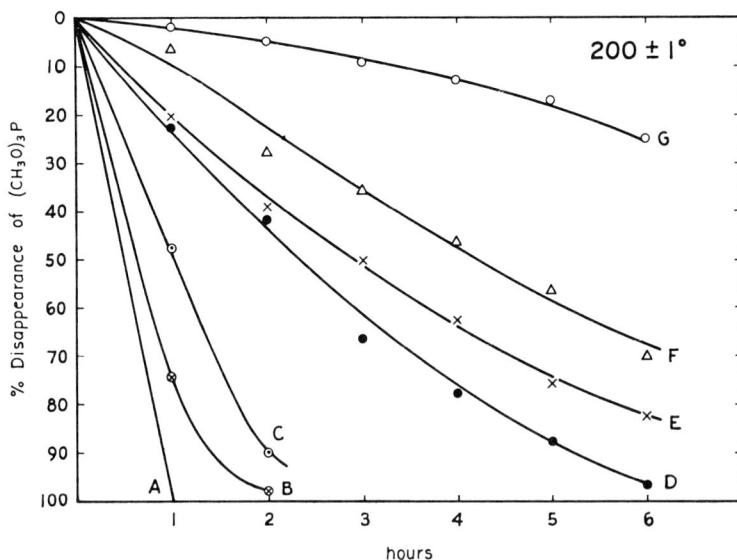

Fig. 13. The rearrangement of trimethyl phosphite in the presence (equimolar) of tetrasubstituted phosphorus (phosphoryl) compounds: (*A*) trimethyl phosphate; (*B*) triphenyl phosphate; (*C*) dimethyl methylphosphonate; (*D*) triethyl phosphate; (*E*) trioctylphosphine oxide; (*F*) triphenylphosphine oxide; (*G*) diluted with diphenyl ether, 1:4 (wt/wt).

In order to distinguish between the two mechanisms, both of which were assumed to be started via a nucleophilic attack by the phosphoryl group, several kinds of pure, tetrasubstituted, phosphoryl compounds were sealed in NMR tubes with equimolar amounts of **40**, brought to reaction temperature, and analyzed by phosphorus and proton NMR. The results of the experiments are reproduced graphically in Fig. 13.

It is evident that trimethyl phosphate (**44**) is a very effective agent to convert **40** to **43**. It is also evident that phosphoryl compounds, for which no concerted mechanism similar to 17 can be formulated (**47, 48**, and especially **45**), convert readily **40** to **43** and thus partake in the reaction via a presumably stepwise mechanism (Eqs. 20 and 21).

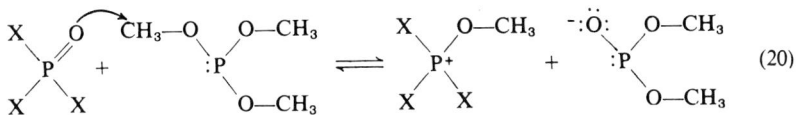

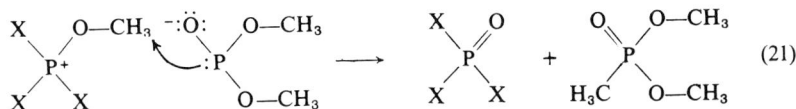

As was the case before, the reaction mixtures contained **40** and **43**, and the added phosphoryl compound (**44, 45, 47, 48**) only.

Compounds **43** and **44** could participate in the conversion of **40** by both mechanisms and the experiments described do not distinguish between the two routes, which, however, could be solved by ^{18}O experiments. The high efficiency of **44**, compared with that of **43**, can be ascribed partly to statistical features.*

Further support for the stepwise mechanism was provided by experiments in which phosphites and phosphates with different alkyl groups were used. Both the qualitative and the quantitative aspects of the results appear to be significant, as evidenced by the following findings.

An equimolar mixture of triethyl phosphite (**41**) and trimethyl phosphate (**44**) reacted readily at 200° (higher than 90% conversion in 2 hr) and yielded dimethyl ethyl phosphate (**49**) and diethyl methylphosphonate (**50**):

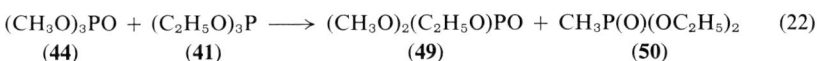

$$(CH_3O)_3PO + (C_2H_5O)_3P \longrightarrow (CH_3O)_2(C_2H_5O)PO + CH_3P(O)(OC_2H_5)_2 \quad (22)$$
$$\text{(44)} \qquad \text{(41)} \qquad\qquad \text{(49)} \qquad\qquad \text{(50)}$$

No diethyl ethylphosphonate, $C_2H_5P(O)(OC_2H_5)_2$ (**51**), was detected by NMR in the reaction mixture. The reaction between **41** and **44** proceeded readily at even 150°; the extent of conversions of these reactants is illustrated in Figs. 14 and 15.

An equimolar mixture of trimethyl phosphate and triisopropyl phosphite (**42**) behaved similarly and yielded at 150° dimethyl isopropyl phosphate (**52**) and diisopropyl methylphosphonate (**53**) only (Fig. 15).

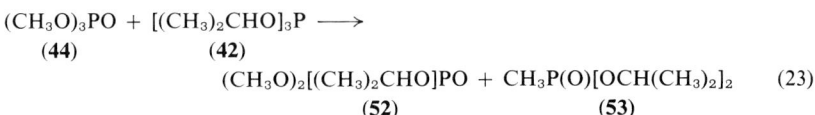

$$(CH_3O)_3PO + [(CH_3)_2CHO]_3P \longrightarrow$$
$$\text{(44)} \qquad\qquad \text{(42)}$$
$$(CH_3O)_2[(CH_3)_2CHO]PO + CH_3P(O)[OCH(CH_3)_2]_2 \quad (23)$$
$$\text{(52)} \qquad\qquad\qquad \text{(53)}$$

Again, the hypothetical Michaelis-Arbuzov rearrangement product, diisopropyl isopropylphosphonate, was not detected in the reaction mixture. The rate of reaction of **44** with **42** was somewhat slower than with **41** (cf. Figs. 14 and 15). At 200° much decomposition of **42** was noted.

As can be anticipated from the reaction of triethyl phosphate (**46**) on the isomerization of trimethyl phosphite (**40**), a much reduced effect was noted when the isomerization of triethyl phosphite (**41**) was carried out in the presence of **46** instead of **44**. The expected product, diethyl ethylphosphonate (**51**), was produced only in 5% conversion after 5 hr at 200° (Fig. 14). At the same temperature neither pure **41** nor pure **42** showed change during 5 hr of heating periods. It is known from scrambling experiments that neither does an exchange of alkyl groups between triethyl

---

* The often encountered deterioration in the assay of **40** on storage is very likely caused by the presence of **44** and **43** and possibly by hydrolysis products.

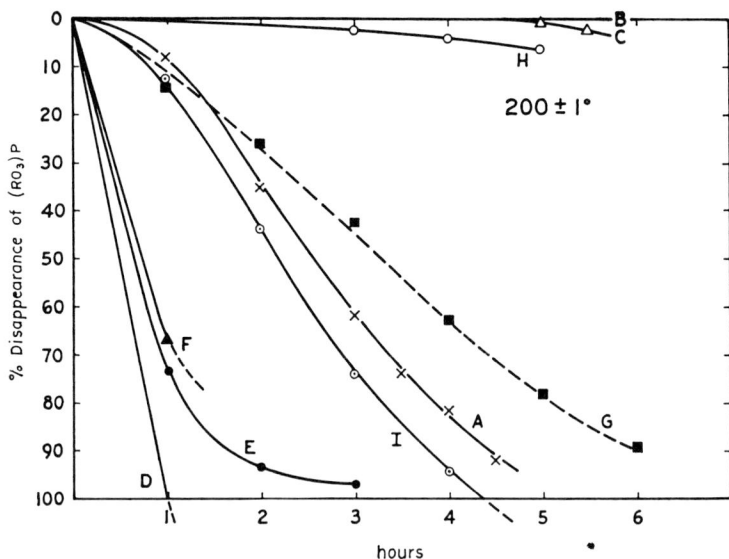

Fig. 14. Thermolysis of trialkyl phosphites, at 200°: (A) trimethyl phosphite; (B) triethyl phosphite; (C) triisopropyl phosphite; trimethyl phosphite and equimolar amounts of (D) trimethyl phosphite, (E) triethyl phosphite, and (F) triisopropyl phosphite; triethyl phosphate and equimolar amounts of (G) trimethyl phosphite and triethyl phosphite; (I) dimethyl methylphosphonate and triethyl phosphite in 1:2 molar ratio.

and trimethyl phosphate take place at 200° within a few hours of heating (104).

The decreasing sequence in rates in the isomerization of trimethyl, triethyl, and triisopropyl phosphites at 200° (and 150°) parallels the order of decreasing rates found in bimolecular nucleophilic displacement reactions, where the methyl group is about thirtyfold more reactive than the ethyl group, which in turn is favored over the isopropyl group by about the same factor (105). The decrease in rates observed in the series can be attributed to step "a" of the displacement mechanism (mechanisms 18 and 20), since not much difference (or, possibly, a reversal) in rates would be expected if step "b" (mechanisms 19 and 21) were rate determining.*

The high selectivity encountered in the reaction of trimethyl phosphate with triethyl and triisopropyl phosphites has its basis, in addition to the preferential displacement on the methyl group in the second step of the

* It was observed qualitatively that triisopropyl phosphite is more reactive than triethyl phosphite toward methyl iodide (106). The inductive effect of the alkyl groups in the anions of the postulated stepwise mechanism (mechanisms 19 and 21) would render the isopropyl compound more reactive than the ethyl homolog.

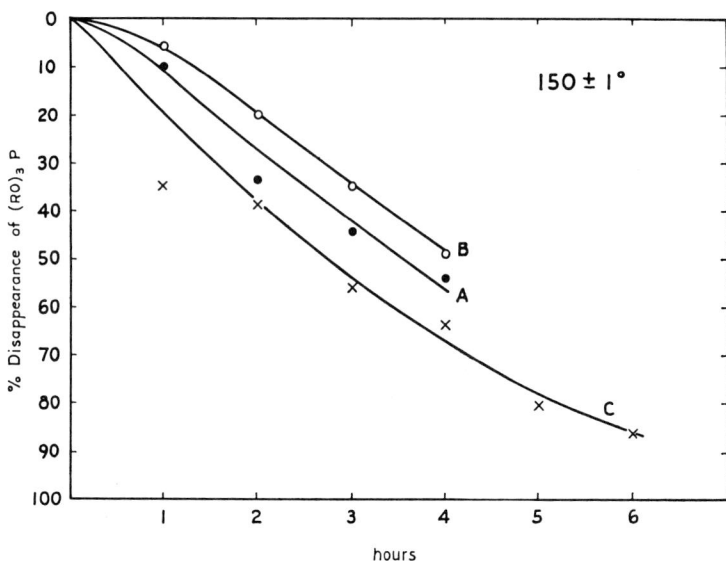

Fig. 15. Thermolysis of trialkyl phosphites at 150°: trimethyl phosphate and equimolar amounts of (*A*) triethyl phosphite, and (*B*) triisopropyl phosphite; (*C*) trimethyl phosphate and triethyl phosphite in 1:3 molar ratio.

postulated mechanism, also on statistical effects, which favor methyls over the other alkyl by a 3:1 ratio (Eq. 22).

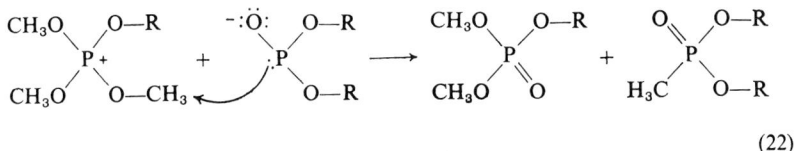

$$\tag{22}$$

Displacement on methyl is a prerequisite if the reaction followed a concerted, instead of a stepwise, pathway.

Since the trialkyl phosphate products of the reaction of **44** with **41** and **42** possess still two methoxy groups, on which a preferred displacement could occur, experiments were carried out (81) to utilize completely all or most of the methyl substituents in these esters. Similar considerations apply to dimethyl methylphosphonate (**43**). Thus when a 1:2 molar mixture of **43** and triethyl phosphite was heated at 200°, more than 50% of the methoxy groups reacted in 5 hr, indicating the participation of the mixed ester primary product, ethyl methyl methylphosphonate (**54**) in the conversion of **41** to **50**.

$$
\text{(43)} \quad + \quad \text{(41)} \longrightarrow
$$

$$
\text{(54)} \quad + \quad \text{(50)}
$$

$$
\text{(54)} \quad + \quad \text{(41)} \longrightarrow
$$

$$
\text{(50)} \quad + \quad \text{(50)}
$$

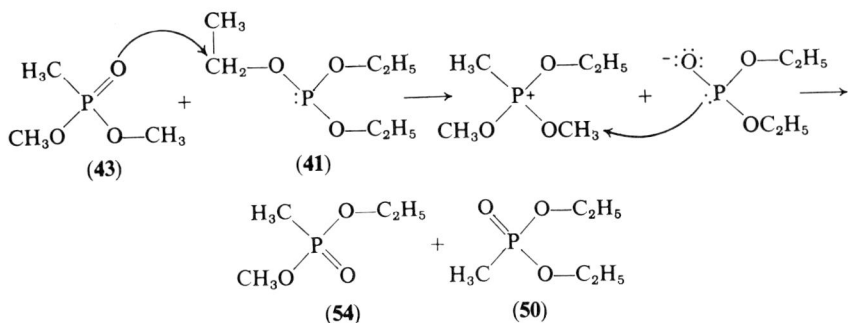

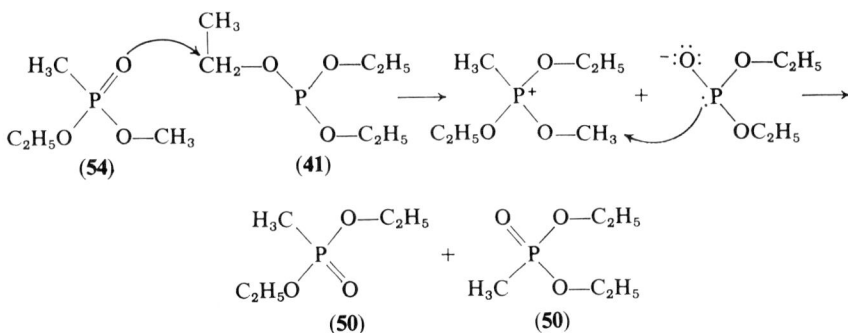

In the mechanism of the conversion of trialkyl phosphites to dialkyl alkylphosphonates, the leading role was assigned to the nucleophilicity of the phosphoryl group. To test the possibility that other nucleophilic agents could act similarly, two systems were investigated (81).

To replace the phosphoryl by a carbonyl group, triethyl phosphite was sealed with equimolar amount of methyl benzoate (55) in an NMR tube and heated at 200°. Reaction was slow, but did result in the formation of ethyl benzoate and diethyl methylphosphonate (50) (Eq. 23).

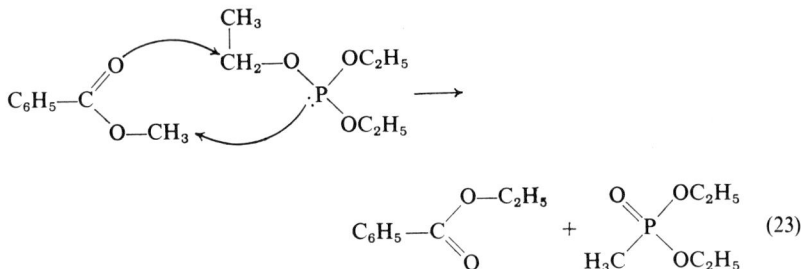

$$
\tag{23}
$$

Reaction between trimethyl phosphite and O,O,O-trimethylthio-phosphate (56), a compound with the well-known nucleophilic $P{=}S$

function [e.g., Pistschimuka reaction; (83)], proceeded much more readily, at even 120° and yielded the anticipated thiol ester **57** (Eq. 24).

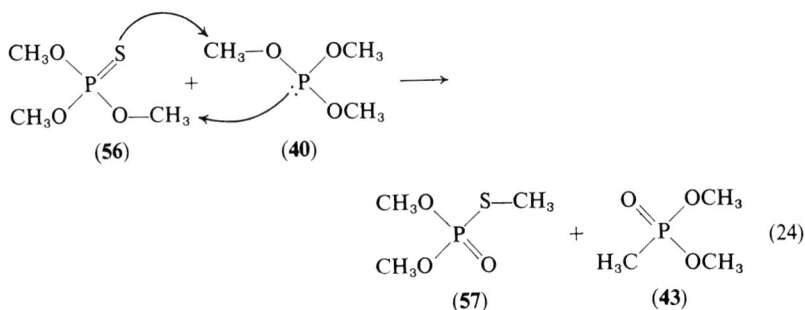

$$
\begin{array}{cc}
\underset{\text{(56)}}{\overset{\displaystyle CH_3O}{\underset{\displaystyle CH_3O}{\diagdown}}\!\!\!\!\overset{S}{\underset{O-CH_3}{\diagup}}\!\!P} & + & \underset{\text{(40)}}{\overset{\displaystyle CH_3-O}{\underset{\displaystyle}{\diagdown}}\!\!\!\!\overset{OCH_3}{\underset{OCH_3}{\diagup}}\!\!\cdot P} \longrightarrow
\end{array}
$$

$$
\underset{\text{(57)}}{\overset{\displaystyle CH_3O}{\underset{\displaystyle CH_3O}{\diagdown}}\!\!\!\!\overset{S-CH_3}{\underset{O}{\diagup}}\!\!P} \quad + \quad \underset{\text{(43)}}{\overset{\displaystyle O}{\underset{\displaystyle H_3C}{\diagdown}}\!\!\!\!\overset{OCH_3}{\underset{OCH_3}{\diagup}}\!\!P} \qquad (24)
$$

   The conversion of **56** to **57** at 120° in 5.5 hr was 35% in the presence of **40**, but only about 3% or less when **56** was heated alone or with equi-molar amount of **43**.

   Thus while it is apparent that phosphoryl compounds, formed under pyrolytic conditions or added deliberately, can readily effect the conversion of alkyl esters of tervalent phosphorus acids into stable, tetrasubstituted phosphorus compounds, the unaided isomerization reaction of pure trialkyl phosphites takes place only with great difficulty, if at all. The high temperatures required to effect possible isomerization result in degradation reactions and in the formation of phosphoryl compounds, which, as shown above, rapidly consume the trivalent ester in bimolecular displace-ment reactions. Although a bimolecular interaction in the tervalent ester has been suggested (107) and could be applied to initiate the reaction sequence illustrated in Fig. 12a, one cannot readily exclude, even with very careful experimental technique, the presence of minute amounts of phosphoryl compounds (phosphate, hydrogen- and alkylphosphonates), which, due to their high efficiency in reacting with the trivalent esters (*vide supra*), could start off the sigma shaped autocatalytic curve. It is very likely that the reported (108) formation in large amounts of diethyl ethylphos-phonate (**51**) in the thermolysis of triethyl phosphite (**41**) was due primarily to the presence of diethyl phosphonate, generated in a competing side reaction (81) or present as a possible impurity in the starting material (109). The conversion of **41** to **51** in high yield on the addition of diethyl phos-phonate, $HP(O)(OC_2H_5)_2$, has been demonstrated (109). On the basis of the data presented above, it is apparent that in addition to diethyl phos-phonate, postulated as an impurity in the starting material (109), triethyl phosphate, or any compound with a phosphoryl group, can also trigger the isomerization sequence of triethyl phosphite resulting eventually in high conversion (70%) to the isomeric phosphonate (108). Oxidation of tervalent phosphorus esters to trialkyl phosphates may take place during the thermolysis experiments proper if no precaution has been taken to deaerate the reactant and to exclude air from the equipment, as might have been the case in (108).*

While the isomerization of trialkyl phosphites thus does not appear to be uncatalyzed mechanistically, the section dealing with them is included in the chapter since it complements the rearrangement series of the unsaturated esters, and since, taking a broader view, the expression "uncatalyzed" might also be interpreted to indicate the nonaddition of a second material to the species undergoing a reaction.

Comparison of the four classes of tervalent phosphorus esters indicates the following order in their ease of rearrangement and the following types of mechanisms:

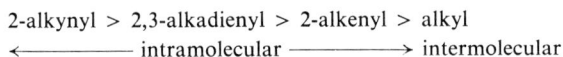

2-alkynyl > 2,3-alkadienyl > 2-alkenyl > alkyl
←——————— intramolecular ————————→ intermolecular

In all cases the reaction products possess significantly better bonds than the tervalent esters, but to undergo rearrangement into the stable, tetrasubstituted phosphorus compounds, only for the unsaturated esters is there an intramolecular mechanistic pathway available. To accomplish the same, saturated esters require outside help; this, however, as seen above, is readily provided, sometimes all too readily, by several kinds of willing partners.

VI. RELATED REARRANGEMENTS

The cyclic, intramolecular mechanistic pathway which was utilized by the acetylenic, allenic, and allylic esters of tervalent phosphorus acids in their isomerization to more stable structures is available for other phosphorus compounds as well. Instead of forming the five-membered cyclic transition state required by the unsaturated esters, other phosphorus compounds might utilize six or four-membered cycles in their intramolecular rearrangement.†

* The validity of control experiments carried out under carbon dioxide (109) might remain somewhat in a doubt unless, and until it is demonstrated that, the blanket gas is really neutral and does not act as a possible inhibitor of the isomerization reaction of phosphites. It was shown previously (*vide supra*) that methyl benzoate is not without effect on triethyl phosphite and yields interaction products on prolonged heating at high temperature (81).

† Although the inversion of the unsaturated moieties has been demonstrated, the limited information available on these rearrangements does not rigorously exclude other mechanistic possibilities, such as an intermolecular or a fragmentation–recombination pathway.

Thus the heating O-allyl-O,O-diethyl thiophosphate for 3–6 hr at 120–140° resulted in the formation of the S-allyl ester in 30% yield (152):

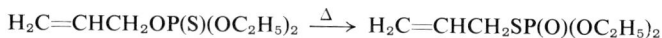

$$H_2C{=}CHCH_2OP(S)(OC_2H_5)_2 \xrightarrow{\Delta} H_2C{=}CHCH_2SP(O)(OC_2H_5)_2$$

That there is an inversion of the allyl substituent was shown by the use of the crotyl ester:

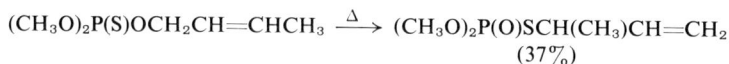

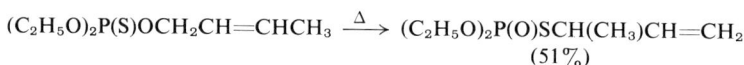

$$(CH_3O)_2P(S)OCH_2CH{=}CHCH_3 \xrightarrow{\Delta} (CH_3O)_2P(O)SCH(CH_3)CH{=}CH_2$$
$$(37\%)$$

$$(C_2H_5O)_2P(S)OCH_2CH{=}CHCH_3 \xrightarrow{\Delta} (C_2H_5O)_2P(O)SCH(CH_3)CH{=}CH_2$$
$$(51\%)$$

It was suggested that the reaction takes place by a concerted mechanism involving a six-membered cyclic transition state (152):

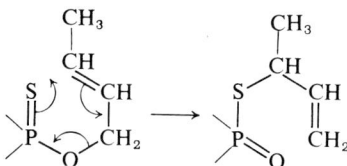

The same mechanism was suggested for the thermal isomerization of allyl esters of N-phenylimidophosphoric acids as well (136):

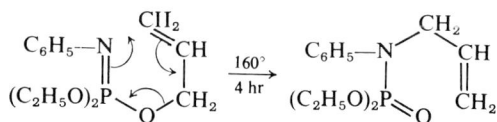

As it was the case in the rearrangement of the tervalent unsaturated esters, much of the driving force is provided by the formation of the very stable phosphoryl (P=O) moiety.

The starting point for the study of the isomerization of unsaturated phosphines was an early observation of L. Horner and co-workers on the racemization of optically active allylmethylphenylphosphine in refluxing toluene (153).

$$H_2C{=}CHCH_2P^*(C_6H_5)CH_3 \xrightarrow{\Delta} \text{racemization}$$

The authors suggested a four membered cyclic transition state for the isomerization underlying the racemization

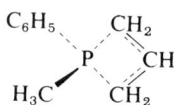

The isomerization of unsaturated phosphines was investigated with the help of unsymmetrically substituted olefinic moieties by Savage and Trippett (139), who confirmed the inversion of the allylic moieties in the rearrangement.

$$(C_6H_5)_2PCH(C_6H_5)CH=CH_2 \xrightarrow[5\ hr]{210°} (C_6H_5)_2PCH_2CH=CHC_6H_5$$

$$(C_6H_5)_2PCH(CH_3)CH=CH_2 \xrightarrow[3\ hr]{200°} (C_6H_5)_2PCH_2CH=CHCH_3$$

$$(C_6H_5)_2PC(CH_3)_2CH=CH_2 \xrightarrow[4\ hr]{200°} (C_6H_5)_2PCH_2CH=C(CH_3)_2$$

Although the authors concluded that the crude phosphines, Ph_2-$PCRR'CH=CH_2$, undergo rearrangement at 200–210° to the isomeric phosphines, $Ph_2PCH_2CH=CRR'$, the mechanism of isomerization is not understood. Purified phosphines remained unaffected at 210°, and both acids and bases failed to catalyze the rearrangement, which, however, was brought about by the addition of phenylsilane.

The rearrangement of the lesser into the higher substituted olefinic phosphines is analogous to the similar isomerization of hydrocarbons and substituted hydrocarbons (154).

$$(CH_3)_2CXCR=CH_2 \rightleftharpoons (CH_3)_2C=CRCH_2X$$
$$R = H, CH_3 \qquad \sim 100\% \text{ at equilibrium}$$

The driving force for the isomerization is provided by the increased stabilization of the double bond by the alkyl groups, which for one methyl group is estimated to be 1–2 kcal/mole (154).

References

1. R. C. Miller, Abstracts, 140th Meeting, American Chemical Society, Chicago, Illinois, September 1961, p. 43Q.
2. (a) V. Mark, *Tetrahedron Letters*, **1962**, 281; *Chem. Abstr.*, **57**, 9876b (1962); (b) V. Mark, Abstracts, 142nd Meeting, American Chemical Society, Atlantic City, New Jersey, September 1962, p. 4N; (c) V. Mark, U.S. Pat. 3,197,497 (1965); *Chem. Abstr.*, **63**, 13318d (1965).
3. A. P. Boisselle and N. A. Meinhardt, *J. Org. Chem.*, **27**, 1828 (1962); *Chem. Abstr.*, **57**, 2246h (1962); A. P. Boisselle, U.S. Pat. 3,189,636 (1965); *Chem. Abstr.*, **63**, 18155c (1965); U.S. Pat. 3,271,313 (1966); *Chem. Abstr.*, **65**, 15427b (1966).
4. (a) A. N. Pudovik and I. M. Aladzheva, *J. Gen. Chem.*, **33**, 700 (1963); *Chem. Abstr.*, **59**, 2851f (1963); (b) A. N. Pudovik and I. M. Aladzheva, *J. Gen. Chem.*, **33**, 702 (1963); *Chem. Abstr.*, **59**, 2852g (1963).
5. R. C. Morris and J. L. Van Winkle, U.S. Pat. 2,728,789 (1955); *Chem. Abstr.*, **50**, 10759 (1956).
6. D. C. Rowlands, U.S. Pat. 2,728,791 (1955); *Chem. Abstr.*, **50**, 13984 (1956).
7. F. J. Lowes and R. F. Monroe, U.S. Pat. 2,809,982 (1957); *Chem. Abstr.*, **52**, 2902 (1958).

8. G. Kamai and E. A. Gerasimova, *Tr. Kazan. k. Khim. Tekhnol. Inst.*, **23**, 138 (1957); *Chem. Abstr.*, **52**, 9946 (1958).

9. A. N. Pudovik, I. M. Aladzheva, and L. N. Yakovenko, *J. Gen. Chem.*, **33**, 3373 (1963); *Chem. Abstr.*, **60**, 5543d.

10. B. T. Ionin and A. A. Petrov, *J. Gen. Chem.*, **34**, 1165 (1964); *Chem. Abstr.*, **61**, 1890c.

11. A. N. Pudovik, I. M. Aladzheva, and N. A. Patrusheva, *J. Gen. Chem.*, **34**, 2940 (1964); *Chem. Abstr.*, **61**, 16089e.

12. A. N. Pudovik, I. M. Aladzheva, and L. N. Yakovenko, *J. Gen. Chem.*, **35**, 1214 (1965); *Chem. Abstr.*, **63**, 11609f.

13. E. Cherbuliez, S. Jaccard, R. Prince, and J. Rabinowitz, *Helv. Chim. Acta*, **48**, 632 (1965).

14. E. Cherbuliez, A. Buchs, S. Caccard, D. Janjic, and J. Rabinowitz, *Helv. Chim. Acta*, **49**, 2395 (1966).

15. C. L. Chernick and H. A. Skinner, *J. Chem. Soc.*, **1956**, 1401.

16. C. T. Mortimer, *Reaction Heats and Bond Strengths*, Pergamon Press, New York, 1962, p. 189.

17. S. B. Hartley, W. S. Holmes, J. K. Jacques, M. F. Mole, and J. C. McCoubrey, *Quart. Rev.*, **17**, 209 (1963).

18. L. Pauling, *The Nature of the Chemical Bond*, Cornell University Press, Ithaca, New York, 1960.

19. (a) C. T. Mortimer, *Pure Appl. Chem.*, **2**, 71 (1961); (b) P. A. Fowell and C. T. Mortimer, *J. Chem. Soc.*, **1959**, 2913.

20. M. L. Huggins, *J. Am. Chem. Soc.*, **75**, 4123 (1953).

21. H. A. Bent, *Chem. Rev.*, **61**, 275 (1961).

22. M. J. S. Dewar and H. N. Schmeising, *Tetrahedron*, **11**, 96 (1960).

23. (a) V. Mark, Abstracts, 139th Meeting, American Chemical Society, St. Louis, Missouri, March 1961, p. 46-O; (b) V. Mark, *Tetrahedron Letters*, **1961**, 295; *Chem. Abstr.*, **56**, 2341f.

24. V. Mark, unpublished results.

25. F. O. Rice and E. Teller, *J. Chem. Phys.*, **6**, 489 (1938); **7**, 199 (1939). For some recent, cogent examples see ref. 26.

26. J. Hine, *J. Org. Chem.*, **31**, 1236 (1966); *J. Am. Chem. Soc.*, **88**, 5525 (1966).

27. A. N. Pudovik and I. M. Aladzheva, *Proc. Acad. Sci., USSR*, **151**, 634 (1963); *Chem. Abstr.*, **59**, 13798d.

28. D. S. Tarbell, *Organic Reactions*, Vol. 2, Wiley, New York, 1944, p. 1.

29. (a) I. Iwai and J. Ide, *Chem. Pharm. Bull. (Tokyo)*, **11**, 1042 (1963); *Chem. Abstr.*, **59**, 13930c; **10**, 926 (1962) and references quoted; cf. Y. Okajima, *Yakugaku Zasshi*, **80**, 318 (1960), *Chem. Abstr.*, **54**, 18487h; (b) B. S. Thyagarajan, K. K. Balasubramanian, and R. B. Rao, *Tetrahedron Letters*, **1963**, 1393; B. S. Thyagarajan, K. K. Balasubramanian, and R. B. Rao, *Tetrahedron*, **21**, 2289 (1965).

30. (a) L. J. Bellamy, *The Infra-Red Spectra of Complex Molecules*, Wiley, New York, 1962; (b) K. Nakanishi, *Infrared Absorption Spectroscopy*, Holden-Day, San Francisco, 1964; (c) N. B. Colthup, L. H. Daly, and S. E. Wiberley, *Introduction to Infrared and Raman Spectroscopy*, Academic Press, New York, 1964; (d) C. N. R. Rao, *Chemical Applications of Infrared Spectroscopy*, Academic Press, New York, 1963; (e) J. H. Wotiz and D. E. Mancuso, *J. Org. Chem.*, **22**, 207 (1957).

31. V. Mark, in preparation for publication.

32. E. B. Whipple, J. H. Goldstein, and W. E. Stewart, *J. Am. Chem. Soc.*, **81**, 4761 (1959).
33. E. L. Allred, D. M. Grant, and W. Goodlett, *J. Am. Chem. Soc.*, **87**, 673 (1965).
34. E. B. Whipple, J. H. Goldstein, L. Mandell, G. S. Reddy, and G. R. McClure, *J. Am. Chem. Soc.*, **81**, 1321 (1959).
35. E. I. Snyder and J. D. Roberts, *J. Am. Chem. Soc.*, **84**, 1582 (1962).
36. R. C. Hirst, D. M. Grant, and E. G. Paul, *J. Chem. Phys.*, **44**, 4305 (1966).
37. A. Almenningen, O. Bastiansen, and M. Traetteberg, *Acta Chem. Scand.*, **13**, 1699 (1959).
38. W. A. Anderson, R. E. Freeman, and C. A. Reilly, *J. Chem. Phys.*, **39**, 1518 (1963).
39. S. L. Manatt, G. L. Juvinall, and D. D. Elleman, *J. Am. Chem. Soc.*, **85**, 2664 (1963).
40. H. C. Allen and E. K. Plyler, *J. Am. Chem. Soc.*, **80**, 2673 (1958).
41. J. M. Dowling and B. P. Stoicheff, *Can. J. Phys.*, **37**, 703 (1959).
42. (a) R. M. Lynden-Bell and N. Sheppard, *Proc. Roy. Soc.*, *Ser. A*, **269**, 385 (1962); (b) D. M. Graham and C. E. Holloway, *Can. J. Chem.*, **41**, 2114 (1963).
43. J. A. Pople and A. A. Bothner-By, *J. Chem. Phys.*, **42**, 1339 (1965).
44. R. C. Cookson, T. A. Crabb, J. J. Frankel, and J. Hudec, *Tetrahedron*, **7**, 355 (1966).
45. Taken from a compilation of a chapter on the proton NMR spectroscopy of phosphorus compounds by V. Mark and C. E. Griffin in *Topics in Phosphorus Chemistry*, M. Grayson and E. J. Griffith, Eds., Interscience, New York, to be published.
46a. R. Freeman and H. D. Whiffen, *Mol. Phys.*, **4**, 321 (1961); R. Freeman, *ibid.*, **4**, 385 (1961); (b) D. F. Evans and J. P. Maher, *Proc. Chem. Soc.*, **1961**, 208.
47. V. S. Watts and J. H. Goldstein, *J. Chem. Phys.*, **42**, 228 (1965).
48. M. Karplus, *J. Chem. Phys.*, **30**, 11 (1959); *J. Am. Chem. Soc.*, **85**, 2870 (1963).
49. M. Karplus, *J. Am. Chem. Soc.*, **82**, 4431 (1960); M. Karplus, *J. Chem. Phys.*, **33**, 1842 (1960).
50. J. B. Hendrickson, M. L. Maddox, J. J. Sims, and H. D. Kaesz, *Tetrahedron*, **20**, 449 (1964).
51. P. L. Corio, *Chem. Rev.*, **60**, 363 (1960).
52. Taken from a compilation of ^{31}P chemical shift data by V. Mark, C. H. Dungan, M. M. Crutchfield, and J. R. Van Wazer in *P^{31} Nuclear Magnetic Resonance* (*Topics in Phosphorus Chemistry*, Vol. 5, M. Grayson and E. J. Griffith, Eds.), Interscience, New York, 1967, p. 227.
53. H. H. Jaffé and M. Orchin, *Theory and Applications of Ultraviolet Spectroscopy*, Wiley, New York, 1962, p. 499.
54. (a) W. D. Celmer and I. A. Solomons, *J. Am. Chem. Soc.*, **75**, 1372 (1953); (b) H. Fischer and H. Fischer, *Chem. Ber.*, **97**, 2975 (1964); (c) H. Fischer in *The Chemistry of Alkenes*, S. Patai, Ed., Interscience, New York, 1964, p. 1122.
55. M. I. Kabachnik, *Tetrahedron*, **20**, 655 (1964).
56. (a) *Organic Electronic Spectral Data*, O. H. Wheeler and L. A. Kaplan, Eds., Interscience, New York, 1966, Vol. 3; (b) *ibid.*, J. Phillips and F. C. Nachod, Eds., Vol. 4; (c) *ibid.*, H. E. Ungade, Ed., Vol. 2; (d) *ibid.*, M. J. Kamlet, Ed., Vol. 1.
57. V. Mark and H. Pines, *J. Am. Chem. Soc.*, **78**, 5946 (1956).
58. L. Horner, H. Hoffmann, W. Klink, H. Ertel, and V. G. Toscano, *Chem. Ber.*, **95**, 581 (1962).

59. W. S. Wadsworth and W. D. Emmons, *J. Org. Chem.*, **29**, 2861 (1964).

60. B. I. Ionin, K. S. Mingaleva, and A. A. Petrov, *J. Gen. Chem.*, **34**, 2651 (1964); *Chem. Abstr.*, **61**, 14506a.

61. B. I. Ionin and A. A. Petrov, *J. Gen. Chem.*, **35**, 1910 (1965); *Chem. Abstr.*, **64**, 6683d (1965).

62. B. C. Saunders and P. Simpson, *J. Chem. Soc.*, **1963**, 3351.

63. B. I. Ionin and A. A. Petrov, *J. Gen. Chem.*, **35**, 2247 (1965); *Chem. Abstr.*, **64**, 11240a (1965).

64. B. I. Ionin and A. A. Petrov, *J. Gen. Chem.*, **33**, 2791 (1963); *Chem. Abstr.*, **60**, 6863d, (1963).

65. B. I. Ionin and A. A. Petrov, *J. Gen. Chem.*, **32**, 2355 (1962); *Chem. Abstr.*, **58**, 9115b (1963).

66. B. I. Ionin, V. B. Lebedev, and A. A. Petrov, *Proc. Akad. Sci. USSR*, **152**, 831 (1963); *Chem. Abstr.*, **60**, 1560d (1963).

67. G. M. Bogolyubov and A. A. Petrov, *J. Gen. Chem.*, **35**, 705 (1965); *Chem. Abstr.*, **63**, 4330a (1965).

68. W. Voskuil and J. F. Arens, *Rec. Trav. Chim.*, **83**, 1301 (1964).

69. M. P. Simonnin, *J. Organomet. Chem.*, **5**, 155 (1966).

70. M. Gordon and C. E. Griffin, *J. Org. Chem.*, **31**, 333 (1966).

71. (a) W. R. Waughan and R. C. Taylor, *J. Chem. Phys.*, **31**, 1425 (1959); (b) J. N. Shoolery, L. F. Johnson, and W. A. Anderson, *J. Mol. Spectr.*, **5**, 110 (1960).

72. N. Muller and D. E. Pritchard, *J. Chem. Phys.*, **31**, 768 (1959); 1425 (1959).

73. G. H. Whitesides, J. L. Beauchamp, and J. D. Roberts, *J. Am. Chem. Soc.*, **85**, 2665 (1963).

74. B. Silver and Z. Luz, *J. Am. Chem. Soc.*, **83**, 786 (1961).

75. (a) L. M. Jackman, *Applications of Nuclear Magnetic Resonance Spectroscopy in Organic Chemistry*, Pergamon Press, New York, 1959; (b) J. D. Roberts, *Nuclear Magnetic Resonance*, McGraw-Hill, New York, 1959; (c) R. H. Bible, Jr., *Interpretation of NMR Spectra*, Plenum Press, New York, 1965.

76. A. N. Pudovik, N. G. Khusainova, and I. M. Aladzheva, *J. Gen. Chem.*, **33**, 1034 (1963); *Chem. Abstr.*, **59**, 10115a (1963).

77. A. N. Pudovik, N. G. Khusainova, and A. B. Ageeva, *J. Gen. Chem.*, **34**, 3998 (1964); *Chem. Abstr.*, **62**, 7792g (1964).

78. A. N. Pudovik, N. G. Khusainova, and R. G. Galeeva, *J. Gen. Chem.*, **36**, 73 (1966); *Chem. Abstr.*, **64**, 14210h (1966).

79. A. N. Pudovik, N. G. Khusainova, and I. M. Aladzheva, *J. Gen. Chem.*, **34**, 2484 (1964); *Chem. Abstr.*, **61**, 9522e (1964).

80. A. N. Pudovik, E. A. Ishmaeva, R. S. Akhmerova, and I. M. Aladzheva, *J. Gen. Chem.*, **36**, 168 (1966); *Chem. Abstr.*, **64**, 14208f (1966).

81. V. Mark, Abstracts, 147th Meeting, American Chemical Society, Philadelphia, Pennsylvania, April 1964, p. 29L.

82. V. Mark and J. R. Van Wazer, *J. Org. Chem.*, **29**, 1006 (1964).

83. (a) R. G. Harvey and E. R. De Sombre, in *Topics in Phosphorus Chemistry*, Vol. 1, M. Grayson and E. J. Griffith, Eds., Interscience, New York, 1964, pp. 63, 75; (b) p. 81.

84. A. N. Pudovik and I. M. Aladzheva, *J. Gen. Chem.*, **33**, 3022 (1963); *Chem. Abstr.*, **60**, 1788c (1963).

85. A. L. Lemper and H. Tieckelmann, *Tetrahedron Letters*, **1964**, 3053; *Chem. Abstr.*, **62**, 1547c (1964).

86. A. E. Arbuzov and K. V. Nikonorov, *Zh. Obshch. Khim.*, **18**, 2008 (1948); *Chem. Abstr.*, **43**, 3801i (1949) (1948).

87. A. L. Lemper, Thesis, State University of New York at Buffalo, 1966.
88. M. P. Savage and S. Trippett, *J. Chem. Soc.* (*C*), **1966**, 1842.
89. V. Mark, *Dev. Appl. Spectry.*, **5**, 285 (1966).
90. V. Mark and J. R. Van Wazer, *J. Org. Chem.*, **32**, 1187 (1967).
91. B. I. Ionin and A. A. Petrov, *J. Gen. Chem.*, **33**, 426 (1963); *Chem. Abstr.*, **59**, 656d (1963).
92. N. T. Thuong, F. Convert, G. Martin, and P. Chabrier, *Bull. Soc. Chim. France*, **1965**, 1925.
93. A. Meisters and J. M. Swan, *Australian J. Chem.*, **18**, 155 (1965).
94. F. A. Cotton and R. A. Schunn, *J. Am. Chem. Soc.*, **85**, 2394 (1963).
95. A. N. Pudovik, *Usp. Khim.*, **23**, 547 (1954).
96. E. L. Gefter, *Organophosphorus Monomers and Polymers*, trans. by G. M. Kosolapoff, Associated Technical Services, Glen Ridge, New Jersey, 1962.
97. A. N. Pudovik and I. V. Konovalova, *J. Gen. Chem.*, **33**, 3371 (1963); *Chem. Abstr.*, **60**, 4179d (1963).
98. A. N. Pudovik and R. D. Gareev, *J. Gen. Chem.*, **33**, 3370 (1963); *Chem. Abstr.*, **60**, 4178f (1963).
99. A. N. Pudovik and I. V. Konovalova, *J. Gen. Chem.*, **31**, 1580 (1961); *Chem. Abstr.*, **55**, 24540b (1961).
100. Gil'm Kamai, V. S. Tsivunin, and S. K. Nurtdinov, *J. Gen. Chem.*, **35**, 1812 (1965); *Chem. Abstr.*, **64**, 3587e (1965).
101. B. G. Liorber and A. I. Razumov, *J. Gen. Chem.*, **36**, 323 (1966).
102. (a) H. J. Harwood and D. W. Grisley, *J. Am. Chem. Soc.*, **82**, 423 (1960); (b) R. G. Laughlin, *J. Org. Chem.*, **27**, 1005 (1962); (c) M. Green and R. F. Hudson, *Proc. Chem. Soc.*, **1962**, 217; (d) A. D. F. Toy, *J. Am. Chem. Soc.*, **71**, 2268 (1949).
103. K. Moedritzer, *J. Inorg. Nucl. Chem.*, **22**, 19 (1961).
104. K. Moedritzer, G. M. Burch, J. R. Van Wazer, and H. K. Hofmeister, *Inorg. Chem.*, **2**, 1152 (1963).
105. A. Streitwieser, *Solvolytic Displacement Reactions*, McGraw-Hill, New York, 1962.
106. A. H. Ford-Moore and J. H. Williams, *J. Chem. Soc.*, **1947**, 1465.
107. P. Rumpf, *Bull. Soc. Chim. France*, **18**, 128 (1951).
108. A. Simon and W. Schulze, *Chem. Ber.*, **94**, 3251 (1961).
109. A. N. Pudovik and A. P. Rakov, *Proc. Acad. Sci., USSR*, **1965**, 389; *Chem. Abstr.*, **63**, 4151d (1965).
110. D. J. Martin, M. Gordon, and C. E. Griffin, *Tetrahedron*, **23**, 831 (1967).
111. J. E. Lancaster, *Spectrochim. Acta*, **23A**, 1449 (1967).
112. D. Seyferth and J. Fogel, *J. Orgmet. Chem.*, **6**, 205 (1966).
113. W. Drenth and D. Rosenberg, *Rec. Trav. Chim.*, **86**, 26 (1967).
114. A. A. Petrov, B. I. Ionin, and V. M. Ignatyev, *Tetrahedron Letters*, **1968**, 15.
115. V. S. Zavgorodnii, B. I. Ionin, and A. A. Petrov, *J. Gen. Chem. USSR* (*Eng. Transl.*), **37**, 988 (1967).
116. G. M. Bogolyubov and A. A. Petrov, *J. Gen. Chem. USSR* (*Eng. Transl.*), **37**, 211 (1967).
117. C. Charrier, W. Chodkiewicz, and P. Cadiot, *Bull. Soc. Chim. France*, **1966**, 1002.
118. V. B. Lebedev and B. I. Ionin, *Izv. Vysshikh Priborostroenie*, **10**, 29 (1967).
119. M. P. Simonnin and B. Borecka, *Bull. Soc. Chim. France*, **1966**, 3842.
120. (a) V. M. Ignatyev, B. I. Ionin, and A. A. Petrov, *J. Gen. Chem. USSR* (*Eng. Transl.*), **36**, 1510 (1966); (b) **37**, 1807 (1967).
121. A. Sevin and W. Chodkiewicz, *Tetrahedron Letters*, **1967**, 2975.

122. B. I. Ionin, V. B. Lebedev, and A. A. Petrov, *J. Gen. Chem. USSR (Eng. Transl.)*, **37**, 1117 (1967).
123. A. N. Pudovik and O. S. Durova, *J. Gen. Chem. USSR (Eng. Transl.)*, **36**, 1465 (1966).
124. Y. A. Kondratev, Y. K. Knobel, and S. Z. Ivin, *J. Gen. Chem., USSR (Eng. Transl.)*, **37**, 1037 (1967).
125. F. A. Miller and D. H. Lemmon, *Spectrochim. Acta*, **23A**, 1099 (1967).
126. Y. S. Arbisman, Y. A. Kondratev, and S. Z. Ivin, *J. Gen. Chem., USSR (Eng. Transl.)*, **37**, 478 (1967).
127. A. N. Pudovik and N. G. Khusainova, *J. Gen. Chem., USSR (Eng. Transl.)*, **36**, 1359 (1966).
128. A. N. Pudovik and N. G. Khusainova, *J. Gen. Chem., USSR (Eng. Transl.)*, **36**, 1251 (1966).
129. A. N. Pudovik, N. G. Khusainova, and T. A. Abdulina, *J. Gen. Chem., USSR (Eng. Transl.)*, **37**, 809 (1967).
130. A. N. Pudovik, I. V. Guryanova, and M. G. Zimin, *J. Gen. Chem., USSR (Eng. Transl.)*, **37**, 381 (1967).
131. C. G. Krespan, *Tetrahedron*, **23**, 4243 (1967).
132. R. K. Hill and N. W. Gilman, *Tetrahedron Letters*, **1967**, 1421.
133. Y. Makisumi, *Tetrahedron Letters*, **1966**, 6413.
134. Y. Makisumi, *Tetrahedron Letters*, **1966**, 6399.
135. A. N. Pudovik, I. M. Aladzheva, and L. V. Spirina, *J. Gen. Chem., USSR (Eng. Transl.)*, **37**, 656 (1967).
136. A. N. Pudovik, I. M. Aladzheva, and V. G. Kotova, *J. Gen. Chem., USSR, (Eng. Transl.)*, **37**, 1115 (1967).
137. P. P. Montijn, L. Brandsma, and J. F. Arens, *Rec. Trav. Chim.*, **86**, 129 (1967).
138. B. I. Ionin, V. M. Ignatyev, and V. B. Lebedev, *J. Gen. Chem., USSR (Eng. Transl.)*, **37**, 1774 (1967).
139. M. P. Savage and S. Trippett, *J. Chem. Soc. (C)*, **1967**, 1998.
140. R. Gardi, R. Vitali, and P. P. Castelli, *Tetrahedron Letters*, **1966**, 3203.
141. P. Cresson, *Compt. rend.*, **261**, 1707 (1965).
142. D. K. Black and S. R. Landor, *J. Chem. Soc.*, **1965**, 6784.
143. D. D. Des Marteau and G. H. Cady, *Inorg. Chem.*, **5**, 1829 (1966).
144. N. Muller and D. T. Carr, *J. Phys. Chem.*, **67**, 112 (1963).
145. P. Cadiot, W. Chodkiewicz, B. Borecka, C. Charrier, and M. P. Simonnin, *Composés Organiques du Phosphore*, Centre National de la Recherche Scientifique, p. 99 (1966).
146. L. Crombie, P. A. Jenkins, D. A. Mitchard, and J. C. Williams, *Tetrahedron Letters*, **1967**, 4297.
147. M. P. Savage and S. Trippett, *J. Chem. Soc. (C)*, **1968**, 591.
148. N. M. Ivakina, Y. A. Kondratev, and S. Z. Ivin, *J. Gen. Chem., USSR (Eng. Transl.)*, **37**, 1612 (1967).
149. B. I. Ionin, G. M. Bogolyubov, and A. A. Petrov, *Russ. Chem. Rev. (English Transl.)*, **1967**, 249.
150. M. V. Mavrov and V. F. Kucherov, *Russ. Chem. Rev. (English Transl.)*, **1967**, 233.
151. W. E. Davidsohn and M. C. Henry, *Chem. Rev.*, **67**, 73 (1967).
152. A. N. Pudovik and I. M. Aladzheva, *J. Gen. Chem., USSR (Eng. Transl.)*, **30**, 2599 (1960).
153. L. Horner, H. Winkler, A. Rapp, A. Mentrup, H. Hoffmann, and P. Beck, *Tetrahedron Letters*, **1961**, 161.

154. P. B. D. de la Mare, "Rearrangements in the Chemistry of Allylic Compounds" in *Molecular Rearrangements*, P. de Mayo, Ed., Interscience, New York, 1963, p. 36.
155. F. A. L. Anet, *J. Am. Chem. Soc.*, **84**, 3767 (1962).
156. S. Forsén, T. Alm, B. Gestblom, S. Rodmar, and R. A. Hoffman, *J. Mol. Spectry.*, **17**, 13 (1965).
157. R. A. Hoffman, S. Forsén, B. Gestblom, and S. Rodmar, *J. Chem. Phys.*, **42**, 1695 (1965).
158. R. Kaiser, *J. Chem. Phys.*, **39**, 2435 (1963).
159. R. A. Hoffman and S. Forsén, "High Resolution Nuclear Magnetic Double and Multiple Resonance" in *Progress in Nuclear Magnetic Resonance Spectroscopy*, J. W. Emsley, J. Feeney, and L. H. Sutcliffe, Eds., Pergamon, New York, 1966, Vol. 1, p. 15.
160. C. N. Banwell, "The Calculation of ABX and Related Spectra" in *Nuclear Magnetic Resonance for Organic Chemists*, D. W. Mathieson, Ed., Academic Press, New York, 1967, p. 98.
161. J. D. Swalen, "Computer Techniques in the Analysis of NMR Spectra" in *Progress in Nuclear Magnetic Resonance Spectroscopy*, J. W. Emsley, J. Feeney, and L. H. Sutcliffe, Eds., Pergamon, New York, 1966, Vol. I, p. 205.
162. M. P. Williamson, S. Castellano, and C. E. Griffin, *J. Phys. Chem.*, **72**, 175 (1968).
163. S. L. Manatt, G. L. Juvinall, R. I. Wagner, and D. D. Elleman, *J. Am. Chem. Soc.*, **88**, 2689 (1966).
164. W. McFarlane, *Comm.*, **1967**, 58.
165. S. L. Stafford and J. D. Baldeschwieler, *J. Am. Chem. Soc.*, **83**, 4473 (1961).
166. R. R. Dean and W. McFarlane, *Chem. Comm.*, **1967**, 840.
167. W. McFarlane, *J. Chem. Soc. (A)*, **1967**, 1148.
168. T. J. Katz, C. R. Nicholson, and C. A. Reilley, *J. Am. Chem. Soc.*, **88**, 3832 (1966).
169. E. Duval and E. A. C. Lucken, *Mol. Phys.*, **10**, 499 (1966).
170. E. G. Finer and R. K. Harris, *Chem. Comm.*, **1968**, 110.

Author Index

Numbers in parentheses are reference numbers and show that an author's work is referred to although his name is not mentioned in the text. Numbers in *italics* indicate the pages on which the full references appear.

A

Abdel-Rahman, M. O., 239(68), *247*
Abdulina, T. A., 389(129), *436*
Abell, P. I., 158(55), 176(86), *189*
Abrahamson, E. W., 169(80), *189*
Abramovitch, R. A., 267(3), 271–273(3), 279(3), 284(3), 296(3), 297(3), *313*
Advani, B. G., 272(17), 294(17), *314*
Ageeva, A. B., 388(77), *434*
Ahn, M.-K., 7, 8(28), 9(28), *40*
Aivazova, R. A., 107(86), *115*
Akasaki, Y., 151(39), *188*
Akawie, R., 78(11), 79(11), 81(19), *113, 114*
Akhmerova, R. S., 395(80), *434*
Akımoto, Y., 24(76), *41*
Aladzheva, I. M., 321(4,9,11,12), 322(4a,12), 323(12), 324(12), 325(11), 326(11), 331(4), 333(12), 336(12,27), 339–341(9,12), 343(4a,12), 345(11), 348(9,12), 373(9,12), 376(4a,12), 378(4a,12), 379(12), 388(76), 389(27), 391(11), 392–394(4b,11), 395(4b,80), 400(84), 401(135), 402–405(84,135), 406(135), 408–410(84), 430(136,152), *431, 432, 434, 436*
Alemagna, A., 272(16), 292(111), 293(117), 294(117), *314, 316*
Alexander, W. A., 66(8), 67(8), 70(8), *72*
Allan, Z. J., 202(33), 230(33), *246*
Allen, H. C., 358(40), *433*
Allen, R. G., 158(56), *189*
Allred, E. L., 356(33), 360(33), *433*
Alm, T., 360(156), *437*
Anastassiou, A. G., 268(7), 271(7), 272(7), *313*
Anderson, W. A., 358(38), *433, 434*
Anet, F. A. L., 360(155), *437*
Anet, R., 150(36), *187*

Angus, H. J. F., 152(42), *188*
Anselme, J. P., 288(96), 289(98), *316*
Antkowiak, W., 287(85), *316*
Appl, M., 296(126), *317*
ApSimon, J. W., 287(85), *316*
Arbisman, Y. S., 388(126), *436*
Arbuzov, A. E., 55, *63*, 400(86), 402(86), 404(86), *434*
Arcker, S., 55(32), 60(32), *63*
Arens, J. F., 81(18), 83(32,33), *114*, 356(137), 360(137), 361(137), 378(68), 382(68), *434, 436*
Arndt, F., 46(13), *62*
Arnold, D. R., 151(37), *188*
Ash, A. B., 38(109), *42*
Ash, A. S. F., 255(27), *266*
Atkinson, J. G., 148(28), *187*
Auken, T. V. van, 154(51), *188*
Ayer, D. E., 148(28), *187*
Aylward, J. B., 292(113), *316*

B

Babayan, A. T., 107, *115*
Bacchetti, T., 272(16), 292(111), 293(117), 294(117), *314, 316*
Bachman, G. B., 67(2), *71*
Back, H., 310(163), *318*
Badger, G. M., 58(20), *63*
Bagby, M. O., 82(25), *114*
Baer, R., 56(45), *63*
Bain, B. M., 3, 7(11), *40*
Baker, W., 308(158), *318*
Balabanov, G. P., 311(170), *318*
Balasubramanian, K. K., 162(61a), *189*, 336(29b), 389(29), *432*
Baldeschwieler, J. D., 362(165), *437*
Baldwin, C. M., 199(26), *246*
Bamberger, E., 273(21), 274(21), *314*
Banks, R. E., 281(59), *315*

439

Subject Index

Mechanisms of Molecular Migrations

Cumulative Index, Volumes 1 and 2

Author Index

Subject Index